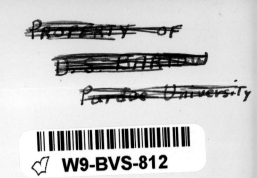

QUANTUM MECHANICS

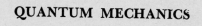

INTERNATIONAL SERIES IN PURE AND APPLIED PHYSICS
Leonard I. Schiff, *Consulting Editor*

The late F. K. Richtmyer was Consulting Editor of the series from its inception in 1929 to his death in 1939. Lee A. DuBridge was Consulting Editor from 1939 to 1946; and G. P. Harnwell from 1947 to 1954.

QUANTUM MECHANICS

LEONARD I. SCHIFF

Professor of Physics
Stanford University

McGRAW-HILL BOOK COMPANY, INC.

New York   Toronto   London

1955

QUANTUM MECHANICS

Library of Congress Catalog Card Number 55-6170

IV

THE MAPLE PRESS COMPANY, YORK, PA.

PREFACE ·

This volume has a threefold purpose: to explain the physical concepts of quantum mechanics, to describe the mathematical formalism, and to present illustrative examples of both the ideas and the methods. The book is intended to serve as a text at the graduate level and also as a reference book. It is assumed that the reader is reasonably familiar with atomic structure, classical mechanics, and differential equations. In addition, he should have had some contact with electromagnetic theory and, for the latter part of the book, with the special theory of relativity.

The author believes that the analytical methods employed in the book will satisfy most theoretical physicists even though no attempt is made to achieve mathematical rigor. For example, there is little or no discussion of the justification for the interchange of sum, derivative, and integral operations, or for the use of the δ function. On the other hand, the physical reasons for the nature of the results obtained are investigated wherever possible.

Problems are given at the end of each chapter. They are often used to illustrate or amplify points discussed in the text. Original theoretical papers are referred to throughout the book; the list is representative rather than exhaustive. Experimental results are, for the most part, quoted without reference, since the large amount of documentation required for an adequate survey seems out of place in a book on theoretical physics. Several other books on quantum mechanics and related subjects are referred to for more detailed discussions of particular topics.

The scope of this volume is best outlined if the book is divided into three parts. The first three chapters constitute an introduction to quantum mechanics, in which the physical concepts are discussed and the Schrödinger wave formalism is established. The detailed treatment of the wave function (Chap. III) may be omitted in a first reading. The next eight chapters comprise the central part of the book. This part presents exact solutions of the wave equation for both energy-level and collision problems, the Heisenberg matrix formalism and transformation theory, approximation methods, radiation theory, and some applications to atomic systems. Since the first eleven chapters correspond to a typical one-year graduate course, it seemed desirable to include a semi-classical treatment of electromagnetic radiation in the central part of the book (Chap. X) even though some of the results are obtained again in Chap. XIV. The last part of the book corresponds to a short course in what is often called advanced quantum mechanics. It consists of relativistic particle theory and an introduction to quantized field theory and quantum electrodynamics.

Since the preparation of the first edition, there have been no changes in the fundamental ideas underlying the first 48 sections of the book, which deal with the quantum mechanics of particles and linear wave fields. This is not true of the last two sections, which are an introduction to the quantum mechanics of interacting wave fields. Here the subject matter has undergone drastic revision with the introduction and successful application of covariant renormalization techniques, especially in quantum electrodynamics. In spite of this, it was decided after serious consideration not to alter the presentation in Secs. 49 and 50. This was partly because a coherent account of covariant field theory would require a great deal of additional space, and partly because it should at the present time be written by someone who has taken an active part in the development of the subject. Moreover, it was felt that the present treatment serves a useful purpose in providing the student with a firm basis for the newer work.

In the revision, several changes have been made, some of which describe improvements in calculational methods that have appeared in the intervening years. The more important additions are a momentum determination experiment (Sec. 4), the relation between total cross section and forward scattered amplitude (Sec. 19), the virial theorem (Sec. 23), definition of angular momentum in terms of infinitesimal rotations (Sec. 24), Green's function and integral equation for the radial wave function (Sec. 26), variation principle for the phase shift (Sec. 27), photoelectric effect and the use of an ingoing spherical wave in the final state (Sec. 37), and the theory of the effective range in the neutron-proton system (Sec. 41). The more general discussion of nuclear properties in Sec. 41 has been considerably shortened. Two of the problems have been deleted, and seventeen new ones added.

The author owes a particular debt of gratitude to three persons in connection with the appearance of the first edition of this book. He wishes to express his appreciation to Prof. J. R. Oppenheimer for introducing him to several of the ideas and examples which helped give the book its form, to Prof. R. Serber for many discussions of both the conceptual and formal aspects of quantum mechanics, and to Dr. G. P. Harnwell for continued encouragement while the book was being written. The author is also grateful to some of the reviewers of the first edition and to several of those who have studied and taught from it, for suggestions that were helpful in the preparation of the revision.

LEONARD I. SCHIFF

CONTENTS

CHAPTER IV
DISCRETE EIGENVALUES: ENERGY LEVELS

CHAPTER V
CONTINUOUS EIGENVALUES: COLLISION THEORY

at the turning point.   Asymptotic connection formulas.   Energy levels of a
potential well.   A quantization rule.   Special boundary conditions.

Conservation of angular momentum. Selection rules for many-particle systems. Cerenkov effect. Expression for the current density. Fourier analysis of the radiation field. Radiated energy. Photoelectric effect. Angular distribution. Cross section for the atomic photoelectric effect. Improvement on the Born approximation.

CHAPTER XI

ATOMS, MOLECULES, AND ATOMIC NUCLEI

CHAPTER XII

RELATIVISTIC WAVE EQUATIONS

CHAPTER XIII

THE QUANTIZATION OF WAVE FIELDS

CHAPTER XIV
QUANTUM ELECTRODYNAMICS

QUANTUM MECHANICS

CHAPTER I

THE PHYSICAL BASIS OF QUANTUM MECHANICS

At the present stage of human knowledge, quantum mechanics can be regarded as the fundamental theory of atomic phenomena. The experimental data on which it is based are derived from physical events that lie almost entirely beyond the range of direct human perception. It is not surprising, therefore, that the theory embodies physical concepts that are foreign to common daily experience. These concepts did not appear in the historical development of quantum mechanics, however, until a quite complete mathematical formalism had been evolved. The need for quantitative comparison with observation, which is the ultimate test of any physical theory, in this case led first to the formalism and only later to its interpretation in physical terms.

It seems desirable in introducing the subject of quantum mechanics to depart from the historical order and preface the mathematical development with a discussion of the physical concepts. In this chapter we first review briefly the experimental background and the ideas of the old quantum theory, then discuss the newer physical concepts of uncertainty and complementarity, and finally lay the groundwork for the formalism that will be developed in its most familiar form in Chap. II. No attempt will be made to deduce the structure of the formalism from the fundamental experiments; we shall try to make the theoretical development seem plausible rather than unique. The justification for the theory, then, will rest on the agreement between deductions made from it and experiments, and on the simplicity (in principle more than in practice) and consistency of the formalism.

1. EXPERIMENTAL BACKGROUND

Experimental physics prior to 1900 had demonstrated the existence of a wide variety of phenomena, which for the most part were believed to be explicable in terms of what we now call *classical* theoretical physics. The motions of mechanical objects were successfully discussed in terms of Newton's equations on both celestial and terrestrial scales. Application of this theory to molecular motions produced useful results in the kinetic theory of gases, and the discovery of the electron by J. J. Thomson in 1897 consisted in showing that it behaved like a Newtonian particle.

1

The wave nature of light had been strongly suggested by the diffraction experiments of Young in 1803, and was put on a firmer foundation by Maxwell's discovery in 1864 of the connection between optical and electrical phenomena.

Inadequacy of Classical Physics.   The difficulties in the understanding of experimental results that remained at the beginning of this century were largely concerned with the development of a suitable atomic model and with the late discoveries of X rays and radioactivity.   However, there were also difficulties associated with phenomena that should have been understood but actually were not: such things as the spectral distribution of thermal radiation from a black body, the low-temperature specific heats of solids, and the appearance of only 5 degrees of freedom in the motion of a free diatomic molecule at ordinary temperatures.

The beginning of an understanding of the second class of difficulties was made by Planck in 1900, when he was able to explain the black-body spectrum in terms of the assumed emission and absorption of electromagnetic radiation in discrete *quanta*, each of which contains an amount of energy E that is equal to the frequency of the radiation ν multiplied by a universal constant h (called *Planck's constant*):

$$E = h\nu \tag{1.1}$$

This quantum idea was later used by Einstein in accounting for some of the experimental observations on the photoelectric effect.   In this way the dual character of electromagnetic radiation became established: it sometimes behaves like a wave motion, and sometimes like a stream of corpuscular quanta.

At about this time, the existence of discrete values for the measurable parameters of atomic systems (not only of electromagnetic radiation) became apparent through Einstein's and Debye's theories of the specific heats of solids, Ritz's classification of spectral lines, the experiment of Franck and Hertz on the discrete energy losses of electrons on collision with atoms, and (somewhat later) the experiment of Stern and Gerlach, which showed that the component of the magnetic moment of an atom along an external magnetic field has discrete values.

Summary of Principal Experiments and Inferences.   The theoretical physics of the first quarter of this century thus contained two important inferences, obtained from the experiments and their interpretations, that had not existed in 1900: the dual character of electromagnetic radiation, and the existence of discrete values for physical quantities.   The relations between the principal experimental conclusions and the theoretical inferences are shown schematically in Table 1; for a more detailed discussion and a bibliography, reference should be made to a book on atomic physics.[1]

TABLE 1.   RELATIONS BETWEEN EXPERIMENTAL INTERPRETATIONS AND THEORETICAL INFERENCES

Diffraction (Young 1803, Laue 1912).............................	Electromagnetic waves
Black-body radiation (Planck 1900) Photoelectric effect (Einstein 1904) Compton effect (1923)	Electromagnetic quanta
Combination principle (Ritz-Rydberg 1908) Specific heats (Einstein 1907, Debye 1912) Franck-Hertz experiment (1913) Stern-Gerlach experiment (1922)	Discrete values for physical quantities

A third theoretical inference appeared in 1924 with the suggestion by de Broglie that matter also has a dual (particle-like and wave-like) character; he assumed that the relation between the momentum p of the particle and the length λ of the corresponding wave is[2]

$$\lambda = \frac{h}{p} \tag{1.2}$$

Up to that time all the evidence had indicated that matter was composed of discrete Newtonian particles; in particular, sharp tracks of charged particles such as electrons and helium nuclei had been observed in expansion cloud chambers like that invented by C. T. R. Wilson in 1911. Shortly after this, however, Davisson and Germer (1927) and G. P. Thomson (1928) independently observed the diffraction of electrons by crystals, and thus confirmed de Broglie's principal supposition.

2. THE OLD QUANTUM THEORY

What is now called the *old quantum theory*[3] was initiated by the work of Planck on black-body radiation, and carried farther by Einstein and Debye.   However, it was only after Rutherford's discovery in 1911 that an atom consists of a small, massive, positively charged nucleus surrounded by electrons, that the theory could be applied to a quantitative description of atoms.

[1] See, for example, F. K. Richtmyer, E. H. Kennard, and T. Lauritsen, "Introduction to Modern Physics" (McGraw-Hill, New York, 1955); M. Born, "Atomic Physics" (Hafner, New York, 1951); G. P. Harnwell and W. E. Stephens, "Atomic Physics" (McGraw-Hill, New York, 1955).

[2] Equation (1.2) is also valid for light quanta, as may be seen by dividing both sides of Eq. (1.1) by the velocity of light c; for a directed beam of light $p = E/c$ and $\lambda = c/\nu$.

[3] For a more detailed discussion than is presented in this section, see the books cited above, and L. Pauling and E. B. Wilson, Jr., "Introduction to Quantum Mechanics," Chap. II (McGraw-Hill, New York, 1935).

Bohr-Sommerfeld Quantization Rules.   The first step in this direction was taken by Bohr in 1913, when he made two postulates concerning the electronic or extranuclear structure of an atom.   The first of these was that an atomic system can exist in particular stationary or quantized states, each of which corresponds to a definite energy of the system. Transitions from one stationary state to another are accompanied by the gain or loss, as the case may be, of an amount of energy equal to the energy difference between the two states; the energy gained or lost appears as a quantum of electromagnetic radiation, or as internal or kinetic energy of another system.   The second postulate (in agreement with that of Planck and Einstein) was that a radiation quantum has a frequency equal to its energy divided by Planck's constant h.

These two postulates by themselves provided some insight into the Ritz combination principle and the Franck-Hertz experiment.   To obtain specific results for hydrogen, Bohr proposed a simple rule for the selection of those circular orbits which are to constitute stationary states: the angular momentum must be an integral multiple of $h/2\pi$.   A more general quantization rule was discovered independently by W. Wilson (1915) and by Sommerfeld (1916), thus making possible the application of Bohr's postulates to a wider variety of atomic systems.   This rule is applicable to Hamiltonian systems in which the coordinates are cyclic variables, and states that the integral of each canonical momentum with respect to its coordinate over a cycle of its motion must be an integral multiple of h.   The rule was applied with considerable success to the computation of the fine structure of hydrogen, the spectra of diatomic molecules, and other problems.

Practical Difficulties.   The old quantum theory encountered practical difficulties in several different respects.   It could not be applied to aperiodic systems, it provided only a qualitative and incomplete treatment of the intensities of spectral lines, and it did not give a satisfactory account of the dispersion of light.   Moreover, improvements in experimental techniques soon showed that there were problems, such as the rotational spectra of some diatomic molecules, to which the theory gave unambiguous but incorrect answers.

The correspondence principle was introduced by Bohr in 1923 in an effort to make use of the classical theory as a limiting case to infer some properties of atomic systems, especially the intensities of spectral lines. Although much was achieved in this way, it was clear in the early 1920's that the quantum theory as it then existed was unsatisfactory.

Conceptual Difficulties.   Quite apart from the practical difficulties outlined above, the old quantum theory failed to give a conceptually satisfactory account of the fundamental phenomena.   It was difficult to understand why the electrostatic interaction between a hydrogen nucleus and an electron should be effective when the ability of the accelerated electron to emit electromagnetic radiation disappeared in a stationary state. The mechanism of emission and absorption of radiation in transitions between stationary states was obscure. The quantization rules were arbitrary even when they were most effective. And the assumption of a dual character for light (particle-like on emission and absorption and wave-like in transit) seemed to be self-contradictory.

In order to illustrate the conceptual difficulties and the way in which they are dealt with by the new quantum mechanics, we consider in some detail a simple diffraction experiment, which is illustrated schematically in Fig. 1. A light source S illuminates a diaphragm A in which two slits

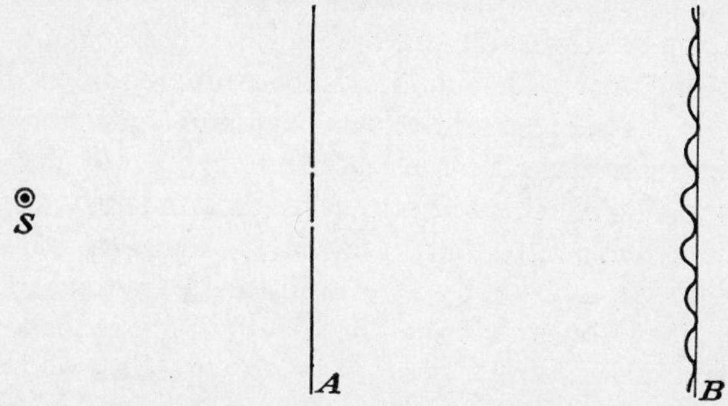

Fig. 1. A diffraction experiment in which light from S passes through the two slits in A to form a diffraction pattern at B.

are cut. A diffraction pattern appears at a photosensitive screen B, and the ejected photoelectrons are most numerous at the diffraction peaks. Here we have the radiation behaving as a wave during its passage from source through slits to screen, but behaving as a stream of light quanta or photons when it ejects electrons from B. We now know that a similar experiment could be set up with matter instead of radiation. The diffraction pattern of electrons scattered from a crystal (analogous to the slits in A) may be detected as a distribution of electron tracks in a Wilson cloud chamber (analogous to the screen B), so that the wave and particle aspects of matter appear in the same experiment.

In the situation illustrated in Fig. 1, we might at first suppose that the diffraction pattern is due to an interference between different photons passing through the two slits, thus explaining the observations entirely in terms of the particle picture. That this is not a sufficient explanation may be shown by decreasing the intensity of the light until an average of only one photon at a time is in transit between source and screen. The diffraction pattern still appears as the distribution of the large number of photons accumulated over a sufficiently long time. Thus we must conclude that diffraction is a statistical property of a single photon, and does not involve an interaction between photons. From the point of view of the particle picture, we may then ask how it is that a stream of independent photons, each of which presumably can go through only one of the slits, can produce a diffraction pattern that appears only when both slits are open. Or to put the question in another way, how can the presence of a slit through which a photon does not go prevent that photon from reaching a part of the screen it would be likely to reach if that slit were closed?

Quantum-mechanical Viewpoint. In this question is implicit the assumption that the photon actually does go through a particular one of the two slits. This assumption is natural from the point of view of the classical theory or the old quantum theory since these theories regard a photon or other particle as having a definite and determinable position at each instant of time. The quantum mechanics, however, discards this assumption, and asserts instead that the position of a photon has meaning only when the experiment includes a position determination. Moreover, this part of the experiment will affect the remainder of the experiment and cannot be considered separately. Thus from the point of view of quantum mechanics, the question asked in the last paragraph is without meaning, since it assumes that the photon goes through a particular one of the two slits (thus making it possible to close the other slit) when there is no provision in the experiment for determining through which slit the photon actually goes.

The quantum mechanics resolves the situation by telling us that the diffraction pattern is destroyed if a sufficiently careful attempt is made to determine through which slit each photon passes (see Sec. 4). We must then be prepared to forego the customary mental picture of a photon (or an electron) as a classical particle that has at each instant of time a position that can be determined without damage to diffraction patterns of the type discussed here. Thus classical causality, which requires that the motion of a particle at any time be uniquely determinable from its motion at an earlier time, must also be abandoned. The new theory that is forced upon us in this way is so successful in other respects as well that, at the present state of knowledge, we must regard such classically incomplete descriptions as a fundamental property of nature.

3. UNCERTAINTY AND COMPLEMENTARITY

Before presenting a more quantitative discussion of the diffraction experiment outlined in Sec. 2, we consider two principles that express in qualitative terms the physical content of the theory of quantum mechanics. We restrict ourselves here to a discussion of their meaning, and give arguments for their validity in Sec. 4.

Uncertainty Principle. The first of these is the *uncertainty principle*, developed by Heisenberg[1] in 1927. According to this principle, it is impossible to specify precisely and simultaneously the values of both members of particular pairs of physical variables that describe the behavior of an atomic system. The members of these pairs of variables are canonically conjugate to each other in the Hamiltonian sense: a rectangular coordinate x of a particle and the corresponding component of momentum p_x, a component J_z of angular momentum of a particle and its angular position ϕ in the perpendicular (xy) plane, the energy E of a particle and the time t at which it is measured, etc. Put more quantitatively, the uncertainty principle states that the order of magnitude of the product of the uncertainties in the knowledge of the two variables must be at least Planck's constant h divided by 2π ($\hbar \equiv h/2\pi = 1.054 \times 10^{-27}$ erg-second),[2] so that

$$\Delta x \cdot \Delta p_x \gtrsim \hbar \qquad (3.1)$$
$$\Delta \phi \cdot \Delta J_z \gtrsim \hbar \qquad (3.2)$$
$$\Delta t \cdot \Delta E \gtrsim \hbar \qquad (3.3)$$

The relation (3.1) means that a component of the momentum of a particle cannot be precisely specified without our loss of all knowledge of the corresponding component of its position at that time, that a particle cannot be precisely localized in a particular direction without our loss of all knowledge of its momentum component in that direction, and that in intermediate cases the product of the uncertainties of the simultaneously measurable values of corresponding position and momentum components is at least of the order of magnitude of $\hbar$. Similarly, Eq. (3.2) means, for example, that the precise measurement of the angular position of a particle in an orbit carries with it the loss at that time of all knowledge of the component of angular momentum perpendicular to the plane of the orbit. Equation (3.3) means that an energy determination that has an accuracy ΔE must occupy at least a time interval $\Delta t \sim \hbar/\Delta E$; thus if a system maintains a particular state of motion not longer than a time Δt, the energy of the system in that state is uncertain by at least the amount $\Delta E \sim \hbar/\Delta t$, since Δt is the longest time interval available for the energy determination. The smallness of h makes the uncertainty principle of interest primarily in connection with systems of atomic size.

[1] W. Heisenberg, *Zeits. f. Physik*, **43**, 172 (1927).
[2] J. W. M. DuMond and E. R. Cohen, *Rev. Mod. Phys.*, **25**, 691 (1953).

As we shall see in Sec. 12, the uncertainty principle may be obtained directly from the mathematical formulation of the theory, and this is actually the way in which it was first obtained by Heisenberg.

Complementarity Principle. In order to understand the implications of the uncertainty principle in more physical terms, Bohr[1] introduced the *complementarity principle* in 1928. This principle states that atomic phenomena cannot be described with the completeness demanded by classical dynamics; some of the elements that complement each other to make up a complete classical description are actually mutually exclusive, and these complementary elements are all necessary for the description of various aspects of the phenomena. From the point of view of the experimenter, the complementarity principle asserts that the physical apparatus available to him has such properties that more precise measurements than those indicated by the uncertainty principle cannot be made.

This is not to be regarded as a deficiency of the experimenter or of his techniques. It is rather a law of nature that, whenever an attempt is made to measure precisely one of the pair of canonical variables, the other is changed by an amount that cannot be too closely calculated without interfering with the primary attempt. This is fundamentally different from the classical situation, in which a measurement also disturbs the system that is under observation, but the amount of the disturbance can be calculated and taken into account. Thus the complementarity principle typifies the fundamental limitations on the classical concept that the behavior of atomic systems can be described independently of the means by which they are observed.

Limitations on Experiment. In the atomic field, we must choose between various experimental arrangements, each designed to measure the two members of a pair of canonical variables with different degrees of precision that are compatible with the uncertainty relations. In particular, there are two extreme arrangements, each of which measures one member of the pair with great precision. According to classical theory, these extreme experimental arrangements complement each other; the results of both may be obtained at once and are necessary to supply a complete classical description of the system. In quantum mechanics, however, the extreme complementary experiments are mutually exclusive and cannot be performed together.

It is in this sense that the classical concept of causality disappears in the atomic field. There is causality in so far as the quantum laws that describe the behavior of atoms are perfectly definite; there is not, however, a causal relationship between successive configurations of an

---

[1] N. Bohr, *Nature*, **121**, 580 (1928); "Atomic Theory and the Description of Nature," especially Part II (Cambridge, London, 1934); *Phys. Rev.*, **48**, 696 (1935).

atomic system when we attempt to describe these configurations in classical terms.

4. DISCUSSION OF MEASUREMENT

In this section we consider three fairly typical measurement experiments from the point of view of the new quantum mechanics. The first two are designed to determine the position and momentum of a particle by optical methods; the third is the diffraction experiment in Sec. 2.

Localization Experiment. We consider a particular example of the validity of the uncertainty principle, making use of a position-momentum determination that is typical of a number of somewhat similar experiments that have been discussed in connection with measurements on particles and radiation fields.[1] We shall consider here the accuracy with which the x components of the position and momentum vectors of a material particle can be determined at the same time by observing the particle through a rather idealized microscope by means of scattered light.

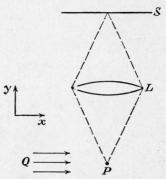

The best resolving power of the lens L shown in Fig. 2 is known (either experimentally or from the theory of wave optics) to provide an accuracy

$$\Delta x \sim \frac{\lambda}{\sin \epsilon} \qquad (4.1)$$

in a position determination, where λ is the wave length of the radiation that enters the lens, and ϵ is the half angle subtended at the particle P by the lens. For simplicity, we consider the case in which only one of the light quanta Q is scattered onto the screen S. Because of the finite aperture of the lens, the precise direction in which the photon is scattered into the lens is not known. Then since Eq. (1.2) states that the momentum of the photon after it is scattered is h/λ,[2] the uncertainty in the x component of its momentum is approximately $(h/\lambda) \sin \epsilon$.

FIG. 2. An experiment for the localization of a particle P by means of one of the scattered quanta Q, which is focused by the lens L to form an image on the screen S.

The x components of the momenta of the photon and the particle can be accurately known before the scattering takes place, since there is no need then to know the x components of their positions. Also, if our position measurement refers to the displacement of the particle with respect to the microscope, there is no reason why the total momentum of

---

[1] See, for example, W. Heisenberg, "The Physical Principles of the Quantum Theory," Chaps. II, III (University of Chicago Press, Chicago, 1930); D. Bohm, "Quantum Theory," Chap. 5 (Prentice-Hall, New York, 1951).

[2] See footnote 2, page 3.

the system (particle, photon, and microscope) need be altered during the scattering. Then the uncertainty Δp_x in the x component of the momentum of the particle after the scattering is equal to the corresponding uncertainty for the photon.

$$\Delta p_x \sim \frac{h}{\lambda} \sin \epsilon \qquad (4.2)$$

If we combine Eq. (4.1) with Eq. (4.2), we see that just after the scattering process,

$$\Delta x \cdot \Delta p_x \sim h \qquad (4.3)$$

is the best that we can do for the particle. Thus a realistic accounting of the properties of the radiation gives a result in agreement with the uncertainty relation (3.1) for the particle.

This experiment may also be considered from the point of view of the complementarity principle. The complementary arrangements differ in the choice of wave length of the observed radiation: sufficiently small λ permits an accurate determination of the position of the particle just after the scattering process, and large λ of its momentum.

Momentum Determination Experiment. The experiment just discussed assumes that the momentum of the particle is accurately known before the measurement takes place, and then measures the position. It is found that the measurement not only gives a somewhat inaccurate position determination but also introduces an uncertainty into the momentum.

We now consider a different experiment in which the position is accurately known at the beginning, and the momentum is measured. We shall see that the measurement not only gives a somewhat inaccurate momentum determination but also introduces an uncertainty into the position. We assume that the particle is an atom in an excited state, which will give off a photon that has the frequency ν_0 if the atom is at rest. Because of the Doppler effect, motion of the atom toward the observer with speed v means that the observed frequency is given approximately by

$$\nu \cong \nu_0 \left(1 + \frac{v}{c}\right) \qquad (4.4)$$

so that

$$v \cong c \left(\frac{\nu}{\nu_0} - 1\right) \qquad (4.5)$$

Accurate measurement of the momentum mv by measurement of the frequency ν requires a relatively long time τ; the minimum error in the frequency measurement can be shown to be

$$\Delta \nu \sim \frac{1}{\tau} \qquad (4.6)$$

Now the instant at which the photon is emitted is uncertain by τ; at this instant, the momentum of the atom decreases by $h\nu/c$, and its velocity decreases by $h\nu/mc$. This makes the subsequent position of the atom uncertain by the amount

$$\Delta x = \frac{h\nu\tau}{mc} \tag{4.7}$$

since the later the photon is emitted, the longer the atom has the higher velocity and the farther it will have traveled. This position uncertainty arises entirely because of the finiteness of τ. If τ were zero, and we knew the velocity and the velocity change on emission of the photon, we would know where the atom is at each instant; it is because τ is finite that we do not know when the velocity changed, and hence where the atom is at later times.

The momentum uncertainty is obtained with the help of Eqs. (4.5) and (4.6):

$$\Delta p_x = m\Delta v \cong \frac{mc\Delta\nu}{\nu_0} \sim \frac{mc}{\nu_0\tau} \tag{4.8}$$

In the nonrelativistic case considered here, $v/c \ll 1$, and Eq. (4.4) shows that $\nu \cong \nu_0$. Then combination of Eqs. (4.7) and (4.8) leads to the minimum uncertainty relation (3.1).

Analysis of Diffraction Experiment. Finally, we analyze the diffraction experiment of Sec. 2 from the point of view of the complementarity principle, assuming that the uncertainty principle is valid. Two contrasting arrangements, which would complement each other classically, are considered here. One of these is illustrated in Fig. 1. Since it is assumed that the distance from A to B is large compared to the distance between the two slits, and this in turn is large compared to the wave length of the light, the distribution of intensity in the diffraction pattern determines to good approximation the angular distribution of the photons leaving the slits in A, and hence determines the distribution of the y components of momentum of the photons beyond A. The second arrangement, shown in Fig. 3, determines through which of the two slits each photon passes, and hence provides information on the y coordinates of the photons.

In the second arrangement each photon registers itself as it passes through a slit by bouncing off one of a number of indicators C placed close to A, and giving up to it a y component of momentum that may be uncertain by the amount Δp_y. If we do not want the resultant diffraction pattern of many such photons to be destroyed by these events, the uncertainty in p_y for a particular photon produced by its encounter with an indicator must be substantially smaller than would be required to throw the photon from a maximum of the diffraction pattern at B into a

neighboring minimum. With a photon of momentum p_x, this requires
that

$$\Delta p_y \ll \theta p_x \tag{4.9}$$

For the simple case in which $R \gg a \gg \lambda$, the angle θ is known experimentally (or from the theory of wave optics) to be given by

$$\theta = \frac{\lambda}{2a} \tag{4.10}$$

in terms of the optical wave length λ and the distance a between the slits.
At the same time, we have not learned through which slit this photon

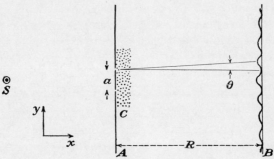

Fig. 3. The experimental arrangement of Fig. 1, modified by the addition of photon
indicators C.

passed unless the uncertainty Δy of the y position of the indicator that
recoiled is less than half the distance between slits.

$$\Delta y < \tfrac{1}{2}a \tag{4.11}$$

It then follows from Eqs. (4.9), (4.10), (4.11), and (1.2) that the
requirement that we be able to determine through which slit each photon
passes without destroying the diffraction pattern at B is equivalent to the
requirement that

$$\Delta y \cdot \Delta p_y \ll \tfrac{1}{4}h \tag{4.12}$$

for each indicator that is used. Since Eq. (4.12) is in disagreement with
the uncertainty relation (3.1), we may conclude that it is impossible
to determine through which slits the photons pass without destroying the
diffraction pattern.

Discussion of Diffraction Experiment. The situation just analyzed
shows the intimate connection between the theoretical principles of
uncertainty and complementarity and the experimental observations
related to localization and diffraction. It provides an explicit demonstration of the validity of the complementarity principle (represented in
this case by the choice between the mutually exclusive but classically
complementary experiments for observing the diffraction and for localizing the photon) when taken in conjunction with the experimentally
observable properties of matter and radiation. For it shows that no

fundamental difficulty need be encountered with the photon picture so long as we do not insist on the degree of detail in describing the situation that is entailed by classical concepts.

It is, of course, still necessary to ascribe unfamiliar properties to the photons in order to explain the experimental observations; the foregoing discussion does not show how an individual photon can interfere with itself to produce the diffraction pattern.[1] Nor on the other hand does it show how an electromagnetic wave can eject photoelectrons from the screen.[2] Such demonstrations lie beyond the scope of the qualitative discussion of this chapter, and require the use of the mathematical formalism of quantum mechanics. However, analysis of the diffraction experiment from the point of view of quantum mechanics removes the difficulty encountered in Sec. 2: the diffraction pattern disappears whenever a successful attempt is made to determine through which slit each photon passes.

5. WAVE PACKETS IN SPACE AND TIME

The relation (1.2) between momentum and wave length, which is known experimentally to be valid for both photons and particles, suggests that it might be possible to use concentrated bunches of waves to describe localized particles of matter and quanta of radiation. To fix our ideas, we shall consider a *wave amplitude* or *wave function* that depends on the space coordinates x,y,z and the time t. This quantity ψ is assumed to have three basic properties. First, it can interfere with itself, so that it can account for the results of diffraction experiments. Second, it is large in magnitude where the particle or photon is likely to be and small elsewhere. And third, ψ will be regarded as describing the behavior of a single particle or photon, not the statistical distribution of a number of such quanta. This last is an essential requirement in view of the conclusion of Sec. 2 that a single quantum of matter or radiation interferes with itself rather than with other quanta. In this section we shall confine ourselves to a qualitative discussion of the one-dimensional case, in which the wave function ψ depends only on x and t, and leave the quantitative development for Chap. II.

Space Packets. A typical form for a concentrated bunch of waves, which we shall call a *wave packet*, is shown in Fig. 4a, where $\psi(x,t)$ is plotted against x for a particular time t. The average wave length λ_0 and the approximate extension Δx of the packet are indicated in the diagram. The Fourier integral analysis[3] of ψ with respect to x is now of

[1] Chapter VI shows the equivalence of the wave theory of Chap. II and the general quantum-mechanical theory of particles, so far as matter is concerned.

[2] Chapter XIV shows how the theory of the electromagnetic field can be modified to include quantum effects.

[3] See, for example, L. A. Pipes, "Applied Mathematics for Engineers and Physicists," Chap. III (McGraw-Hill, New York, 1946).

interest since it shows how ψ may be built up out of continuous harmonic waves of various lengths. This is indicated in Fig. 4b, in which the Fourier transform of ψ is plotted schematically against the *propagation number* $k = 2\pi/\lambda$.

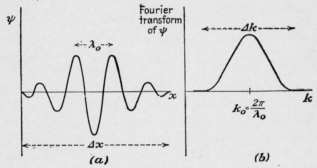

FIG. 4.   Plots of a typical wave packet $\psi(x)$ and its Fourier transform.

It can be shown by standard mathematical methods that

$$\Delta k \gtrsim \frac{1}{\Delta x} \tag{5.1}$$

where Δk is the approximate spread in propagation number associated with the packet. If now we correlate wave length and momentum as in Eq. (1.2) we see that the spread Δk corresponds to a momentun spread

$$\Delta p = \Delta\left(\frac{h}{\lambda}\right) = \frac{h}{2\pi}\,\Delta k = \hbar \cdot \Delta k \tag{5.2}$$

Combination of Eq. (5.1) with Eq. (5.2) gives

$$\Delta x \cdot \Delta p \gtrsim \hbar \tag{5.3}$$

which agrees with the uncertainty relation (3.1). Thus the uncertainty principle for position and momentum of a quantum of matter or radiation follows directly from the wave-packet description and Eq. (1.2).

Time Packets. In analogous fashion, we may examine the dependence of ψ on the time t for a point x that is typical of the packet, and obtain a time Fourier transform that shows how ψ can be built up out of continuous harmonic waves of various frequencies ν. In this case the relation between the spread in time of ψ and the spread in frequency of the time Fourier transform of ψ is

$$\Delta t \cdot \Delta \nu \gtrsim \frac{1}{2\pi} \tag{5.4}$$

Equation (5.4) may be brought into correspondence with the uncertainty principle by associating the energy E of a quantum with the frequency of the wave that represents it in a manner similar to the association of momentum with wave length given by Eq. (1.2). We shall make this connection through Eq. (1.1):

$$E = h\nu \tag{5.5}$$

which may be inferred in the case of photons from the experimental discussion of Sec. 1. Combination of Eq. (5.4) with Eq. (5.5) then gives the uncertainty relation (3.3).

The assumption that Eq. (5.5) is valid for matter as well as for radiation may be made plausible by computing the group velocity[1] of a wave packet that represents a nonrelativistic particle of mass m, kinetic energy E, and momentum p for which λ and ν are given by Eqs. (1.2) and (5.5), respectively. The group velocity, which is the velocity of the center of the packet, is equal to

$$\frac{d\nu}{d(1/\lambda)} = \frac{dE}{dp} = \frac{d(p^2/2m)}{dp} = \frac{p}{m} \tag{5.6}$$

in agreement with the classical expression for the velocity. This shows that with Eq. (5.5), the wave-packet description of the motion of a particle agrees with the classical description when the circumstances are such that we can ignore the size and internal structure of the packet.

Wave Formalism. We see then that quanta of matter or radiation can be represented in agreement with the uncertainty principle by wave packets that may be superposed to produce interference and whose magnitudes give a measure of likelihood of location, provided that use is made of the experimentally inferred relations (1.2) and (5.5). It is then possible to set up a quantitative formalism based on the mathematical analysis of wave motion. This will be done for matter in Chap. II, using the physical principles outlined in this chapter as a guide, and requiring always that the result of any calculation reduce to the result of the corresponding classical calculation in the appropriate limit. This requirement is a way of stating Bohr's correspondence principle, which was mentioned in Sec. 2. At the present time, when a reasonably complete quantum theory exists, the correspondence principle is mainly of interest in assuring that the formalism has the proper classical limit, although it may also be of heuristic value in performing new calculations or extending the boundaries of the theory.

It might at first be thought that the exclusive use of a wave formalism for the description of matter in the next four chapters would conflict with the observed particle-wave duality discussed in Sec. 1 and hence disagree with the complementarity principle. This is not the case, however, for the formalism actually provides an understanding of all of the measurable properties of matter, including, for example, the production of particle tracks in a cloud chamber. Thus it will be shown in Sec. 30 that, if a single material particle is represented by a wave function of definite momentum and hence completely undetermined position, the

---

[1] M. Born, *op. cit.*, pp. 88, 330.

probability of ionization of two or more molecules of the cloud-chamber gas is negligibly small unless the molecules lie very nearly along a line parallel to the momentum vector.

It must be emphasized that these remarks are true only if a wave function of the type described in this section is always interpreted as representing just one particle of matter, and not the statistical distribution of a number of particles. When we wish to describe more than one particle, we must make use of a wave function that depends on the coordinates of all of them. The analogous analytical description of light quanta, which will be taken up quantitatively in Chap. XIV, makes use of a somewhat different approach. This is mainly because photons (unlike particles as we consider them here) can be emitted or absorbed through interaction with matter, so that their number is not fixed. Thus a photon wave function would have to depend on a variable number of parameters, and it is desirable to avoid such a situation.

Problems

1. Give a brief description of each of the experiments referred to in Table 1, together with their interpretations.

2. Describe briefly the Davisson-Germer and Thomson experiments, and the use of the Wilson cloud chamber for the observation of particle tracks.

3. A beam of silver atoms for a Stern-Gerlach experiment is produced by collimating atoms that vaporize from silver held in a furnace at 1200°C. If the beam travels 1 meter, use the uncertainty relation to find the order of magnitude of the smallest spot that can be obtained at the detector.

4. Show that if a component of angular momentum of the electron of a hydrogen atom is known to be $2\hbar$ within 5 per cent error, its angular orbital position in the plane perpendicular to that component cannot be specified at all.

5. A 1-ounce rifle bullet takes 0.5 second to reach its target. Regarding the bullet as a mass point, and neglecting effects of air resistance and earth motion, find the order of magnitude of the spread of successive shots at the target under optimum conditions of aiming and firing.

6. A perfectly elastic ping-pong ball is dropped in vacuum from a height equal to ten times its radius onto a perfectly elastic fixed sphere of the same radius. Neglecting effects due to earth motion, estimate the largest number of bounces against the fixed sphere that the ball can be expected to make under optimum conditions of release.

7. A beam of monoenergetic electrons is used to excite a particular level of an atom in a Franck-Hertz experiment. If this level is of short duration, owing to radiation back to the ground state, show that the inelastically scattered electrons that have lost energy to produce the excited level will not all be expected to have the same final energy. If the excited level lasts about 10^{-10} second, what is the order of magnitude of the electron energy spread, measured in electron-volts?

8. Discuss any connections you can think of that exist between the three uncertainty relations (3.1), (3.2), and (3.3).

9. Derive the expression for the group velocity that is given as the left side of Eq. (5.6).

CHAPTER II

THE SCHRÖDINGER WAVE EQUATION

This and the next several chapters are concerned with the non-relativistic motion of a particle in a force field that can be represented by a potential energy. A quantitative description of the motion in terms of a differential equation, the *Schrödinger wave equation*, is developed in this chapter, and applied to a simple one-dimensional problem. Various assumptions have to be made as regards the structure of the wave equation, the boundary and continuity conditions on its solutions, and the physical meaning of these solutions. These assumptions are given a high degree of plausibility in this chapter and the next by relating them to experimental results, mainly those that deal with the diffraction of material particles and with the existence of a classical limit to the quantum mechanics. However, no attempt is made to derive the formalism uniquely from a consideration of the experiments. The definitive test of the theory must, of course, be its internal consistency and the success with which deductions from it agree with particular experimental measurements; some examples will be worked out in Chaps. IV and V.

6. DEVELOPMENT OF THE WAVE EQUATION

The form of the Schrödinger wave equation is obtained in this section by generalizing the properties of the wave amplitude of Sec. 5. The remainder of this chapter presents a discussion of some of the properties of the equation and its solutions.

Traveling Harmonic Waves. The first task is to develop in more quantitative fashion the properties of the one-dimensional wave function $\psi(x,t)$ that was discussed qualitatively in Sec. 5. It was shown there that for a continuous traveling harmonic wave, the wave length and momentum are related by Eq. (1.2) and the energy and frequency by Eq. (5.5). We rewrite these two equations in terms of the universal constant $\hbar = h/2\pi$:

$$p = \hbar k, \qquad k = \frac{2\pi}{\lambda} \tag{6.1}$$

$$E = \hbar\omega, \qquad \omega = 2\pi\nu \tag{6.2}$$

A wave function $\psi(x,t)$ that represents a particle of completely undetermined position traveling in the positive x direction with precisely

17

known momentum p and kinetic energy E, would then be expected to have one of the forms

$$\cos (kx - \omega t), \qquad \sin (kx - \omega t), \qquad e^{i(kx-\omega t)}, \qquad e^{-i(kx-\omega t)} \qquad (6.3)$$

or some linear combination of them. This follows from diffraction experiments like those of Davisson and Germer and of Thomson (see Sec. 1), and from the requirement that a wave packet of approximately the propagation number k and angular frequency ω has a group velocity equal to that of a classical free particle of momentum p and energy E [see Eq. (5.6)].

Need for a Wave Equation. In order to go beyond the very simplest problem of a continuous harmonic wave, it is very desirable to have an equation of which both the harmonic waves and more complicated waves are solutions. An example from a more familiar field of physics should help to clarify this point. In the case of three-dimensional sound waves in a gas, it is possible to obtain a solution of the problem of the scattering of sound by a rigid sphere by superposing plane harmonic waves traveling in various directions. But it is far simpler to solve the differential equation for sound waves directly in spherical polar coordinates. If the temperature of the gas changes from point to point, no progress can be made in the general case without such a differential equation. The correct underlying equation for sound waves can be found from direct consideration of the mechanical properties of the gas. While this is not the case with the equation of which the wave functions of Sec. 5 are solutions, it is no less imperative to find the form of the equation. The need for this becomes more evident when the wave function is to describe the motion of a particle under the influence of external forces; this situation turns out to be analogous to the propagation of sound waves in an inhomogeneous gas. We shall, therefore, find an equation for ψ, and having found it, shall regard it as a more fundamental attribute of the wave functions than the harmonic forms (6.3).

The equation must have two basic properties. First, it must be linear, in order that solutions of it can be superposed to produce interference effects (in the three-dimensional case) and to permit the construction of wave packets. And second, the coefficients of the equation must involve only constants such as $\hbar$ and the mass and charge of the particle, and not the parameters of a particular kind of motion of the particle (momentum, energy, propagation number, and frequency). The reason for the latter requirement is that we shall want to leave open the possibility of superposing solutions that belong to different values of these parameters; this means that such a more general wave function cannot be a solution of an equation that involves the parameters in its structure.   Since differential equations are the easiest to handle, it is worth while to try this type first, and it turns out that the requirements can be met by a differential equation.

With all these considerations in mind, we look first at the most familiar one-dimensional wave equation, that which describes the motion of transverse waves on a string or plane sound waves in a gas:

$$\frac{\partial^2 \psi}{\partial t^2} = \gamma \frac{\partial^2 \psi}{\partial x^2} \qquad (6.4)$$

where γ is the square of the wave velocity.   Substitution of the forms (6.3) into Eq. (6.4) shows that each of the four harmonic solutions, and hence any linear combination of them, satisfies this differential equation, if and only if we put

$$\gamma = \frac{\omega^2}{k^2} = \frac{E^2}{p^2} = \frac{p^2}{4m^2} \qquad (6.5)$$

where m is the mass of the particle that is to be described by Eq. (6.4). Because of the structure of Eq. (6.5) it is apparent that the coefficient γ that appears in Eq. (6.4) involves the parameters of the motion (E or p); we therefore discard this differential equation.

The One-dimensional Wave Equation.   In looking further for a suitable equation, it is helpful to note that differentiation with respect to x of wave functions like those of (6.3) has the general effect of multiplication of the function by k (and sometimes also interchanging sine and cosine), while differentiation with respect to t has the general effect of multiplication by ω.   Then the relation $E = p^2/2m$, which is equivalent to the relation $\omega = \hbar k^2/2m$, suggests that the differential equation for which we are looking contains a first derivative with respect to t and a second derivative with respect to x.

$$\frac{\partial \psi}{\partial t} = \gamma \frac{\partial^2 \psi}{\partial x^2} \qquad (6.6)$$

Substitution shows that the first two of the wave functions (6.3) are not solutions of Eq. (6.6), but that either of the last two may be (but not both at once) if the constant γ is suitably chosen.   In particular, if we choose

$$\gamma = \frac{i\omega}{k^2} = \frac{i\hbar E}{p^2} = \frac{i\hbar}{2m} \qquad (6.7)$$

then the third of the wave functions (6.3) satisfies Eq. (6.6).   Moreover, the value of γ given by Eq. (6.7) involves only the constants $\hbar$ and m.

We are thus led to the one-dimensional form of the Schrödinger[1] wave

---

[1] E. Schrödinger, *Ann. d. Physik,* **79,** 361, 489 (1926); **81,** 109 (1926).   The present treatment is somewhat different from that originally given by Schrödinger.

equation for a free particle of mass m, which from Eqs. (6.6) and (6.7) may be written

$$i\hbar \frac{\partial \psi}{\partial t} = -\frac{\hbar^2}{2m} \frac{\partial^2 \psi}{\partial x^2} \tag{6.8}$$

The particular form in which Eq. (6.8) is written is significant in so far as its harmonic solution, the third of the wave functions (6.3), makes the left side $E\psi$ and the right side $(p^2/2m)\psi$. The fact that the solution $e^{i(kx-\omega t)}$ is complex is not in itself a defect of the formalism. We shall have to be certain that all predicted results of possible physical observations are expressible in terms of real numbers, and this will supply a condition on the detailed interpretation of ψ.

Extension to Three Dimensions. The foregoing one-dimensional treatment is readily extended to three dimensions. It is natural to rewrite Eq. (6.1) as

$$\mathbf{p} = \hbar\mathbf{k}, \qquad k = |\mathbf{k}| = \frac{2\pi}{\lambda} \tag{6.9}$$

where $\mathbf{k}$ is called the *propagation vector*. Similarly, the third of the wave functions (6.3) becomes

$$\exp{[i(\mathbf{k} \cdot \mathbf{r} - \omega t)]} \tag{6.10}$$

where $\mathbf{r}$ is the position vector for the particle. Then by an obvious extension of the argument that led up to Eq. (6.8), it is seen that the three-dimensional Schrödinger equation for a free particle that is represented by the wave function $\psi(\mathbf{r},t)$ is

$$i\hbar \frac{\partial \psi}{\partial t} = -\frac{\hbar^2}{2m} \nabla^2 \psi. \tag{6.11}$$

A comparison of Eqs. (6.9), (6.10), (6.11), and the classical energy equation

$$E = \frac{\mathbf{p}^2}{2m} \tag{6.12}$$

suggests that, at least for a free particle, the energy and momentum can be represented by differential operators that act on the wave function ψ.

$$E \rightarrow i\hbar \frac{\partial}{\partial t}, \qquad \mathbf{p} \rightarrow -i\hbar \,\mathbf{grad} \tag{6.13}$$

The development of Secs. 7, 8, 10, and 11 will show that these are also valid representations when the particle is not free.

Inclusion of Forces. The next problem is to extend the free-particle wave equation (6.11) so that it includes the effects of external forces that may act on the particle. We shall assume for the present that these forces are of such a nature (electrostatic, gravitational, possibly nuclear) that they can be combined into a single force **F** that is derivable from a potential energy V.

$$\mathbf{F}(\mathbf{r},t) = - \operatorname{grad} V(\mathbf{r},t) \tag{6.14}$$

Just as the classical relation between energy and momentum is used above to infer the structure of Eq. (6.11), so it is desirable now to start from the corresponding classical relation that includes external forces. This is simply expressed in terms of the potential energy

$$E = \frac{\mathbf{p}^2}{2m} + V(\mathbf{r},t) \tag{6.15}$$

where E is now the total energy, and the first and second terms on the right side of Eq. (6.15) are the kinetic and potential energies of the particle, respectively.

Since V does not depend on $\mathbf{p}$ or E, Eqs. (6.15) and (6.13) suggest that Eq. (6.11) be generalized into

$$i\hbar \frac{\partial \psi}{\partial t} = - \frac{\hbar^2}{2m} \nabla^2 \psi + V(\mathbf{r},t)\psi \tag{6.16}$$

This is the Schrödinger wave equation that describes the motion of a particle of mass m in a force field given by Eq. (6.14).[1] While the introduction of Eq. (6.16) cannot claim as high a degree of plausibility as the derivation of the free-particle equation (6.11), the further discussion of the next section should make it more convincing. It is, of course, the agreement of solutions of Eq. (6.16) with experiment in particular cases that eventually demonstrates the validity and usefulness of this wave equation.

7. INTERPRETATION OF THE WAVE FUNCTION

The wave function $\psi(\mathbf{r},t)$, which is a solution of the wave equation (6.16), is now assumed to provide a quantum-mechanically complete description of the behavior of a particle of mass m with the potential energy $V(\mathbf{r},t)$, and hence is analogous to the classical trajectory $\mathbf{r}(t)$. Thus far, the only interpretative guide available to us is that the wave function be large where the particle is likely to be and small elsewhere. This has to be supplemented with more detailed statements that enable us to get out of ψ the maximum amount of information permitted by nature, as was discussed in Sec. 3. As with the structure of the wave equation, the correctness of our interpretation of the wave function must be judged by logical consistency and appeal to experimental results.

---

[1] The development of the wave function in time can also be related to integrals over all possible paths of the particle; see R. P. Feynman, *Rev. Mod. Phys.*, **20**, 367 (1948).

Statistical Interpretation. The phrase "likely to be" in the preceding paragraph, together with the discussion of Sec. 3, indicates the need for interpreting ψ in statistical terms. We can imagine a very large number of identical, independent, nonoverlapping regions of space, each large enough to contain all the physically interesting features of the motion, in each of which the behavior of a particle with the potential energy $V(\mathbf{r},t)$ is described by the same wave function $\psi(\mathbf{r},t)$; in each case $\mathbf{r}$ is referred to the origin of the particular region. We then make the assumption, due to Born[1], that the numerical result of the measurement at a particular time t (in so far as the time at which the measurement is made can be specified) of any physically meaningful quantity, such as position, momentum, or energy, will in general not be the same for all the regions. Rather, there will be a distribution of these numbers that can be described by a probability function.

For example, we have seen in Sec. 5 that the result of a position determination is to be regarded as uncertain by an amount of the order of the linear dimensions of the wave function. It is natural therefore to regard ψ as a measure of the probability of finding a particle at a particular position with respect to the origin of its region. However, a probability must be real and nonnegative, whereas ψ is complex in general. We therefore assume that the product of ψ and its complex conjugate $\bar\psi$ is the *position probability density*.

$$P(\mathbf{r},t) = |\psi(\mathbf{r},t)|^2 \qquad (7.1)$$

This means that $P(\mathbf{r},t)dxdydz$ is to be the probability of finding a particle in its volume element $dxdydz$ about its point $\mathbf{r}$ at the time t, when a large number of precise position measurements are made on independent particles each of which is described by the one-particle wave function $\psi(\mathbf{r},t)$.

Normalization of ψ. The probability of finding the particle somewhere in the region must be unity, so that Eq. (7.1) implies that the wave function is *normalized*:

$$\int|\psi(\mathbf{r},t)|^2d\tau = 1 \qquad (7.2)$$

where the integral extends over the entire region; here $d\tau$ is the volume element $dxdydz$. If ψ is a wave packet of the type discussed in Sec. 5, the integral in Eq. (7.2) converges, and the numerical coefficient of ψ may be adjusted so that the integral is unity; such normalization does not of course change the fact that ψ is a solution of Eq. (6.16), which is homogeneous in ψ. There are, however, wave functions like that given in Eq. (6.10) for which the integral in Eq. (7.2) does not converge if taken over an infinite volume. Such wave functions require special considera-

[1] M. Born, *Zeits. f. Physik*, **37**, 863 (1926); *Nature*, **119**, 354 (1927).

tion, and will be discussed further in Secs. 10 and 11. For the present, we may think of the region of space in which such a wave function is defined as being arbitrarily large, but finite; then the integral in Eq. (7.2) is over the finite volume of this region and converges, so that normalization is always possible.

The coefficient of ψ that normalizes it must be independent of the time in order that ψ may satisfy the wave equation (6.16). Thus if Eq. (7.2) is satisfied at one instant of time, the interpretation of $|\psi|^2$ as a position probability density requires that the normalization integral be independent of the time. That this is actually the case may be shown by computing the time derivative of the integral of P over any fixed volume V.

$$
\frac{\partial}{\partial t} \int_V P(\mathbf{r},t)\, d\tau = \int_V \left(\bar{\psi}\frac{\partial \psi}{\partial t} + \frac{\partial \bar{\psi}}{\partial t}\psi \right) d\tau
$$

$$
= \frac{i\hbar}{2m} \int_V [\bar{\psi}\nabla^2\psi - (\nabla^2\bar{\psi})\psi]\, d\tau
$$

$$
= \frac{i\hbar}{2m} \int_V \operatorname{div}[\bar{\psi}\operatorname{grad}\psi - (\operatorname{grad}\bar{\psi})\psi]\, d\tau
$$

$$
= \frac{i\hbar}{2m} \int_A [\bar{\psi}\operatorname{grad}\psi - (\operatorname{grad}\bar{\psi})\,\psi]_n\, dA.
$$

Here substitution has been made for $\partial\psi/\partial t$ from Eq. (6.16), and for $\partial\bar{\psi}/\partial t$ from the complex conjugate of Eq. (6.16). The last integral is obtained by partial integration (use of Green's theorem), where A is the bounding surface of the region of integration and $[\ ]_n$ denotes the component of the vector in brackets in the direction of the outward normal to the surface element dA.[1]

We define a vector $\mathbf{S}(\mathbf{r},t)$,

$$
\mathbf{S}(\mathbf{r},t) = \frac{\hbar}{2im} [\bar{\psi}\operatorname{grad}\psi - (\operatorname{grad}\bar{\psi})\psi] \tag{7.3}
$$

in terms of which

$$
\frac{\partial}{\partial t} \int_V P(\mathbf{r},t)\, d\tau = -\int_V \operatorname{div}\mathbf{S}\, d\tau = -\int_A S_n\, dA \tag{7.4}
$$

In the case of a wave packet, for which ψ vanishes at great distances and the normalization integral converges, the surface integral is evidently zero when V is the entire space. For a wave function of the type given in Eq. (6.10), ψ can be defined in a finite region V so that it vanishes or has a periodic structure along the bounding surfaces (see Sec. 10). In all these cases, it can be shown without difficulty that the surface integral in

---

[1] It is convenient to adopt an order of factors such that $\bar{\psi}$ precedes ψ [see the discussion of Eq. (7.7) below].

Eq. (7.4) is zero, so that the normalization integral in Eq. (7.2) is constant in time.

Probability Current Density. The derivation of Eq. (7.4) also shows that the differential relation

$$\frac{\partial P(\mathbf{r},t)}{\partial t} + \text{div } \mathbf{S}(\mathbf{r},t) = 0$$

is valid. This has the familiar form associated with the conservation of flow of a fluid of density P and current density $\mathbf{S}$, in which there are no sources or sinks. It is thus reasonable to interpret $\mathbf{S}(\mathbf{r},t)$ given by Eq. (7.3) as a *probability current density*. This interpretation makes more plausible the identification of $-i\hbar$ **grad** with the momentum in Eq. (6.13), even when a force is present. For then $(\hbar/im)$ **grad** is the velocity operator, and it is apparent that

$$\mathbf{S}(\mathbf{r},t) = \text{real part of } \left(\bar{\psi}\, \frac{\hbar}{im}\, \textbf{grad } \psi \right)$$

While this interpretation of $\mathbf{S}$ is suggestive, it must be realized that $\mathbf{S}$ is not susceptible to direct measurement in the sense in which P is. It would be misleading, for example, to say that $\mathbf{S}(\mathbf{r},t)$ is the average measured particle flux at the point $\mathbf{r}$ and the time t, for a measurement of average local flux implies simultaneous high-precision measurements of position and velocity (which is equivalent to momentum) and is therefore inconsistent with the uncertainty relation (3.1). Nevertheless, it is sometimes helpful to think of $\mathbf{S}$ as a flux vector, especially when it depends only slightly or not at all on $\mathbf{r}$, so that an accurate velocity determination can be made without impairing the usefulness of the concept of flux.

Expectation Value. The existence of the position probability density $P(\mathbf{r},t)$ makes it possible to calculate what we shall call the *expectation value* of the position vector of a particle, which is defined as the vector whose components are the weighted averages of the corresponding components of the position of the particle. The expectation value is the mathematical expectation (in the sense of probability theory) for the result of a single measurement, or it is the average of the results of a large number of measurements on independent systems of the type discussed at the beginning of this section. We write the expectation value of $\mathbf{r}$ as

$$\langle \mathbf{r} \rangle = \int \mathbf{r}P(\mathbf{r},t)d\tau = \int \bar{\psi}(\mathbf{r},t)\mathbf{r}\psi(\mathbf{r},t)d\tau \qquad (7.5)$$

which is equivalent to the three equations

$$\langle x \rangle = \int \bar{\psi}x\psi d\tau, \qquad \langle y \rangle = \int \bar{\psi}y\psi d\tau, \qquad \langle z \rangle = \int \bar{\psi}z\psi d\tau$$

where ψ is normalized.   The expectation value is a function only of the time, since ψ and P depend on t and the space coordinates have been integrated out.

The expectation values of any other physically meaningful quantities can be found in a similar way if they are functions only of the particle coordinate $\mathbf{r}$.   Thus the expectation value of the potential energy is

$$\langle V \rangle = \int V(\mathbf{r},t)P(\mathbf{r},t)d\tau = \int \bar{\psi}(\mathbf{r},t)V(\mathbf{r},t)\psi(\mathbf{r},t)d\tau \qquad (7.6)$$

A quantity such as momentum or energy must, however, be expressed in terms of $\mathbf{r}$ and t before a calculation of this type can be made.   We assume that it is possible to use the differential-operator representations given in Eq. (6.13) for this purpose, and justify this assumption with the help of the corresponding probability functions in Sec. 10 (for the energy) and in Sec. 11 (for the momentum).   The question immediately arises, however, as to how such differential operators are to be combined with the position probability density P.

This question may be answered by imposing on the expectation values the reasonable requirement that

$$\langle E \rangle = \left\langle \frac{\mathbf{p}^2}{2m} \right\rangle + \langle V \rangle$$

in analogy with the classical energy equation (6.15).   In terms of differential operators, this may be written

$$\left\langle i\hbar \frac{\partial}{\partial t} \right\rangle = \left\langle -\frac{\hbar^2}{2m}\nabla^2 \right\rangle + \langle V \rangle \qquad (7.7)$$

It is apparent that Eq. (7.7) is consistent with the wave equation (6.16) only if the expectation value is defined in the general case with the operator acting on ψ, and multiplied on the left by $\bar{\psi}$.   We therefore obtain, for example,

$$\langle E \rangle = \int \bar{\psi} i\hbar \frac{\partial \psi}{\partial t}\,d\tau, \qquad \langle \mathbf{p} \rangle = \int \bar{\psi}(-i\hbar)\,\mathbf{grad}\,\psi d\tau \qquad (7.8)$$

Like Eq. (7.5), the second of Eqs. (7.8) is equivalent to the three component equations

$$\langle p_x \rangle = -i\hbar \int \bar{\psi} \frac{\partial \psi}{\partial x}\,d\tau, \qquad \langle p_y \rangle = -i\hbar \int \bar{\psi} \frac{\partial \psi}{\partial y}\,d\tau$$

$$\langle p_z \rangle = -i\hbar \int \bar{\psi} \frac{\partial \psi}{\partial z}\,d\tau$$

Ehrenfest's Theorem.[1]   It is reasonable to expect the motion of a wave packet to agree with the motion of the corresponding classical

[1] P. Ehrenfest, *Zeits. f. Physik*, **45**, 455 (1927).

particle whenever the potential energy changes by a negligible amount over the dimensions of the packet. If we mean by the "position" and "momentum" vectors of the packet the weighted averages or expectation values of these quantities, we can show that the classical and quantum motions always agree. A component of the "velocity" of the packet will be the time rate of change of the expectation value of that component of the position; since $\langle x \rangle$ depends only on the time, and the x in the integrand of Eq. (7.5) is a variable of integration, this is

$$\frac{d}{dt}\langle x \rangle = \frac{d}{dt}\int \bar{\psi}x\psi d\tau = \int \bar{\psi}x\frac{\partial\psi}{\partial t}\,d\tau + \int \frac{\partial\bar{\psi}}{\partial t}\,x\psi d\tau$$

This may be simplified by substituting for the time derivatives of the wave function and its complex conjugate from Eq. (6.16) and canceling the V terms.

$$\frac{d}{dt}\langle x \rangle = -\frac{i}{\hbar}\left[\int \bar{\psi}x\left(-\frac{\hbar^2}{2m}\nabla^2\psi + V\psi\right)d\tau \right.$$
$$\left. - \int \left(-\frac{\hbar^2}{2m}\nabla^2\bar{\psi} + V\bar{\psi}\right)x\psi d\tau\right]$$
$$= \frac{i\hbar}{2m}\int [\bar{\psi}x(\nabla^2\psi) - (\nabla^2\bar{\psi})x\psi]d\tau$$

The second integral can be integrated by parts:

$$\int (\nabla^2\bar{\psi})x\psi d\tau = -\int (\mathbf{grad}\ \bar{\psi})\cdot\mathbf{grad}\ (x\psi)d\tau + \int_A (x\psi\ \mathbf{grad}\ \bar{\psi})_n\,dA$$

where the integral of the normal component of $x\psi\ \mathbf{grad}\ \bar{\psi}$ over the infinite bounding surface A is zero because a wave packet ψ vanishes at great distances. A second partial integration, in which the surface integral again vanishes, results in

$$\int(\nabla^2\bar{\psi})x\psi d\tau = \int\bar{\psi}\nabla^2(x\psi)d\tau$$

Thus

$$\frac{d}{dt}\langle x \rangle = \frac{i\hbar}{2m}\int \bar{\psi}[x\nabla^2\psi - \nabla^2(x\psi)]d\tau$$
$$= -\frac{i\hbar}{m}\int \bar{\psi}\frac{\partial\psi}{\partial x}\,d\tau = \frac{1}{m}\langle p_x \rangle \qquad (7.9)$$

Since $\langle x \rangle$ is seen always to be a real number from the structure of Eq. (7.5), Eq. (7.9) shows quite incidentally that $\langle p_x \rangle$ is real; this can also be shown from the second of Eqs. (7.8) when ψ represents a wave packet, by means of partial integration.

In similar fashion we can calculate the time rate of change of a component of the "momentum" of the particle as

$$\frac{d}{dt}\langle p_x\rangle = -i\hbar\frac{d}{dt}\int\bar{\psi}\frac{\partial\psi}{\partial x}\,d\tau$$

$$= -i\hbar\left(\int\bar{\psi}\frac{\partial}{\partial x}\frac{\partial\psi}{\partial t}\,d\tau + \int\frac{\partial\bar{\psi}}{\partial t}\frac{\partial\psi}{\partial x}\,d\tau\right)$$

$$= -\int\bar{\psi}\frac{\partial}{\partial x}\left(-\frac{\hbar^2}{2m}\nabla^2\psi + V\psi\right)d\tau + \int\left(-\frac{\hbar^2}{2m}\nabla^2\bar{\psi} + V\bar{\psi}\right)\frac{\partial\psi}{\partial x}\,d\tau$$

$$= -\int\bar{\psi}\left[\frac{\partial}{\partial x}(V\psi) - V\frac{\partial\psi}{\partial x}\right]d\tau$$

$$= -\int\bar{\psi}\frac{\partial V}{\partial x}\psi d\tau = \left\langle -\frac{\partial V}{\partial x}\right\rangle \tag{7.10}$$

again substituting from the wave equation and integrating twice by parts.

Equations (7.9) and (7.10), together with their other components, are analogous to the classical equations of motion,

$$\frac{d\mathbf{r}}{dt} = \frac{\mathbf{p}}{m}, \qquad \frac{d\mathbf{p}}{dt} = -\text{ grad } V$$

They provide an example of the correspondence principle, since they show that a wave packet moves like a classical particle whenever the expectation value gives a good representation of the classical variable; this is usually the macroscopic limit in which the finite size and the internal structure of the packet can be ignored.

8. ENERGY EIGENFUNCTIONS

The Schrödinger wave equation (6.16) admits of considerable simplification when the potential energy $V(\mathbf{r})$ does not depend on the time. It is then possible to express its general solution as a sum of products of functions of $\mathbf{r}$ and t separately.

Separation of the Wave Equation. We consider a particular solution of Eq. (6.16) that can be written as a product: $\psi(\mathbf{r},t) = u(\mathbf{r})f(t)$; a general solution can then be written as a sum of such separated solutions. If we substitute into Eq. (6.16) and divide through by the product, we obtain

$$\frac{i\hbar}{f}\frac{df}{dt} = \frac{1}{u}\left(-\frac{\hbar^2}{2m}\nabla^2 u + V(\mathbf{r})u\right) \tag{8.1}$$

Since the left side of Eq. (8.1) depends only on t and the right side only on $\mathbf{r}$, both sides must be equal to the same separation constant, which we call E. Then the equation for f is readily integrated to give

$$f(t) = Ce^{-\frac{iEt}{\hbar}}$$

where C is an arbitrary constant, and the equation for u becomes

$$\left[-\frac{\hbar^2}{2m} \nabla^2 + V(\mathbf{r}) \right] u(\mathbf{r}) = Eu(\mathbf{r}) \tag{8.2}$$

Since Eq. (8.2) is homogeneous in u, the constant C may be chosen to normalize u. Then a particular solution of the wave equation is

$$\psi(\mathbf{r},t) = u(\mathbf{r})e^{-\frac{iEt}{\hbar}} \tag{8.3}$$

Significance of the Separation Constant E. The time-derivative operator given in Eq. (6.13) as a representation of the total energy may be applied to the ψ of Eq. (8.3) to give

$$i\hbar \frac{\partial \psi}{\partial t} = E\psi \tag{8.4}$$

An equation of the type of Eq. (8.4) is called an *eigenvalue equation; ψ* is said to be an *eigenfunction* of the operator that appears on the left, and the multiplying constant E that appears on the right is called the corresponding *eigenvalue*.[1] An energy eigenfunction, like the ψ in Eq. (8.3), is said to represent a *stationary state* of the particle, since $|\psi|^2$ is constant in time.

Equation (8.2) is also an eigenvalue equation. It states that u (and hence also ψ) is an eigenfunction of the operator $[-(\hbar^2/2m)\nabla^2 + V(\mathbf{r})]$ with the same eigenvalue E. It is, of course, to be expected that ψ is an eigenfunction of this operator if it is an eigenfunction of the time-derivative operator, since according to the wave equation (6.16), the two operators are equivalent not only for separated functions of the form of Eq. (8.3) but also for more general solutions.

We now anticipate the discussion of the physical significance of eigenfunctions and eigenvalues that will be presented in Chap. III, and assume that the energy eigenvalues E are the only possible results of precise measurements of the total energy of the particle. It is then of interest to inquire whether or not physically interesting solutions $u(\mathbf{r})$ of Eq. (8.2) exist for all real values of E. An answer cannot be obtained until a specification of "physical interest" is found in terms of the boundary conditions that are imposed on $u(\mathbf{r})$. This specification, and the general character of the energy eigenvalues that are associated with various types of potential energy function $V(\mathbf{r})$, are considered in the remainder of this section.

---

[1] The terms *characteristic function* and *characteristic value* are often used in place of *eigenfunction* and *eigenvalue*.

Boundary Conditions at Great Distances.   We have thus far encountered two classes of wave functions: wave packets that are well localized and for which the normalization integral $\int |\psi|^2 d\tau$ converges, and traveling harmonic waves like the function (6.10) that have a constant magnitude at great distances so that the normalization integral taken over an infinite volume diverges.   The first class may be interpreted as representing particles that, if free, are initially well localized, or that are restrained to a particular region of space by external forces derived from the potential energy $V(\mathbf{r})$.   The second class represents particles that are neither localized nor restrained, but travel through the region under consideration from one distant part of space to another; such wave functions will be useful in describing the scattering of particles by a field of force.[1]   In either case, the wave functions are bounded at great distances in all directions.

Continuity Conditions.   The time-independent wave equation (8.2) is a second-order linear differential equation in $\mathbf{r}$.   Thus so long as $V(\mathbf{r})$ is finite, whether or not it is continuous, a knowledge of the wave function and its gradient along a surface makes it possible to integrate the equation to obtain the wave function at any point.   It is reasonable, therefore, to require that the wave function and its gradient be continuous, finite, and single-valued at every point in space, in order that a definite physical situation can be represented uniquely by a wave function.   These requirements also have the consequence that the position probability density $P(\mathbf{r})$ and the probability current density $\mathbf{S}(\mathbf{r})$, defined in Sec. 7, are finite and continuous everywhere.

Boundary Conditions for Infinite Potential Energy.   If $V(\mathbf{r})$ is infinite anywhere, the appropriate boundary condition can be established by a limiting process that starts from a finite V and the above continuity conditions.

Suppose, for example, that there is an infinite discontinuity in V across a continuous surface, so that the potential energy is finite on one side of it and $+\infty$ on the other, and we wish to determine the boundary conditions on $u(\mathbf{r})$ and **grad** u at this surface.   The essential features of the problem are retained if we replace the continuous surface by the plane that is tangent to it at the point of interest, and the continuously changing potential energy on one side of the surface by a constant potential, which can, without loss of generality, be chosen to be zero since any constant change in V is equivalent to an equal change in E.   We choose

---

[1] Another possible class consists of wave functions that become infinite at large distances; however, these are not of physical interest, since we have no reason to be concerned with particles for which the position probability density becomes indefinitely large in remote regions of space.

the origin of coordinates at the point of interest and the x axis perpendicular to the tangent plane.

The wave equation (8.2) then separates in the three space coordinates, and the dependence of u on y and z is not affected by the discontinuity in V at the plane $x = 0$. We wish therefore to solve the one-dimensional wave equation

$$-\frac{\hbar^2}{2m}\frac{d^2u}{dx^2} + V(x)u = Eu \qquad (8.5)$$

where $V(x) = 0$ for $x < 0$, $V(x) = V_0$ for $x > 0$, and we eventually pass to the limit $V_0 \rightarrow +\infty$. If we assume that $0 \leqq E < V_0$, the general solutions of Eq. (8.5) are

$$u(x) = A \sin \alpha x + B \cos \alpha x, \qquad x < 0, \qquad \alpha = +\left(\frac{2mE}{\hbar^2}\right)^{\frac{1}{2}}$$

$$u(x) = Ce^{-\beta x} + De^{\beta x}, \qquad x > 0, \qquad \beta = +\left[\frac{2m(V_0 - E)}{\hbar^2}\right]^{\frac{1}{2}}$$

The boundary condition that u be bounded at great distances requires that we set $D = 0$. Then the continuity of u at $x = 0$ gives the relation $B = C$, while the continuity of du/dx gives the relation $\alpha A = -\beta C$. Since β becomes infinite when V_0 does, and the solution for $x < 0$ must be finite, the second relation shows that C becomes zero as $V_0 \rightarrow \infty$, thus also making B zero; A is not determined from these relations, but might be fixed by normalization.

Thus the boundary conditions at a surface at which there is an infinite potential step are that the wave function is zero and the component of the gradient of the wave function normal to the surface is not determined. The assumption above that $E < V_0$ is evidently not a restriction since V_0 eventually becomes infinite. For $E < 0$, the sine and cosine in the solution for $x < 0$ are replaced by hyperbolic sine and cosine (which is permissible since the solution need hold only near $x = 0$), with no change in the final result. It should be noted that both P and S_x vanish as $x \rightarrow 0$ from the negative side, so that they are continuous at $x = 0$ even though du/dx is not.

A boundary surface of this type represents a perfectly rigid, impenetrable wall, since in the analogous classical situation a particle of any finite energy would have its x component of momentum reversed instantaneously on contact with the surface.

Energy Eigenvalues in One Dimension. Energy eigenfunctions that represent particles that are restrained to a particular region of space by the potential energy (first class) are always characterized by discrete eigenvalues, while eigenfunctions that do not vanish at great distances (second class) possess a continuous range of eigenvalues. This may be seen qualitatively by considering the nature of the solutions of the one-dimensional wave equation (8.5).

We shall suppose at first that $V(x)$ becomes equal to some constant value, which may be taken to be zero, for sufficiently large positive and negative x, and that $E < 0$. A classical particle with this total energy E cannot escape to infinity, and indeed can exist in the region only if E is greater than or equal to the smallest value V_{min} of $V(x)$. The permitted form of the wave function for $|x|$ large enough that $V = 0$ is evidently $e^{-\beta|x|}$, where $\beta = +(-2mE/\hbar^2)^{\frac{1}{2}}$. These two solutions for large positive and negative x can be extended in toward some intermediate point, say $x = 0$, by making use of the wave equation and the continuity conditions. At this point, u can always be made continuous by choosing the arbitrary multiplying constants for the positive and negative x solutions appropriately. Then a little reflection shows that for an arbitrary value of E, they will not meet with the same value of du/dx. There may, however, be particular values of E for which both u and du/dx are continuous at $x = 0$. The conditions for this can be seen in the following way.

In the regions in which $E < V(x)$, $(d^2u/dx^2)/u$ is positive, and so u is convex towards the x axis. Thus the two solutions that are continued in from $\pm \infty$ have opposite signs for their ratios of slope to value,

$$\frac{1}{u}\frac{du}{dx},$$

so long as they are in regions for which E is always less than V. This is illustrated in Fig. 5b for the potential shown in Fig. 5a; both choices of the sign of u are shown for $x < 0$. The points at which $E = V(x)$ are called the *turning points* (*TP*) of the classical motion, since they are the limits of the motion of a classical particle of energy E, at which the particle turns around or reverses its motion. At these points $d^2u/dx^2 = 0$, and u has zero curvature.

Clearly what is needed to make the two solutions join smoothly is a region in which $E > V(x)$, in order that $(d^2u/dx^2)/u$ may be negative and u be concave toward the x axis; this may permit the ratios of slope to value to become equal. Figure 5c shows the two solutions carried in until they meet, but for a somewhat small value of E, so that when the u's are made the same at $x = 0$, the slopes are not equal (solid curves), or when the slopes are made the same at $x = 0$, the u's are not equal (dotted curve on left and solid curve on right). Figure 5d shows a somewhat larger (less negative) value of E, and Fig. 5e a still larger value. The values of E

and V_{min} are indicated on the u axis, and the turning points are indicated on the x axis, in the last three cases.

Discrete Energy Levels. We see then that an eigenfunction that satisfies the boundary and continuity conditions and that represents a particle bound by the potential energy $V(x)$, can exist for the particular

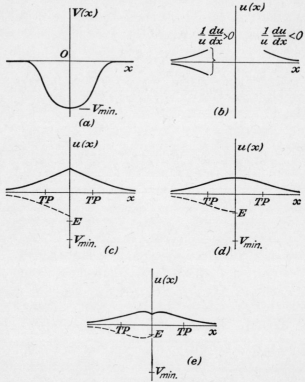

Fig. 5. (a) Potential energy function and (b) solutions for large $|x|$; (c) and (e) show that either the wave function or its slope is discontinuous at $x = 0$ for values of E that are smaller (more negative) and larger, respectively, than the energy eigenvalue shown in (d).

value of E illustrated in Fig. 5d. In analogy with the classical situation, a necessary condition that such an eigenfunction exist is that $V_{min} < 0$, in which case E lies between V_{min} and 0; as in the classical case, this condition is also sufficient in one dimension although it is not in three dimensions (see Prob. 10, Chap. IV, and Secs. 9 and 15).

If the *potential energy well* illustrated in Fig. 5a is sufficiently broad or deep, there will exist another eigenfunction corresponding to a larger energy eigenvalue that is still negative. Figures 6a, b, and c show a series of wave functions analogous to those shown in Figs. 5c, d, and e for successively increasing (successively less negative) values of E; both signs

of u are shown for $x < 0$.   Thus Figs. 5d and 6b show the eigenfunctions
for the two lowest energy eigenvalues or *energy levels* of a particle bound
by the potential well $V(x)$.   It is easy to see by an extension of the foregoing qualitative arguments that if there are any higher discrete energy
levels, each eigenfunction has one more node than that corresponding to
the next lowest eigenvalue.

Thus for a potential energy that approaches a finite constant value as
$x \to \pm \infty$, there may be a finite number of discrete energy levels, or in

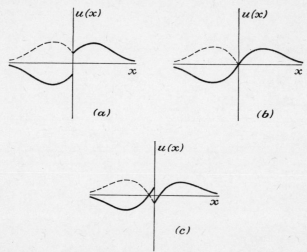

Fig. 6.   Solutions for sufficiently broad or deep potential and larger (less negative) values
of E than those shown in Fig. 5. E increases in going from (a) to (b) to (c) and is an
eigenvalue in (b), where the wave function and its slope can both be continuous at $x = 0$.

some cases an infinite number (if $V(x)$ falls off slowly enough for large
$|x|$), depending on $V(x)$ and the mass of the particle.   However, if
$V(x) \to + \infty$ as $x \to \pm \infty$, an argument like that given above shows that
there will always be an infinite number of discrete energy levels; apart
from arbitrary multiplying constants there will be just one eigenfunction
$u(x)$ for each of these.

Continuous Energy Eigenvalues.   It is possible to find eigenfunctions
that obey the boundary and continuity conditions for all energy eigenvalues that exceed the smaller of the two numbers $V(+\infty)$ and $V(-\infty)$.
If, for example, the potential energy has the form illustrated in Fig. 5a,
then solutions of the wave equation can be found for all positive values
of E.   This is because the solutions for large $|x|$ are of the form

$$A \sin \alpha|x| + B \cos \alpha|x|, \qquad \alpha = + \left(\frac{2mE}{\hbar^2}\right)^{\frac{1}{2}} \qquad (8.6)$$

and there is no reason why both terms should not be kept. Thus it is always possible to adjust the phase of each of the wave functions for large $|x|$ (which is equivalent to adjusting the ratios A/B for the solutions for large positive and negative x) so that they join together smoothly when continued in to $x = 0$.

The classical terms *periodic* (or *multiply periodic*) and *aperiodic* are sometimes used to designate the particle motions associated with discrete and continuous energy eigenvalues, respectively.

Discrete and Continuous Eigenvalues in Three Dimensions. We shall assume without further discussion that all the foregoing results can

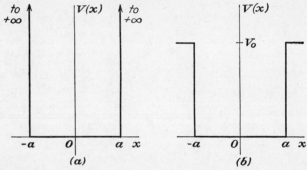

Fig. 7. One-dimensional square well potential with (a) perfectly rigid walls and (b) finite potential step.

be taken over in a natural way for the three-dimensional wave equation (8.2). We can expect that if $V(\mathbf{r}) \rightarrow +\infty$ as $r \rightarrow \infty$ in all directions, there will be an infinite set of discrete energy levels extending to $+\infty$. If $V(\mathbf{r})$ is bounded as $r \rightarrow \infty$ in some direction, there may be a finite or an infinite number of discrete levels, depending on the form of V. In this case, the discrete energy levels cannot exceed the smallest value that $V(\infty)$ has in any direction. For values of E larger than this smallest $V(\infty)$, the energy eigenvalues cover a continuous range extending to $+\infty$.

9. ONE-DIMENSIONAL SQUARE WELL POTENTIAL

As a simple explicit example of the calculation of discrete energy levels of a particle in quantum mechanics, we consider the one-dimensional motion of a particle that is restrained by reflecting walls that terminate a region of constant potential energy. Two simple types of potential energy are considered. Figure 7a shows a situation in which $V(x) = 0$ for $-a < x < a$, and $V(x) = +\infty$ for $|x| > a$, corresponding to perfectly rigid, impenetrable walls at the points $x = \pm a$. In Fig. 7b the increase in potential energy at the walls is abrupt, but finite, so that $V(x) = V_0$ for $|x| > a$; because of its appearance, this is often called a *square well potential*. The motion of a classical particle with total energy

E less than V_0 is the same for both these potentials; but as we shall see, the quantum-mechanical behavior is different. In general, an abrupt finite increase in potential energy at the boundaries of a region forces a particle toward the interior of the region. Such a potential may be thought of as a limiting case of a potential of the type shown in Fig. 5a, for which the force $-dV/dx$ is always directed in toward $x = 0$. The force associated with a square well potential is zero except at the boundaries, so that the particle is acted on by no force except a sudden impulse directed toward the origin as it passes the points $x = \pm a$.

Perfectly Rigid Walls. It was shown in Sec. 8 that the wave function must vanish at the points $x = \pm a$, when the potential energy has the form shown in Fig. 7a. From Eq. (8.5) the wave equation for $|x| < a$ is simply

$$-\frac{\hbar^2}{2m}\frac{d^2u}{dx^2} = Eu \tag{9.1}$$

which has the general solution

$$u(x) = A \sin \alpha x + B \cos \alpha x, \quad \alpha = + \left(\frac{2mE}{\hbar^2}\right)^{\frac{1}{2}} \tag{9.2}$$

Application of the boundary conditions at $x = \pm a$ gives

$$A \sin \alpha a + B \cos \alpha a = 0,$$
$$-A \sin \alpha a + B \cos \alpha a = 0,$$

from which we obtain

$$A \sin \alpha a = 0, \quad B \cos \alpha a = 0$$

Now we do not want both A and B to be zero, since this would give the physically uninteresting solution $u = 0$ everywhere. Also, we cannot make both sin αa and cos αa zero for a given value of α or E. There are then two possible classes of solutions: For the first class

$$A = 0 \quad \text{and} \quad \cos \alpha a = 0$$

and for the second class

$$B = 0 \quad \text{and} \quad \sin \alpha a = 0$$

Thus $\alpha a = n\pi/2$, where n is an odd integer for the first class and an even integer for the second class. The two classes of solutions and their energy eigenvalues are then

$$u(x) = B \cos \frac{n\pi x}{2a} \qquad n \text{ odd}$$

$$u(x) = A \sin \frac{n\pi x}{2a} \qquad n \text{ even}$$

$$E = \frac{\pi^2 \hbar^2 n^2}{8ma^2} \qquad \text{in both cases}$$

It is evident that $n = 0$ gives the physically uninteresting result $u = 0$, and that solutions for negative values of n are not linearly independent of those for positive n. The constants A and B can easily be chosen in each case so that the eigenfunctions $u(x)$ are normalized.

There is thus an infinite sequence of discrete energy levels that correspond to all positive integer values of the quantum number n. There is just one eigenfunction for each level, and the number of nodes of the nth eigenfunction that are within the potential well is $n - 1$. These results are in agreement with the discussion of Sec. 8. It is interesting to note that the order of magnitude of the lowest or ground-state energy level is in agreement with the uncertainty relation (3.1). The position uncertainty of order a implies a momentum uncertainty at least of order $\hbar/a$, which in turn implies a minimum kinetic energy of order $\hbar^2/ma^2$.

Finite Potential Step. When the potential energy has the form shown in Fig. 7b, it is necessary to supplement the general solution (9.2), which is still valid for $|x| < a$ since Eq. (9.1) is unaltered there, by a solution for $|x| > a$. The wave equation in this region is

$$-\frac{\hbar^2}{2m}\frac{d^2u}{dx^2} + V_0 u = Eu$$

which has the general solution for $E < V_0$ (bound states)

$$u(x) = Ce^{-\beta x} + De^{\beta x}, \qquad \beta = +\left[\frac{2m(V_0 - E)}{\hbar^2}\right]^{\frac{1}{2}} \tag{9.3}$$

The boundary conditions at $x = \pm \infty$ discussed in Sec. 8 require that we set $D = 0$ if Eq. (9.3) is to represent the solution for $x > a$, and $C = 0$ if the solution is for $x < -a$.

We now impose on the solutions (9.2) and (9.3) the requirements that u and du/dx be continuous at $x = \pm a$.

$$A \sin \alpha a + B \cos \alpha a = Ce^{-\beta a}, \qquad \alpha A \cos \alpha a - \alpha B \sin \alpha a = -\beta C e^{-\beta a}$$
$$-A \sin \alpha a + B \cos \alpha a = De^{-\beta a}, \qquad \alpha A \cos \alpha a + \alpha B \sin \alpha a = \beta D e^{-\beta a}$$

from which we obtain

$$2A \sin \alpha a = (C - D)e^{-\beta a}, \qquad 2\alpha A \cos \alpha a = -\beta(C - D)e^{-\beta a} \tag{9.4}$$
$$2B \cos \alpha a = (C + D)e^{-\beta a}, \qquad 2\alpha B \sin \alpha a = \beta(C + D)e^{-\beta a} \tag{9.5}$$

Unless $A = 0$ and $C = D$, Eqs. (9.4) have as their consequence

$$\alpha \cot \alpha a = -\beta \tag{9.6}$$

Similarly, unless $B = 0$ and $C = -D$, Eqs. (9.5) give

$$\alpha \tan \alpha a = \beta \tag{9.7}$$

Now it is impossible for Eqs. (9.6) and (9.7) to be valid at once, since on elimination of β this would require that $\tan^2 \alpha a = -1$, which in turn would make α imaginary and β negative, contrary to Eq. (9.3). Also, we do not want A, B, C, and D all to vanish. Thus the solutions may again be divided into two classes: For the first class

$$A = 0, \qquad C = D, \qquad \text{and} \qquad \alpha \tan \alpha a = \beta$$

and for the second class

$$B = 0, \qquad C = -D, \qquad \text{and} \qquad \alpha \cot \alpha a = -\beta$$

Energy Levels. The energy levels are found from a numerical or graphical solution of Eqs. (9.6) and (9.7) with the definitions for α and β

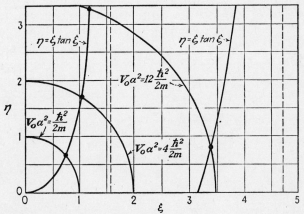

Fig. 8. Graphical solution of Eq. (9.7) for three values of $V_0 a^2$; vertical dashed lines are the first two asymptotes of $\eta = \xi \tan \xi$.

given in Eqs. (9.2) and (9.3). A simple graphical method for effecting this solution is described here, since it shows quite clearly the way in which the number of discrete levels depends on V_0 and a. We put $\xi = \alpha a$, $\eta = \beta a$, whence Eq. (9.7) becomes $\xi \tan \xi = \eta$, with

$$\xi^2 + \eta^2 = \frac{2m V_0 a^2}{\hbar^2}$$

Since ξ and η are restricted to positive values, the energy levels may be found in this case from the intersections in the first quadrant of the curve of $\xi \tan \xi$ plotted against ξ, with the circle of known radius $(2m V_0 a^2/\hbar^2)^{\frac{1}{2}}$. The construction is drawn in Fig. 8 for three values of $V_0 a^2$; for each of the two smaller of these values, there is one solution of Eq. (9.7) and for the largest there are two.

Figure 9 is a similar construction for the solution of Eq. (9.6) in which the energy levels are obtained from the intersections of the same circles with the curve of $-\xi \cot \xi$ in the first quadrant. The smallest value of $V_0 a^2$ gives no solution, and the two larger values each give one. Thus the three increasing values of $V_0 a^2$ give altogether one, two, and three energy levels, respectively.

It is clear from Figs. 8 and 9 that for a given particle mass, the energy levels depend on the parameters of the potential energy through the combination $V_0 a^2$. For $V_0 a^2$ between zero and $\pi^2 \hbar^2 / 8m$, there is just one

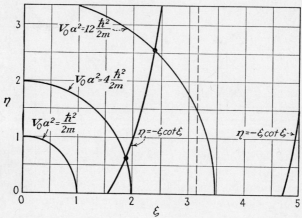

Fig. 9. Graphical solution of Eq. (9.6) for three values of $V_0 a^2$; vertical dashed line is the first asymptote of $\eta = -\xi \cot \xi$.

energy level of the first class; for $V_0 a^2$ between $\pi^2 \hbar^2 / 8m$ and four times this value, there is one energy level of each class, or two altogether. As $V_0 a^2$ increases, energy levels appear successively, first of one class and then of the other. It is not difficult to see from Eq. (9.2) that when ordered according to increasing eigenvalues, the nth eigenfunction has $n - 1$ nodes.

Parity. It follows from the foregoing discussion that the eigenfunctions of the first class are even with respect to change in sign of x $[u(-x) = u(x)]$, while the eigenfunctions of the second class are odd $[u(-x) = -u(x)]$. This division of the eigenfunctions into even and odd types is not accidental, and will now be shown to be a direct consequence of the fact that the potential energy function $V(x)$ is symmetric about $x = 0$. If we change the sign of x in the wave equation (8.5)

$$-\frac{\hbar^2}{2m} \frac{d^2 u(x)}{dx^2} + V(x) u(x) = E u(x) \qquad (9.8)$$

and if $V(-x) = V(x)$, we obtain

$$-\frac{\hbar^2}{2m}\frac{d^2u(-x)}{dx^2} + V(x)u(-x) = Eu(-x)$$

Then $u(x)$ and $u(-x)$ are solutions of the same wave equation with the same eigenvalue E. Unless there are two or more linearly independent eigenfunctions that correspond to this energy level, these two solutions can differ only by a multiplicative constant:

$$u(-x) = \epsilon u(x). \tag{9.9}$$

Changing the sign of x in Eq. (9.9) gives $u(x) = \epsilon u(-x)$. From these two equations it follows at once that

$$\epsilon^2 = 1 \qquad \text{or} \qquad \epsilon = \pm 1$$

Thus all such eigenfunctions of a symmetric potential are either even or odd with respect to changes of sign of x. Such wave functions are said to have even or odd *parity*.

If an eigenvalue has more than one linearly independent eigenfunction, these eigenfunctions need not have a definite parity: they need not be even or odd. However, we can easily see that linear combinations of such eigenfunctions can be found such that each has even or odd parity. Suppose that an eigenfunction $u(x)$ does not have a definite parity. It can always be written

$$u(x) = u_e(x) + u_o(x),$$

where $u_e(x) = \frac{1}{2}[u(x) + u(-x)]$ is even and $u_o(x) = \frac{1}{2}[u(x) - u(-x)]$ is odd. Then if the wave equation (9.8) is symmetric, we can write it as

$$-\frac{\hbar^2}{2m}\frac{d^2u_e}{dx^2} + (V - E)u_e - \frac{\hbar^2}{2m}\frac{d^2u_o}{dx^2} + (V - E)u_o = 0 \tag{9.10}$$

On changing the sign of x in Eq. (9.10), we obtain

$$-\frac{\hbar^2}{2m}\frac{d^2u_e}{dx^2} + (V - E)u_e + \frac{\hbar^2}{2m}\frac{d^2u_o}{dx^2} - (V - E)u_o = 0 \tag{9.11}$$

Addition and subtraction of Eqs. (9.10) and (9.11) shows that u_e and u_o are separately solutions of the wave equation with the same eigenvalue E.

A Simplified Solution. Knowledge that the solutions possess a definite parity sometimes simplifies the determination of the energy levels, since then we need only find the solution for positive x. Even solutions have zero slope and odd solutions have zero value at $x = 0$. If, for example, we wish to find the even solutions, Eqs. (9.2) and (9.3) can be replaced at once by

$$u(x) = B \cos \alpha x, \qquad 0 < x < a$$
$$u(x) = Ce^{-\beta x}, \qquad x > a$$

Instead of making both u and du/dx continuous at $x = a$, it is enough to make the ratio $(1/u)(du/dx)$ continuous at $x = a$, since the normalizing constants B and C are eliminated thereby. This gives Eq. (9.7) at once. Similarly, the odd solutions are

$$u(x) = A \sin \alpha x, \qquad 0 < x < a$$
$$u(x) = Ce^{-\beta x}, \qquad x > a$$

Then continuity of $(1/u)(du/dx)$ at $x = a$ immediately gives Eq. (9.6).

Problems

1. Use the arguments of Sec. 6 to set up a differential equation for ψ that involves a second time derivative of ψ, in the case of a free particle. Discuss any solutions that this equation has that are not shared by the free-particle Schrödinger equation.

2. Show that the free-particle one-dimensional Schrödinger wave equation (6.8) is invariant with respect to Galilean transformations. Do this by showing that, when the transformation $x' = x - vt$, $t' = t$ is applied, the transformed wave function $\psi'(x',t') = \psi(x',t') \exp if(x',t')$ satisfies Eq. (6.8) with respect to the primed variables, where f involves only x', t', $\hbar$, m, and v. Find the form of f, and show that the traveling wave solution $\psi(x,t) = A \exp i(kx - \omega t)$ transforms as expected.

3. How must a wave packet ψ fall off for large r in order that the volume integral of P and the surface integral of S_n in Eq. (7.4) converge?

4. Show directly that $\langle p_x \rangle$ is real for a wave packet.

5. Show that for a three-dimensional wave packet

$$\frac{d}{dt} \langle x^2 \rangle = \frac{1}{m} (\langle x p_x \rangle + \langle p_x x \rangle).$$

6. Calculate the energy levels and plot the eigenfunctions for the three bound states in the potential of Fig. 7b when $V_0 a^2 = 6\hbar^2/m$. Compare with the first three states for the potential of Fig. 7a.

7. Discuss the relation between the energy levels for the potential of Fig. 7b and those for the potential: $V(x) = +\infty$, $x < 0$; $V(x) = 0$, $0 < x < a$; $V(x) = V_0$, $x > a$.

8. Show that if the potential energy $V(\mathbf{r})$ is changed by a constant amount everywhere, the time-independent wave functions are unchanged. What is the effect on the energy eigenvalues?

CHAPTER III

EIGENFUNCTIONS AND EIGENVALUES

In Chap. II, the Schrödinger wave equation was developed and applied to a simple problem. Some discussion of the physical interpretation of the wave function was given in Sec. 7. This relied for the most part on the computation of average or expectation values of operators that represent various physical quantities. In addition, however, a position probability density was introduced. Thus at the present point we are in a position to calculate from the wave function any property that depends on the spatial distribution of a particle (for example, the mean-square deviation of its position from the average), whereas we can only calculate average values of operators other than position. Clearly what is needed to round out our interpretation of the wave function is a means of computing probability functions for operators in general; this would incidentally enable us to obtain the expressions for expectation values used in Sec. 7 without separate assumptions.

In this chapter, we first set up three physical postulates from which a complete interpretation of the wave function can be derived, and then apply them to a discussion of the total energy and momentum of a particle, and to an illustrative problem. The interpretation presented in Sec. 7 can then be seen to be a special case of the more general treatment given here.

10. INTERPRETATIVE POSTULATES AND ENERGY EIGENFUNCTIONS

We start with the wave function $\psi(\mathbf{r},t)$, which is a solution of Eq. (6.16) and describes the motion of a particle that has mass m and potential energy $V(\mathbf{r})$. From this wave function we wish to obtain as complete a description of the properties of the motion of the particle as is consistent with the uncertainty relations discussed in Sec. 3.

Dynamical Variables as Operators. We first postulate that *each dynamical variable that relates to the motion of the particle can be represented by a linear operator.* The operator may be simply a multiplication operator such as $\mathbf{r}$ for the position, or it may be a differential operator such as $-i\hbar \,\mathbf{grad}$ for the momentum.

With each operator can be associated a linear eigenvalue equation, defined near the beginning of Sec. 8. Thus with the operator Ω may be associated the equation

$$\Omega u_\omega = \omega u_\omega \tag{10.1}$$

41

where u_ω is the eigenfunction of Ω corresponding to the eigenvalue ω.

Our second postulate is that *one or another of the eigenvalues ω is the only possible result of a precise measurement of the dynamical variable represented by Ω.* This implies that the eigenvalues of all operators that represent physically significant variables are real numbers.

Expansion in Eigenfunctions. We assume that all the eigenfunctions of any dynamical variable constitute a *complete set of functions* in the sense that an arbitrary continuous function can be expanded in terms of them. This is a mathematical, not a physical, assumption, and will be discussed further below in connection with energy and momentum eigenfunctions.

Suppose now that a particular wave function ψ is expanded in terms of the eigenfunctions u_ω of the operator Ω. We adopt the statistical interpretation of ψ given at the beginning of Sec. 7, according to which there are a large number of identical, nonoverlapping regions of space, in each of which is a particle described by ψ. We then make measurements of the dynamical variable represented by Ω on each of these particles. Our third physical postulate is that *the number of measurements that result in the eigenvalue ω is proportional to the square of the magnitude of the coefficient of u_ω in the expansion of ψ.* This postulate, due to M. Born (see page 22), enables us to associate a probability function with any dynamical variable.[1] A corollary is that we are certain to measure a particular eigenvalue ω only when the wave function that describes the particle is the corresponding eigenfunction u_ω.

Rather than develop the consequences of these postulates for an arbitrary operator Ω, we consider here the total energy of the particle, and in Sec. 11 the momentum. Most of the results obtained are readily applicable to other physical operators.

The Total Energy Operator. According to the uncertainty relation (3.3), a precise measurement of the total energy of a particle cannot be made in a finite length of time. Thus if the total energy is to have a definite value, it is essential that the potential energy $V(\mathbf{r})$ be independent of the time. Then the operator $-(\hbar^2/2m)\nabla^2 + V(\mathbf{r})$, which is shown in Sec. 8 to be equivalent to the total energy operator $i\hbar\, \partial/\partial t$, has eigenfunctions $u(\mathbf{r})$ that need not involve the time. The energy-eigenvalue equation is Eq. (8.2),

$$\left[-\frac{\hbar^2}{2m}\nabla^2 + V(\mathbf{r}) \right] u_E(\mathbf{r}) = E u_E(\mathbf{r}) \qquad (10.2)$$

[1] An alternative deterministic interpretation in terms of "hidden variables" rather than the dynamical variables, which has not been widely accepted, has been proposed by D. Bohm, *Phys. Rev.*, **85**, 166, 180 (1952).

where the eigenfunction $u_E(\mathbf{r})$ corresponds to the eigenvalue E, and obeys the boundary and continuity conditions of Sec. 8.

As discussed in Sec. 8, the energy eigenfunctions can be divided into two classes: those which are well localized and are associated with discrete eigenvalues, and those which remain finite at great distances and possess a continuous range of eigenvalues.

Normalization in a Box. It is often desirable to be able to treat these two classes on the same basis; this can be accomplished by enclosing the particle under investigation in a box of arbitrarily large but finite volume. The simplest physical situation to which this approach is applicable is one in which the walls of the box are perfectly rigid, so that, as shown in Sec. 8, the wave function vanishes there. Then the discussion of Sec. 8 shows that all the eigenvalues are discrete. If the box is large in comparison with the dimensions of physical interest in the problem, the eigenvalues that were discrete in the absence of the box are practically unaffected, since before the walls were introduced the wave functions were extremely small there. Also, the eigenvalues that were continuously distributed in the absence of the box are very closely spaced; this is shown explicitly for a free particle in Sec. 11.

It is more convenient to assume that the wave functions obey *periodic boundary conditions* at the walls of the box than that they vanish there, since it is then possible to get a simpler description of the momentum eigenfunctions (see Sec. 11). We choose the finite region to be a cube of edge length L centered at the origin, and require each wave function to have the same value at corresponding points of opposite faces of the cube, and the same derivative normal to the wall. These boundary conditions make the otherwise continuous eigenvalues discrete, since the phase of the eigenfunction at great distances is no longer arbitrary [see the discussion of Eq. (8.6)]. As with the rigid-walled box, the presence of the walls has a negligible effect apart from imparting discreteness to the otherwise continuous eigenvalues and providing a finite volume in which these wave functions can be normalized; we shall continue to use the word "continuous" to describe these functions, even when box normalization is used.

Orthonormality of Energy Eigenfunctions. The integral $\int |u_E(\mathbf{r})|^2 d\tau$, which converges in any case for the discrete set of eigenfunctions, converges for all eigenfunctions when they are normalized in the box of finite volume L^3. The coefficient of u_E can then be chosen so that this integral is equal to unity, and the $u_E(\mathbf{r})$ are normalized.

We now show that the eigenfunctions corresponding to two different eigenvalues E and E' are *orthogonal*; that is, that the integral of the product of one of them and the complex conjugate of the other over the common domain of the functions is zero. From Eq. (10.2) we have that $\bar{u}_{E'}(\mathbf{r})$ satisfies the equation

$$\left[-\frac{\hbar^2}{2m} \nabla^2 + V(\mathbf{r}) \right] \bar{u}_{E'}(\mathbf{r}) = E'\bar{u}_{E'}(\mathbf{r}) \tag{10.3}$$

where we assume in accordance with our physical interpretation that E' is real; this is verified below. We multiply Eq. (10.2) by $\bar{u}_{E'}$ and Eq. (10.3) by u_E, integrate over the volume L^3, and take the difference between the two resulting equations. The V terms cancel, and leave

$$-\frac{\hbar^2}{2m} \int (\bar{u}_{E'} \nabla^2 u_E - u_E \nabla^2 \bar{u}_{E'}) d\tau = (E - E') \int \bar{u}_{E'} u_E d\tau \tag{10.4}$$

The integral on the left side of Eq. (10.4) can be transformed by Green's theorem into a surface integral over the surface A of the cube.

$$\int (\bar{u}_{E'} \nabla^2 u_E - u_E \nabla^2 \bar{u}_{E'}) d\tau$$

$$= \int \mathrm{div}\ (\bar{u}_{E'}\ \mathbf{grad}\ u_E - u_E\ \mathbf{grad}\ \bar{u}_{E'}) d\tau$$

$$= \int_A (\bar{u}_{E'}\ \mathbf{grad}\ u_E - u_E\ \mathbf{grad}\ \bar{u}_{E'})_n dA \tag{10.5}$$

where the subscript n designates the component of the vector in the direction of the outward normal to the element of area dA. Since the imposition of periodic boundary conditions gives each wave function and its normal derivative the same values at corresponding points of opposite faces of the cube, the outward normal derivative has opposite signs on opposite faces, and the surface integral in Eq. (10.5) vanishes. Then Eq. (10.4) tells us that if $E \neq E'$, u_E and $u_{E'}$ are orthogonal.[1]

An energy eigenvalue E is said to be *degenerate* when two or more linearly independent eigenfunctions $u_1, u_2, \ldots$ correspond to it. Orthogonal linear combinations of degenerate eigenfunctions can be found in many different ways. For example, $u_a = a_1 u_1 + a_2 u_2$ can be made orthogonal to u_1 by choosing the constant coefficients a_1 and a_2 such that

$$\frac{a_1}{a_2} = - \frac{\int \bar{u}_1 u_2 d\tau}{\int |u_1|^2 d\tau}$$

this choice does not interfere with the normalization of u_a, and u_a is still an energy eigenfunction with the eigenvalue E. Evidently the choice

---

[1] It is apparent that this proof of orthogonality can be applied to a *discrete* set of eigenfunctions even though the box is not introduced, since the u's vanish rapidly at great distances and the surface integral, which is then over a sphere of infinite radius, is zero. The continuous set of energy eigenfunctions can also be treated without using the box normalization (as is the continuous set of momentum eigenfunctions in Sec. 11). See E. C. Kemble, "The Fundamental Principles of Quantum Mechanics" (McGraw-Hill, New York, 1937); Sec. 30 of Kemble's book presents a discussion of this problem and references to the original papers.

of orthogonal linear combinations is not unique.   By an extension of this procedure, all the energy eigenfunctions can be made orthogonal to each other even though some of the eigenvalues are degenerate.

Such a set of eigenfunctions, each of which is normalized and orthogonal to each of the others, is called an *orthonormal* set of functions.   We specify an orthonormal set of nondegenerate energy eigenfunctions by the relation

$$\int \bar{u}_{E'}(\mathbf{r})u_E(\mathbf{r})d\tau = \delta_{EE'} \tag{10.6}$$

where $\delta_{EE'}$ is the Kronecker δ symbol that equals unity if $E = E'$ and is zero otherwise.   If there is degeneracy, Eq. (10.6) must be replaced by

$$\int \bar{u}_{E's'}(\mathbf{r})u_{Es}(\mathbf{r})d\tau = \delta_{EE'}\delta_{ss'} \tag{10.7}$$

where the index s distinguishes between orthogonal degenerate eigenfunctions.   It is often convenient to omit explicit mention of s and use Eq. (10.6) for degenerate situations as well, in which case the index s is implied.

Reality of the Energy Eigenvalues.   We can now see directly that E is a real number, as has been assumed.   We multiply Eq. (10.2) by $\bar{u}_E(\mathbf{r})$ and integrate over the box of volume L^3.   If u_E is normalized, the result is

$$E = -\frac{\hbar^2}{2m} \int \bar{u}_E\nabla^2 u_E d\tau + \int V(\mathbf{r})|u_E|^2 d\tau$$

which may be expressed in terms of expectation values as $(1/2m)\langle \mathbf{p}^2 \rangle + \langle V \rangle$.

The second term $\langle V \rangle$ is real since its integrand is real.   The first term can be shown explicitly to be real by means of a partial integration.

$$-\int \bar{u}_E\nabla^2 u_E d\tau = \int (\mathbf{grad}\ \bar{u}_E) \cdot (\mathbf{grad}\ u_E)d\tau - \int_A \bar{u}_E(\mathbf{grad}\ u_E)_n dA.$$

The volume integral is evidently real, and the surface integral [like that in Eq. (10.5)] vanishes because of the periodic boundary conditions at the walls of the box.   It is interesting to note that $\langle \mathbf{p}^2 \rangle$ cannot be negative.

Expansion in Energy Eigenfunctions.   As mentioned near the beginning of this section, we make the mathematical assumption that all the eigenfunctions $u_E(\mathbf{r})$ of the total energy operator constitute a complete set of functions in the sense that an arbitrary continuous function can be expanded in terms of them.[1]   Then if we have any wave function $\psi(\mathbf{r})$ at a particular instant of time that is normalized in the box L^3 and obeys periodic boundary conditions at the walls, the assumed existence of the expansion

$$\psi(\mathbf{r}) = \sum_E A_E u_E(\mathbf{r}) \tag{10.8}$$

---

[1] For further discussion see E. C. Kemble, *op. cit.*, Chap. IV and Sec. 30.

makes it possible to find unique coefficients A_E that do not depend on $\mathbf{r}$.

The coefficients in the expansion (10.8) can be determined by multiplying both sides by $\bar{u}_{E'}$ and integrating over the box. We assume that the order of $\sum_E$ and $\int d\tau$ can be reversed[1] and obtain

$$\int \bar{u}_{E'}(\mathbf{r})\psi(\mathbf{r})d\tau = \sum_E A_E \int \bar{u}_{E'}(\mathbf{r})u_E(\mathbf{r})\, d\tau = \sum_E A_E\delta_{EE'} = A_{E'}. \quad (10.9)$$

with the help of Eq. (10.6) or (10.7).

The Closure Property. Substitution of the expression (10.9) for A_E back into Eq. (10.8) gives

$$\psi(\mathbf{r}) = \sum_E \left[\int \bar{u}_E(\mathbf{r}')\psi(\mathbf{r}')d\tau' \right] u_E(\mathbf{r})$$

which we rearrange to give

$$\psi(\mathbf{r}) = \int \psi(\mathbf{r}') \left[\sum_E \bar{u}_E(\mathbf{r}')u_E(\mathbf{r}) \right] d\tau' \quad (10.10)$$

Since $\psi(\mathbf{r})$ is an arbitrary continuous function, Eq. (10.10) implies that the bracketed part of the integrand vanishes unless $\mathbf{r}' = \mathbf{r}$, since otherwise the value of ψ at the point $\mathbf{r}$ given by Eq. (10.10) would change when the values of ψ at other points $\mathbf{r}' \neq \mathbf{r}$ are changed, and this is contrary to the assumption that ψ can have an arbitrary form. Moreover, the integral of the term in brackets must be unity when the volume of integration includes the point $\mathbf{r}' = \mathbf{r}$. We conclude therefore that

$$\sum_E \bar{u}_E(\mathbf{r}')u_E(\mathbf{r}) = 0, \qquad \mathbf{r}' \neq \mathbf{r};$$

$$\int \sum_E \bar{u}_E(\mathbf{r}')u_E(\mathbf{r})d\tau' = 1$$

$$(10.11)$$

if the volume of integration includes the point $\mathbf{r}' = \mathbf{r}$.

Equations (10.11) describe the *closure* property of the orthonormal functions $u_E(\mathbf{r})$ and are seen to follow directly from their completeness as expressed by Eq. (10.8), whether or not they happen to be energy eigenfunctions.

Probability Function and Expectation Value. The second and third physical postulates presented at the beginning of this section state that the energy eigenvalues are the only possible results of precise measure-

[1] The propriety of changing the order of summations and integrations must in principle be investigated separately in each case. The mathematical considerations entailed are beyond the scope of this book, and we shall always assume that such interchanges are permissible in situations of physical interest.

ment of the total energy, and that the probability of finding a particular value E when the particle is described by the wave function $\psi(\mathbf{r})$ is proportional to $|A_E|^2$. It is easily seen that the proportionality factor is unity, for if we put for the energy probability function

$$P(E) = |A_E|^2 \tag{10.12}$$

we see that $P(E)$ sums to unity.

$$
\begin{aligned}
\sum_E P(E) &= \sum_E \int \bar{u}_E(\mathbf{r})\psi(\mathbf{r})d\tau \int u_E(\mathbf{r}')\bar{\psi}(\mathbf{r}')d\tau' \\
&= \int \int \bar{\psi}(\mathbf{r}')\psi(\mathbf{r}) \left[\sum_E \bar{u}_E(\mathbf{r})u_E(\mathbf{r}') \right] d\tau d\tau' \\
&= \int |\psi(\mathbf{r})|^2 d\tau = 1
\end{aligned}
$$

since ψ is normalized; use has been made here of Eqs. (10.11).

We can also compute the average or expectation value of the energy from the probability function.

$$\langle E \rangle = \sum_E E P(E) = \sum_E \int E\bar{u}_E(\mathbf{r})\psi(\mathbf{r})d\tau \int u_E(\mathbf{r}')\bar{\psi}(\mathbf{r}')d\tau' \tag{10.13}$$

If we substitute for $E\bar{u}_E$ from Eq. (10.3), the first integral in Eq. (10.13) can be integrated twice by parts as follows:

$$
\begin{aligned}
\int E\bar{u}_E(\mathbf{r})\psi(\mathbf{r})d\tau &= \int \psi(\mathbf{r})\left[-\frac{\hbar^2}{2m}\nabla^2 + V(\mathbf{r}) \right]\bar{u}_E(\mathbf{r})d\tau \\
&= \int \bar{u}_E(\mathbf{r})\left[-\frac{\hbar^2}{2m}\nabla^2 + V(\mathbf{r}) \right]\psi(\mathbf{r})d\tau
\end{aligned}
$$

The two surface integrals that result from the partial integrations vanish because of the periodic boundary conditions on u_E and ψ. Thus with the help of Eqs. (10.11), Eq. (10.13) becomes

$$
\begin{aligned}
\langle E \rangle &= \sum_E \int \bar{u}_E(\mathbf{r})\left[-\frac{\hbar^2}{2m}\nabla^2 + V(\mathbf{r}) \right]\psi(\mathbf{r})d\tau \int u_E(\mathbf{r}')\bar{\psi}(\mathbf{r}')d\tau' \\
&= \int \int \bar{\psi}(\mathbf{r}')\left\{ \left[-\frac{\hbar^2}{2m}\nabla^2 + V(\mathbf{r}) \right]\psi(\mathbf{r}) \right\}\left[\sum_E \bar{u}_E(\mathbf{r})u_E(\mathbf{r}') \right]d\tau d\tau' \\
&= \int \bar{\psi}(\mathbf{r})\left[-\frac{\hbar^2}{2m}\nabla^2 + V(\mathbf{r}) \right]\psi(\mathbf{r})d\tau \tag{10.14}
\end{aligned}
$$

The result embodied in Eq. (10.14) confirms the supposition made in Sec. 7 that the expectation value of an operator is to be calculated by inserting the operator between $\bar{\psi}(\mathbf{r})$ and $\psi(\mathbf{r})$, so that it operates just on the latter, and integrating over $\mathbf{r}$.

General Solution of the Schrödinger Equation. If the potential energy $V(\mathbf{r})$ is independent of t and we know the solution of the Schrödinger equation (6.16) at a particular time, we can write down a formal expression for the solution at any time. We expand $\psi(\mathbf{r},t)$ in energy eigenfunctions at the time t, in which case the expansion coefficients depend on the time.

$$\psi(\mathbf{r},t) = \sum_E A_E(t)u_E(\mathbf{r}), \qquad A_E(t) = \int \bar{u}_E(\mathbf{r})\psi(\mathbf{r},t)d\tau \qquad (10.15)$$

Substitution of Eq. (10.15) into the wave equation (6.16) gives

$$i\hbar \sum_E u_E(\mathbf{r}) \frac{d}{dt} A_E(t) = \sum_L A_E(t)Eu_E(\mathbf{r}) \qquad (10.16)$$

Because of the orthonormality of the u_E, Eq. (10.16) is equivalent to

$$i\hbar \frac{d}{dt} A_E(t) = EA_E(t)$$

which may be integrated at once to give

$$A_E(t) = A_E(t_0)e^{-\frac{iE(t-t_0)}{\hbar}} \qquad (10.17)$$

Note that $P(E) = |A_E(t)|^2 = |A_E(t_0)|^2$ is constant in time.

Thus if $\psi(\mathbf{r},t)$ is known at the time $t = t_0$, the solution at any time t is given in terms of Eqs. (10.15) and (10.17):

$$\psi(\mathbf{r},t) = \sum_E A_E(t_0)e^{-\frac{iE(t-t_0)}{\hbar}} u_E(\mathbf{r})$$
$$A_E(t_0) = \int \bar{u}_E(\mathbf{r}')\psi(\mathbf{r}',t_0)d\tau' \qquad (10.18)$$

or

$$\psi(\mathbf{r},t) = \int \left[\sum_E \bar{u}_E(\mathbf{r}')u_E(\mathbf{r})e^{-\frac{iE(t-t_0)}{\hbar}} \right] \psi(\mathbf{r}',t_0)d\tau' \qquad (10.19)$$

The solution (10.18) is a linear combination of the separated solutions (8.3) obtained earlier.

11. MOMENTUM EIGENFUNCTIONS

The eigenfunctions of the linear momentum operator $-i\hbar$ **grad** provide a second instructive example of the application of the general ideas developed at the beginning of the last section. They also are of considerable usefulness in solving problems of physical interest.

Form of the Eigenfunctions. The momentum eigenfunctions are solutions of the three eigenvalue equations

$$-i\hbar \ \mathbf{grad} \ u_\mathbf{p}(\mathbf{r}) = \mathbf{p}u_\mathbf{p}(\mathbf{r}) \qquad (11.1)$$

or:

$$-i\hbar \frac{\partial}{\partial x} u_{\mathbf{p}}(\mathbf{r}) = p_x u_{\mathbf{p}}(\mathbf{r}), \qquad -i\hbar \frac{\partial}{\partial y} u_{\mathbf{p}}(\mathbf{r}) = p_y u_{\mathbf{p}}(\mathbf{r})$$

$$-i\hbar \frac{\partial}{\partial z} u_{\mathbf{p}}(\mathbf{r}) = p_z u_{\mathbf{p}}(\mathbf{r})$$

They have the form

$$u_{\mathbf{p}}(\mathbf{r}) = C \exp \frac{i(\mathbf{p} \cdot \mathbf{r})}{\hbar}$$

where C is a normalization constant.

It is convenient, as in Sec. 6, to change from the momentum vector $\mathbf{p}$ to the propagation vector $\mathbf{k} = \mathbf{p}/\hbar$, and rewrite the momentum eigenfunctions

$$u_{\mathbf{k}}(\mathbf{r}) = C \exp i\mathbf{k} \cdot \mathbf{r} \tag{11.2}$$

These are eigenfunctions of the momentum operator with the eigenvalues $\hbar\mathbf{k}$.

Box Normalization.   As with the energy eigenfunctions discussed in Sec. 10, we can restrict the domain of the $u_{\mathbf{k}}(\mathbf{r})$ to an arbitrarily large but finite cubical box of volume L^3 centered at the origin, at the walls of which the functions obey periodic boundary conditions. Then $u_{\mathbf{k}}$ is normalized if $C = L^{-\frac{3}{2}}$. Also, $\mathbf{k}$ is no longer an arbitrary real vector; its components are restricted to the values

$$k_x = \frac{2\pi n_x}{L}, \qquad k_y = \frac{2\pi n_y}{L}, \qquad k_z = \frac{2\pi n_z}{L} \tag{11.3}$$

where n_x, n_y, and n_z are positive or negative integers or zero. The spacing of neighboring $\mathbf{k}$ vectors and of their energy eigenvalues $\hbar^2 k^2/2m$ can be made as small as desired by making L sufficiently large.

It is interesting to note that the momentum eigenfunctions (11.2) cannot exist within a box that has perfectly rigid walls, since these eigenfunctions do not vanish anywhere. This is analogous to the classical situation in which the momentum of a particle that is reflected from a rigid wall is not conserved. On the other hand, the cubical box with periodic boundary conditions is equivalent to a situation in which the entire infinite space is divided up into adjacent cubes and all wave functions are periodic throughout space with the period L along each of the three cartesian axes. If the periodicity of the space is carried over to the analogous classical situation, a particle passing through a wall would be equivalent to one that strikes that wall and appears at the corresponding point of the opposite wall with its momentum vector unchanged.

The orthonormality of the momentum eigenfunctions

$$u_{\mathbf{k}}(\mathbf{r}) = L^{-\frac{3}{2}} \exp i\mathbf{k} \cdot \mathbf{r} \tag{11.4}$$

is readily established.   For integration over the volume L^3

$$\int \bar{u}_\mathbf{l}(\mathbf{r}) u_\mathbf{k}(\mathbf{r}) d\tau = \frac{1}{L^3} \int_{-\frac{1}{2}L}^{\frac{1}{2}L} e^{i(k_x-l_x)x} dx \int_{-\frac{1}{2}L}^{\frac{1}{2}L} e^{i(k_y-l_y)y} dy \int_{-\frac{1}{2}L}^{\frac{1}{2}L} e^{i(k_z-l_z)z} dz$$
$$= \delta_{k_x l_x} \delta_{k_y l_y} \delta_{k_z l_z} \equiv \delta_{\mathbf{kl}} \tag{11.5}$$

where the δ's are Kronecker δ symbols and use is made of Eqs. (11.3). Orthogonality could also have been shown by the more general method used in Sec. 10 for the energy eigenfunctions [see Eq. (10.4)].

The Dirac δ Function.   It was stated in Sec. 10 that continuous sets of eigenfunctions can be handled without introducing the box with periodic boundary conditions (which has the effect of making the set discrete with an arbitrarily small spacing of eigenvalues).   This can be shown explicitly for the momentum eigenfunctions with the help of the Dirac δ function,[1] which can be defined by the relations

$$\delta(x) = 0 \quad \text{if} \quad x \neq 0, \qquad \int \delta(x)\, dx = 1 \tag{11.6}$$

where the region of integration includes the point $x = 0$.   An equivalent definition is that for an arbitrary function $f(x)$ that is continuous at $x = 0$, the equation

$$\int f(x) \delta(x) dx = f(0) \tag{11.7}$$

is valid, where again the integration includes the point $x = 0$.

It is apparent from a comparison of Eqs. (11.6) and (10.11), or of Eqs. (11.7) and (10.10), that the bracketed quantity in Eq. (10.10) can be expressed in terms of δ functions:

$$\sum_E \bar{u}_E(\mathbf{r}') u_E(\mathbf{r}) = \delta(x - x')\delta(y - y')\delta(z - z') \equiv \delta(\mathbf{r} - \mathbf{r}') \tag{11.8}$$

Comparison of Eqs. (11.8) and (10.6) shows that the closure property is a kind of orthonormality of the eigenfunctions with respect to summation over the eigenvalues.

A Representation of the δ Function.   The definition (11.6) or (11.7) shows that $\delta(x)$ is an exceedingly singular function.[2]   It may be thought of qualitatively as being zero everywhere except at $x = 0$, and being so large there that the area between it and the x axis is finite and equal to unity.   More formally, it can be represented in a number of different ways as the limit of a sequence of analytic functions.

A particular representation that is quite useful involves $(\sin gx)/\pi x$ as a function of x, where g is a positive real number.   This has the value g/π at $x = 0$, oscillates with decreasing amplitude and with period $2\pi/g$

---

[1] P. A. M. Dirac, "The Principles of Quantum Mechanics," 3d ed., Sec. 15 (Oxford, New York, 1947).

[2] A rigorous mathematical basis has recently been provided for the δ function by L. Schwartz; see, for example, I. Halperin and L. Schwartz, "Introduction to the Theory of Distributions" (University of Toronto Press, Toronto, 1952).

as $|x|$ increases, and has unit integral from $x = -\infty$ to $x = +\infty$ independently of the value of g.   Thus the limit of this function as $g \to \infty$ has all the properties of the δ function: it becomes infinitely large at $x = 0$, it has unit integral, and the infinitely rapid oscillations as $|x|$ increases mean that the entire contribution to an integral containing this function comes from the infinitesimal neighborhood of $x = 0$.   We can therefore put

$$\delta(x) = \lim_{g \to \infty} \frac{\sin gx}{\pi x} \tag{11.9}$$

Normalization in Terms of the δ Function.   The representation (11.9) of the δ function can be used to set up an orthonormality integral like that given in Eq. (11.5), where now we do not impose the box normalization but allow the momentum eigenfunctions to have the form (11.2) over all space with all real vectors **k**.   The integral $\int \bar{u}_l(\mathbf{r}) u_\mathbf{k}(\mathbf{r}) d\tau$ is the product of three integrals, each of which can be expressed in terms of a δ function:

$$\int_{-\infty}^{\infty} e^{i(k_x - l_x)x}\, dx = \lim_{g \to \infty} \int_{-g}^{g} e^{i(k_x - l_x)x}\, dx$$

$$= \lim_{g \to \infty} \frac{2 \sin g(k_x - l_x)}{k_x - l_x}$$

$$= 2\pi \delta(k_x - l_x) \tag{11.10}$$

Thus the momentum eigenfunctions in infinite space can be written

$$u_\mathbf{k}(\mathbf{r}) = (8\pi^3)^{-\frac{1}{2}} \exp i\mathbf{k} \cdot \mathbf{r} \tag{11.11}$$

in which case the orthonormality relation becomes

$$\int \bar{u}_l(\mathbf{r}) u_\mathbf{k}(\mathbf{r}) d\tau = \delta(k_x - l_x)\delta(k_y - l_y)\delta(k_z - l_z) \equiv \delta(\mathbf{k} - \mathbf{l}) \tag{11.12}$$

It will be shown in Sec. 12 that the box and δ-function normalizations of the momentum eigenfunctions give the same final result in a typical problem.

Some Properties of the δ Function.   It is important to note that, because of its singular character, the δ function cannot be the end result of a calculation, and has meaning only so long as a subsequent integration over its argument is carried out.   With this understanding we can write down some relations between δ functions.[1]

$$\begin{aligned}
\delta(x) &= \delta(-x) \\
\delta'(x) &= -\delta'(-x) \\
x\delta(x) &= 0 \\
x\delta'(x) &= -\delta(x) \\
\delta(ax) &= a^{-1}\delta(x), \qquad\qquad\qquad a > 0 \\
\delta(x^2 - a^2) &= (2a)^{-1}[\delta(x - a) + \delta(x + a)], \qquad a > 0 \\
\int \delta(a - x)\delta(x - b)dx &= \delta(a - b) \\
f(x)\delta(x - a) &= f(a)\delta(x - a)
\end{aligned} \tag{11.13}$$

Here, a prime denotes differentiation with respect to the argument.

[1] Dirac, *op. cit.*, p. 60.

Each of the first six of these equations can be established by multiplying both sides by a continuous, differentiable function $f(x)$ and integrating over x. For example, the fourth of Eqs. (11.13) gives

$$\int f(x)x\delta'(x)dx = -\int \delta(x)\frac{d}{dx}[xf(x)]dx$$
$$= -\int\delta(x)[f(x) + xf'(x)]dx = -\int f(x)\delta(x)dx$$

where the boundary terms that result from the partial integration vanish. Thus $x\delta'(x)$ has the same effect when it is a factor in an integrand as has $-\delta(x)$. Similarly the seventh of Eqs. (11.13) means that the two sides give the same result when multiplied by $f(a)$ or $f(b)$ and integrated over a or b. The last equation is verified by integrating both sides over either x or a.

Closure. The closure property of the momentum eigenfunctions, with both box and δ function normalization, can be established without the help of the completeness assumption that was made in Sec. 10 for the energy eigenfunctions. With box normalization, the expression analogous to the left side of Eq. (11.8) is

$$\sum_k \bar{u}_k(\mathbf{r}')u_k(\mathbf{r}) = L^{-3}\sum_{n_x=-\infty}^{\infty}\sum_{n_y=-\infty}^{\infty}\sum_{n_z=-\infty}^{\infty}e^{2\pi i[n_x(x-x')+n_y(y-y')+n_z(z-z')]/L}$$

This is readily evaluated in the limit of large L, in which case the summand changes by a negligible amount as each n changes by one unit.

We can then regard n_x as a continuous variable and replace $\sum_{n_x=-\infty}^{\infty}$ by $\int_{-\infty}^{\infty}dn_x = (L/2\pi)\int_{-\infty}^{\infty}dk_x$. We thus obtain

$$\sum_k \bar{u}_k(\mathbf{r}')u_k(\mathbf{r}) \xrightarrow[L\to\infty]{} (8\pi^3)^{-1}\int_{-\infty}^{\infty}\int_{-\infty}^{\infty}\int_{-\infty}^{\infty}e^{i[k_x(x-x')+k_y(y-y')+k_z(z-z')]}dk_xdk_ydk_z$$
$$= \delta(x-x')\delta(y-y')\delta(z-z') = \delta(\mathbf{r}-\mathbf{r}') \quad (11.14)$$

on making use of Eq. (11.10).

A similar calculation can be carried through, using the δ-function normalization, in which case we obtain from Eqs. (11.11) and (11.10)

$$\int \bar{u}_k(\mathbf{r}')u_k(\mathbf{r})d\tau_k = \int\int\int \bar{u}_k(\mathbf{r}')u_k(\mathbf{r})\,dk_x\,dk_y\,dk_z = \delta(\mathbf{r}-\mathbf{r}') \quad (11.15)$$

The closure relation (11.14) or (11.15) shows that the momentum eigenfunctions are orthonormal with respect to summation or integration over the eigenvalue $\mathbf{k}$ as well as with respect to integration over the position vector $\mathbf{r}$.

Expansion in Momentum Eigenfunctions. An arbitrary continuous function $\psi(\mathbf{r})$ can be written in terms of the δ function as

$$\psi(\mathbf{r}) = \int \psi(\mathbf{r}')\delta(\mathbf{r} - \mathbf{r}')d\tau' \tag{11.16}$$

If we substitute the left side of Eq. (11.14) in place of $\delta(\mathbf{r} - \mathbf{r}')$ in Eq. (11.16), we obtain

$$\psi(\mathbf{r}) = \int \psi(\mathbf{r}') \sum_k \bar{u}_k(\mathbf{r}')u_k(\mathbf{r})d\tau' = \sum_k A_k u_k(\mathbf{r})$$
$$A_k = \int \bar{u}_k(\mathbf{r}')\psi(\mathbf{r}')d\tau' \tag{11.17}$$

Similarly, if we substitute for $\delta(\mathbf{r} - \mathbf{r}')$ from Eq. (11.15), we obtain

$$\psi(\mathbf{r}) = \int \psi(\mathbf{r}')\int \bar{u}_k(\mathbf{r}')u_k(\mathbf{r})d\tau_k d\tau' = \int A_k u_k(\mathbf{r})d\tau_k \tag{11.18}$$

with the same expression for A_k. Equations (11.17) and (11.18) show that it is possible to expand an arbitrary function in momentum eigenfunctions that are normalized either in a box or by means of δ functions.[1]

Probability Function and Expectation Value. The momentum probability function associated with a normalized wave function $\psi(\mathbf{r})$ is proportional to $|A_k|^2$. The proportionality factor is unity, since if we put

$$P(\mathbf{k}) = |A_k|^2 \tag{11.19}$$

it is easily shown in analogy with the summation of Eq. (10.12) that

$$\sum_k P(\mathbf{k}) = 1 \qquad \text{and} \qquad \int P(\mathbf{k})d\tau_k = 1 \tag{11.20}$$

for the box and δ-function normalization, respectively.

The expectation value of the momentum when box normalization is used is

$$\langle \mathbf{p} \rangle = \hbar \sum_k \mathbf{k} P(\mathbf{k}) = \hbar \sum_k \int \mathbf{k}\bar{u}_k(\mathbf{r})\psi(\mathbf{r})d\tau \int u_k(\mathbf{r}')\bar{\psi}(\mathbf{r}')d\tau' \tag{11.21}$$

From the complex conjugate of Eq. (11.2), we can replace $\mathbf{k}\bar{u}_k(\mathbf{r})$ by $i \, \text{grad} \, \bar{u}_k(\mathbf{r})$. Then the first integral in Eq. (11.21) can be integrated by parts and the surface integral vanishes because of the periodic boundary conditions on ψ and $\bar{u}_k$. Thus with the help of Eq. (11.14), Eq. (11.21) becomes

$$\langle \mathbf{p} \rangle = -i\hbar \sum_k \int \bar{u}_k(\mathbf{r}) \, \text{grad} \, \psi(\mathbf{r})d\tau \int u_k(\mathbf{r}')\bar{\psi}(\mathbf{r}')d\tau'$$
$$= -i\hbar \int\int \bar{\psi}(\mathbf{r}')[\text{grad} \, \psi(\mathbf{r})]\delta(\mathbf{r} - \mathbf{r}')d\tau d\tau'$$
$$= -i\hbar \int \bar{\psi}(\mathbf{r}) \, \text{grad} \, \psi(\mathbf{r})d\tau \tag{11.22}$$

[1] These results, while not rigorously established here, are equivalent to the mathematical theorems on the expansibility of functions in Fourier series and Fourier integrals.

This is in agreement with the second of Eqs. (7.8).

When δ-function normalization is used, the details of the calculation are very similar to those given above, except that the surface integral that results from the partial integration is over a sphere of infinite radius; it is zero because ψ becomes vanishingly small at great distances. This is consistent with the supposition that ψ is normalized; otherwise neither $\int P(\mathbf{k})d\tau_k$ nor $\langle \mathbf{p} \rangle$ have any physical meaning. The result of the calculation in this case is the same as Eqs. (11.22) and (7.8).

12. MOTION OF A FREE WAVE PACKET IN ONE DIMENSION

The motion of a free particle (no external forces) in one dimension is described by the Schrödinger wave equation (6.8). The study of this motion provides an interesting application of the expansion techniques developed in Secs. 10 and 11. As a first step, we find the minimum value of the uncertainty product given in Eq. (3.1), and the possible forms of the one-dimensional wave packet that correspond to it, all at a definite instant of time. The structure of this minimum packet is the same whether or not the particle is free, since this form can be regarded simply as an initial condition on the solution of the Schrödinger equation for any V. However, the analytical work involved in finding ψ at other times is especially simple in the force-free case.

The Minimum Uncertainty Product.[1] In order to find the minimum value for the uncertainty product $\Delta x \cdot \Delta p$, we must first define what we mean by Δx and Δp. While many expressions are possible, the simplest to handle analytically is the root-mean-square deviation from the mean, where the word "mean" implies the expectation value of Sec. 7.

$$(\Delta x)^2 = \langle (x - \langle x \rangle)^2 \rangle = \langle x^2 \rangle - \langle 2x\langle x \rangle \rangle + \langle \langle x \rangle^2 \rangle = \langle x^2 \rangle - \langle x \rangle^2$$
$$(\Delta p)^2 = \langle (p - \langle p \rangle)^2 \rangle = \langle p^2 \rangle - \langle p \rangle^2 \tag{12.1}$$

Here the equalities follow directly from the general definition of expectation value given in Sec. 7. If now we put

$$\alpha \equiv x - \langle x \rangle, \qquad \beta \equiv p - \langle p \rangle = -i\hbar \left[\frac{d}{dx} - \left\langle \frac{d}{dx} \right\rangle \right] \tag{12.2}$$

then

$$(\Delta x)^2 (\Delta p)^2 = \int_{-\infty}^{\infty} \bar{\psi}\alpha^2\psi \, dx \int_{-\infty}^{\infty} \bar{\psi}\beta^2\psi \, dx$$
$$= \int_{-\infty}^{\infty} (\bar{\alpha}\bar{\psi})(\alpha\psi) \, dx \int_{-\infty}^{\infty} (\bar{\beta}\bar{\psi})(\beta\psi) \, dx \tag{12.3}$$

The transformation of the α integral in Eq. (12.3) is obvious; the similar transformation of the β integral follows from a partial integration when

---

[1] W. Heisenberg, "The Physical Principles of the Quantum Theory," pp. 17–19 (University of Chicago Press, Chicago, 1930).

we remember that ψ is a normalized wave packet, which vanishes at $x = \pm\infty$.

The inequality

$$\int \left| f - g\,\frac{\int f\bar{g}dx}{\int|g|^2dx} \right|^2 dx \geqq 0$$

where all integrals are from $x = -\infty$ to $+\infty$, is obviously true, and the equality is applicable only if $f = \gamma g$, where γ is a constant. From this inequality we obtain at once

$$\int|f|^2dx\int|g|^2dx \geqq |\int f\bar{g}dx|^2$$

If now we replace f by $\alpha\psi$ and g by $\beta\psi$, Eq. (12.3) becomes

$$(\Delta x)^2(\Delta p)^2 \geqq |\int(\bar{\alpha\psi})(\beta\psi)dx|^2 = |\int\bar{\psi}\alpha\beta\psi dx|^2 \qquad (12.4)$$

The last term in Eq. (12.4) can be written

$$|\int\bar{\psi}[\tfrac{1}{2}(\alpha\beta - \beta\alpha) + \tfrac{1}{2}(\alpha\beta + \beta\alpha)]\psi dx|^2$$
$$= \tfrac{1}{4}|\int\bar{\psi}(\alpha\beta - \beta\alpha)\psi dx|^2 + \tfrac{1}{4}|\int\bar{\psi}(\alpha\beta + \beta\alpha)\psi dx|^2 \qquad (12.5)$$

The cross term in the product that is omitted on the right side of Eq. (12.5) can be seen to vanish when use is made of the relation

$$\overline{\int\bar{\psi}\alpha\beta\psi\,dx} = \int\psi\bar{\alpha}\bar{\beta}\bar{\psi}\,dx = \int(\bar{\beta\psi})(\alpha\psi)\,dx = \int\bar{\psi}\beta\alpha\psi\,dx,$$

which is obtained by using partial integration and remembering that α is real. Now from Eq. (12.2)

$$(\alpha\beta - \beta\alpha)\psi = -i\hbar\left[x\frac{d\psi}{dx} - \frac{d}{dx}(x\psi)\right] = i\hbar\psi \qquad (12.6)$$

We thus obtain from Eqs. (12.4), (12.5), and (12.6)

$$(\Delta x)^2(\Delta p)^2 \geqq \tfrac{1}{4}\hbar^2 \qquad \text{or} \qquad \Delta x \cdot \Delta p \geqq \tfrac{1}{2}\hbar \qquad (12.7)$$

where the equality can hold only if the second term on the right side of Eq. (12.5) is zero. This is the precise expression of the Heisenberg uncertainty relation (3.1), when the uncertainties Δx and Δp are defined as in Eq. (12.1).

Form of the Minimum Packet. It follows from the foregoing derivation that the minimum uncertainty product is attained only when two conditions are fulfilled.

$$\alpha\psi = \gamma\beta\psi \qquad (12.8)$$
$$\int\bar{\psi}(\alpha\beta + \beta\alpha)\psi dx = 0 \qquad (12.9)$$

Equations (12.8) and (12.2) give us a differential equation for ψ

$$\frac{d\psi}{dx} = \left[\frac{i}{\gamma\hbar} (x - \langle x \rangle) + \frac{i\langle p \rangle}{\hbar} \right] \psi$$

which is readily integrated to give

$$\psi(x) = N \exp \left[\frac{i}{2\gamma\hbar} (x - \langle x \rangle)^2 + \frac{i\langle p \rangle x}{\hbar} \right] \tag{12.10}$$

where N is an arbitrary constant.

Equation (12.9), with the help of Eq. (12.8), becomes

$$\left(\frac{1}{\gamma} + \frac{1}{\bar{\gamma}} \right) \int \bar{\psi} \alpha^2 \psi dx = 0$$

which evidently requires that γ be pure imaginary. Then since we want Eq. (12.10) to represent a wave packet for which the integral of $|\psi|^2$ converges, γ must be negative imaginary. The magnitude of the constant N can now be fixed by normalizing ψ.

$$\int |\psi|^2 dx = 1$$

Similarly, γ can be determined by requiring that

$$\int (x - \langle x \rangle)^2 |\psi|^2 dx = (\Delta x)^2$$

The integrals are readily evaluated, and lead to the normalized minimum wave packet

$$\psi(x) = [2\pi(\Delta x)^2]^{-\frac{1}{4}} \exp \left[-\frac{(x - \langle x \rangle)^2}{4(\Delta x)^2} + \frac{i\langle p \rangle x}{\hbar} \right] \tag{12.11}$$

Momentum Expansion Coefficients. The one-dimensional momentum eigenfunctions analogous to Eqs. (11.4) and (11.11) are

$$u_k(x) = L^{-\frac{1}{2}} e^{ikx} \tag{12.12}$$

for normalization in a one-dimensional "box" of length L, and

$$u_k(x) = (2\pi)^{-\frac{1}{2}} e^{ikx} \tag{12.13}$$

for δ-function normalization. Since for a free particle the wave equation has the simple form of Eq. (6.8)

$$i\hbar \frac{\partial \psi}{\partial t} = -\frac{\hbar^2}{2m} \frac{\partial^2 \psi}{\partial x^2} \tag{12.14}$$

the momentum eigenfunctions are also eigenfunctions of the energy.[1]

---

[1] The converse is not necessarily true, since there are two solutions of Eq. (12.16) for k (positive and negative) for each value of E_k.

Thus any solution of the wave equation can be written in a form analogous to Eq. (10.18),

$$\psi(x,t) = \left(\sum_k \text{ or } \int dk\right) A_k e^{-\frac{iE_k t}{\hbar}} u_k(x), \tag{12.15}$$

where the A_k are independent of x and t; the entire time dependence is contained in the exponential factor. Equation (12.15) is readily verified to be a solution of Eq. (12.14) by direct substitution, provided that

$$E_k = \frac{\hbar^2 k^2}{2m} \tag{12.16}$$

The problem of finding the motion of a wave packet is thus resolved into finding the expansion coefficient A_k at some particular time, say $t = 0$, and then using Eqs. (12.15) and (12.16) to find $\psi(x,t)$ at other times. At $t = 0$, the exponential factors in Eq (12.15) are unity, and we may use the one-dimensional analogue of the second of Eqs. (11.17) to find A_k.

$$A_k = \int \bar{u}_k(x)\psi(x,0)dx \tag{12.17}$$

The limits on the integral are $x = \pm\frac{1}{2}L$ or $x = \pm\infty$, according as box or δ-function normalization is used. The momentum probability function $P(k) = |A_k e^{-\frac{iE_k t}{\hbar}}|^2 = |A_k|^2$ is independent of the time, so that $\langle p \rangle$ and Δp, for example, are constants.

Change with Time of a Minimum Packet. As a simple specific example, we take $\psi(x,0)$ to have the form of Eq. (12.11) with $\langle x \rangle = \langle p \rangle = 0$, so that the wave packet initially is centered at $x = 0$ and has zero average momentum. Then using box normalization, Eq. (12.17) gives

$$A_k = [2\pi L^2 (\Delta x)^2]^{-\frac{1}{4}} \int_{-\frac{1}{2}L}^{\frac{1}{2}L} \exp\left[-\frac{x^2}{4(\Delta x)^2} - ikx \right] dx$$

$$= \left[\frac{8\pi(\Delta x)^2}{L^2} \right]^{\frac{1}{4}} e^{-k^2(\Delta x)^2} \tag{12.18}$$

where L is assumed to be so large that the contribution to the integral from $|x| > \frac{1}{2}L$ can be neglected. Substitution into Eq. (12.15) gives the wave function for general values of t

$$\psi(x,t) = \sum_k A_k e^{-\frac{i\hbar k^2 t}{2m}} u_k(x) \tag{12.19}$$

where $k = 2\pi n/L$ and n takes on all positive and negative integer values and zero. As in Sec. 11, L may be taken arbitrarily large, n can be regarded as a continuous variable and the summation replaced by $\int dn$, which in turn is the same as $(L/2\pi)\int dk$. Thus

$$
\psi(x,t) = \left[\frac{(\Delta x)^2}{2\pi^3}\right]^{\frac{1}{4}} \int_{-\infty}^{\infty} \exp\left[-k^2(\Delta x)^2 - \frac{i\hbar k^2 t}{2m} + ikx\right] dk
$$

$$
= (2\pi)^{-\frac{1}{4}}\left(\Delta x + \frac{i\hbar t}{2m\Delta x}\right)^{-\frac{1}{2}} \exp\left[-\frac{x^2}{4(\Delta x)^2 + (2i\hbar t/m)}\right] \quad (12.20)
$$

The position probability density is then

$$
|\psi(x,t)|^2 = \left\{2\pi\left[(\Delta x)^2 + \frac{\hbar^2 t^2}{4m^2(\Delta x)^2}\right]\right\}^{-\frac{1}{2}}
$$

$$
\cdot \exp\left\{-\frac{x^2}{2\left[(\Delta x)^2 + \frac{\hbar^2 t^2}{4m^2(\Delta x)^2}\right]}\right\}. \quad (12.21)
$$

Equation (12.21) is of the same form as $|\psi(x,0)|^2$, except that $(\Delta x)^2$ is replaced by $(\Delta x)^2 + \hbar^2 t^2/4m^2(\Delta x)^2$, which is equal to $(\Delta x)^2 + (\Delta p)^2 t^2/m^2$. Thus the center of the packet remains at $x = 0$ while the breadth of the packet increases as t departs from zero in both past and future directions. The smaller the initial uncertainty in position, the larger the uncertainty in momentum and the more rapidly the packet spreads; the time-dependent part of the above expression, $t(\Delta p)/m$, is simply the distance traveled by a classical particle of momentum Δp in the time t.

Use of the δ-function normalization does not alter the results of the foregoing calculation. The expression for A_k given in Eq. (12.18) is to be multiplied by $(L/2\pi)^{\frac{1}{2}}$; in Eq. (12.19) the summation is to be replaced directly by $\int dk$, thus eliminating a factor $L/2\pi$; finally, u_k in Eq. (12.19) is to be multiplied by $(L/2\pi)^{\frac{1}{2}}$. These three factors cancel, and so Eqs. (12.20) and (12.21) are unaffected by the choice of normalization of the momentum eigenfunctions.

Classical Limit. We have seen in Sec. 7 that a wave packet always moves like a classical particle in so far as the expectation values of its position and momentum are concerned. However, classical dynamics is only useful as a description of the motion if the spreading of the wave packet can be neglected over times of interest in the particular problem.

As a simple example of the kind of parameter that indicates when the classical limit is realized, we consider a wave packet that corresponds to a classical particle moving in a circular orbit of radius a and period T. We shall assume that this packet is sufficiently well localized so that the potential energy does not vary appreciably over its dimensions. Then the classical theory can provide a useful description of the motion only if a wave packet like that discussed above spreads by an amount that is small in comparison with a during a time that is large in comparison with T. The smallest spread of a packet during a time interval of magnitude t is attained when Δx is chosen to be of order $(\hbar t/m)^{\frac{1}{2}}$. We thus require that $(\hbar t/m)^{\frac{1}{2}} \ll a$ when $t \gg T$. This condition may be simply expressed by saying that the angular momentum $2\pi ma^2/T$ of the particle must be very large in comparison with $\hbar$. Thus for most atomic systems, where the angular momentum of each electron is of order $\hbar$, a wave packet corresponding to a well-localized particle spreads so much in one period that this type of description of the motion is not of physical interest.

Problems

1. Given three degenerate eigenfunctions that are linearly independent although not necessarily orthogonal. Find three linear combinations of them that are orthogonal to each other and are normalized. Are the three new combinations eigenfunctions? If so, are they degenerate?

2. Show that so far as the one-dimensional motion of a particle is concerned, the functions $u_{x'}(x) = \delta(x - x')$ for all real x' constitute a complete orthonormal set, and that each of them is an eigenfunction of the position variable x with the eigenvalue x'. Set up the position probability function and compare with that obtained in Sec. 7.

3. If the potential energy $V(x)$ in a one-dimensional problem is a monotonic increasing function of x and independent of the time, show that the functions $u_{V'}(x) = (dV/dx)^{-\frac{1}{2}}_{x=x'}\,\delta(x - x')$ for all real x', where $V' = V(x')$, constitute a complete orthonormal set of eigenfunctions of the potential energy with eigenvalues V'. Find the probability function for the potential energy, and show that it has the properties that would be expected of it.

4. What changes are needed in the discussion of the momentum eigenfunctions given in Sec. 11 if normalization is carried through in a box of rectangular parallelepiped shape rather than in a box of cubical shape?

5. Find two other representations for the Dirac δ function like that given in Eq. (11.9).

6. Verify each of Eqs. (11.13) involving δ functions.

7. Show that the two Eqs. (11.20) are correct: that the momentum probability function defined in Eqs. (11.19) and (11.17) for a normalized ψ sums or integrates to unity.

8. The expression in square brackets in the integrand of Eq. (10.19) enables one to calculate ψ at time t in terms of ψ at time t_0. If this expression is called $G(x,x',t,t_0)$ in the one-dimensional case, then $\psi(x,t) = \int G(x,x',t,t_0)\psi(x',t_0)dx'$. Show that for a free particle in one dimension

$$G(x,x',t,t_0) = \left[\frac{-im}{2\pi\hbar(t - t_0)}\right]^{\frac{1}{2}} \exp\left[\frac{im(x - x')^2}{2\hbar(t - t_0)}\right]$$

Assume that ψ has the form of the normalized minimum wave packet (12.11) at $t_0 = 0$; use the above result to find ψ and $|\psi|^2$ at another time t.

CHAPTER IV

DISCRETE EIGENVALUES: ENERGY LEVELS

The formalism that was developed in Chap. II and elaborated in Chap. III will now be applied to the explicit computation of discrete energy levels and the corresponding eigenfunctions. The next chapter will take up situations in which the energy eigenvalues are continuously distributed. Thus we are concerned here with bound states in which the particle is restrained by the external forces (potential energy) to a particular region of space, and in the next chapter with collision problems in which the particle can approach from and recede to infinite distance.

The relatively few potential energy functions $V(\mathbf{r})$ for which analytic solutions of the wave equation (8.2) are possible, are important beyond these immediate problems, since they often serve as bases for approximate calculations on more complicated systems.

13. LINEAR HARMONIC OSCILLATOR

The one-dimensional motion of a point mass attracted to a fixed center by a force that is proportional to the displacement from that center, provides one of the fundamental problems of classical dynamics. Its study is important not only for itself, but also because more complicated systems can often be analyzed in terms of normal modes of motion that are formally equivalent to harmonic oscillators. The linear harmonic oscillator in quantum mechanics is similarly of importance both for the study of such problems as the vibrations of individual atoms in a molecule, and for the analysis of more complicated systems such as crystals and (as we shall see in Chap. XIII) quantized wave fields.

Asymptotic Behavior. The force $F = -Kx$ can be represented by the potential energy $V(x) = \frac{1}{2}Kx^2$ so that Eq. (8.5) becomes

$$-\frac{\hbar^2}{2m}\frac{d^2u}{dx^2} + \frac{1}{2}Kx^2u = Eu \qquad (13.1)$$

It is convenient in dealing with an equation of this type to rewrite it in dimensionless form. To this end we introduce a dimensionless independent variable $\xi = \alpha x$, and a dimensionless eigenvalue λ, and attempt to put Eq. (13.1) in the form

$$\frac{d^2u}{d\xi^2} + (\lambda - \xi^2)u = 0 \qquad (13.2)$$

60

Comparison of Eqs. (13.1) and (13.2) shows that this is possible if

$$\alpha^4 = \frac{mK}{\hbar^2}, \qquad \lambda = \frac{2E}{\hbar}\left(\frac{m}{K}\right)^{\frac{1}{2}} = \frac{2E}{\hbar\omega_c} \qquad (13.3)$$

where $\omega_c = (K/m)^{\frac{1}{2}}$ is the angular frequency of the corresponding classical harmonic oscillator.

The solution of Eq. (13.2) is facilitated by first examining the dominant behavior of u in the asymptotic region $\xi \to \pm \infty$.[1] For sufficiently large ξ it is apparent that $u(\xi) = \xi^n e^{\pm \frac{1}{2}\xi^2}$ satisfies Eq. (13.2) so far as the leading terms (which are of order $\xi^2 u$) are concerned, when n has any finite value. The boundary conditions of Sec. 8 permit us to keep only the minus sign in the exponent. This suggests that it might be possible to find an exact solution of Eq. (13.2) of the form

$$u(\xi) = H(\xi)e^{-\frac{1}{2}\xi^2} \qquad (13.4)$$

where $H(\xi)$ is a polynomial of finite order in ξ. Substitution of Eq. (13.4) into Eq. (13.2) gives as the equation for $H(\xi)$

$$H'' - 2\xi H' + (\lambda - 1)H = 0 \qquad (13.5)$$

where primes denote differentiation with respect to ξ.

Energy Levels. We now find a solution for H in the form

$$H(\xi) = \xi^s(a_0 + a_1\xi + a_2\xi^2 + \cdots), \qquad a_0 \neq 0, \qquad s \geqq 0 \quad (13.6)$$

This is necessarily finite for $\xi = 0$. Equation (13.5) is to be valid for all values of ξ, so that when Eq. (13.6) is substituted into it, the coefficient of each power of ξ can be equated to zero.

$$s(s - 1)a_0 = 0$$
$$(s + 1)sa_1 = 0$$
$$(s + 2)(s + 1)a_2 - (2s + 1 - \lambda)a_0 = 0 \qquad (13.7)$$
$$(s + 3)(s + 2)a_3 - (2s + 3 - \lambda)a_1 = 0$$
$$\cdots \cdots \cdots \cdots \cdots \cdots \cdots \cdots \cdots \cdots \cdots$$
$$(s + \nu + 2)(s + \nu + 1)a_{\nu+2} - (2s + 2\nu + 1 - \lambda)a_\nu = 0$$

where ν is an integer. Since a_0 cannot be zero, the first of Eqs. (13.7) tells us that $s = 0$ or $s = 1$. The second equation tells us that $s = 0$, or $a_1 = 0$, or both. Then the third equation gives us a_2 in terms of a_0, the fourth gives us a_3 in terms of a_1, and the general equation gives us $a_{\nu+2}$ in terms of a_ν.

It follows from Eqs. (13.7) that the presence in the series (13.6) of a finite or an infinite number of terms depends on the choice of s, a_1, and

[1] We follow the polynomial method of A. Sommerfeld, "Wave Mechanics," p. 11 (Dutton, New York, 1929).

the eigenvalue λ.   If the series does not terminate, its dominant asymptotic behavior can be inferred from the coefficients of its high terms

$$\frac{a_{\nu+2}}{a_\nu} \xrightarrow[\nu \to \infty]{} \frac{2}{\nu}$$

This ratio is the same as that of the series for $\xi^n e^{\xi^2}$ with any finite value of n.   Equation (13.4) shows that this behavior for H violates the boundary conditions on u for large $|\xi|$.

Thus the series (13.6) must terminate.   This means that

$$\lambda = 2s + 2\nu + 1;$$

ν must be an even integer, since $a_0 \neq 0$ and otherwise the even-subscript terms would form an infinite series.   Since the odd-subscript series cannot then terminate, we must choose $a_1 = 0$.   The index s can still be either 0 or 1, and corresponding to these two values λ is equal to $2\nu + 1$ or $2\nu + 3$, where ν is an even integer.   We may express both cases in terms of a quantum number n

$$\lambda = 2n + 1, \qquad E_n = (n + \tfrac{1}{2})\hbar\omega_c, \qquad n = 0, 1, 2, \ldots \qquad (13.8)$$

Zero-point Energy.   The infinite sequence of energy levels (13.8) has the equal spacing postulated in 1900 by Planck, which is in agreement with the quantization rules of the old quantum theory.   However, the finite value of the ground-state energy level $\tfrac{1}{2}\hbar\omega_c$, which is called the *zero-point energy*, is characteristic of the quantum mechanics, and is related to the uncertainty principle in the same manner as is the finite lowest energy level for the square well with perfectly rigid walls (Sec. 9).   The total energy is of order $(\Delta p)^2/m + K(\Delta x)^2$, where Δp and Δx are measures of the spreads in momentum and position, as defined in Sec. 12; if this is minimized, taking account of the uncertainty relation (3.1), it is easily seen that the minimum Δp is of order $(Km\hbar^2)^{\frac{1}{4}}$, so that the minimum total energy is of order $\hbar(K/m)^{\frac{1}{2}}$ or $\hbar\omega_c$.

Parity.   It follows from Eqs. (13.8) and (13.7) that n is the highest value of $s + \nu$ in the series (13.6) for H.   If we denote the corresponding polynomial by $H_n(\xi)$, we see that H_n is of degree n in ξ, and is wholly even or odd according as n is even or odd.   Since $e^{-\frac{1}{2}\xi^2}$ is even and has no nodes, the corresponding eigenfunction $u_n(\xi)$ has the parity of n, and has n nodes.   These conclusions are in agreement with the earlier results of Secs. 8 and 9.

Hermite Polynomials.   The polynomial of order n that has the parity of n and is a solution of Eq. (13.5) with $\lambda = 2n + 1$

$$H_n'' - 2\xi H_n' + 2nH_n = 0, \qquad (13.9)$$

is called the nth *Hermite polynomial* $H_n(\xi)$. It is clear from the foregoing solution of Eq. (13.5) that these conditions define H_n uniquely except for an arbitrary multiplying constant. It is not necessary, then, to use the recursion relations (13.7) to study the detailed properties of the H_n, if some other formulation of them can be found that is consistent with these conditions. A far more convenient formulation is actually available, which expresses the H_n in terms of a *generating function* $S(\xi,s)$.

$$S(\xi,s) = e^{\xi^2-(s-\xi)^2} = e^{-s^2+2s\xi}$$

$$= \sum_{n=0}^{\infty} \frac{H_n(\xi)}{n!} s^n \qquad (13.10)$$

If the exponential in Eq. (13.10) is expanded out in powers of s and ξ, it is seen that a given power of s is associated only with powers of ξ that are equal to that power or less than it by an even integer. Thus $H_n(\xi)$ defined in this way is a polynomial of order n that has the parity of n.

To show that this H_n satisfies the differential equation (13.9), we differentiate both sides of Eq. (13.10) first with respect to ξ and then with respect to s.

$$\frac{\partial S}{\partial \xi} = 2se^{-s^2+2s\xi} = \sum_n \frac{2s^{n+1}}{n!} H_n(\xi) = \sum_n \frac{s^n}{n!} H_n'(\xi)$$

$$\frac{\partial S}{\partial s} = (-2s + 2\xi)e^{-s^2+2s\xi} = \sum_n \frac{(-2s + 2\xi)s^n}{n!} H_n(\xi) = \sum_n \frac{s^{n-1}}{(n-1)!} H_n(\xi)$$

Equating equal powers of s in the sums of these two equations gives respectively

$$H_n' = 2nH_{n-1}$$
$$H_{n+1} = 2\xi H_n - 2nH_{n-1} \qquad (13.11)$$

The lowest order differential equation involving only H_n that can be constructed from Eqs. (13.11) is easily seen to be Eq. (13.9). Thus the $H_n(\xi)$ given by Eq. (13.10) are the Hermite polynomials.

The relations (13.11) may be used for the calculation of the H_n and their derivatives, or an explicit expression obtainable directly from the generating function may be used. If $S(\xi,s)$ is differentiated n times with respect to s and s is then set equal to 0, Eq. (13.10) shows that the result is simply $H_n(\xi)$. Now for any function of the form $f(s - \xi)$ it is apparent that

$$\frac{\partial f}{\partial s} = -\frac{\partial f}{\partial \xi}$$

Thus

$$\frac{\partial^n S}{\partial s^n} = e^{\xi^2} \frac{\partial^n}{\partial s^n} e^{-(s-\xi)^2} = (-1)^n e^{\xi^2} \frac{\partial^n}{\partial \xi^n} e^{-(s-\xi)^2}$$

This gives an expression for the nth Hermite polynomial

$$H_n(\xi) = (-1)^n e^{\xi^2} \frac{\partial^n}{\partial \xi^n} e^{-\xi^2} \tag{13.12}$$

The first three polynomials calculated from Eq. (13.12) are

$$H_0(\xi) = 1, \qquad H_1(\xi) = 2\xi, \qquad H_2(\xi) = 4\xi^2 - 2$$

Harmonic-oscillator Wave Functions. The generating function is also useful for the calculation of integrals involving the harmonic-oscillator wave functions (13.4)

$$u_n(x) = N_n H_n(\alpha x) e^{-\frac{1}{2}\alpha^2 x^2} \tag{13.13}$$

Suppose, for example, that we wish to normalize $u_n(x)$; this is equivalent to choosing the constant N_n such that

$$\int_{-\infty}^{\infty} |u_n(x)|^2 dx = \frac{|N_n|^2}{\alpha} \int_{-\infty}^{\infty} H_n^2(\xi) e^{-\xi^2} d\xi = 1$$

The integral on the right can be expressed as a series coefficient in the expansion of an integral containing the product of two generating functions.

$$\int_{-\infty}^{\infty} e^{-s^2+2s\xi} e^{-t^2+2t\xi} e^{-\xi^2} d\xi = \sum_{n=0}^{\infty} \sum_{m=0}^{\infty} \frac{s^n t^m}{n!m!} \int_{-\infty}^{\infty} H_n(\xi) H_m(\xi) e^{-\xi^2} d\xi \tag{13.14}$$

The integral on the left of Eq. (13.14) is readily evaluated directly to give

$$\pi^{\frac{1}{2}} e^{2st} = \pi^{\frac{1}{2}} \sum_{n=0}^{\infty} \frac{(2st)^n}{n!} \tag{13.15}$$

If equal powers of s and t are equated in the series on the right sides of Eqs. (13.14) and (13.15), we obtain the results

$$\int_{-\infty}^{\infty} H_n^2(\xi) e^{-\xi^2} d\xi = \pi^{\frac{1}{2}} 2^n n!,$$
$$\int_{-\infty}^{\infty} H_n(\xi) H_m(\xi) e^{-\xi^2} d\xi = 0, \qquad n \neq m \tag{13.16}$$

The first of Eqs. (13.16) tells us that the normalizing constant can be chosen to be

$$N_n = \left(\frac{\alpha}{\pi^{\frac{1}{2}} 2^n n!} \right)^{\frac{1}{2}} \tag{13.17}$$

where a constant multiplicative complex phase factor of unit magnitude is still arbitrary. The second of these equations tells us that $u_n(x)$ and $u_m(x)$ are orthogonal to each other if $n \neq m$; this is in agreement with the general result obtained in Sec. 10 for nondegenerate energy eigenfunctions, since in accordance with Eq. (13.8), $E_n \neq E_m$ if $n \neq m$, and so there is no degeneracy.

The integral

$$\int_{-\infty}^{\infty} \bar{u}_n(x) x u_m(x) dx = \frac{\bar{N}_n N_m}{\alpha^2} \int_{-\infty}^{\infty} \xi H_n(\xi) H_m(\xi) e^{-\xi^2} d\xi$$

is typical of others that can be evaluated with the help of the generating function. The two series expressions for the integral,

$$\int_{-\infty}^{\infty} e^{-s^2 + 2s\xi} e^{-t^2 + 2t\xi} \xi e^{-\xi^2} d\xi = \sum_{n=0}^{\infty} \sum_{m=0}^{\infty} \frac{s^n t^m}{n! m!} \int_{-\infty}^{\infty} \xi H_n(\xi) H_m(\xi) e^{-\xi^2} d\xi$$

and

$$\pi^{\frac{1}{2}} (s + t) e^{2st} = \pi^{\frac{1}{2}} \sum_{n=0}^{\infty} \frac{2^n (s^{n+1} t^n + s^n t^{n+1})}{n!}$$

may be equated term by term. With the help of Eq. (13.17), we get

$$\int_{-\infty}^{\infty} \bar{u}_n(x) x u_m(x) dx = \begin{cases} \dfrac{1}{\alpha} \left(\dfrac{n+1}{2} \right)^{\frac{1}{2}}, & m = n + 1 \\[2ex] \dfrac{1}{\alpha} \left(\dfrac{n}{2} \right)^{\frac{1}{2}}, & m = n - 1 \\[2ex] 0, & \text{otherwise} \end{cases} \quad (13.18)$$

$\dfrac{1}{\alpha} \left(\dfrac{2}{n} \right)^{1/2}$

Correspondence with Classical Theory. Plots of the first six harmonic oscillator wave functions are shown in Fig. 10. It is apparent that the position probability densities $|u_n|^2$ associated with these stationary wave functions have little resemblance to the corresponding densities for the classical harmonic oscillator; the latter are proportional to $(\xi_0^2 - \xi^2)^{-\frac{1}{2}}$, where ξ_0 is the amplitude of the classical oscillator whose energy is equal to the quantum-mechanical eigenvalue. The agreement between classical and quantum probability densities improves rapidly with increasing n. Figure 11 contains a plot of $|u_n|^2$ for $n = 10$ (solid curve), and of the density of a classical oscillator of total energy $\frac{21}{2} \hbar \omega_c$ (dashed curve). The agreement is quite good on the average, the principal discrepancy being the rapid oscillations in $|u_n|^2$.

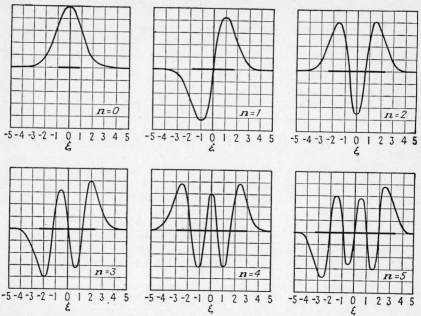

FIG. 10. Energy eigenfunctions for the first six states of the harmonic oscillator. [*After L. Pauling and E. B. Wilson, Jr., "Introduction to Quantum Mechanics," pp. 74–75 (McGraw-Hill, New York, 1935).*]

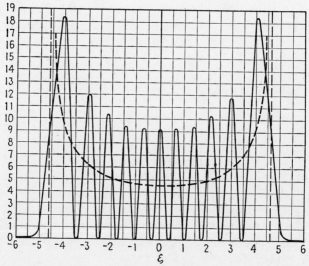

FIG. 11. Position probability density for the state $n = 10$ of a harmonic oscillator (solid curve) and for a classical oscillator of the same total energy (dashed curve). (*After L. Pauling and E. B. Wilson, Jr., op. cit., p. 76.*)

The expectation value for the potential energy can be obtained from Eq. (7.6):

$$\langle V \rangle_n = \int_{-\infty}^{\infty} \bar{u}_n(x) \tfrac{1}{2} K x^2 u_n(x) dx$$

$$= \tfrac{1}{2} K \left(\frac{2n+1}{2\alpha^2} \right) = \tfrac{1}{2}(n + \tfrac{1}{2})\hbar\omega_c = \tfrac{1}{2} E_n$$

where $\int x^2 |u_n|^2 dx$ can be calculated with the help of the generating function in analogy with the evaluation of Eq. (13.18). Thus for any value of n, the average potential and kinetic energies are each half of the total energy, just as is the case with the classical oscillator.

In similar fashion it can be shown that $\langle x \rangle = \langle p \rangle = 0$ for any harmonic-oscillator wave function, so that Eq. (12.1) tells us that $(\Delta x)^2 = \langle x^2 \rangle$, and $(\Delta p)^2 = \langle p^2 \rangle$. It is then easy to see that the uncertainty product is

$$\Delta x \cdot \Delta p = (n + \tfrac{1}{2})\hbar$$

This has the minimum possible value $\tfrac{1}{2}\hbar$ of Eq. (12.7) for the ground-state eigenfunction

$$u_0(x) = \frac{\alpha^{\frac{1}{2}}}{\pi^{\frac{1}{4}}} e^{-\frac{1}{2}\alpha^2 x^2} \tag{13.19}$$

which, as would be expected, is of the form of the minimum packet (12.11). Thus the minimum packet happens to be an eigenfunction of the harmonic-oscillator wave equation if its Δx is properly related to K and m.

Oscillating Wave Packet. In accordance with Eq. (10.18), the general solution of the time-dependent Schrödinger equation for the harmonic oscillator

$$i\hbar \frac{\partial}{\partial t} \psi(x,t) = \left(-\frac{\hbar^2}{2m} \frac{\partial^2}{\partial x^2} + \tfrac{1}{2} K x^2 \right) \psi(x,t)$$

can be expanded in terms of stationary wave functions

$$\psi(x,t) = \sum_{n=0}^{\infty} A_n u_n(x) e^{-\frac{iE_n t}{\hbar}} = e^{-\frac{1}{2}i\omega_c t} \sum_{n=0}^{\infty} A_n u_n(x) e^{-in\omega_c t} \tag{13.20}$$

where the A_n are arbitrary constants. Thus apart from the phase factor $e^{-\frac{1}{2}i\omega_c t}$, $\psi(x,t)$ is a periodic function of t with the period of the classical oscillator $2\pi/\omega_c$. This suggests that it might be possible to find a solution in the form of a wave packet whose center of gravity oscillates with the period of the classical motion.

To investigate this possibility, we assume that at $t = 0$ the ψ of Eq. (13.20) has the form of the normalized minimum packet (13.19), except that the center of gravity is displaced in the positive x direction by an amount a.

$$\psi(x,0) = \sum_{n=0}^{\infty} A_n u_n(x) = \frac{\alpha^{\frac{1}{2}}}{\pi^{\frac{1}{4}}} e^{-\frac{1}{2}\alpha^2(x-a)^2} \tag{13.21}$$

We can make use of the orthonormality of the u_n to calculate a particular coefficient A_m by multiplying Eq. (13.21) through by $\bar{u}_m(x)$ and integrating over x.

$$A_m = \int_{-\infty}^{\infty} \bar{u}_m(x)\psi(x,0)dx = \frac{\bar{N}_m}{\pi^{\frac{1}{4}}\alpha^{\frac{1}{2}}} \int_{-\infty}^{\infty} H_m(\xi)e^{-\frac{1}{2}\xi^2}e^{-\frac{1}{2}(\xi-\xi_0)^2}d\xi, \quad \xi_0 \equiv \alpha a$$

The integral on the right can be evaluated with the help of the generating function by equating term by term the two series expressions for the integral

$$\int_{-\infty}^{\infty} e^{-s^2+2s\xi}e^{-(\xi^2-\xi\xi_0+\frac{1}{2}\xi_0^2)}d\xi = \sum_{n=0}^{\infty} \frac{s^n}{n!} \int_{-\infty}^{\infty} H_n(\xi)e^{-(\xi^2-\xi\xi_0+\frac{1}{2}\xi_0^2)}d\xi,$$

and

$$\pi^{\frac{1}{2}}e^{-\frac{1}{4}\xi_0^2+s\xi_0} = \pi^{\frac{1}{2}}e^{-\frac{1}{4}\xi_0^2}\sum_{n=0}^{\infty} \frac{(s\xi_0)^n}{n!}.$$

On making use of Eq. (13.17), we obtain

$$A_n = \frac{\xi_0^n e^{-\frac{1}{4}\xi_0^2}}{(2^n n!)^{\frac{1}{2}}} \tag{13.22}$$

Substitution of these A_n into Eq. (13.20) gives

$$\psi(x,t) = \frac{\alpha^{\frac{1}{2}}}{\pi^{\frac{1}{4}}} e^{-\frac{1}{2}\xi^2-\frac{1}{4}\xi_0^2-\frac{1}{2}i\omega_c t}\sum_{n=0}^{\infty} \frac{H_n(\xi)}{n!}\left(\tfrac{1}{2}\xi_0 e^{-i\omega_c t}\right)^n$$

$$= \frac{\alpha^{\frac{1}{2}}}{\pi^{\frac{1}{4}}} \exp\left(-\tfrac{1}{2}\xi^2 - \tfrac{1}{4}\xi_0^2 - \tfrac{1}{2}i\omega_c t - \tfrac{1}{4}\xi_0^2 e^{-2i\omega_c t} + \xi\xi_0 e^{-i\omega_c t}\right)$$

$$= \frac{\alpha^{\frac{1}{2}}}{\pi^{\frac{1}{4}}} \exp\left[-\tfrac{1}{2}(\xi - \xi_0 \cos \omega_c t)^2\right.$$
$$\left. - i(\tfrac{1}{2}\omega_c t + \xi\xi_0 \sin \omega_c t - \tfrac{1}{4}\xi_0^2 \sin 2\omega_c t)\right]$$

where the sum is evaluated with the help of the generating function (13.10). The absolute square of this wave function gives a position probability density

$$|\psi(x,t)|^2 = \frac{\alpha}{\pi^{\frac{1}{2}}} e^{-\alpha^2(x-a \cos \omega_c t)^2}$$

This shows that ψ represents a wave packet that oscillates without change of shape about $x = 0$, with amplitude a and the classical frequency.

As $a \to 0$, ψ approaches the lowest energy eigenfunction $u_0(x)e^{-\frac{1}{2}i\omega_c t}$. The larger a becomes, the larger the number of stationary states that contribute significantly to the packet, and the larger the quantum number n_0 for which A_n of Eq. (13.22) has a maximum. For $n \gg 1$, we can use Stirling's formula to maximize $\ln A_n$; neglecting terms of order $\ln n$ and lower

$$\ln A_n \cong n(\ln \xi_0 - \tfrac{1}{2} \ln 2) - \tfrac{1}{2}n(\ln n - 1)$$
$$n_0 \cong \tfrac{1}{2}\xi_0^2 = \frac{Ka^2}{2\hbar\omega_c} \tag{13.23}$$

Thus the energy level $E_{n_0} = (n_0 + \tfrac{1}{2})\hbar\omega_c$, from whose neighborhood most of the contribution to ψ comes, is approximately equal to the energy $\tfrac{1}{2}Ka^2$ of the classical oscillator that has the same amplitude.

14. SPHERICALLY SYMMETRIC POTENTIALS IN THREE DIMENSIONS

It is generally impossible to obtain analytic solutions of the three-dimensional wave equation (8.2) unless it can be separated into total differential equations in each of the three space coordinates. It has been shown[1] that there are 11 coordinates systems in which the free-particle wave equation [Eq. (8.2) with $V = 0$] can be separated. One of the most important of these is the spherical polar-coordinate system, in terms of which the rectangular coordinates are given by (see Fig. 12)

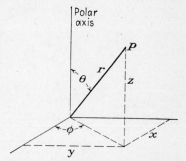

$$x = r \sin \theta \cos \phi$$
$$y = r \sin \theta \sin \phi$$
$$z = r \cos \theta$$

Fig. 12. Relation between rectangular and spherical polar coordinates of a point P.

If the potential energy is spherically symmetric, so that $V(\mathbf{r}) = V(r)$ is a function only of the magnitude r of $\mathbf{r}$ measured from some origin, the wave equation can always be separated in spherical coordinates. Many problems of physical interest can be represented exactly or approximately in terms of spherically symmetric potentials of various shapes. In this section we effect the separation, and solve the resulting total dif-

[1] L. P. Eisenhart, *Phys. Rev.*, **45**, 428 (1934). See also L. Pauling and E. B. Wilson, Jr., "Introduction to Quantum Mechanics," Appendix IV (McGraw-Hill, New York, 1935).

ferential equations in θ and ϕ. The next two sections deal with the solution of the radial equation for particular forms of $V(r)$.

Separation of the Wave Equation. The wave equation (8.2) with a spherically symmetric potential energy may be written in spherical coordinates

$$-\frac{\hbar^2}{2m}\left[\frac{1}{r^2}\frac{\partial}{\partial r}\left(r^2\frac{\partial}{\partial r}\right) + \frac{1}{r^2\sin\theta}\frac{\partial}{\partial\theta}\left(\sin\theta\frac{\partial}{\partial\theta}\right) + \frac{1}{r^2\sin^2\theta}\frac{\partial^2}{\partial\phi^2}\right]u$$
$$+ V(r)u = Eu \quad (14.1)$$

We first separate the radial and the angular parts by substituting

$$u(r,\theta,\phi) = R(r)Y(\theta,\phi)$$

into Eq. (14.1) and dividing through by u.

$$\frac{1}{R}\frac{d}{dr}\left(r^2\frac{dR}{dr}\right) + \frac{2mr^2}{\hbar^2}[E - V(r)]$$
$$= -\frac{1}{Y}\left[\frac{1}{\sin\theta}\frac{\partial}{\partial\theta}\left(\sin\theta\frac{\partial Y}{\partial\theta}\right) + \frac{1}{\sin^2\theta}\frac{\partial^2 Y}{\partial\phi^2}\right] \quad (14.2)$$

Since the left side of Eq. (14.2) depends only on r, and the right side depends only on θ and ϕ, both sides must be equal to a constant that we call λ. Thus Eq. (14.2) gives us a radial equation

$$\frac{1}{r^2}\frac{d}{dr}\left(r^2\frac{dR}{dr}\right) + \left\{\frac{2m}{\hbar^2}[E - V(r)] - \frac{\lambda}{r^2}\right\}R = 0 \quad (14.3)$$

and an angular equation

$$\frac{1}{\sin\theta}\frac{\partial}{\partial\theta}\left(\sin\theta\frac{\partial Y}{\partial\theta}\right) + \frac{1}{\sin^2\theta}\frac{\partial^2 Y}{\partial\phi^2} + \lambda Y = 0 \quad (14.4)$$

The angular equation (14.4) can be further separated by substituting $Y(\theta,\phi) = \Theta(\theta)\Phi(\phi)$ into it and following the same procedure to obtain

$$\frac{d^2\Phi}{d\phi^2} + \nu\Phi = 0 \quad (14.5)$$

$$\frac{1}{\sin\theta}\frac{d}{d\theta}\left(\sin\theta\frac{d\Theta}{d\theta}\right) + \left(\lambda - \frac{\nu}{\sin^2\theta}\right)\Theta = 0 \quad (14.6)$$

The ϕ equation (14.5) can be solved at once; its general solution may be written

$$\Phi(\phi) = Ae^{i\nu^{\frac{1}{2}}\phi} + Be^{-i\nu^{\frac{1}{2}}\phi}, \qquad \nu \neq 0$$
$$\Phi(\phi) = A + B\phi, \qquad \nu = 0 \quad (14.7)$$

The requirement of Sec. 8 that $\Phi(\phi)$ and $d\Phi/d\phi$ be continuous throughout the domain 0 to 2π of ϕ demands that ν be chosen equal to the square of an integer. We thus replace Eqs. (14.7) by

$$\Phi_m(\phi) = (2\pi)^{-\frac{1}{2}} e^{im\phi} \qquad (14.8)$$

where now all physical meaningful solutions are included if m is allowed to be a positive or negative integer or zero;[1] the multiplying constant is chosen equal to $(2\pi)^{-\frac{1}{2}}$ in order that Φ be normalized to unity over the range of ϕ.

Legendre Polynomials. Unless $V(r)$ is specified, the farthest we can carry our treatment is the solution of the θ equation (14.6), where now $\nu = m^2$. It is convenient to substitute $w = \cos\theta$ for θ, and put

$$\Theta(\theta) = P(w),$$

when Eq. (14.6) becomes

$$\frac{d}{dw}\left[(1 - w^2)\frac{dP}{dw}\right] + \left(\lambda - \frac{m^2}{1 - w^2}\right)P = 0 \qquad (14.9)$$

Since the domain of θ is 0 to π, the domain of w is 1 to -1. The procedure for solving Eq. (14.9) is in many respects similar to the solution of the harmonic-oscillator wave equation presented in Sec. 13, and will not be given in detail here.[2] Since Eq. (14.9) is a second-order differential equation, it has two linearly independent solutions. Except for particular values of λ, both of these are infinite at $w = \pm 1$, and in accordance with Sec. 8 are not physically acceptable. If however $\lambda = l(l + 1)$, where l is a positive integer or zero, one of the solutions is finite at $w = \pm 1$ (the other is not); this finite solution has the form $(1 - w^2)^{\frac{1}{2}|m|}$ times a polynomial of order $l - |m|$ in w, and has the parity of $l - |m|$.

The physically acceptable solutions of Eq. (14.9) when $m = 0$ are called the *Legendre polynomials* $P_l(w)$. Just as is the case with the Hermite polynomials, their properties may be discussed in terms of a generating function

$$T(w,s) = (1 - 2sw + s^2)^{-\frac{1}{2}}$$

$$= \sum_{l=0}^{\infty} P_l(w)s^l, \qquad s < 1. \qquad (14.10)$$

---

[1] At the very slight risk of confusion with the mass of the particle, we make use of the customary symbol m for the quantum number associated with the coordinate ϕ.

[2] For a complete discussion of this equation, see E. T. Whittaker and G. N. Watson, "A Course of Modern Analysis," 4th ed., Chap. XV (Cambridge, London, 1935).

Differentiation of the generating function with respect to w and s leads to relations that are analogous to Eqs. (13.11) for the Hermite polynomials.

$$(1 - w^2)P_l' = - lwP_l + lP_{l-1}$$
$$(l + 1)P_{l+1} = (2l + 1)wP_l - lP_{l-1} \qquad (14.11)$$

where primes denote differentiation with respect to w. The lowest order differential equation involving only P_l that can be constructed from Eqs. (14.11) is easily seen to be Eq. (14.9) with $\lambda = l(l + 1)$ and $m = 0$.

For m not necessarily equal to zero, Eq. (14.9) has physically acceptable solutions if $\lambda = l(l + 1)$ and $|m| \leq l$. These solutions, which are called *associated Legendre functions*, are expressible in terms of the Legendre polynomials

$$P_l^m(w) = (1 - w^2)^{\frac{1}{2}|m|} \frac{d^{|m|}}{dw^{|m|}} P_l(w) \qquad (14.12)$$

This can be shown by substitution of Eq. (14.12) into the equation that is obtained by differentiating $|m|$ times the equation for $P_l(w)$. The generating function for the associated Legendre functions is obtained by differentiating Eq. (14.10) $|m|$ times with respect to w and multiplying by $(1 - w^2)^{\frac{1}{2}|m|}$.

$$T_m(w,s) = \frac{(2|m|)!(1 - w^2)^{\frac{1}{2}|m|}s^{|m|}}{2^{|m|}(|m|)!(1 - 2sw + s^2)^{|m|+\frac{1}{2}}}$$

$$= \sum_{l=|m|}^{\infty} P_l^m(w)s^l \qquad (14.13)$$

Spherical Harmonics. The angular part $Y_{lm}(\theta,\phi)$ of the complete wave function, which is a solution of Eq. (14.4) when $\lambda = l(l + 1)$, is called a *spherical harmonic.* It is apparent that

$$Y_{lm}(\theta,\phi) = N_{lm}P_l^m(\cos \theta)\Phi_m(\phi) \qquad (14.14)$$

where $\Phi_m(\phi)$ is given by Eq. (14.8), and N_{lm} is the normalization constant for the associated Legendre function.

The same proof that was given in Sec. 10 for the orthogonality of the energy eigenfunctions may be used to show that solutions of Eq. (14.4) corresponding to different eigenvalues λ or l are orthogonal. The eigenvalue l is, however, $(2l + 1)$-fold degenerate, since there exist linearly independent solutions $Y_{lm}(\theta,\phi)$ for this value of l and all integer values of m between $+l$ and $-l$. The choice of Eq. (14.8) for $\Phi_m(\phi)$ makes these degenerate eigenfunctions orthogonal. We have then that the integral

$$\int_0^\pi \int_0^{2\pi} \bar{Y}_{lm}(\theta,\phi)Y_{l'm'}(\theta,\phi) \sin \theta d\theta d\phi = \int_{-1}^1 \int_0^{2\pi} \bar{Y}_{lm}Y_{l'm'}dwd\phi$$

vanishes unless $l = l'$ and $m = m'$. It is interesting to note that there is no more orthogonality present than is necessary to make this integral vanish when it should. Thus the ϕ part of the integral vanishes when $m \neq m'$ without regard for the l values; the θ or w part of the integral vanishes only when $l \neq l'$ and $|m| = |m'|$, since for $m \neq m'$ the orthogonality is taken care of by the integration over ϕ.

The integral

$$\int_{-1}^{1} P_l^m(w) P_{l'}^m(w) \, dw \tag{14.15}$$

can be evaluated in various ways, for example, by using the generating function (14.13) in a manner similar to that described in Sec. 13. As expected, the integral (14.15) vanishes unless $l = l'$, when it has the value $[2/(2l + 1)][(l + |m|)!/(l - |m|)!]$; thus N_{lm}, which contains an arbitrary complex phase factor of unit magnitude, may be taken to be the reciprocal of the square root of this quantity. The normalized spherical harmonics are then

$$Y_{lm}(\theta, \phi) = \left[\frac{2l + 1}{4\pi} \frac{(l - |m|)!}{(l + |m|)!} \right]^{\frac{1}{2}} P_l^m(\cos \theta) e^{im\phi} \tag{14.16}$$

The first four spherical harmonics are

$$Y_{0,0} = \frac{1}{(4\pi)^{\frac{1}{2}}}, \qquad Y_{1,1} = \left(\frac{3}{8\pi} \right)^{\frac{1}{2}} \sin \theta e^{i\phi}$$

$$Y_{1,0} = \left(\frac{3}{4\pi} \right)^{\frac{1}{2}} \cos \theta, \qquad Y_{1,-1} = \left(\frac{3}{8\pi} \right)^{\frac{1}{2}} \sin \theta e^{-i\phi}$$

Parity. The concept of parity introduced in Sec. 9 can now be extended to three-dimensional problems of the type discussed in this section. Suppose that the position coordinate $\mathbf{r}$ is reflected through the origin so that $\mathbf{r}$ is replaced by $-\mathbf{r}$; this corresponds to replacing x by $-x$, y by $-y$, and z by $-z$, or to replacing θ by $\pi - \theta$, ϕ by $\phi + \pi$, and leaving r unchanged. It is clear that the only change in the wave equation (14.1) is that $u(r, \theta, \phi)$ is replaced by $u(r, \pi - \theta, \phi + \pi)$, the rest of the equation being unaffected. Then the discussion of Sec. 9 shows that orthogonal linear combinations of degenerate eigenfunctions can be found that have definite parities, and that a nondegenerate eigenfunction must have a definite parity.

· The energy levels for a spherically symmetric potential are degenerate at least with respect to the quantum number m, for $l > 0$. In this case, the degenerate eigenfunctions all have the same parity, which we now show to be the parity of l. When $\mathbf{r}$ is reflected through the origin, the radial part $R(r)$ of the solution is unchanged, the ϕ part $\Phi(\phi)$ given by

Eq. (14.8) has the parity of $|m|$, and the θ part $P_l^m(\cos\theta)$ has the parity of $l - |m|$, since $P_l^m(w)$ is equal to an even part $(1 - w^2)^{\frac{1}{2}|m|}$ times a polynomial in w that has the parity of $l - |m|$ with respect to change in sign of w or $\cos\theta$. Thus $Y_{lm}(\theta,\phi)$, and hence $u(\mathbf{r})$, has the parity of l.

Angular Momentum. The radial wave equation (14.3) may be rewritten in a form that resembles the one-dimensional wave equation (8.5). If we put $R(r) = \chi(r)/r$, the equation for the modified radial wave function χ may be written

$$-\frac{\hbar^2}{2m}\frac{d^2\chi}{dr^2} + \left[V(r) + \frac{l(l+1)\hbar^2}{2mr^2}\right]\chi = E\chi \qquad (14.17)$$

Thus the radial motion is similar to the one-dimensional motion of a particle in a potential

$$V(r) + \frac{l(l+1)\hbar^2}{2mr^2} \qquad (14.18)$$

The additional "potential energy" can be seen physically to be connected with the angular momentum in the following way. A classical particle that has angular momentum M about the axis through the origin perpendicular to the plane of its orbit has the angular velocity $\omega = M/mr^2$ when its radial distance from the origin is r. An inward force

$$m\omega^2 r = \frac{M^2}{mr^3}$$

is required to keep the particle in this path; this "centripetal force" is supplied by the potential energy, and hence adds to the $V(r)$ that appears in the radial motion an additional "centrifugal potential energy" $M^2/2mr^2$. This has exactly the form of the extra term in (14.18) if we put

$$M = [l(l+1)]^{\frac{1}{2}}\hbar$$

The foregoing physical argument for identifying the quantum number l with the angular momentum of the particle can be put in quantitative form by finding the operators that correspond to the three components of the angular momentum vector. Classically, we have that $\mathbf{M} = \mathbf{r} \times \mathbf{p}$, so that we take in quantum mechanics

$$M_x = yp_z - zp_y = -i\hbar\left(y\frac{\partial}{\partial z} - z\frac{\partial}{\partial y}\right)$$

$$M_y = zp_x - xp_z = -i\hbar\left(z\frac{\partial}{\partial x} - x\frac{\partial}{\partial z}\right) \qquad (14.19)$$

$$M_z = xp_y - yp_x = -i\hbar\left(x\frac{\partial}{\partial y} - y\frac{\partial}{\partial x}\right)$$

Equations (14.19) can be transformed into spherical polar coordinates to give

$$M_x = i\hbar \left(\sin \phi \frac{\partial}{\partial \theta} + \cot \theta \cos \phi \frac{\partial}{\partial \phi} \right)$$

$$M_y = i\hbar \left(- \cos \phi \frac{\partial}{\partial \theta} + \cot \theta \sin \phi \frac{\partial}{\partial \phi} \right) \qquad (14.20)$$

$$M_z = -i\hbar \frac{\partial}{\partial \phi}$$

The operator that represents the square of the total angular momentum is then found from Eqs. (14.20) to be

$$\mathbf{M}^2 = M_x^2 + M_y^2 + M_z^2$$

$$= -\hbar^2 \left[\frac{1}{\sin \theta} \frac{\partial}{\partial \theta} \left(\sin \theta \frac{\partial}{\partial \theta} \right) + \frac{1}{\sin^2 \theta} \frac{\partial^2}{\partial \phi^2} \right] \qquad (14.21)$$

Comparison of Eqs. (14.21) and (14.4) shows that $Y_{lm}(\theta,\phi)$ is an eigenfunction of $\mathbf{M}^2$ with the eigenvalue $l(l + 1)\hbar^2$.

$$\mathbf{M}^2 Y_{lm}(\theta,\phi) = l(l + 1)\hbar^2 Y_{lm}(\theta,\phi) \qquad (14.22)$$

In similar fashion, it follows from the structure of Eq. (14.8) and the last of Eqs. (14.20) that $\Phi_m(\phi)$, and hence also $Y_{lm}(\theta,\phi)$, is an eigenfunction of M_z with the eigenvalue $m\hbar$.

$$M_z Y_{lm}(\theta,\phi) = m\hbar Y_{lm}(\theta,\phi) \qquad (14.23)$$

Thus the separation of the wave equation in spherical polar coordinates results in wave functions that are eigenfunctions of both the total angular momentum and the component of angular momentum along the polar axis. The quantum number l that appears in Eq. (14.22) is called the *azimuthal* or *orbital angular-momentum quantum number*. The quantum number m that appears in Eq. (14.23) is called the *magnetic quantum number*, since it is of importance in the theory of the Zeeman effect (see Sec. 39), which involves the component of angular momentum along the magnetic field (z axis). It should be noted that the wave equation cannot in general be separated in this way and angular-momentum eigenfunctions obtained if the potential energy $V(r)$ is not spherically symmetric. This corresponds to the classical result that the angular momentum is a constant of the motion only for a central field of force (which is describable by a spherically symmetric potential). There is, however, the characteristic difference between classical and quantum theory that all three components of $\mathbf{M}$ can be precisely specified at once in the classical theory, whereas only M_z and $\mathbf{M}^2$ can in general be precisely specified at once in the quantum theory, since $Y_{lm}(\theta,\phi)$ is not an eigenfunction of M_x and M_y (except for the case $l = 0$). It is possible to relate this result to the uncertainty principle. The choice of the direction of the polar axis that distinguishes M_z from M_x and M_y is, of course, completely arbitrary; it corresponds to the arbitrariness of the direction of space quantization in the absence of external fields in the old quantum theory.

15. THREE-DIMENSIONAL SQUARE WELL POTENTIAL

We are now in a position to find the bound-state energy levels that correspond to particular choices of the potential energy $V(r)$ and of the angular-momentum quantum number l, by solving the radial wave equation (14.3). As a first example, we consider the square well potential of finite depth, for which $V(r) = -V_0$, $r < a$, $V(r) = 0$, $r > a$, where V_0 is positive (see Fig. 13). A spherical region of this type in which the potential is less than that of the surroundings serves to attract a particle just as in the one-dimensional case considered in Sec. 9.

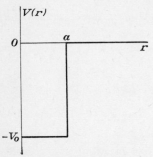

Fig. 13. Spherically symmetric square well potential of depth V_0 and radius a.

Zero Angular Momentum. When $l = 0$, it is easier to solve the wave equation in the form (14.17) than in the form (14.3). In this case, $R(r) = \chi(r)/r$, and the wave equation is

$$-\frac{\hbar^2}{2m}\frac{d^2\chi}{dr^2} - V_0\chi = E\chi, \qquad r < a$$

$$-\frac{\hbar^2}{2m}\frac{d^2\chi}{dr^2} = E\chi, \qquad r > a \qquad (15.1)$$

The solution of Eqs. (15.1) is the same as that obtained for the finite potential step in Sec. 9, except for three points: first, the energy scale is lowered everywhere in the present problem by an amount V_0; second, the domain of r is 0 to $+\infty$, in place of the domain $-\infty$ to $+\infty$ for x; and third, the boundary condition that the wave function not become infinite at $x = -\infty$ is now replaced by the same condition at $r = 0$.

From the discussion of Sec. 9, it is apparent that the solutions of Eqs. (15.1) are

$$\chi(r) = A \sin \alpha r + B \cos \alpha r, \qquad \alpha = \left[\frac{2m(V_0 - |E|)}{\hbar^2}\right]^{\frac{1}{2}}, \qquad r < a,$$

$$\chi(r) = Ce^{-\beta r}, \qquad \beta = \left(\frac{2m|E|}{\hbar^2}\right)^{\frac{1}{2}}, \qquad r > a \qquad (15.2)$$

where we are interested in bound-state energy levels for which $E < 0$. The requirement that $R(r)$ be finite at $r = 0$ demands that we set $B = 0$ in the first of Eqs. (15.2). Thus the solution has the form of the odd parity solution of the one-dimensional problem. The energy levels are obtained by equating the two values of $(1/\chi)(d\chi/dr)$ at $r = a$ (this is equivalent to making $(1/R)(dR/dr)$ continuous there), and are given by solving

$$\alpha \cot \alpha a = -\beta \qquad (15.3)$$

which is the same as Eq. (9.6). Then it follows from the discussion of Fig. 9 that there is no energy level unless $V_0 a^2 > \pi^2 \hbar^2 / 8m$; there is one bound state if $\pi^2 \hbar^2 / 8m < V_0 a^2 \leqq 9\pi^2 \hbar^2 / 8m$, etc.

Interior Solutions for Arbitrary l. For nonzero values of l, it is more convenient to work with the original radial equation (14.3) than with the equation for χ. If we put $\rho = \alpha r$, where α is defined in Eq. (15.2), the wave equation for $r < a$ becomes

$$\frac{d^2 R}{d\rho^2} + \frac{2}{\rho} \frac{dR}{d\rho} + \left[1 - \frac{l(l+1)}{\rho^2} \right] R = 0 \qquad (15.4)$$

The strong resemblance between Eq. (15.4) and Bessel's equation suggests that $R(r)$ can be expressed in terms of Bessel functions. This is in fact the case; if we define the "spherical Bessel function" $j_l(\rho)$ that is regular at $\rho = 0$ by[1]

$$j_l(\rho) = \left(\frac{\pi}{2\rho} \right)^{\frac{1}{2}} J_{l+\frac{1}{2}}(\rho) \qquad (15.5)$$

where J is an ordinary Bessel function of half-odd-integer order, it is easily verified that $j_l(\rho)$ satisfies Eq. (15.4). In similar fashion, the "spherical Neumann function" is

$$n_l(\rho) = (-1)^{l+1} \left(\frac{\pi}{2\rho} \right)^{\frac{1}{2}} J_{-l-\frac{1}{2}}(\rho)$$

It can be shown[2] that $J_{l+\frac{1}{2}}(\rho)$, where l is a positive or negative integer or zero, is expressible as a sum of products of $\sin \rho$ and $\cos \rho$ with polynomials of odd order in $\rho^{-\frac{1}{2}}$. In particular, explicit expressions for the first three j's and n's are

$$j_0(\rho) = \frac{\sin \rho}{\rho}, \qquad\qquad n_0(\rho) = -\frac{\cos \rho}{\rho}$$

$$j_1(\rho) = \frac{\sin \rho}{\rho^2} - \frac{\cos \rho}{\rho}, \qquad n_1(\rho) = -\frac{\cos \rho}{\rho^2} - \frac{\sin \rho}{\rho}$$

$$\qquad\qquad\qquad\qquad\qquad\qquad\qquad\qquad\qquad\qquad (15.6)$$

$$j_2(\rho) = \left(\frac{3}{\rho^3} - \frac{1}{\rho} \right) \sin \rho$$

$$- \frac{3}{\rho^2} \cos \rho, \qquad n_2(\rho) = -\left(\frac{3}{\rho^3} - \frac{1}{\rho} \right) \cos \rho - \frac{3}{\rho^2} \sin \rho$$

The leading terms for small ρ are[3]

---

[1] This definition and the properties of the j_l and n_l are taken from P. M. Morse, "Vibration and Sound," 2d ed., pp. 316–317 (McGraw-Hill, New York, 1948).

[2] G. N. Watson, "Theory of Bessel Functions," 2d ed., p. 52 (Macmillan, New York, 1945).

[3] Equations (15.7) are useful approximations for ρ^2 somewhat less than $4l + 6$ and 2, respectively (G. N. Watson, *op. cit.*, p. 44).

$$j_l(\rho) \xrightarrow[\rho \to 0]{} \frac{\rho^l}{1 \cdot 3 \cdot 5 \cdots (2l + 1)},$$

$$n_l(\rho) \xrightarrow[\rho \to 0]{} - \frac{1 \cdot 1 \cdot 3 \cdot 5 \cdots (2l - 1)}{\rho^{l+1}}, \tag{15.7}$$

and the leading terms in the asymptotic expansions are[1]

$$j_l(\rho) \xrightarrow[\rho \to \infty]{} \frac{1}{\rho} \cos [\rho - \tfrac{1}{2}(l + 1)\pi]$$

$$n_l(\rho) \xrightarrow[\rho \to \infty]{} \frac{1}{\rho} \sin [\rho - \tfrac{1}{2}(l + 1)\pi] \tag{15.8}$$

Some properties of the j's and n's are

$$\int j_0^2(\rho)\rho^2 d\rho = \tfrac{1}{2}\rho^3[j_0^2(\rho) + n_0(\rho)j_1(\rho)]$$

$$\int n_0^2(\rho)\rho^2 d\rho = \tfrac{1}{2}\rho^3[n_0^2(\rho) - j_0(\rho)n_1(\rho)]$$

$$n_{l-1}(\rho)j_l(\rho) - n_l(\rho)j_{l-1}(\rho) = \frac{1}{\rho^2}, \qquad l > 0 \tag{15.9}$$

$$j_l(\rho) \frac{d}{d\rho} n_l(\rho) - n_l(\rho) \frac{d}{d\rho} j_l(\rho) = \frac{1}{\rho^2}$$

The following are properties of both the j's and the n's:

$$j_{l-1}(\rho) + j_{l+1}(\rho) = \frac{2l + 1}{\rho} j_l(\rho), \qquad\qquad l > 0$$

$$\frac{d}{d\rho} j_l(\rho) = \frac{1}{2l + 1} [lj_{l-1}(\rho) - (l + 1)j_{l+1}(\rho)]$$

$$\frac{d}{d\rho} [\rho^{l+1}j_l(\rho)] = \rho^{l+1}j_{l-1}(\rho), \qquad\qquad l > 0 \tag{15.10}$$

$$\frac{d}{d\rho} [\rho^{-l}j_l(\rho)] = -\rho^{-l}j_{l+1}(\rho)$$

$$\int j_1(\rho)d\rho = -j_0(\rho)$$

$$\int j_0(\rho)\rho^2 d\rho = \rho^2 j_1(\rho)$$

$$\int j_l^2(\rho)\rho^2 d\rho = \tfrac{1}{2}\rho^3[j_l^2(\rho) - j_{l-1}(\rho)j_{l+1}(\rho)] \qquad l > 0$$

Since $R(r)$ must be finite for $r = 0$, the desired solution for $r < a$ is

$$R(r) = Aj_l(\alpha r) \tag{15.11}$$

Exterior Solutions for Arbitrary l. The wave equation for $r > a$ can be put in the form (15.4) if we redefine ρ to be $i\beta r$, where β is given in Eq. (15.2). Since the domain of ρ does not now extend in to zero, there is

---

[1] Equations (15.8) are useful approximations for ρ somewhat larger than $\tfrac{1}{2}l(l + 1)$ (G. N. Watson, *op. cit.*, p. 199); however, the magnitudes (although not the phases) of j_l and n_l are given to good approximation by (15.8) if ρ is somewhat larger than l, which is approximately the value of ρ for which the magnitude of j_l is greatest.

no reason why n_l cannot appear in the solution. The linear combination of j_l and n_l to be selected will be determined by the asymptotic form, which must fall off exponentially for large r. This suggests that we define *spherical Hankel functions*

$$h_l^{(1)}(\rho) = j_l(\rho) + in_l(\rho)$$
$$h_l^{(2)}(\rho) = j_l(\rho) - in_l(\rho) \qquad (15.12)$$

which from Eqs. (15.8) have the asymptotic forms

$$h_l^{(1)}(\rho) \xrightarrow[\rho \to \infty]{} \frac{1}{\rho} e^{i[\rho - \frac{1}{2}(l+1)\pi]}$$

$$h_l^{(2)}(\rho) \xrightarrow[\rho \to \infty]{} \frac{1}{\rho} e^{-i[\rho - \frac{1}{2}(l+1)\pi]} \qquad (15.13)$$

It can be shown that the asymptotic expansions, of which Eqs. (15.13) give the leading terms, contain no terms for which the exponent has the opposite sign to that given.

The desired solution for $r > a$ is then

$$R(r) = Bh_l^{(1)}(i\beta r) = B[j_l(i\beta r) + in_l(i\beta r)] \qquad (15.14)$$

The first three of these functions are

$$h_0^{(1)}(i\beta r) = -\frac{1}{\beta r} e^{-\beta r}$$

$$h_1^{(1)}(i\beta r) = i \left(\frac{1}{\beta r} + \frac{1}{\beta^2 r^2} \right) e^{-\beta r} \qquad (15.15)$$

$$h_2^{(1)}(i\beta r) = \left(\frac{1}{\beta r} + \frac{3}{\beta^2 r^2} + \frac{3}{\beta^3 r^3} \right) e^{-\beta r}$$

Energy Levels. The energy levels are obtained by requiring that $(1/R)(dR/dr)$ be continuous at $r = a$. When this condition is applied to the interior solution (15.11) and the exterior solution (15.15) with $l = 0$, we obtain Eq. (15.3). This may be written as

$$\xi \cot \xi = -\eta, \qquad \xi^2 + \eta^2 = \frac{2mV_0a^2}{\hbar^2} \qquad (15.16)$$

where, as in Sec. 9, we have put $\xi = \alpha a$ and $\eta = \beta a$. The same condition applied to the solutions for $l = 1$ reduces, with the help of Eqs. (15.6) and (15.15) to

$$\frac{\cot \xi}{\xi} - \frac{1}{\xi^2} = \frac{1}{\eta} + \frac{1}{\eta^2}, \qquad \xi^2 + \eta^2 = \frac{2mV_0a^2}{\hbar^2} \qquad (15.17)$$

Equations (15.17) may be solved numerically or graphically, by the methods indicated for the solution of Eqs. (15.16) in Sec. 9. In general, there is no degeneracy between the eigenvalues obtained from the solution of equations like (15.16) and (15.17) for various values of l.

It is easy to see how many energy levels Eqs. (15.17) give for various values of V_0a^2 without going through the numerical work. A new level appears whenever η is zero or cot ξ is infinite. This occurs at $\xi = \pi$, $2\pi, \ldots$. Thus there is no energy level with $l = 1$ when

$$V_0a^2 \leqq \frac{\pi^2\hbar^2}{2m};$$

there is one bound state with $l = 1$ if $\pi^2\hbar^2/2m < V_0a^2 \leqq 2\pi^2\hbar^2/m$, etc.

The smallest value of V_0a^2 for which there exists a bound state with $l = 1$, is greater than the corresponding value of V_0a^2 for $l = 0$; this is reasonable from a physical point of view. The interpretation in Sec. 14 of the l term in the radial wave equation as an additional potential energy, which corresponds to the repulsive "centrifugal force," suggests that a particle possessing angular momentum requires a stronger attractive potential to bind it than a particle with no angular momentum. Indeed, it turns out that the minimum square well potential "strength" V_0a^2 required to bind a particle of orbital angular-momentum quantum number l increases monotonically with increasing l.[1]

16. THE HYDROGEN ATOM

The potential energy $V(r) = -Ze^2/r$, which represents the attractive Coulomb interaction between an atomic nucleus of charge $+Ze$ and an electron of charge $-e$, provides another wave equation that can be solved analytically. This problem is of direct physical interest, since apart from relativistic effects (see Chap. XII), the calculated energy eigenvalues are in agreement with the observed energy levels of the hydrogen atom ($Z = 1$), the singly charged helium ion ($Z = 2$), etc.

Reduced Mass. The Schrödinger wave equation developed in Sec. 6 describes the motion of a single particle in an external field of force. Now, however, we are interested in the motion of two particles (nucleus and electron) that are attracted to each other by a force that depends only on the distance between them. The form of the wave equation to be used for two particles is suggested by the extension of the wave equation from one to three dimensions that was given in Sec. 6. This extension involved making the wave function depend on the three rectangular coordinates x, y, and z instead of just on x, and introducing

---

[1] It can be shown that bound states appear with zero energy for a particular l value when $[(1/R)(dR/dr)]_{r=a} = -(l+1)/a$; for $l > 0$ this is equivalent to the condition $j_{l-1}(\xi) = 0$ where now $\xi = (2mV_0a^2/\hbar^2)^{\frac{1}{2}}$.

the momenta corresponding to the new coordinates as they appear in the classical expression for the energy.

A similar extension from three to six rectangular coordinates leads directly to the Schrödinger wave equation for two particles of masses m_1 and m_2:

$$i\hbar \frac{\partial}{\partial t} \psi(x_1,y_1,z_1,x_2,y_2,z_2,t) = \left[-\frac{\hbar^2}{2m_1}\left(\frac{\partial^2}{\partial x_1^2} + \frac{\partial^2}{\partial y_1^2} + \frac{\partial^2}{\partial z_1^2}\right) \right.$$

$$\left. -\frac{\hbar^2}{2m_2}\left(\frac{\partial^2}{\partial x_2^2} + \frac{\partial^2}{\partial y_2^2} + \frac{\partial^2}{\partial z_2^2}\right) + V(x_1,y_1,z_1,x_2,y_2,z_2,t) \right] \psi(x_1,y_1,z_1,x_2,y_2,z_2,t) \quad (16.1)$$

where the potential energy is assumed to depend in an arbitrary manner on all six coordinates and the time. If now the potential energy depends only on the relative coordinates, so that $V = V(x_1 - x_2, y_1 - y_2, z_1 - z_2)$, an important simplification can be made. We define relative coordinates x,y,z and coordinates of the center of mass X,Y,Z by

$$x = x_1 - x_2, \qquad y = y_1 - y_2, \qquad z = z_1 - z_2$$
$$MX = m_1x_1 + m_2x_2, \quad MY = m_1y_1 + m_2y_2, \quad MZ = m_1z_1 + m_2z_2 \quad (16.2)$$

Here, $M = m_1 + m_2$ is the total mass of the system. Equation (16.1) can be rewritten in terms of the new coordinates

$$i\hbar \frac{\partial \psi}{\partial t} = \left[-\frac{\hbar^2}{2M}\left(\frac{\partial^2}{\partial X^2} + \frac{\partial^2}{\partial Y^2} + \frac{\partial^2}{\partial Z^2}\right) \right.$$

$$\left. -\frac{\hbar^2}{2\mu}\left(\frac{\partial^2}{\partial x^2} + \frac{\partial^2}{\partial y^2} + \frac{\partial^2}{\partial z^2}\right) + V(x,y,z) \right] \psi \quad (16.3)$$

where

$$\mu = \frac{m_1 m_2}{m_1 + m_2} \quad (16.4)$$

is called the *reduced mass*.

Two separations of the wave equation (16.3) can now be made. First, the time dependence can be separated out, as in Sec. 8; and second, a separation can be made into a product of functions of the relative coordinates and center-of-mass coordinates. The process is straightforward and simple, and results in

$$\psi(x,y,z,X,Y,Z,t) = u(x,y,z)U(X,Y,Z)e^{-\frac{i(E+E')t}{\hbar}}$$

$$-\frac{\hbar^2}{2\mu} \nabla^2 u + Vu = Eu \quad (16.5)$$

$$-\frac{\hbar^2}{2M} \nabla^2 U = E'U$$

where the ∇^2 operators in the second and third equations imply differentiation with respect to the relative and center-of-mass coordinates, respectively. The second of Eqs. (16.5) describes the relative motion of the two particles, and is the same as the equation for the motion of a particle that has the reduced mass μ in an external potential energy V. The third of Eqs. (16.5) tells us that the center of mass of the system of two particles moves like a free particle of mass M.

In the hydrogen-atom problem, we shall be interested in the energy levels E associated with the relative motion. In this case, the reduced mass μ is only slightly smaller than the electronic mass, since atomic nuclei are far more massive than electrons.

Asymptotic Behavior. The separation of the relative motion in spherical coordinates is made as in Sec. 14. The radial equation that corresponds to the angular-momentum quantum number l is then

$$-\frac{\hbar^2}{2\mu}\frac{1}{r^2}\frac{d}{dr}\left(r^2\frac{dR}{dr}\right) - \frac{Ze^2}{r}R + \frac{l(l+1)\hbar^2}{2\mu r^2}R = ER \qquad (16.6)$$

where $E < 0$ for a bound state. We follow the polynomial method used in the treatment of the harmonic-oscillator equation that was given in Sec. 13, and first attempt to rewrite Eq. (16.6) in dimensionless form by introducing a dimensionless independent variable $\rho = \alpha r$. Unlike Eq. (13.1), however, where the leading term for large x was the potential energy term $\frac{1}{2}Kx^2$, the leading term in Eq. (16.6) for large r is the eigenvalue term E. We therefore choose α so that the E term becomes a fixed number; this makes the dominant asymptotic behavior of the solution independent of the eigenvalue. We rewrite Eq. (16.6) as

$$\frac{1}{\rho^2}\frac{d}{d\rho}\left(\rho^2\frac{dR}{d\rho}\right) + \left(\frac{\lambda}{\rho} - \frac{1}{4} - \frac{l(l+1)}{\rho^2}\right)R = 0 \qquad (16.7)$$

where the particular choice of the number $\frac{1}{4}$ for the eigenvalue term is arbitrary but convenient for the following development. Comparison of Eqs. (16.6) and (16.7) shows that

$$\alpha^2 = \frac{8\mu|E|}{\hbar^2}, \qquad \lambda = \frac{2\mu Ze^2}{\alpha\hbar^2} = \frac{Ze^2}{\hbar}\left(\frac{\mu}{2|E|}\right)^{\frac{1}{2}} \qquad (16.8)$$

As with the harmonic-oscillator equation, we first find the dominant behavior of $R(\rho)$ in the asymptotic region $\rho \to \infty$. For sufficiently large ρ, it is apparent that $R(\rho) = \rho^n e^{\pm\frac{1}{2}\rho}$ satisfies Eq. (16.7) so far as the leading terms (which are of order R) are concerned, when n has any finite value. This suggests that we look for an exact solution of Eq. (16.7) of the form

$$R(\rho) = F(\rho)e^{-\frac{1}{2}\rho} \qquad (16.9)$$

where $F(\rho)$ is a polynomial of finite order in ρ.   Substitution of Eq. (16.9) into Eq. (16.7) gives as the equation for $F(\rho)$

$$F'' + \left(\frac{2}{\rho} - 1\right)F' + \left[\frac{\lambda - 1}{\rho} - \frac{l(l + 1)}{\rho^2}\right] F = 0 \qquad (16.10)$$

where primes denote differentiation with respect to ρ.

Energy Levels.   We now find a solution for F in the form

$$F(\rho) = \rho^s(a_0 + a_1\rho + a_2\rho^2 + \cdots)$$
$$\equiv \rho^s L(\rho), \qquad a_0 \neq 0, \qquad s \geqq 0 \quad (16.11)$$

This is necessarily finite for $\rho = 0$.   Substitution of Eq. (16.11) into Eq. (16.10) gives as the equation for L

$$\rho^2 L'' + \rho[2(s + 1) - \rho]L' + [\rho(\lambda - s - 1) + s(s + 1) - l(l + 1)]L = 0$$

If ρ is set equal to zero in this equation, it follows from the form of L implied by Eq. (16.11) that $s(s + 1) - l(l + 1) = 0$.   This quadratic equation in s has two roots: $s = l$ and $s = -(l + 1)$.   The boundary condition that $R(\rho)$ be finite at $\rho = 0$ requires that we choose $s = l$. The equation for L then becomes

$$\rho L'' + [2(l + 1) - \rho]L' + (\lambda - l - 1)L = 0 \qquad (16.12)$$

Equation (16.12) can be solved by substituting in a power series of the form indicated by Eq. (16.11).   The recursion relation between the coefficients of successive terms of the series is readily seen to be

$$a_{\nu+1} = \frac{\nu + l + 1 - \lambda}{(\nu + 1)(\nu + 2l + 2)} a_\nu \qquad (16.13)$$

If the series does not terminate, its dominant asymptotic behavior can be inferred from the coefficients of its high terms:

$$\frac{a_{\nu+1}}{a_\nu} \xrightarrow[\nu \to \infty]{} \frac{1}{\nu}$$

This ratio is the same as that of the series for $\rho^n e^\rho$ with any finite value of n.   Equations (16.9) and (16.11) show that this behavior for L violates the boundary condition on R for large ρ.

Thus the series for L must terminate.   If the highest power of ρ in L is $\rho^{n'}(n' \geqq 0)$, we must choose λ equal to a positive integer n,[1] such that

$$\lambda = n = n' + l + 1 \qquad (16.14)$$

---

[1] The result that the allowed values of λ are integers, rather than multiples of integers, derives from the choice of $\frac{1}{4}$ for the eigenvalue term in the dimensionless radial wave equation (16.7).

n' is called the *radial quantum number* and n the *total quantum number*. Since n' and l can take on positive integer or zero values, n can have the values 1, 2, ... The energy eigenvalues are given by Eq. (16.8)

$$E_n = - |E_n| = - \frac{\mu Z^2 e^4}{2\hbar^2 n^2} \qquad (16.15)$$

in agreement with the old quantum theory and with experiment. Unlike the square well potential problem considered in Sec. 15, the Coulomb field problem gives rise to an infinite number of discrete energy levels extending from $-\mu Z^2 e^4 / 2\hbar^2$ up to zero, for any finite value of Z. This is due to the slow decrease in magnitude of the Coulomb potential at large r.

Laguerre Polynomials. The physically acceptable solutions of Eq. (16.12) with $\lambda = n$ may be expressed in terms of the *Laguerre polynomials* $L_q(\rho)$, which can be defined in terms of a generating function

$$U(\rho,s) = \frac{e^{-\frac{\rho s}{1-s}}}{1-s}$$

$$= \sum_{q=0}^{\infty} \frac{L_q(\rho)}{q!} s^q, \qquad s < 1 \qquad (16.16)$$

Differentiation of the generating function with respect to ρ and s leads to relations that are analogous to Eqs. (13.11) for the Hermite polynomials and (14.11) for the Legendre polynomials

$$L'_q - qL'_{q-1} = -qL_{q-1}$$
$$L_{q+1} = (2q + 1 - \rho)L_q - q^2 L_{q-1} \qquad (16.17)$$

The lowest order differential equation involving only L_q that can be constructed from Eqs. (16.17) is easily seen to be

$$\rho L''_q + (1 - \rho)L'_q + qL_q = 0 \qquad (16.18)$$

Equation (16.18) resembles Eq. (16.12) but is not quite the same. We define the *associated Laguerre polynomial*

$$L_q^p(\rho) = \frac{d^p}{d\rho^p} L_q(\rho) \qquad (16.19)$$

on differentiating Eq. (16.18) p times, it is seen that $L_q^p(\rho)$ satisfies

$$\rho L_q^{p''} + (p + 1 - \rho)L_q^{p'} + (q - p)L_q^p = 0 \qquad (16.20)$$

Comparison of Eq. (16.12) with $\lambda = n$ and Eq. (16.20) shows that the desired polynomial solutions are the associated Laguerre polynomials $L_{n+l}^{2l+1}(\rho)$, which are of order $(n + l) - (2l + 1) = n - l - 1$ in agreement with Eq. (16.14).

Differentiation of Eq. (16.16) p times with respect to ρ gives the generating function for the associated Laguerre polynomials,

$$U_p(\rho,s) = \frac{(-s)^p e^{-\frac{\rho s}{1-s}}}{(1-s)^{p+1}} = \sum_{q=p}^{\infty} \frac{L_q^p(\rho)}{q!} s^q \qquad (16.21)$$

The following explicit expression may be verified by substituting it into Eq. (16.21) with $n + l = q$ and $2l + 1 = p$, and interchanging the order of the two summations:

$$L_{n+l}^{2l+1}(\rho) = \sum_{k=0}^{n-l-1} (-1)^{k+1} \frac{[(n+l)!]^2 \rho^k}{(n-l-1-k)!(2l+1+k)!k!} \qquad (16.22)$$

Hydrogen-atom Wave Functions.   The radial wave function is of the form $e^{-\frac{1}{2}\rho}\rho^l L_{n+l}^{2l+1}(\rho)$.   The normalization constant may be found by using the generating function to evaluate the integral

$$\int_0^{\infty} e^{-\rho}\rho^{2l}[L_{n+l}^{2l+1}(\rho)]^2\rho^2 d\rho = \frac{2n[(n+l)!]^3}{(n-l-1)!} \qquad (16.23)$$

Thus the normalized energy eigenfunctions for the hydrogen atom are

$$u_{nlm}(r,\theta,\phi) = R_{nl}(r)Y_{lm}(\theta,\phi)$$

$$R_{nl}(r) = -\left\{\left(\frac{2Z}{na_0}\right)^3 \frac{(n-l-1)!}{2n[(n+l)!]^3}\right\}^{\frac{1}{2}} e^{-\frac{1}{2}\rho}\rho^l L_{n+l}^{2l+1}(\rho) \qquad (16.24)$$

$$a_0 = \frac{\hbar^2}{\mu e^2}, \qquad \rho = \frac{2Z}{na_0} r$$

where $Y_{lm}(\theta,\phi)$ is the normalized spherical harmonic given in Eq. (14.16); a_0 is the radius of the first (circular) Bohr orbit for hydrogen ($Z = 1$) in the old quantum theory.   The energy levels (16.15) may be written

$$E_n = -\frac{Z^2 e^2}{2a_0 n^2}$$

The first three radial functions, which are found from Eqs. (16.22) and (16.24), are

$$R_{10}(r) = \left(\frac{Z}{a_0}\right)^{\frac{3}{2}} 2e^{-\frac{Zr}{a_0}}$$

$$R_{20}(r) = \left(\frac{Z}{2a_0}\right)^{\frac{3}{2}} \left(2 - \frac{Zr}{a_0}\right) e^{-\frac{Zr}{2a_0}}$$

$$R_{21}(r) = \left(\frac{Z}{2a_0}\right)^{\frac{3}{2}} \frac{Zr}{a_0\sqrt{3}} e^{-\frac{Zr}{2a_0}}$$

A much more complete set of these functions, with graphs of some of them, is given by Pauling and Wilson.[1]

It is interesting to note that each of the eigenfunctions for which $l = 0$ has a discontinuous gradient at $r = 0$, since $dR_{n0}/dr \neq 0$ there and Y_{00} is independent of θ and ϕ. This is a consequence of the infinite potential energy at that point, as can be shown by means of a limiting process similar to that used in Sec. 8 to derive the boundary conditions at a perfectly rigid wall.

Degeneracy. The energy eigenvalues (16.15) depend only on n, and so are degenerate with respect to both l and m. Thus for each value of n, l can vary from 0 to $n - 1$, and for each of these l values, m can vary from $-l$ to $+l$. The total degeneracy of the energy level E_n is then

$$\sum_{l=0}^{n-1} (2l + 1) = 2\,\frac{n(n - 1)}{2} + n = n^2$$

It follows from the discussion of Sec. 14 that the degeneracy with respect to m is characteristic of any central force field, for which V depends only on the radial distance r from some point. The l degeneracy, however, is characteristic of the Coulomb field, as distinguished from most other central force fields. In some problems, such as the motion of the valence electron of an alkali atom, the potential energy of the electron is central, but only approximately of the Coulomb form. This prevents the n energy levels that have the same total quantum number n and different l from being coincident, so that the nth hydrogen-like level splits up into n distinct levels. If also some external field (such as a magnetic field) that destroys the spherical symmetry is imposed, the $(2l + 1)$-fold m degeneracy disappears, and the nth hydrogen-like level is split up into n^2 distinct levels.

The existence of degenerate energy eigenvalues means that linear combinations of the corresponding eigenfunctions are solutions of the wave equation with the same energy. In the case of the m degeneracy, such linear combinations of the spherical harmonics $Y_{lm}(\theta,\phi)$ can be found that correspond to a new choice of the polar axis. It is reasonable to expect that linear combinations of the degenerate hydrogen-atom eigenfunctions that have the same n and different l exist that also correspond to some new choice of the coordinates. This is, in fact, the case, since it turns out that the hydrogen-atom wave equation can be separated in parabolic coordinates. In general, degeneracy will occur whenever the wave equation can be solved in more than one way (in different

---

[1] Pauling and Wilson, *op. cit.*, Sec. 21.

coordinate systems, or in a single coordinate system oriented in different ways), since if there were no degeneracy the wave functions obtained in the different coordinate systems would have to be identical except for a multiplying constant, and that is usually not possible.   For a general central field, an exception occurs when $l = 0$, since then the wave function is spherically symmetric and has the same form for all orientations of the polar axis, so that there is no degeneracy.   A similar exception occurs in the hydrogen atom problem when $n = 1$, in which case it turns out that the solutions obtained by spherical and parabolic separation of the wave equation are identical.

Separation in Parabolic Coordinates.   The parabolic coordinates ξ, η, ϕ are given in terms of the spherical polar coordinates by the relations

$$\xi = r - z = r(1 - \cos \theta)$$
$$\eta = r + z = r(1 + \cos \theta) \tag{16.25}$$
$$\phi = \phi$$

The surfaces of constant ξ are a set of confocal paraboloids of revolution about the z or polar axis, with focus at the origin, that open in the direction of positive z or $\theta = 0$.   The surfaces of constant η are a similar set of confocal paraboloids that open in the direction of negative z or $\theta = \pi$. The surfaces of constant ϕ are the same as in the spherical coordinate system: planes through the polar axis.

The wave equation for the hydrogen atom in parabolic coordinates is

$$- \frac{\hbar^2}{2\mu} \left\{ \frac{4}{\xi + \eta} \left[\frac{\partial}{\partial \xi} \left(\xi \frac{\partial u}{\partial \xi} \right) + \frac{\partial}{\partial \eta} \left(\eta \frac{\partial u}{\partial \eta} \right) \right] \right.$$
$$\left. + \frac{1}{\xi\eta} \frac{\partial^2 u}{\partial \phi^2} \right\} - \frac{2Ze^2}{\xi + \eta} u = Eu, \qquad E < 0 \tag{16.26}$$

The separation is accomplished by substituting

$$u(\xi, \eta, \phi) = f(\xi) g(\eta) \Phi(\phi)$$

into Eq. (16.26) and dividing through by u; the ϕ part of the equation separates at once:

$$\frac{4\xi\eta}{\xi + \eta} \left[\frac{1}{f} \frac{d}{d\xi} \left(\xi \frac{df}{d\xi} \right) + \frac{1}{g} \frac{d}{d\eta} \left(\eta \frac{dg}{d\eta} \right) \right]$$
$$+ \frac{4\mu Ze^2 \xi\eta}{\hbar^2(\xi + \eta)} - \frac{2\mu |E| \xi\eta}{\hbar^2} = - \frac{1}{\Phi} \frac{d^2\Phi}{d\phi^2} \tag{16.27}$$

Since the left side of Eq. (16.27) depends only on ξ and η, and the right side only on ϕ, both sides must be equal to a constant that we call m^2; in accordance with the discussion of Sec. 14, this gives normalized ϕ solutions that are the same as (14.8)

$$\Phi_m(\phi) = (2\pi)^{-\frac{1}{2}} e^{im\phi}, \qquad m = 0, \pm 1, \pm 2, \ldots \qquad (16.28)$$

The rest of Eq. (16.27) can be separated into ξ and η parts:

$$\frac{1}{f} \frac{d}{d\xi} \left(\xi \frac{df}{d\xi} \right) - \frac{m^2}{4\xi} - \frac{\mu|E|}{2\hbar^2} \xi + \frac{\mu Z e^2}{\hbar^2}$$
$$= - \left[\frac{1}{g} \frac{d}{d\eta} \left(\eta \frac{dg}{d\eta} \right) - \frac{m^2}{4\eta} - \frac{\mu|E|}{2\hbar^2} \eta \right] = \nu \qquad (16.29)$$

where the separation constant ν is to be determined by the boundary conditions. Thus the equations for f and g are

$$\frac{d}{d\xi} \left(\xi \frac{df}{d\xi} \right) - \left(\frac{m^2}{4\xi} + \frac{\mu|E|\xi}{2\hbar^2} - \frac{\mu Z e^2}{\hbar^2} + \nu \right) f = 0$$
$$\frac{d}{d\eta} \left(\eta \frac{dg}{d\eta} \right) - \left(\frac{m^2}{4\eta} + \frac{\mu|E|\eta}{2\hbar^2} - \nu \right) g = 0 \qquad (16.30)$$

Since these two equations are of the same form, and differ only in their constant terms, it is sufficient to solve one of them.

Energy Levels. The first of Eqs. (16.30) may be solved by the method used to solve (16.6). The substitution $\zeta = \alpha\xi$ puts it into the dimensionless form

$$\frac{1}{\zeta} \frac{d}{d\zeta} \left(\zeta \frac{df}{d\zeta} \right) + \left(\frac{\lambda_1}{\zeta} - \frac{1}{4} - \frac{m^2}{4\zeta^2} \right) f = 0 \qquad (16.31)$$

if we choose the parameters α and λ_1 to be given by

$$\alpha^2 = \frac{2\mu|E|}{\hbar^2}, \qquad \lambda_1 = \frac{1}{\alpha} \left(\frac{\mu Z e^2}{\hbar^2} - \nu \right) \qquad (16.32)$$

The second of Eqs. (16.30) is also of the form (16.31) if we put $\zeta = \alpha\eta$ with α given by (16.32); λ_1 is replaced by

$$\lambda_2 = \frac{\nu}{\alpha} \qquad (16.33)$$

We now treat Eq. (16.31) as we did (16.7). The asymptotic behavior is dominated by the factor $e^{\pm \zeta}$, where we must take the minus sign in the exponent. The series that multiplies this starts with a term ζ^s, where it is readily shown that $s = \pm\frac{1}{2}m$. We therefore substitute

$$f(\zeta) = e^{-\frac{1}{2}\zeta} \zeta^{\frac{1}{2}|m|} L(\zeta) \qquad (16.34)$$

into (16.31) and obtain as the equation for L

$$\zeta L'' + (|m| + 1 - \zeta)L' + [\lambda_1 - \frac{1}{2}(|m| + 1)]L = 0 \qquad (16.35)$$

As with Eq. (16.12), the nonterminating solutions for L cause the wave function (16.34) to becomes infinite for large ζ. The terminating solutions are the associated Laguerre polynomials; comparison of Eqs. (16.20) and (16.35) shows that they are $L_{n_1+|m|}^{|m|}(\zeta)$, where

$$n_1 = \lambda_1 - \tfrac{1}{2}(|m| + 1) \tag{16.36}$$

is a positive integer or zero.

In similar fashion, the solution of the η equation shows that the number

$$n_2 = \lambda_2 - \tfrac{1}{2}(|m| + 1) \tag{16.37}$$

is a positive integer or zero. From Eqs. (16.36) and (16.37) we obtain

$$\lambda_1 + \lambda_2 = n_1 + n_2 + |m| + 1 \equiv n \tag{16.38}$$

where n is a nonzero positive integer. The energy levels are given by combining Eqs. (16.32), (16.33), and (16.38):

$$E_n = -|E_n| = -\frac{\hbar^2\alpha^2}{2\mu} = -\frac{\mu Z^2 e^4}{2\hbar^2 n^2}$$

in agreement with Eq. (16.15). The energy level E_n is degenerate, since according to (16.38) there are various ways in which the three quantum numbers n_1, n_2, and m can be combined to make up n. For $m = 0$, there are n ways of choosing n_1 and n_2; for $|m| > 0$, there are two ways of choosing m ($= \pm|m|$), and $n - |m|$ ways of choosing n_1 and n_2. Thus the total degeneracy of the energy level E_n is

$$n + 2 \sum_{|m|=1}^{n-1} (n - |m|) = n + 2\left[n(n-1) - \frac{n(n-1)}{2}\right] = n^2$$

in agreement with the earlier result.

Wave Functions. It is clear from the foregoing discussion that the unnormalized hydrogen-atom wave functions in parabolic coordinates are

$$u_{n_1 n_2 m}(\xi,\eta,\phi) = e^{-\frac{1}{2}\alpha(\xi+\eta)}(\xi\eta)^{\frac{1}{2}|m|}L_{n_1+|m|}^{|m|}(\alpha\xi)L_{n_2+|m|}^{|m|}(\alpha\eta)e^{im\phi}$$

$$\alpha = \frac{\mu Z e^2}{\hbar^2(n_1 + n_2 + |m| + 1)}$$

For a particular energy level E_n and magnetic quantum number m ($n > |m|$), the parabolic quantum numbers n_1 and n_2 can be chosen such that $n_1 + n_2 = n - |m| - 1$; that is, in $n - |m|$ different ways. Similarly, for given n and m, the azimuthal quantum number l in the spherical solution can be chosen such that $|m| \leqq l \leqq n - 1$, and so also in $n - |m|$ different ways. Thus the $n - |m|$ products of the ξ and η functions are linear combinations of the $n - |m|$ products of the r and θ functions.

The ground-state energy level provides a particularly simple illustration of the connection between the parabolic and spherical solutions. In this case, $n_1 = n_2 = m = 0$, and the parabolic solution is simply $e^{-\frac{\mu Z e^2 (\xi + \eta)}{2\hbar^2}}$. Also, $n = 1$, $l = \bar{m} = 0$, and the spherical solution is $e^{-\frac{\mu Z e^2 r}{\hbar^2}}$. It is apparent from Eq. (16.25) that these two solutions are identical.

Problems

1. Apply the Bohr-Sommerfeld quantization rules (see Sec. 2) to the determination of the energy levels of a harmonic oscillator and of the circular orbits in a hydrogen atom. Compare with the results obtained in this chapter.

2. What is the order of magnitude of the spread of quantum numbers and energies of the states that contribute significantly to the oscillating-wave-packet solution for the harmonic oscillator?

3. Use the generating function for the Hermite polynomials to evaluate

$$\int_{-\infty}^{\infty} \bar{u}_n(x) x^2 u_m(x) dx,$$

where the u's are normalized harmonic-oscillator wave functions.

4. Use the generating function for the Legendre polynomials to evaluate

$$\int_{-1}^{1} P_l(w) P_{l'}(w) dw.$$

5. Obtain an approximate analytic expression for the energy level in a square well potential $(l = 0)$ when $V_0 a^2$ is slightly greater than $\pi^2 \hbar^2 / 8m$.

6. Show that for a square well potential the values of $V_0 a^2$ that just bind new energy levels with an l value greater than zero are given by $\hbar^2 z^2 / 2m$, where the numbers z are the nonvanishing solutions of the equation $j_{l-1}(z) = 0$ (see footnote 1, page 80).

7. Assume that the interaction between the neutron and the proton that make up a deuteron can be represented by a square well potential with $a = 2.00 \times 10^{-13}$ cm. If the lowest $(l = 0)$ energy level of the system is -2.23 Mev (million electron-volts), calculate V_0 in Mev to three significant figures. How does the answer compare with that which would be obtained from the approximate formula derived in Prob. 5?

8. Consider Eq. (14.17) with $l = 0$ and $V(r) = -V_0 e^{-\frac{r}{a}}$. Change variables from r to $z = e^{-\frac{r}{2a}}$, and show that Bessel's equation results. What boundary conditions are to be imposed on χ as a function of z, and how can these be used to determine the energy levels? What is the lower limit to V_0 for which a bound state exists?

9. Find expressions for the eigenfunctions and energy levels of a particle in a two-dimensional circular box that has perfectly rigid walls.

10. It is shown in Sec. 9 that a one-dimensional square well potential has a bound state for any positive $V_0 a^2$, and in Sec. 15 that a three-dimensional square well potential has a bound state only for $V_0 a^2 > \pi^2 \hbar^2 / 8m$. What is the analogous situation for a two-dimensional square well potential? What, if any, is the physical significance of these results?

11. The Schrödinger equation for a rigid body that is constrained to rotate about a fixed axis and that has a moment of inertia I about this axis is

$$i\hbar \frac{\partial \psi}{\partial t} = -\frac{\hbar^2}{2I} \frac{\partial^2 \psi}{\partial \phi^2}$$

where $\psi(\phi,t)$ is a function of the time t and of the angle of rotation ϕ about the axis. What boundary conditions must be applied to the solutions of this equation? Find the normalized energy eigenfunctions and eigenvalues. Is there any degeneracy?

12. Find the energy levels of a three-dimensional isotropic harmonic oscillator $(V(r) = \frac{1}{2}Kr^2)$, by solving the wave equation in cartesian coordinates. What is the degeneracy of each level? Show that this equation can also be separated in spherical and in cylindrical coordinates.

13. Show that the expectation value of the potential energy of an electron in the nth quantum state of a hydrogen atom is $-Z^2e^2/a_0n^2$. From this result, find the expectation value of the kinetic energy.

$\longrightarrow$ **14.** Find the normalized hydrogen-atom wave functions in parabolic coordinates for $n = 2$, $m = 0$. Express them as linear combinations of the corresponding wave functions in spherical coordinates.

15. Discuss the parities, if any, of the hydrogen-atom wave functions in parabolic coordinates.

CHAPTER V

CONTINUOUS EIGENVALUES: COLLISION THEORY

Problems for which the energy eigenvalues are continuously distributed usually arise in connection with the collision of a particle with a force field. The method of approach is different from that employed in the preceding chapter. There the boundary conditions at great distances were used to determine the discrete energy levels of the particle. In a collision problem, the energy is specified in advance, and the behavior of the wave function at great distances is found in terms of it. This asymptotic behavior can then be related to the amount of scattering of the particle by the force field.

As in Chap. IV, the relatively few exact solutions that are obtained here are of wider application than might at first seem to be the case, since they can serve as foundations for approximate calculations on more complicated systems. It is interesting to note that the study of collisions is particularly important in connection with atomic nuclei (see Sec. 41) where relatively little information can be obtained in other ways.

17. ONE-DIMENSIONAL SQUARE POTENTIAL BARRIER

We consider first the one-dimensional collision of a particle with the square potential barrier $V(x)$ shown in Fig. 14. In this problem we are interested in a particle that approaches from the region of negative x and is reflected or transmitted by the barrier. In the corresponding classical problem, the particle is always reflected if its energy is less than that of the top of the barrier, and always transmitted if its energy is greater. We shall see that in the quantum problem, both reflection and transmission occur with finite probability for most energies of the particle. Because of the lack of symmetry between positive and negative x that is introduced from the beginning, it is disadvantageous to deal with solutions that have definite parities, and so there is no reason for making $V(x)$ symmetrical about $x = 0$, as

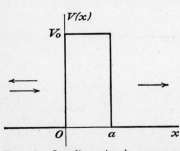

Fig. 14. One-dimensional square potential barrier of height V_0 and thickness a.

92

was done in Sec. 9.   We assume, therefore, that $V(x) = 0$ for $x < 0$ and $x > a$, and $V\ x) = V_0$ for $0 < x < a$, where V_0 is positive.

Asymptotic Behavior.   We are interested in representing a particle that approaches from the left with energy $E > 0$, and may be turned back by the potential barrier or penetrate through it.   Thus the asymptotic behavior (in the regions where $V(x) = 0$) is as follows: for $x < 0$, we want the wave function to represent a particle moving to the left (reflected particle) as well as to the right (incident particle); for $x > a$, we want the wave function to represent only a particle moving to the right (transmitted particle).

A particle in a force-free region that is moving in a definite direction with a definite energy necessarily has a definite momentum, and hence can be represented by a one-dimensional momentum eigenfunction $u(x) \propto e^{\frac{ipx}{\hbar}}$ if the particle is moving in the positive x direction with the momentum p, and $u(x) \propto e^{-\frac{ipx}{\hbar}}$ if the particle is moving in the negative x direction with the same energy.   Thus since the wave equation in the regions where $V(x) = 0$ is

$$-\frac{\hbar^2}{2m}\frac{d^2u}{dx^2} = Eu$$

our asymptotic solutions are

$$
\begin{aligned}
u(x) &= Ae^{ikx} + Be^{-ikx}, &\qquad x \leqq 0\\
u(x) &= Ce^{ikx}, &\qquad x \geqq a
\end{aligned}
\qquad (17.1)
$$

where $k = p/\hbar = (2mE/\hbar^2)^{\frac{1}{2}}$ is the magnitude of the propagation number. The solutions (17.1) are appropriate for the force-free regions that are external to any scattering potential, whether or not it has the simple form shown in Fig. 14.

Normalization.   The physical meaning of the coefficients A, B, and C can be inferred by substituting (17.1) into the one-dimensional form of the probability current density given by Eq. (7.3).

$$
\begin{aligned}
S(x) &= v(|A|^2 - |B|^2), &\qquad x < 0\\
S(x) &= v|C|^2 &\qquad x > a
\end{aligned}
\qquad (17.2)
$$

where $v = \hbar k/m$ is the speed of a particle with propagation number k. Since these expressions are independent of x, the discussion of Sec. 7 shows that they may be interpreted as the net flux (positive to the right) in the two regions.   This interpretation is consistent with the statement above that A, B, and C are the amplitudes of the incident, reflected, and transmitted wave functions, respectively.

The absolute normalization of the wave functions (17.1) is unimportant for this problem; this is because we are interested only in the ratios of $|B|^2$ and $|C|^2$ to $|A|^2$, which are respectively the reflection and transmission coefficients for the barrier. It is sometimes convenient, however, to normalize the incident wave function to unit flux; this corresponds to taking $A = 1/v^{\frac{1}{2}}$. Such a normalization must not be interpreted as indicating that $u(x)$ represents more than one particle; rather it means that we choose a large enough number of systems [each described by $u(x)$] that are identical, independent, and nonoverlapping in the sense of Sec. 7, so that the total incident flux in all of them is unity. A more precise but sometimes less convenient normalization would assume a one-dimensional "box" of length L with periodic boundary conditions, and require that $\int_{(L)} |u(x)|^2 dx = 1$.

Scattering Coefficients. The character of the solution inside the potential barrier depends on whether E is greater or less than V_0. Suppose first that $E > V_0$, so that we can define a propagation number inside the barrier: $\alpha = [2m(E - V_0)/\hbar^2]^{\frac{1}{2}}$. Then the solution inside is

$$u(x) = Fe^{i\alpha x} + Ge^{-i\alpha x}, \qquad 0 \leq x \leq a \qquad (17.3)$$

The continuity of u and du/dx at $x = 0$ and $x = a$ required by the boundary conditions provides four relations between the five coefficients. We can eliminate F and G, and solve for the ratios B/A and C/A.

$$\frac{B}{A} = \frac{(k^2 - \alpha^2)(1 - e^{2i\alpha a})}{(k + \alpha)^2 - (k - \alpha)^2 e^{2i\alpha a}}$$

$$\frac{C}{A} = \frac{4k\alpha e^{i(\alpha - k)a}}{(k + \alpha)^2 - (k - \alpha)^2 e^{2i\alpha a}} \qquad (17.4)$$

The absolute squares of the ratios (17.4) are the scattering (reflection and transmission) coefficients

$$\left|\frac{B}{A}\right|^2 = \left[1 + \frac{4k^2\alpha^2}{(k^2 - \alpha^2)^2 \sin^2 \alpha a}\right]^{-1} = \left[1 + \frac{4E(E - V_0)}{V_0^2 \sin^2 \alpha a}\right]^{-1}$$

$$\left|\frac{C}{A}\right|^2 = \left[1 + \frac{(k^2 - \alpha^2)^2 \sin^2 \alpha a}{4k^2\alpha^2}\right]^{-1} = \left[1 + \frac{V_0^2 \sin^2 \alpha a}{4E(E - V_0)}\right]^{-1} \qquad (17.5)$$

It is readily verified from (17.5) that $|B/A|^2 + |C/A|^2 = 1$, as would be expected.

Equations (17.5) show that the transmission coefficient approaches

$$\left(1 + \frac{mV_0a^2}{2\hbar^2}\right)^{-1} \qquad (17.6)$$

when the particle energy approaches the energy of the top of the barrier $(E \rightarrow V_0)$. For increasing E $(E > V_0)$, the transmission coefficient oscillates between a steadily increasing lower envelope and unity (see Fig.

15).   There is perfect transmission when $\alpha a = \pi, 2\pi, \ldots$; *i.e.*, whenever the barrier contains an integral number of half wave lengths.[1] Interference phenomena of this type are well known in the transmission of light through thin refracting layers.

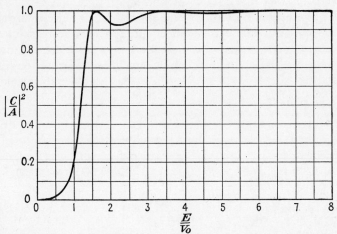

FIG. 15.   Transmission coefficient of a square barrier as a function of particle energy for $mV_0a^2/\hbar^2 = 8$.

The reflection and transmission coefficients for $0 < E < V_0$ are most easily obtained by replacing α by $i\beta$ in Eqs. (17.4), where

$$\beta = \left[\frac{2m(V_0 - E)}{\hbar^2} \right]^{\frac{1}{2}}.$$

The result for the transmission coefficient is

$$\left| \frac{C}{A} \right|^2 = \left[1 + \frac{V_0^2 \sinh^2 \beta a}{4E(V_0 - E)} \right]^{-1} \tag{17.7}$$

This decreases monotonically from the value (17.6) as E decreases below V_0. When $\beta a \gg 1$, the transmission coefficient (17.7) becomes very small and is given approximately by

$$\frac{16E(V_0 - E)}{V_0^2} e^{-2\beta a} \tag{17.8}$$

Figure 15 is a plot of the transmission coefficient computed from Eqs. (17.5) and (17.7) for a rather "opaque" barrier: $mV_0a^2/\hbar^2 = 8$.

[1] This effect also occurs when $V_0 < 0$, in which case the square barrier becomes a square well.   The scattering coefficients are given by (17.5) if the sign of V_0 is changed there and in the expression for α.

18. COLLISIONS IN THREE DIMENSIONS

We are primarily concerned in this chapter with collisions in three dimensions, in which a particle collides with a fixed force field, or two particles collide with each other. It was shown in Sec. 16 that the problem of the nonrelativistic motion of two particles, when the only forces present depend on their relative positions, can be broken up into two one-particle problems, of which one describes the motion of the particles relative to each other or to their center of mass, and the other describes the free motion of the center of mass. While the center of mass can be taken to be at rest in calculating the energy levels of the internal motion, as in Sec. 16, it has a definite motion in a collision that cannot be ignored in calculating the outcome of such an experiment. This is because the customary laboratory procedure consists in bombarding a particle that is initially at rest with another particle that carries the total energy $E_0 = E + E'$ of Eq. (16.5). Thus the energy E of the relative motion of the two particles is different from the bombarding energy E_0, and the observed scattering depends on whether the struck particle or the center of mass is initially at rest.

We call the coordinate system in which the bombarded particle is initially at rest the *laboratory coordinate system* and the coordinate system in which the center of mass of the two colliding particles is (initially and always) at rest the *center-of-mass coordinate system*. It is evidently easier to calculate the result of a collision experiment in the center-of-mass system than in the laboratory system, since only 3 degrees of freedom appear in the former as compared with 6 in the latter system. The collision process in the center-of-mass system may then be thought of as one in which a particle that has the reduced mass $\mu = m_1 m_2/(m_1 + m_2)$ of Eq. (16.4) and an initial velocity v collides with a fixed scattering center [see the discussion of Eq. (18.9) below]. The distribution in angle of the scattered particles will be affected by the transformation between the center-of-mass coordinate system, in which the calculations are made, and the laboratory coordinate system, in which the observations are made.

Scattering Cross Section. The angular distribution of particles scattered by a fixed center of force or by other particles is conveniently described in terms of a scattering cross section. Suppose that we bombard a group of n particles or scattering centers with a parallel flux of N particles per unit area per unit time, and count the number of incident particles that emerge per unit time in a small solid angle $\Delta\omega_0$ centered about a direction that has polar angles θ_0 and ϕ_0 with respect to the bombarding direction as polar axis. This number will be proportional to N, n, and $\Delta\omega_0$, provided that the flux is small enough so that there is no interference between bombarding particles and no appreciable diminution of the bombarded particles by their recoil out of the target region, and provided also that the bombarded particles are far enough apart so that each collision process involves only one of them.

Then the number of incident particles that emerge per unit time in $\Delta\omega_0$ can be written

$$nN\sigma_0(\theta_0,\phi_0)\Delta\omega_0 \tag{18.1}$$

where the proportionality factor $\sigma_0(\theta_0,\phi_0)$ is called the *differential scattering cross section*. Since (18.1) has the dimensions of reciprocal time, $\sigma_0(\theta_0,\phi_0)$ has the dimensions of an area. $\sigma_0(\theta_0,\phi_0)\Delta\omega_0$ is equal to the cross-sectional area of the parallel incident beam that contains the number of particles scattered into $\Delta\omega_0$ by a single target particle or scattering center. The integral of $\sigma_0(\theta_0,\phi_0)$ over the sphere is called the *total scattering cross section*

$$\sigma_0 = \int\sigma_0(\theta_0,\phi_0)d\omega_0 \tag{18.2}$$

For the collision of a particle with a fixed scattering center, the definition (18.1) of differential scattering cross section is equally valid in the laboratory and center-of-mass coordinate systems, since a scattering center that is fixed has an infinite effective mass and so the center of mass of the system does not move. For a collision between two particles of finite mass, however, the differential cross section (18.1) applies in general only to the laboratory coordinate system and to the observation of the scattered incident particle. It does not describe the observation of the recoil bombarded particle in the laboratory system, although it is of course possible to obtain a differential cross section for the recoil particle from $\sigma_0(\theta_0,\phi_0)$. In the center-of-mass system the differential cross section $\sigma(\theta,\phi)$ may be defined in analogy with (18.1), where again the scattered incident particle is the one that is observed and the flux N of the incident particle is computed with respect to the bombarded particle, not the center of mass. Since in this coordinate system the two particles move in opposite directions away from each other after the collision, it is clear that the differential cross section for observation of the recoil bombarded particle in the direction θ,ϕ is just $\sigma(\pi - \theta, \phi + \pi)$.

Relations between Angles in the Laboratory and Center-of-mass Systems. The relation between the differential cross sections and angles in the laboratory system and in the center-of-mass system can be found by translating the laboratory system in the direction of the incident particle with sufficient speed to bring the center of mass to rest. Figure 16(a) shows a particle of mass m_1 and initial speed v striking a particle of

mass m_2 that is initially at rest; the center of mass moves to the right with
the speed $v' = m_1v/(m_1 + m_2)$, as may be seen from the conservation of

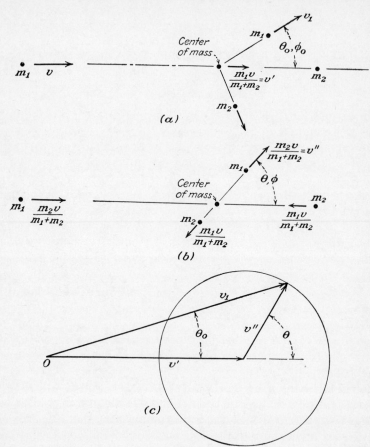

FIG. 16. (a) Laboratory coordinate system, in which the target particle of mass m_2 is
initially at rest.   (b) Center-of-mass coordinate system, in which the center of mass is
initially and always at rest.   (c) Vector addition of velocity of center of mass in laboratory
system (v') to velocity of observed particle in center-of-mass system (v'') to give velocity
observed in laboratory system (v₁); if $v'' < v'$, θ_0 cannot exceed the angle $\sin^{-1} (v''/v')$.

momentum.   Thus in the center-of-mass system the particles of masses
m_1 and m_2 approach the center of mass with speeds

$$v'' = v - v' = \frac{m_2v}{(m_1 + m_2)},$$

and v', respectively; they evidently recede from the center of mass after
the collision with the same speeds [see Fig. 16(b)].   It follows from the

geometry of the situation that θ and ϕ are related to θ_0 and ϕ_0 by

$$v'' \cos \theta + v' = v_1 \cos \theta_0$$
$$v'' \sin \theta = v_1 \sin \theta_0 \qquad (18.3)$$
$$\phi = \phi_0$$

From the first two of Eqs. (18.3) we obtain on elimination of v_1

$$\tan \theta_0 = \frac{\sin \theta}{\gamma + \cos \theta}, \qquad \gamma = \frac{v'}{v''} = \frac{m_1}{m_2} \qquad (18.4)$$

Equations (18.3) and (18.4) can be generalized by considering a collision (for example, a nuclear reaction) in which a particle of mass m_1 strikes a particle of mass m_2 initially at rest, and after the collision, particles of masses m_3 and m_4 emerge, where $m_1 + m_2 = m_3 + m_4$. If also an amount of energy, Q, is converted from internal energy to kinetic energy of the emergent particles (Q is positive for exothermic and negative for endothermic collisions), and the particle of mass m_3 is observed, the first of Eqs. (18.4) is still valid. In this case γ is still equal to the ratio of the speed of the center of mass in the laboratory system to the speed of the observed particle in the center-of-mass system. However, γ is no longer m_1/m_2, but can be shown to be given by

$$\gamma = + \left(\frac{m_1 m_3}{m_2 m_4} \frac{E}{E + Q} \right)^{\frac{1}{2}} \qquad (18.5)$$

where $E = m_1 m_2 v^2 / 2(m_1 + m_2)$ is the energy initially associated with the relative motion in the center-of-mass system [see the discussion of Eq. (18.9) below].

Relation between Cross Sections. The relation between the cross sections in the laboratory and center-of-mass coordinate systems can be obtained from their definitions, which imply that the same number of particles are scattered into the differential solid angle $d\omega_0$ about θ_0, ϕ_0 as are scattered into $d\omega$ about θ, ϕ.

$$\sigma_0(\theta_0, \phi_0) \sin \theta_0 d\theta_0 d\phi_0 = \sigma(\theta, \phi) \sin \theta d\theta d\phi \qquad (18.6)$$

With the help of the last of Eqs. (18.3) and the first of Eqs. (18.4), Eq. (18.6) gives

$$\sigma_0(\theta_0, \phi_0) = \frac{(1 + \gamma^2 + 2\gamma \cos \theta)^{\frac{3}{2}}}{|1 + \gamma \cos \theta|} \sigma(\theta, \phi) \qquad (18.7)$$

where in general γ is given by Eq. (18.5). It should be noted that the total cross section is the same for both laboratory and center-of-mass systems, and also for both the outgoing particles, since the total number of collisions that take place is independent of the mode of description of the process.

Dependence on γ. For $\gamma < 1$, Eq. (18.4) shows that θ_0 increases monotonically from 0 to π as θ increases from 0 to π. For $\gamma = 1$, $\theta_0 = \frac{1}{2}\theta$ and varies from 0 to $\frac{1}{2}\pi$ as θ varies from 0 to π; in this case

$$\sigma_0(\theta_0,\phi_0) = 4 \cos \theta_0 \sigma(2\theta_0,\phi_0),$$

and no particles appear in the backward hemisphere in the laboratory system. For $\gamma > 1$, θ_0 first increases from 0 to a maximum value $\sin^{-1}(1/\gamma)$, which is less than $\frac{1}{2}\pi$, as θ increases from 0 to $\cos^{-1}(-1/\gamma)$; θ_0 then decreases to 0 as θ increases further to π. In this case $\sigma_0(\theta_0,\phi_0)$ is usually infinite at the maximum value of θ_0, although this singularity gives a finite contribution to the total cross section; no particles appear beyond the maximum θ_0 in the laboratory system. The two values of θ that give rise to a particular value of θ_0 between 0 and $\sin^{-1}(1/\gamma)$ can be distinguished by the energy of the observed particle, which is greater for the smaller θ.

This last case ($\gamma > 1$) is illustrated schematically in Fig. 16c. The resultant of the velocity $\mathbf{v}''$ of the observed particle in the center-of-mass system and the velocity $\mathbf{v}'$ of the center of mass in the laboratory system gives the velocity $\mathbf{v}_1$ of the observed particle in the laboratory system. The locus of the terminal points of $\mathbf{v}_1$ when its origin is at the point O is the circle of radius v''. Thus when $v'' < v'$, the angle θ_0 of the resultant $\mathbf{v}_1$ with the bombarding direction cannot exceed the angle

$$\sin^{-1}\left(\frac{v''}{v'}\right) = \sin^{-1}\left(\frac{1}{\gamma}\right).$$

As the ratio $\gamma = v'/v''$ decreases, the circle gets relatively larger and the angular range of $\mathbf{v}_1$ increases.

The use of geometrical relationships in the foregoing discussion is valid in a quantum-mechanical system as well as in a classical system. This is because they are essentially relations between momentum vectors that are applied in the asymptotic region where the particles need not be precisely localized in space and hence can have definite momenta.

It is interesting to note that the difference between laboratory and center-of-mass systems is negligible in the collisions of electrons with atoms, because of the large mass ratio of the colliding particles. In nuclear collisions, however, the difference between the two coordinate systems is usually significant.

Asymptotic Behavior. The differential scattering cross section $\sigma(\theta,\phi)$ in the center-of-mass coordinate system can be found from the asymptotic form of the solution of the second of Eqs. (16.5),

$$-\frac{\hbar^2}{2\mu} \nabla^2 u + Vu = Eu \tag{18.8}$$

which is the wave equation for the relative motion.   The wave function u may be written as a function of the angles θ, ϕ of Fig. 16(b) and the radial distance r between the two particles.   From Eq. (16.4) the reduced mass is $\mu = m_1 m_2 / (m_1 + m_2)$.   The energy E associated with the relative motion is easily seen from Fig. 16 to be

$$E = \frac{m_2}{m_1 + m_2} E_0 \qquad (18.9)$$

where E_0 is the initial energy of the bombarding particle.   It is interesting to note that E is equal to the kinetic energy of a particle whose mass is the reduced mass μ and whose speed is the relative speed v.   Thus we can think of Eq. (18.8) as representing the collision of a particle of mass μ, initial speed v, and kinetic energy $E = \frac{1}{2}\mu v^2$, with a fixed scattering center that is described by the potential energy $V(\mathbf{r})$; then $\mathbf{r}$ is the vector distance from the fictitious particle μ to the origin of the scattering potential.

As in Sec. 17, the scattering is determined by the asymptotic form of $u(r,\theta,\phi)$ in the region where $V = 0$.   When the colliding particles are far apart, we want u to contain a part that represents an incident particle of mass μ moving in a particular direction with speed v, and a part that represents a radially outgoing particle:

$$u(r,\theta,\phi) \xrightarrow[r \to \infty]{} A[e^{ikz} + r^{-1}f(\theta,\phi)e^{ikr}], \qquad k = \frac{\mu v}{\hbar} \qquad (18.10)$$

The first term in Eq. (18.10) represents a particle moving in the positive z direction, or along the polar axis $\theta = 0$, since $z = r \cos \theta$; it is an infinite plane wave of the form of the momentum eigenfunction (11.2), where the propagation vector $\mathbf{k}$ has the magnitude k and is directed along the polar axis.   The second term in Eq. (18.10) represents a particle that is moving radially outward; its amplitude depends on θ and ϕ, and is inversely proportional to r since the radial flux must fall off as the inverse square of the distance.   It is readily verified that Eq. (18.10) satisfies the wave equation (18.8) asymptotically through terms of order $1/r$ in the region in which $V = 0$, for any form of the function $f(\theta,\phi)$.

Normalization.   The physical meaning of the coefficient A and the angular function f can be inferred from a calculation of the particle flux, as in Sec. 17.   A straightforward substitution of Eq. (18.10) into Eq. (7.3), however, yields interference terms between the incident and scattered waves that do not appear in most experimental arrangements; that they do not appear can be seen in the following way.

In practice, the incident and scattered particles are separated from each other by collimating one or the other.   Suppose, for example, that the experimental arrangement is as shown schematically in Fig. 17, so that the bombarding particles from the source S are collimated by diaphragms DD into a fairly well-defined beam. Such a collimated beam is not an infinite plane wave of the form e^{ikz}, but can be made up by superposing infinite plane waves that have propagation vectors of slightly different magnitudes and directions. The total angular spread in radians will be of the order of the ratio of the wave length of the particle to the diameter of the collimating aperture, and so can be made extremely small in a practical case. Now f usually does not vary rapidly with angle, so that the small directional spread of the incident propagation vectors does not affect f significantly. Thus at the point of observation, P, only the f term is present, and it is essentially the same as that which appears in Eq. (18.10). The incident flux can be calculated from the plane wave term alone, since if we go far enough from the scattering region, the f

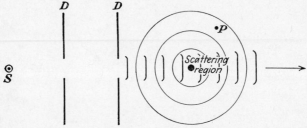

Fig. 17. Schematic diagram of a laboratory arrangement for the measurement of scattering, in which there is no interference between the incident and scattered waves at the point of observation P.

term can be made negligible. Thus in the region of observation, the interference terms are a consequence of the idealization implicit in assuming an infinite plane wave in Eq. (18.10), and usually have no physical significance.[1]

Substitution of the two terms of Eq. (18.10) separately into Eq. (7.3) shows that the incident flux is of magnitude $v|A|^2$ along the polar axis, and that the leading term in the scattered flux is of magnitude

$$v|A|^2|f(\theta,\phi)|^2/r^2$$

along the outward radius. From the definition of cross section, it follows that

$$\sigma(\theta,\phi) = |f(\theta,\phi)|^2 \qquad (18.11)$$

As discussed in Sec. 17, the choice of the coefficient A is unimportant so far as the calculation of the scattering is concerned. The wave function may be normalized to unit incident flux by choosing $A = 1/v^{\frac{1}{2}}$, or it may be normalized by making $\int|u|^2d\tau = 1$ over a large box that has periodic boundary conditions. We shall often simply set A equal to unity.

[1] For a somewhat exceptional case, see the discussion of Eqs. (19.14) and (19.24) in the next section.

19. SCATTERING BY SPHERICALLY SYMMETRIC POTENTIALS

The asymptotic behavior of the wave function determines the differential scattering cross section, but cannot itself be found without solving the wave equation (18.8) throughout all space. As was the case with the calculation of energy levels considered in Chap. IV, this can be done only when the wave equation is separable, and a particular case of great physical interest is that in which the potential energy is spherically symmetric. We assume here that V is a function only of r, and find the connection between the solutions separated in spherical polar coordinates and the asymptotic form (18.10); this procedure is called the *method of partial waves*.

In the remainder of this chapter we shall not, for the most part, distinguish between collisions of a particle with a fixed scattering center, and collisions between two particles treated in the center-of-mass coordinate system.

Asymptotic Behavior. It is apparent that the problem now possesses symmetry about the polar axis, so that u, f, and σ are independent of the angle ϕ. The general solution of Eq. (18.8) has the form (see Sec. 14)

$$u(r,\theta) = \sum_{l=0}^{\infty} R_l(r) P_l(\cos\theta) = \sum_{l=0}^{\infty} r^{-1}\chi_l(r) P_l(\cos\theta) \qquad (19.1)$$

where P_l is the Legendre polynomial of order l, and χ_l satisfies the equation

$$\frac{d^2\chi_l}{dr^2} + \left[k^2 - U(r) - \frac{l(l+1)}{r^2} \right] \chi_l = 0$$

$$k = \left(\frac{2\mu E}{\hbar^2} \right)^{\frac{1}{2}}, \qquad U(r) = \frac{2\mu V(r)}{\hbar^2} \xrightarrow[r\to\infty]{} 0 \qquad (19.2)$$

The boundary condition at $r = 0$ that R_l be finite or χ_l vanish determines the asymptotic form of the solution (19.2) except for an arbitrary multiplicative constant.

In order to find the general nature of this asymptotic behavior, we consider r to be so large that the U and l terms in Eq. (19.2) can be neglected. Then the solution of Eq. (19.2) is one of the forms $e^{\pm ikr}$. To get a better approximation, we put

$$\chi_l(r) = A \exp\left[\int_a^r f(r')dr' \right] e^{\pm ikr} \qquad (19.3)$$

where A and a are constants. The first exponential is assumed to be a slowly varying function of r for large r, which implies that $f(r)$ falls off more rapidly than r^{-1} as $r \to \infty$. Substitution of (19.3) into (19.2) gives the following equation for f:

$$f' + f^2 \pm 2ikf = U(r) + \frac{l(l+1)}{r^2} \equiv W(r) \qquad (19.4)$$

where the prime denotes differentiation with respect to r. If now $W(r)$ falls off like r^{-s} for large r ($s > 0$), the last term on the left side is the leading term, and f also falls off like r^{-s}. In this case, χ_l varies like $e^{\pm ikr}$ for large r if $s > 1$, since then the integral in the exponent of Eq. (19.3) converges for large r. If, on the other hand, W falls off like an exponential or error function of r (which implies that $l = 0$), the first and third terms on the left side of Eq. (19.4) may both have to be considered. It can then be shown without difficulty that χ_l again varies like $e^{\pm ikr}$ for large r. The Coulomb field, for which U and W vary like r^{-1} for large r regardless of the value of l, is the only case of physical interest which requires special attention and will be discussed in Sec. 20.

The asymptotic form of $\chi_l(r)$ can then be written quite generally

$$\chi_l(r) \xrightarrow[r \to \infty]{} A_l' \sin (kr + \delta_l') \tag{19.5}$$

where thus far A_l' and δ_l' can be complex. The solution of (19.2) that vanishes at $r = 0$ is unique except for a multiplying constant. It can be shown that this solution is real everywhere if it starts out to be real at $r = 0$, since k, U, and l are all real. Thus δ_l' must be real, although A_l' need not be. This being the case, it is readily verified that the total radial flux of particles through a large sphere vanishes:

$$\lim_{r \to \infty} 2\pi r^2 \int_0^\pi S_r \sin \theta d\theta = 0 \tag{19.6}$$

where S_r is the radial component of the vector (7.3) calculated by substituting $u(r,\theta)$ from Eq. (19.1) into it. This means that there are no sources or sinks of particles present, and the particles that are scattered radially outward are supplied by the incident plane wave.

Differential Cross Section. It is convenient to redefine the amplitude A_l' and phase angle δ_l' that appear in Eq. (19.5) in terms of a somewhat more specialized problem. It will be assumed that $U(r)$ can be neglected for r greater than some distance a; in cases of practical interest, a may be small enough so that the l term in (19.2) is not negligible. For $r > a$, the most general form for $R_l(r)$ that is real (except possibly for a complex multiplying constant) is shown in Sec. 15 to be

$$R_l(r) = A_l[\cos \delta_l j_l(kr) - \sin \delta_l n_l(kr)] \tag{19.7}$$

where δ_l is real; according to (15.8), this has the asymptotic form

$$R_l(r) \xrightarrow[r \to \infty]{} (kr)^{-1} A_l \sin (kr - \tfrac{1}{2}l\pi + \delta_l) \tag{19.8}$$

Equations (19.5) and (19.8) agree if $A_l = kA_l'$ and $\delta_l = \delta_l' + \tfrac{1}{2}l\pi$.

We now wish to identify the asymptotic form of (19.1) with (18.10). To do this, we require an expansion of $e^{ikz} = e^{ikr \cos \theta}$ in Legendre polynomials:[1]

$$e^{ikr \cos \theta} = \sum_{l=0}^{\infty} (2l + 1)i^l j_l(kr) P_l(\cos \theta) \tag{19.9}$$

Substituting the asymptotic form of (19.9) into (18.10) with $A = 1$, and

[1] G. N. Watson, "Theory of Bessel Functions," rev. ed., p. 128 (Macmillan, New York, 1944).

equating this to the asymptotic form of (19.1), we obtain

$$\sum_{l=0}^{\infty} (2l + 1)i^l(kr)^{-1} \sin\,(kr - \tfrac{1}{2}l\pi)P_l(\cos\,\theta) + r^{-1}f(\theta)e^{ikr}$$

$$= \sum_{l=0}^{\infty} A_l(kr)^{-1} \sin\,(kr - \tfrac{1}{2}l\pi + \delta_l)P_l(\cos\,\theta)$$

When the sine functions are written in complex exponential form, the coefficients of e^{ikr} and of e^{-ikr} on the two sides of this equation must be equal to each other:

$$2ikf(\theta) + \sum_{l=0}^{\infty} (2l + 1)i^l e^{-\frac{1}{2}il\pi}P_l(\cos\,\theta) = \sum_{l=0}^{\infty} A_l e^{i(\delta_l - \frac{1}{2}l\pi)}P_l(\cos\,\theta)$$

$$(19.10)$$

$$\sum_{l=0}^{\infty} (2l + 1)i^l e^{\frac{1}{2}il\pi}P_l(\cos\,\theta) = \sum_{l=0}^{\infty} A_l e^{-i(\delta_l - \frac{1}{2}l\pi)}P_l(\cos\,\theta)$$

Since these are true for all values of θ and the Legendre polynomials are orthogonal to each other, the second of Eqs. (19.10) becomes

$$A_l = (2l + 1)i^l e^{i\delta_l}$$

Substitution of this into the first of Eqs. (19.10) gives for the scattering amplitude

$$f(\theta) = (2ik)^{-1} \sum_{l=0}^{\infty} (2l + 1)(e^{2i\delta_l} - 1)P_l(\cos\,\theta) \qquad (19.11)$$

Thus the differential cross section is

$$\sigma(\theta) = |f(\theta)|^2 = \frac{1}{k^2}\left| \sum_{l=0}^{\infty} (2l + 1)e^{i\delta_l} \sin\,\delta_l P_l(\cos\,\theta) \right|^2 \qquad (19.12)$$

Total Cross Section. The total cross section is the integral of Eq. (19.12) over the sphere. Because of the orthogonality of the Legendre polynomials, it contains no products of factors involving different values of l.

$$\sigma = 2\pi \int_0^{\pi} \sigma(\theta) \sin\,\theta d\theta = \frac{4\pi}{k^2} \sum_{l=0}^{\infty} (2l + 1) \sin^2\,\delta_l \qquad (19.13)$$

The total cross section can also be related to $f(0)$. It follows from the generating function (14.10) for the Legendre polynomials that $P_l(1) = 1$ for all l, so that Eq. (19.11) gives for $\theta = 0$

$$f(0) = (2ik)^{-1} \sum_{l=0}^{\infty} (2l + 1)(e^{2i\delta_l} - 1)$$

Comparison with Eq. (19.13) then shows that

$$\sigma = \frac{2\pi}{ik} [f(0) - \bar{f}(0)] = \frac{4\pi}{k} Im\,[f(0)] \qquad (19.14)$$

where Im denotes the imaginary part of the expression that follows.

The physical interpretation of Eq. (19.14) is as follows: In order for scattering to take place, particles must be removed in an amount proportional to σ from the incident beam, so that its intensity is smaller behind the scattering region ($\theta \cong 0$) than in front of it. This can only occur by interference between the two terms in the asymptotic expression (18.10). Since such an interference term must be a linear function of the forward scattered amplitude, we expect a relation of the general form of Eq. (19.14). An actual calculation of this interference term shows that Eq. (19.14) holds much more generally: when f depends on ϕ as well as on θ, and when σ includes inelastic scattering and absorption as well as elastic scattering.[1]

Phase Shifts. The angle δ_l is called the *phase shift* of the lth partial wave, since according to (19.8) it is the difference in phase between the asymptotic forms of the actual radial function $R_l(r)$, and the radial function $j_l(kr)$ in the absence of scattering potential ($U = 0$). The phase shifts completely determine the scattering, and the scattering cross section vanishes when each of the δ_l is 0° or 180°.

It should be noted that the derivation of (19.11) is valid whether or not there exists the assumed radius a beyond which $U(r)$ is negligible, provided that $U(r)$ falls off more rapidly than $1/r$. However, the method of partial waves is most useful for computing scattering cross sections if such a radius a does exist, especially if ka is of the order of or less than unity. The reason for this is that the first and largest maximum of $j_l(kr)$ lies roughly at $r = l/k$, and that for r much smaller than this, j_l is small and increases about as r^l [see Eq. (15.7)]. Thus if $a \ll l/k$, j_l will be very small where U is appreciable; then the lth partial wave will hardly be affected by the potential, the phase shift δ_l will be very small, and the contribution to the scattering from that l will be negligible. It follows then that the scattering cross section consists of a series of terms extending from $l = 0$ to a maximum l that is of the order of ka. Since the computation of the phase shifts is usually a tedious affair, the smaller the magnitude of ka the easier the method is to apply. Thus this method of partial waves is most useful at low bombarding energies.

It is interesting to note that the classical distance of closest approach of a free particle of mass μ, velocity v, and angular momentum $l\hbar$ to the origin is $l\hbar/\mu v = l/k$. Thus the foregoing remarks are analogous to the statement that a classical particle is not scattered if it has sufficient angular momentum so that it does not enter the potential region $r < a$.

Calculation of δ_l. The phase shift δ_l is computed by fitting the radial wave function $R_l(r)$ for $r < a$, which may have an analytic form and can always be found numerically if necessary, to the exterior solution (19.7). The boundary condition at $r = a$ is that $(1/R_l)(dR_l/dr)$ be continuous.

[1] E. Feenberg, *Phys. Rev.*, **40**, 40 (1932); L. I. Schiff, *Progress of Theor. Physics* (Kyoto), **11**, 288 (1954).

Thus if γ_l is the ratio of slope to value of the interior wave function, we have that

$$\frac{k[j_l'(ka)\cos\delta_l - n_l'(ka)\sin\delta_l]}{j_l(ka)\cos\delta_l - n_l(ka)\sin\delta_l} = \gamma_l$$

where the derivatives j_l' and n_l' may be rewritten with the help of (15.10). Then δ_l is given by

$$\tan\delta_l = \frac{kj_l'(ka) - \gamma_l j_l(ka)}{kn_l'(ka) - \gamma_l n_l(ka)} \tag{19.15}$$

Equation (19.15) can be used at once to obtain an approximate expression for δ_l when $l \gg ka$ and δ_l is expected to be small. In this case, γ_l will differ little from the ratio of slope to value of the solution in the absence of a scattering potential, so that we put

$$\gamma_l = k\left[\frac{j_l'(ka)}{j_l(ka)} + \epsilon_l\right], \qquad |\epsilon_l| \ll \left|\frac{j_l'(ka)}{j_l(ka)}\right| \tag{19.16}$$

Equation (19.15) can be rewritten with the help of (15.9) as

$$\tan\delta_l = \frac{\epsilon_l(ka)^2 j_l^2(ka)}{\epsilon_l(ka)^2 j_l(ka)n_l(ka) - 1} \tag{19.17}$$

which is still exact. If now we make use of the power series expansion for j_l from (15.7) when $l \gg (ka)^2$, and use (15.7) and (15.8) to estimate the order of magnitude of n_l, the inequality in (19.16) becomes

$$|\epsilon_l| \ll \frac{l}{ka} \tag{19.18}$$

and (19.17) may be approximated as

$$\delta_l \cong -\frac{\epsilon_l(ka)^{2l+2}}{[1\cdot 3\cdot 5\cdots(2l+1)]^2} = -\frac{\epsilon_l 2^{2l}(l!)^2(ka)^{2l+2}}{[(2l+1)!]^2} \tag{19.19}$$

Equation (19.19) can be used to verify the convergence of the sums over partial waves such as appear in (19.11). We use Stirling's formula to find the leading terms in $\ln|\delta_l|$ when l is large, and neglect terms of order $\ln l$ and lower.

$$\ln|\delta_l| \cong \ln|\epsilon_l| + 2l[\ln(ka) + 1 - \ln 2] - 2l\ln l$$

Thus even if $|\epsilon_l|$ has the maximum value indicated by (19.18), δ_l falls off like the inverse factorial of l (faster than exponentially), and the series that appear in the expressions for the scattering converge quite rapidly for large l.

Relation between Signs of δ_l and $V(r)$. It is apparent from (19.19) that when $l \gg (ka)^2$, δ_l has the opposite sign from ϵ_l. If now the potential energy term V or U is positive, corresponding to forces that are mainly repulsive, Eq. (19.2) shows that the ratio of curvature to value for the radial wave function is more positive than in the force-free case. This means that the ratio of slope to value is more positive at $r = a$ than is the case if $U = 0$. Thus a repulsive potential makes ϵ_l positive and δ_l

negative. A negative phase shift means that the radial wave function is "pushed out" in comparison with the force-free wave function.

In similar fashion, we see that a negative potential makes ϵ_l negative and δ_l positive. This means that the radial wave function is "pulled in" by the attractive potential.

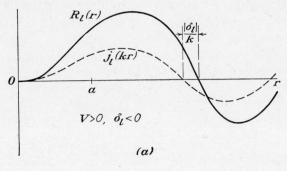

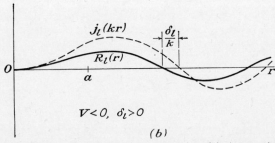

FIG. 18. Schematic plots of the effects of (a) positive (repulsive) potential, and (b) negative (attractive) potential, on the force-free radial wave function $j_l(kr)$; the range of the potential is a in each case. $R_l(r)$ is drawn arbitrarily to start out like $j_l(kr)$ at $r = 0$, and is bent up more rapidly in (a) so that it has a greater amplitude and a retarded phase (pushed out) with respect to $j_l(kr)$. In (b), $R_l(r)$ bends over sooner, and thus has a smaller amplitude than $j_l(kr)$ and an advanced phase (pulled in). The amplitudes have no direct physical significance, whereas the phases determine the scattering. The difference between neighboring nodes of j_l and R_l is not precisely equal to the phase shift divided by k (as indicated) until j_l has gone through several oscillations and attained its asymptotic form.

These conclusions are valid even when l is not large compared to ka and δ_l is not small. This may be seen graphically by comparing $j_l(kr)$ and $R_l(r)$ when they are arbitrarily made to start out in the same way at $r = 0$. Figure 18(a) shows a schematic comparison for positive V, and Fig. 18(b) for negative V.

Ramsauer-Townsend Effect. The construction in Fig. 18(b) suggests that an attractive potential might be strong enough so that one of the radial partial waves is pulled in by just half a cycle and its phase shift is 180°. If this were the case, the corresponding term in the expression

(19.11) for $f(\theta)$ would vanish, and there would be no contribution to the scattering.   It is clear from the foregoing discussion that the phase shift is largest for $l = 0$.   The possibility then arises that ka can be small enough and the attractive potential large enough in magnitude so that $\delta_0 = 180°$ and all other phase shifts are negligibly small.   In such a case, the scattered amplitude $f(\theta)$ vanishes for all θ, and there is no scattering.

This is the explanation[1] of the *Ramsauer-Townsend effect*, the extremely low minimum observed in the scattering cross section of electrons by rare-gas atoms at about 0.7 electron-volt bombarding energy.[2]   A rare-gas atom, which consists entirely of closed shells, is relatively small,

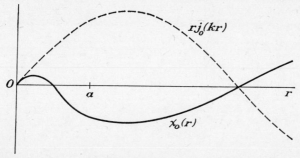

Fig. 19.   Schematic plot of the effect of the potential of a rare-gas atom of "radius" a on the $l = 0$ partial wave of an incident electron that has the minimum cross section observed in the Ramsauer-Townsend effect.   As in Fig. 18, the actual and force-free wave functions start out in the same way at $r = 0$; the former is "pulled in" by 180° of phase.   In an actual case, the quantity ka would be somewhat smaller than is indicated here.

and the combined force of nucleus and atomic electrons exerted on an incident electron is strong and sharply defined as to range.   Thus it is reasonable to expect that a situation such as that illustrated in Fig. 19 could occur.   Here the partial wave with $l = 0$ has exactly a half cycle more of oscillation inside the atomic potential than the corresponding force-free wave, and the wave length of the electron is large enough in comparison with a so that higher l phase shifts are negligible.   It is clear that this minimum cross section will occur at a definite energy, since the shape of the wave function inside the potential is insensitive to the relatively small bombarding energy whereas the phase of the force-free wave function depends rapidly on it.

Physically, the Ramsauer-Townsend effect may be thought of as a diffraction of the electron around the rare-gas atom, in which the wave function inside the atom is distorted in just such a way that it fits on

[1] This explanation, suggested by N. Bohr, was shown to be quantitatively reasonable by H. Faxén and J. Holtsmark, *Zeits. f. Physik*, **45**, 307 (1927).

[2] The experimental results are summarized by R. Kollath, *Phys. Zeits.*, **31**, 985 (1931).

smoothly to an undistorted wave function outside. This effect is analogous to the perfect transmission found at particular energies in the one-dimensional problem considered earlier [see discussion of Eq. (17.5)]. Unlike the situation in one dimension, however, the Ramsauer-Townsend effect cannot occur with a repulsive potential, since ka would have to be at least of order unity to make $\delta_0 = -180°$, and a potential of this large range would produce higher l phase shifts.

Scattering by a Perfectly Rigid Sphere. As a first example of the method of partial waves, we compute the scattering by a perfectly rigid sphere, which is represented by the potential $V(r) = +\infty$ for $r < a$, and $V(r) = 0$ for $r > a$. The solution for $r > a$ is just Eq. (19.7). The boundary condition, obtained in Sec. 8, that $u(a,\theta) = 0$, is equivalent to the requirement that all the radial functions vanish at $r = a$. The phase shifts may then be obtained by setting either $R_l(a)$ given by (19.7) equal to zero, or γ_l in (19.14) equal to infinity:

$$\tan \delta_l = \frac{j_l(ka)}{n_l(ka)} \tag{19.20}$$

The calculation of the scattering is particularly simple in the low-energy limit: $ka = 2\pi a/\lambda \ll 1$. Then substitution of (15.7) into (19.20) gives as an approximation for the phase shifts

$$\tan \delta_l \cong -\frac{(ka)^{2l+1}}{(2l+1)[1\cdot 1\cdot 3\cdot 5\cdots(2l-1)]^2} \tag{19.21}$$

Thus δ_l falls off very rapidly as l increases, in agreement with (19.19). All the phase shifts vanish as $k \to 0$; however, the $l = 0$ partial wave gives a finite contribution to the scattering because of the factor $1/k^2$ that appears in (19.12) and (19.13). We thus obtain

$$\sigma(\theta) \cong a^2, \qquad \sigma \cong 4\pi a^2 \tag{19.22}$$

The scattering is spherically symmetrical, and the total cross section is four times the classical value.

In the high-energy limit ($ka \gg 1$), we might expect to get the classical result, since it is then possible to make wave packets that are small in comparison with the size of the scattering region, and these can follow the classical trajectories without spreading appreciably. This corresponds to the ray limit in the wave theory of light or sound. The differential scattering cross section is rather difficult to find, and we only indicate the computation of the leading term in the total cross section. Substitution of (19.20) into (19.13) gives

$$\sigma = \frac{4\pi}{k^2} \sum_{l=0}^{\infty} \frac{(2l + 1)j_l^2(ka)}{j_l^2(ka) + n_l^2(ka)} \tag{19.23}$$

We can make use of asymptotic expansions of Bessel functions that are valid when the argument is large and the order is smaller than, of the order of, and larger than the argument.[1] The calculation shows that most of the contribution to the sum in (19.23) comes from

$$l < (ka) - C(ka)^{\frac{1}{3}},$$

where C is a number of order unity; the leading term here is $\frac{1}{2}(ka)^2$. The other two parts of the sum, for $(ka) - C(ka)^{\frac{1}{3}} < l < (ka) + C(ka)^{\frac{1}{3}}$, and for $l > (ka) + C(ka)^{\frac{1}{3}}$, each contribute terms of order $(ka)^{\frac{2}{3}}$, and hence may be neglected in the high-energy limit.   Thus

$$\sigma \cong 2\pi a^2 \tag{19.24}$$

which is twice the classical value.

The reason for the apparently anomalous result (19.24) is that the asymptotic form of the wave function is so set up in Eq. (18.10) that in the classical limit the scattering is counted twice: once in the true scattering (which turns out to be spherically symmetric as it is in the classical problem), and again in the shadow of the scattering sphere that appears in the forward direction, since this shadow is produced by interference between the incident plane wave e^{ikz} and the scattered wave $f(\theta)e^{ikr}/r$ [see also the discussion of Eq. (19.14)].   However, so long as ka is finite, diffraction around the sphere in the forward direction actually takes place, and the total measured cross section (if the measurement can be made so that it includes the strong forward maximum) is approximately $2\pi a^2$.

Scattering by a Square Well Potential.   As a second example of the method of partial waves, we consider the somewhat more complicated problem of the scattering from the spherically symmetric square well potential illustrated in Fig. 13 of Sec. 15.   The interior $(r < a)$ wave function that is finite at $r = 0$ is seen by analogy with Eq. (15.11) to be

$$R_l(r) = B_l j_l(\alpha r), \qquad \alpha = \left[\frac{2\mu(E + V_0)}{\hbar^2} \right]^{\frac{1}{2}} \tag{19.25}$$

Thus the phase shifts are given by Eq. (19.14), where the ratio of slope to value of the lth partial wave at $r = a$ is

$$\gamma_l = \frac{\alpha j_l'(\alpha a)}{j_l(\alpha a)} \tag{19.26}$$

[1] Watson, *op. cit.*, Chap. VIII.

In the low-energy limit $(ka \ll 1)$, substitution of (15.7) into (19.14) gives for the first two phase shifts

$$\tan \delta_0 \cong - \frac{\gamma_0 k a^2}{1 + \gamma_0 a}$$

$$\tan \delta_1 \cong \frac{(ka)^3}{3} \frac{1 - \gamma_1 a}{2 + \gamma_1 a} \tag{19.27}$$

Unless $\gamma_0 a = -1$ or $\gamma_1 a = -2$, both of these vanish as $k \to 0$. As with the rigid sphere, however, the $l = 0$ partial wave gives a finite contribution to the scattering because of the factor $1/k^2$ that appears in (19.12) and (19.13). From Eq. (19.26), we see that $\gamma_0 a = \alpha a \cot \alpha a - 1$, so that

$$\sigma \cong 4\pi a^2 \left(1 - \frac{\tan \alpha a}{\alpha a}\right)^2 \tag{19.28}$$

The scattering is spherically symmetrical.

The conclusion reached here and in connection with the rigid sphere that the low-energy scattering is substantially independent of bombarding energy and angle of observation is almost always valid for any potential that has a finite range. Exceptions can arise, as pointed out after Eq. (19.27), if any one of the γ_l is such that the denominator of the expression for $\tan \delta_l$ is very small. In such a situation, the lth partial wave is said to be in *resonance* with the scattering potential; then it usually dominates the scattering.

Resonance Scattering. An approximate expression for the resonance cross section can be obtained by making use of the fact that γ_l decreases linearly with increasing α when α is sufficiently close to $\alpha_0 \equiv (2\mu V_0/\hbar^2)^{\frac{1}{2}}$. Increasing α causes the interior wave function to bend over more rapidly and so decreases the ratio of slope to value at $r = a$. Now

$$\alpha = (\alpha_0^2 + k^2)^{\frac{1}{2}} \cong \alpha_0 + \frac{k^2}{2\alpha_0}$$

when k is small, so that we can write to lowest order in k

$$\gamma_l a \cong \gamma_l^0 a - b_l (ka)^2$$

where γ_l^0 is the value of γ_l when $\alpha = \alpha_0$, and b_l is a positive number of order unity.[1] Substitution into (19.27) and then into (19.12) gives for the leading term in the differential cross section, in the two cases for which the value of l for the partial wave that is in resonance is 0 and is 1,

---

[1] It can be shown that the lth partial wave is exactly in resonance at zero bombarding energy when $\gamma_l^0 a = -(l + 1)$; in this case $b_l = \frac{1}{2}$ for all l. Compare with footnote 1, page 80.

$$\sigma(\theta) \cong \frac{a^2}{(\zeta_0 - b_0 k^2 a^2)^2 + (ka)^2}, \qquad l = 0 \quad (19.29)$$

$$\sigma(\theta) \cong \frac{9a^2 \cos^2 \theta \, (ka)^4}{(\zeta_1 - b_1 k^2 a^2)^2 + (ka)^6}, \qquad l = 1 \quad (19.30)$$

We have put $\zeta_0 = \gamma_0^0 a + 1$ and $\zeta_1 = \gamma_1^0 a + 2$; for resonance, $|\zeta_0|$ and $|\zeta_1|$ are small compared to unity. It is easy to show then that (19.29) is a monotonically decreasing function of ka; however (19.30) has a sharp maximum at $ka \cong (\zeta_1/b_1)^{\frac{1}{2}}$ if ζ_1 is positive, and a much lower maximum at $ka \cong (2|\zeta_1|b_1)^{\frac{1}{4}}$ if ζ_1 is negative.

If we make use of the relation $\zeta_0 = \alpha_0 a \cot \alpha_0 a$, we see from (19.29) that a suitable approximation for the total cross section when the $l = 0$ partial wave is in resonance is

$$\sigma \cong \frac{4\pi}{k^2 + \alpha_0^2 \cot^2 \alpha_0 a} \qquad (19.31)$$

It is apparent that the $l = 0$ partial wave is in resonance at low bombarding energies whenever $\alpha_0 a$ is approximately an odd multiple of $\pi/2$, so that $V_0 a^2 \cong \pi^2 \hbar^2 / 8\mu$, $9\pi^2 \hbar^2 / 8\mu$, etc. The discussion of Eq. (15.3) shows that these are just the values of $V_0 a^2$ for which new energy levels with $l = 0$ appear. It is true quite generally that a potential well (not necessarily square) that has an energy level nearly at zero exhibits a resonance in the low-energy scattering of particles with the same l value (not necessarily zero) as the energy level. From a physical point of view, we can say that an incident particle that has nearly the right energy to be bound by the potential tends to concentrate there and produce a large distortion in the wave function and hence a large amount of scattering.

Sharp resonance maxima in the low-energy scattering like that found above for $l = 1$ with positive ζ_1 can appear for any l value except $l = 0$, provided that the potential well is not quite deep or broad enough to contain a new energy level of that angular momentum (this corresponds in the case of the square well to having ζ_l small and positive). We can think of such a potential physically as containing a *virtual energy level* slightly above zero. While a discrete energy level cannot exist with positive energy, the positive "centrifugal potential" $l(l + 1)\hbar^2/2\mu r^2$ [see the discussion of Eq. (14.18)] for $l > 0$ acts as a potential barrier that impedes the escape of a particle that is in the virtual energy level. Figure 20 illustrates this barrier, which is characterized by a small transmission at low energies in the same way as is the barrier of Fig. 14 [see the discussion of Eq. (17.7)]. Thus the virtual level has a kind of transient existence and produces a greater distortion of the incident wave function at its energy than at neighboring energies.

Angular Distribution at Low Energies.   When the bombarding energy is small but not zero, the partial wave $l = 1$ may have an observable effect on the scattering.   If only δ_0 and δ_1 are appreciably different from zero, Eqs. (19.12) and (19.13) become

$$\sigma(\theta) = \frac{1}{k^2} [\sin^2 \delta_0 + 6 \sin \delta_0 \sin \delta_1 \cos (\delta_1 - \delta_0) \cos \theta$$
$$+ 9 \sin^2 \delta_1 \cos^2 \theta] \quad (19.32)$$
$$\sigma = \frac{4\pi}{k^2} (\sin^2 \delta_0 + 3 \sin^2 \delta_1)$$

In the absence of resonance, we see from Eqs. (19.27) and (19.32) that the ratio of the contributions to the total cross section of the partial waves $l = 1$ and $l = 0$ is of order $(ka)^4$.   However, the ratio of the largest angle-

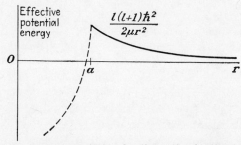

FIG. 20.   Effective potential energy [$V(r)$ plus "centrifugal potential"] for $l > 0$, when $V = 0$ for $r > a$.   The dashed portion for $r < a$ depends on the shape of V.   The effective potential barrier $(r \gtrsim a)$ resembles the barrier of Fig. 14 in that it has a small transmission for E slightly greater than zero.

dependent term in the differential cross section (which is proportional to $\cos \theta$) to the constant term is of order $(ka)^2$.

Thus the partial wave $l = 1$ manifests itself in the angular distribution at a lower energy than that at which it becomes significant in the total cross section; this is because of its interference with the stronger partial wave $l = 0$.   For example, if $\delta_0 = 20°$ and $\delta_1 = 2°$ at a particular bombarding energy, the partial wave $l = 1$ contributes only 3 per cent to the total cross section while it makes the forward scattering $(\theta = 0°)$ 3.5 times as great as the backward scattering $(\theta = 180°)$.

20. SCATTERING BY A COULOMB FIELD

It was noted in Sec. 19 that the Coulomb field is an exceptional scatterer so far as the application of the method of partial waves is concerned. If $V(r) = ZZ'e^2/r$ for a collision between particles of charges Ze and $Z'e$, it is easily seen that Eq. (19.3) becomes asymptotically

$$\chi_l(r) \propto e^{\pm i(kr - n \ln r)} \quad (20.1)$$

Here $n = \mu ZZ'e^2/\hbar^2 k = ZZ'e^2/\hbar v$, where v is the relative velocity and μ is the reduced mass.   Thus the radial solutions never approach the sinusoidal free-particle solutions, since there is always a logarithmic contribution to the phase at great distances that cannot be neglected.   Although it is still possible to obtain a solution of this scattering problem in spherical coordinates (this is given below), the phase shifts δ_l introduced in Sec. 19 are altered in meaning.   This section presents the analytical work in outline, and quotes the principal results from more extended treatments.[1]

Parabolic Coordinates.   So long as $\sigma(\theta)$ for a pure Coulomb field is all that is desired, it is simpler to work with the separation of the wave equation in parabolic coordinates (see Sec. 16) than in spherical coordinates.   The reason for this is that the desired solution depends almost entirely on the variable ξ defined in Eq. (16.25), and not on the other two variables η and ϕ.   It is apparent that the solution will not involve ϕ, because of the axial symmetry of the problem; if now the incident plane wave term e^{ikz} is taken out as a factor, it can be made plausible that the rest of the solution does not involve η.   We put

$$u_c = e^{ikz} f \tag{20.2}$$

where u_c represents the complete Coulomb wave function (incident plus scattered wave).   Now u_c must contain a part whose dominant asymptotic behavior is of the form $r^{-1}e^{ikr}$, but no part that goes like $r^{-1}e^{-ikr}$ [see Eq. (18.10)].   Since an expression $e^{ikz}f(r - z)$ can be of this form, while an expression $e^{ikz}f(r + z)$ cannot, we anticipate that the function f appearing in (20.2) will depend only on $\xi = r - z$.

We substitute Eq. (20.2) into Eq. (16.26) after replacing Z by $-ZZ'$, and remember that $E > 0$.   The differential equation for f is then

$$\xi \frac{d^2 f}{d\xi^2} + (1 - ik\xi) \frac{df}{d\xi} - nkf = 0 \tag{20.3}$$

The confluent hypergeometric equation

$$z \frac{d^2 F}{dz^2} + (b - z) \frac{dF}{dz} - aF = 0 \tag{20.4}$$

which has the solution $F(a,b,z)$, is equivalent to Eq. (20.3) if we put

$$f(\xi) = CF(-in,1,ik\xi) \tag{20.5}$$

where C is a constant.

---

[1] W. Gordon, *Zeits. f. Physik*, **48**, 180 (1928); N. F. Mott and H. S. W. Massey, "The Theory of Atomic Collisions," 2d ed., Chap. III (Oxford, New York, 1949).   For the mathematical background, see E. T. Whittaker and G. N. Watson, "A Course of Modern Analysis," 4th ed., Chap. XVI (Cambridge, London, 1935).

Confluent Hypergeometric Function. The solution of Eq. (20.4) that is regular at $z = 0$ can be written as a power series

$$F(a,b,z) = \sum_{s=0}^{\infty} \frac{\Gamma(a + s)\Gamma(b)z^s}{\Gamma(a)\Gamma(b + s)\Gamma(1 + s)}$$
$$= 1 + \frac{az}{b1!} + \frac{a(a + 1)z^2}{b(b + 1)2!} + \cdots \qquad (20.6)$$

It is convenient to put $F(a,b,z) = W_1(a,b,z) + W_2(a,b,z)$, where W_1 and W_2 are separately solutions of Eq. (20.4). An asymptotic expansion for F can then be obtained from the following relations:

$$W_1(a,b,z) = \frac{\Gamma(b)}{\Gamma(b - a)} (-z)^{-a}g(a, a - b + 1, -z)$$
$$W_2(a,b,z) = \frac{\Gamma(b)}{\Gamma(a)} e^z z^{a-b}g(1 - a, b - a, z) \qquad (20.7)$$
$$g(\alpha,\beta,z) \xrightarrow[z \to \infty]{} 1 + \frac{\alpha\beta}{z1!} + \frac{\alpha(\alpha + 1)\beta(\beta + 1)}{z^2 2!} + \cdots$$

The solution of Eq. (20.4) that is irregular at the origin can be taken to be

$$G(a,b,z) = iW_1(a,b,z) - iW_2(a,b,z) \qquad (20.8)$$

We shall require the irregular solution for problems in which the Coulomb field does not extend in to $r = 0$.

The asymptotic form of the Coulomb wave function can be obtained from Eqs. (20.2), (20.5), and (20.7). The result through terms of order r^{-1} is

$$u_c \xrightarrow[r \to \infty]{} \frac{Ce^{\frac{1}{2}n\pi}}{\Gamma(1 + in)} \left\{ e^{i[kz+n \ln k(r-z)]} \left[1 - \frac{n^2}{ik(r - z)} \right] \right.$$
$$\left. + r^{-1}f_c(\theta) e^{i(kr-n \ln 2kr)} \right\} \qquad (20.9)$$

where

$$f_c(\theta) = \frac{\Gamma(1 + in)}{i\Gamma(- in)} \frac{e^{-in \ln (\sin^2 \frac{1}{2}\theta)}}{2k \sin^2 \frac{1}{2}\theta}$$
$$= \frac{n}{2k \sin^2 \frac{1}{2}\theta} e^{-in \ln (\sin^2 \frac{1}{2}\theta)+i\pi+2i\eta_0} \qquad (20.10)$$
$$\eta_0 = \arg \Gamma(1 + in)$$

Scattering Cross Section and Normalization. The f_c term on the right side of Eq. (20.9) represents the outgoing scattered wave, since it is the only term in which the factor $r^{-1}e^{ikr}$ appears. The first term in Eq. (20.9) similarly corresponds to the incident "plane" wave; the multiplicative factor $-n^2/ik(r - z)$ can be ignored in the asymptotic region.

Both the incident and scattered waves are distorted at infinite distances by logarithmic phase factors.   In accordance with Eq. (18.11), the differential scattering cross section is

$$\sigma_c(\theta) = |f_c(\theta)|^2 = \left(\frac{n}{2k \sin^2 \frac{1}{2}\theta}\right)^2$$

$$= \left(\frac{ZZ'e^2}{2\mu v^2}\right)^2 \csc^4 \tfrac{1}{2}\theta \tag{20.11}$$

This is just the formula obtained by Rutherford from classical dynamics, which was verified experimentally for the collisions of alpha particles (helium nuclei) with heavier nuclei.   It should be noted, however, that the angle-dependent part of the phase factor in the scattered amplitude $f_c(\theta)$ given in Eq. (20.10) can manifest itself in a nonclassical way when the colliding particles are identical (see Sec. 32).

If the incident beam is normalized to unit flux, the constant C must be chosen to be

$$C = v^{-\frac{1}{2}}\Gamma(1 + in)e^{-\frac{1}{2}n\pi}$$

so that the Coulomb wave function is

$$u_c = v^{-\frac{1}{2}}\Gamma(1 + in)e^{-\frac{1}{2}n\pi}e^{ikz}F(-in,1,ik\xi)$$
$$= v^{-\frac{1}{2}}\Gamma(1 + in)e^{-\frac{1}{2}n\pi}e^{ikr \cos\theta}F(-in,1,2ikr \sin^2 \tfrac{1}{2}\theta) \tag{20.12}$$

Then the particle density at $r = 0$ is found from the power series expansion (20.6) to be

$$|u_c(0)|^2 = |C|^2 = v^{-1}|\Gamma(1 + in)|^2 e^{-n\pi}$$

$$= \frac{2n\pi}{v(e^{2n\pi} - 1)} \tag{20.13}$$

For small collision speeds ($|n| \gg 1$), Eq. (20.13) tells us that

$$|u_c(0)|^2 \cong \frac{2\pi|n|}{v} \qquad \text{attractive case, } n < 0$$
$$|u_c(0)|^2 \cong \frac{2\pi n}{v} e^{-2n\pi} \quad \text{repulsive case, } n > 0 \tag{20.14}$$

The second of Eqs. (20.14) is of some practical interest.   The exponential is the dominant factor in the production of reactions between positively charged nuclei at low bombarding energies, when the nuclear radii may be assumed small enough so that the colliding nuclei have to approach to zero distance in order to initiate a reaction.   In this case $\exp(-2\pi ZZ'e^2/\hbar v)$ is called the *Gamow factor*,[1] and is the dominant term in the rate of many nuclear reactions at low bombarding energies.

[1] G. Gamow, *Zeits. f. Physik*, **51**, 204 (1928); R. W. Gurney and E. U. Condon, *Phys. Rev.*, **33**, 127 (1929).

Solution in Spherical Coordinates.   In nuclear collision problems, such as that of the scattering of protons of several million electron-volts energy in hydrogen, the departures from the Coulomb law of interaction at small distances between the colliding particles can affect the scattering cross section.   Such problems can be treated by a modification of the method of partial waves, developed in Sec. 19, in which an expansion in spherical harmonics is made for the pure Coulomb field, and modifications introduced for the first few l values.   In order to apply such a technique, we require first a solution for the pure Coulomb scattering in spherical partial waves.

We put

$$u_c = \sum_{l=0}^{\infty} R_l(r) P_l(\cos \theta) \tag{20.15}$$

where the radial wave equation is

$$\frac{1}{r^2} \frac{d}{dr} \left(r^2 \frac{dR_l}{dr} \right) + \left[k^2 - \frac{2nk}{r} - \frac{l(l+1)}{r^2} \right] R_l = 0 \tag{20.16}$$

If we substitute $R_l(r) = r^l e^{ikr} f_l(r)$, the equation for f_l becomes

$$r \frac{d^2 f_l}{dr^2} + [2ikr + 2(l+1)] \frac{df_l}{dr} + [2ik(l+1) - 2nk] f_l = 0 \tag{20.17}$$

This is equivalent to the confluent hypergeometric equation (20.4), and has as its solution that is regular at $r = 0$

$$f_l(r) = C_l F(l+1+in, 2l+2, -2ikr) \tag{20.18}$$

The asymptotic form of (20.18) can be found from (20.7), and gives for the radial wave function at great distances

$$R_l(r) \xrightarrow[r \to \infty]{} \frac{C_l e^{\frac{1}{2}n\pi + i\eta_l} \Gamma(2l+2)}{(2k)^l \Gamma(l+1+in)kr} \sin \left(kr - \tfrac{1}{2}l\pi - n \ln 2kr + \eta_l \right), \tag{20.19}$$

where $\eta_l = \arg \Gamma(l+1+in)$.

The coefficients C_l must be determined so that the partial wave expansion (20.15) is identical with the solution (20.12) in parabolic coordinates. Because of the orthogonality of the Legendre polynomials, we have the relation

$$R_l(r) = \frac{2l+1}{2} \int_0^\pi P_l(\cos \theta) u_c(r,\theta) \sin \theta d\theta \tag{20.20}$$

where $u_c(r,\theta)$ is given by the second of Eqs. (20.12).   The complete evaluation of this integral can be avoided by making use of the fact that we know all about the function $R_l(r)$ except the constant multiplying factor C_l. C_l can then be found by matching the known form of $R_l(r)$ to Eq. (20.20) near $r = 0$, and turns out to be

$$C_l = \frac{(2ik)^l e^{-\frac{1}{2}n\pi} \Gamma(l + 1 + in)}{v^{\frac{1}{2}}(2l)!}.$$

We thus obtain as an alternative expression to (20.12)

$$u_c = v^{-\frac{1}{2}} e^{-\frac{1}{2}n\pi} \sum_{l=0}^{\infty} \frac{\Gamma(l + 1 + in)}{(2l)!} (2ikr)^l e^{ikr}$$
$$\cdot F(l + 1 + in, 2l + 2, -2ikr) P_l(\cos \theta).   (20.21)$$

Modified Coulomb Field.   If the actual potential deviates from the Coulomb form only at small values of r, we expect in analogy with the partial wave treatment of section 19 that only the first few terms in the sum (20.21) will be altered.   Since each partial radial wave function must be a solution of (20.16) outside of the potential anomaly, the only change we can make in the function f_l and still have it a solution of (20.17) is to add in some of the irregular solution $G(l + 1 + in, 2l + 2, -2ikr)$ defined by (20.8).   The manner in which G is to be added in is determined by the requirement that the complete wave function shall represent asymptotically a Coulomb incident plus scattered wave, plus an extra *outgoing* scattered wave.

We must, therefore, substitute for each F term in (20.21) a linear combination of F and G in which the amount of the ingoing term W_2 is not changed.   Such a combination is

$$e^{i\delta_l}(F \cos \delta_l + G \sin \delta_l) = W_1 e^{2i\delta_l} + W_2.$$

The modified wave function, which is a solution of the wave equation outside of the potential anomaly, can then be written

$$u_m = u_c + v^{-\frac{1}{2}} e^{-\frac{1}{2}n\pi} \sum_{l=0}^{\infty} \frac{\Gamma(l + 1 + in)}{(2l)!} (2ikr)^l e^{ikr}$$
$$\cdot (e^{2i\delta_l} - 1) W_1(l + 1 + in, 2l + 2, -2ikr) P_l(\cos \theta)   (20.22)$$

The asymptotic form of u_m is

$$u_m \xrightarrow[r \to \infty]{} v^{-\frac{1}{2}} \sum_{l=0}^{\infty} (2l + 1) i^l e^{i(\eta_l + \delta_l)} (kr)^{-1}$$
$$\cdot \sin(kr - \tfrac{1}{2}l\pi - n \ln 2kr + \eta_l + \delta_l) P_l(\cos \theta)   (20.23)$$

As shown in connection with Eq. (19.5), each term on the right side of

(20.23) must be a real function of r, except for complex multiplying factors, so that the δ_l must be real.

The additional phase shifts δ_l can be found by matching each partial radial wave in Eq. (20.22) to the interior solution at the edge of the potential anomaly, in just the same way as the phase shifts were found in Sec. 19.   While in Sec. 19 the phase shifts δ_l represented the departure of the wave function from that of a free particle, they here represent the departure from the wave function of a particle scattered by a pure Coulomb field.[1]   It can be shown from Eq. (20.22) that the asymptotic form of u_m may be written in the form of (20.9), where $f_c(\theta)$ is replaced by

$$f_m(\theta) = f_c(\theta) + \sum_{l=0}^{\infty} k^{-1}(2l + 1)e^{i(2\eta_l+\delta_l)} \sin \delta_l P_l(\cos \theta) \qquad (20.24)$$

The differential scattering cross section is just $|f_m(\theta)|^2$, and in general contains interference terms between the Coulomb scattered amplitude $f_c(\theta)$ and the extra terms that are determined by the δ_l.

Classical Limit for a Pure Coulomb Field.   As was discussed in Sec. 12, we expect the results of quantum and classical theory to coincide whenever it is possible to construct wave packets that follow the classical trajectory without spreading appreciably and are small enough so that the forces are sensibly constant over their dimensions.   The smallest spread of a wave packet during a time interval t was found there to be of order $(\hbar t/\mu)^{\frac{1}{2}}$ or $(\hbar d/\mu v)^{\frac{1}{2}} = (\lambda d)^{\frac{1}{2}}$, where $d = vt$ is the distance traveled by the packet in the time t, and $\lambda \equiv \lambda/2\pi = \hbar/\mu v$ is the reduced wave length for the relative motion.   Thus the classical theory can be used when $(\lambda d)^{\frac{1}{2}} \ll d$, or $(d/\lambda)^{\frac{1}{2}} \gg 1$, where d is the distance over which the force varies by an appreciable fraction of itself.   For a repulsive Coulomb field, d is of the order of the classical distance of closest approach $|ZZ'e^2/\frac{1}{2}\mu v^2|$.   This also provides a useful estimate for an attractive Coulomb field, since in all the collisions, except the relatively few for which the particles are scattered through large angles, they never get closer than this distance from each other.

The condition for the validity of the classical theory is then

$$|n|^{\frac{1}{2}} = \left|\frac{ZZ'e^2}{\hbar v}\right|^{\frac{1}{2}} \gg 1$$

Large n implies that the angle-dependent part of the phase of $f_c(\theta)$ given by Eq. (20.10) varies rapidly with θ, so that these rapid oscillations in the scattering amplitude should have little effect on the scattering when the colliding particles are identical (see Prob. 6, Chap. IX).

[1] The computation of the δ_l in Eq. (20.22) requires knowledge of G at small r; useful formulas have been given by F. L. Yost, J. A. Wheeler, and G. Breit, *Phys. Rev.*, **49**, 174 (1936).

It is interesting to note that for the Coulomb field the classical limit is approached for small v, whereas for potentials that have a finite range a, such as are discussed in Sec. 19, the classical limit is approached when $(a/\lambda)^{\frac{1}{2}} \gg 1$, that is, for large v. This is because the "size" $|ZZ'e^2/\mu v^2|$ of the Coulomb field increases more rapidly than $\lambda = \hbar/\mu v$ as v decreases.

Problems

1. Show that the coefficients of scattering by a one-dimensional square well potential (like Fig. 14 except that $V_0 < 0$) are given by Eqs. (17.5) if the sign of V_0 is changed there and in the expression for α. Discuss the dependence of transmission coefficient on E in this case.

2. Show that Eqs. (18.4) and (18.7) are valid for a general binary collision if γ is given by (18.5); make use of conservation of energy and mass.

3. Show that, when a particle of mass m_1 collides elastically with a particle of mass m_2 that is initially at rest, all the recoil (mass m_2) particles are scattered in the forward hemisphere in the laboratory coordinate system. If the angular distribution is spherically symmetrical in the center-of-mass system, what is it for m_2 in the laboratory system?

4. Express the scattering wave function (19.1) outside the scattering potential (but not necessarily in the asymptotic region) as the sum of a plane wave and an infinite series of spherical Hankel functions of the first kind [see Eqs. (15.12)]. From this expression and the discussion of Eqs. (15.13), show that the scattered wave is purely outgoing, even inside of the asymptotic region.

5. What must $V_0 a^2$ be for a three-dimensional square well potential in order that the scattering cross section be zero at zero bombarding energy (Ramsauer-Townsend effect)? Find the leading term in the expression for the total cross section for small bombarding energy. Note that both the $l = 0$ and the $l = 1$ partial waves must be included.

6. State clearly the assumptions that go into the derivation of Eq. (19.31), and verify that it is a suitable approximation for the total cross section at low bombarding energies when the $l = 0$ wave is in resonance.

7. Make use of Eq. (19.31) and the result of Prob. 5, Chap. IV, to obtain an approximate expression for the total scattering cross section by a particular potential in terms of the bombarding energy E and the binding energy ϵ of a particle in that potential, when E and ϵ are small in comparison with V_0.

8. Compute and make a polar plot of the differential scattering cross section for a perfectly rigid sphere when $ka = \frac{1}{2}$, using the first three partial waves ($l = 0, 1, 2$). What is the total cross section in this case, and what is the approximate accuracy of this result when the three terms are used?

9. Find a general expression for the phase shift produced by a scattering potential $V(r) = A/r^2$, where $A > 0$. Is the total cross section finite? If not, does the divergence come from small or large scattering angles, and why? What modifications are necessary in the calculation if $A < 0$? Are any difficulties encountered in this latter case?

10. Protons of 200,000 electron-volts energy are scattered from aluminum. The directly back scattered intensity ($\theta = 180°$) is found to be 96 per cent of that computed from the Rutherford formula. Assume this to be due to a modification of the Coulomb potential that is of sufficiently short range so that only the phase shift for $l = 0$ is affected. Is this modification attractive or repulsive? Find the sign and magnitude of the change in the phase shift for $l = 0$ produced by the modification.

CHAPTER VI

MATRIX FORMULATION OF QUANTUM MECHANICS

In the last four chapters the Schrödinger wave equation was developed and its solutions obtained in some cases of physical interest. We now turn to a different formulation of quantum mechanics, in which dynamical variables such as the coordinates, momentum components, and energy of a particle appear explicitly in the equations of motion of the system without their having to multiply or differentiate a wave function. The classical equations are just of this structure, so it might be expected that there would be a closer resemblance between the classical and quantum formalism here than in the Schrödinger theory.

This is actually the case; the principal formal difference is that the quantum dynamical variables do not obey the commutative law of multiplication. It is convenient to represent such noncommutative dynamical variables, which are often simply called *operators*, as matrices. Matrix theory provides an expecially flexible representation scheme, since there are an arbitrarily large number of ways of choosing the rows and columns of a matrix, all of which are of equal validity. It is because of the close formal resemblance between quantum matrix mechanics and classical dynamics that this was historically the first formulation of quantum theory to be discovered, by Heisenberg in 1925.[1]

In this chapter we first review briefly the more important properties of matrices, and then show their connection with quantum theory and their usefulness in particular problems.

21. MATRIX ALGEBRA

We restrict our discussion at first to matrices that have a finite number of rows and columns, and then indicate how the results obtained can be taken over to matrices that have an infinite number of rows and columns.[2]

---

[1] W. Heisenberg, *Zeits. f. Physik*, **33**, 879 (1925); M. Born, W. Heisenberg, and P. Jordan, *Zeits. f. Phys.* **35**, 557 (1925). The connection between quantum matrix mechanics and the wave equation was established by E. Schrödinger, *Ann. d. Physik*, **79**, 734 (1926), and C. Eckart, *Phys. Rev.*, **28**, 711 (1926).

[2] For a fuller discussion, see J. von Neumann, "Mathematische Grundlagen der Quantenmechanik," Chap. II (Springer, Berlin, 1932; reprinted by Dover, New York).

Matrix Addition and Multiplication.   A *matrix* is a square or rectangular array of numbers that can be added to or multiplied into another matrix according to certain rules.   We denote a matrix by a capital letter, such as A, and the numbers or *elements* that make it up by the same letter with subscripts, such as A_{kl}; here, k designates the row and l the column in which the matrix element A_{kl} appears.   Two matrices can be added when they have the same *rank*, *i.e.*, the same number of rows and the same number of columns.   Addition is commutative:

$$A + B = B + A \tag{21.1}$$

If the sum matrix is called C, then

$$C_{kl} = A_{kl} + B_{kl} \tag{21.2}$$

A matrix A can be multiplied from the left into a matrix B if the number of columns of A is equal to the number of rows of B; then the product matrix C has the number of rows of A and the number of columns of B.

$$C = AB, \qquad C_{kl} = \sum_{m} A_{km} B_{ml} \tag{21.3}$$

where the summation is over the subscript m, which denotes the columns of A and the rows of B.   It follows at once from Eqs. (21.2) and (21.3) that the distributive law of multiplication is valid.

$$A(B + C) = AB + AC \tag{21.4}$$

Also, the associative law of multiplication is seen to be valid:

$$A(BC) = (AB)C \tag{21.5}$$

where the left side means that A is multiplied from the left into the product of B and C, and the right side means that the product of A and B is multiplied from the left into C.   The product (21.5) is written simply as ABC and, from (21.3), has the explicit expression

$$D = ABC, \qquad D_{kl} = \sum_{m,n} A_{km} B_{mn} C_{nl} \tag{21.6}$$

It is clear from Eq. (21.3) that AB is not in general equal to BA; thus the commutative law of multiplication is not generally valid.

Null, Unit, and Constant Matrices.   For an arbitrary square matrix A, the *null matrix* O is defined by the equations

$$OA = O, \qquad AO = O, \tag{21.7}$$

from which it follows that all the elements of O are zero.   If A is not square, the elements of O are still all zero, but the O's that appear at different places in (21.7) do not all have the same numbers of rows and columns.

The *unit matrix* 1 is defined by

$$1A = A, \qquad B1 = B, \tag{21.8}$$

for arbitrary matrices A and B. From Eqs. (21.8) it follows that 1 is a square matrix whose rank (number of rows or columns) equals the number of rows of A or the number of columns of B. Moreover, 1 must have unit elements along its principal diagonal ($k = l$) and zeros elsewhere, so that the elements of 1 equal the Kronecker symbol δ_{kl} introduced in Sec. 10.

The product of a number c and a matrix A is the matrix cA that results from multiplying each element of A by c. Thus if we define a *constant matrix* C to be a multiple of a unit matrix so that each nonvanishing element is c instead of unity, then

$$cA = CA, \qquad \text{where } C_{kl} = c\delta_{kl} \tag{21.9}$$

are the matrix elements of the constant matrix C.

Spur, Determinant, and Inverse of a Matrix. The *spur* of a square matrix, often called the *trace* or the *diagonal sum*, is the sum of the diagonal elements of the matrix:

$$Sp(A) = \sum_k A_{kk} \tag{21.10}$$

The *determinant* of a square matrix is found from the usual rule for the computation of the determinant of a square array of numbers.

A matrix A may or may not possess an *inverse* A^{-1}, which is defined by the relations

$$AA^{-1} = 1, \qquad A^{-1}A = 1 \tag{21.11}$$

A is said to be *nonsingular* if it possesses an inverse, and *singular* if it does not. If A is nonsingular and of finite rank, it can be shown to be square (see Prob. 2), and the kl element of its inverse is just the cofactor of A_{lk} divided by the determinant of A; thus A is singular if its determinant vanishes. It is readily verified that for nonsingular matrices A, B, C

$$(ABC)^{-1} = C^{-1}B^{-1}A^{-1} \tag{21.12}$$

Hermitian and Unitary Matrices. The *Hermitian adjoint* A^* of a matrix A is the matrix obtained by interchanging rows and columns and taking the complex conjugate of each element; thus if

$$B = A^* \qquad \text{then} \qquad B_{kl} = \bar{A}_{lk} \tag{21.13}$$

It is readily verified that the Hermitian adjoint of the product of a series of matrices is the product of their adjoints in the reverse order

$$(ABC)^* = C^*B^*A^* \tag{21.14}$$

A matrix is *Hermitian* or *self-adjoint*, if it is equal to its Hermitian adjoint; thus, A is a Hermitian matrix if

$$A = A^* \tag{21.15}$$

Evidently only square matrices can be Hermitian.

A matrix is *unitary* if its Hermitian adjoint is equal to its inverse; thus A is a unitary matrix if

$$A^* = A^{-1}, \quad \text{or} \quad AA^* = 1 \quad \text{and} \quad A^*A = 1 \tag{21.16}$$

Unitary matrices of finite rank must be square.

Transformation and Diagonalization of Matrices. We define the *transformation* of a square matrix A into a square matrix A' by a non-singular matrix S, by the following equation:

$$SAS^{-1} = A' \tag{21.17}$$

It is evident then that S^{-1} transforms A' back into A.

The form of a matrix equation is unaffected by transformation. Thus the equation

$$AB + CDE = F$$

may be transformed into

$$SABS^{-1} + SCDES^{-1} = SFS^{-1}$$

which is equivalent to

$$SAS^{-1} \cdot SBS^{-1} + SCS^{-1} \cdot SDS^{-1} \cdot SES^{-1} = SFS^{-1}$$

or to

$$A'B' + C'D'E' = F'$$

where the primes denote transformed matrices. This invariance of matrix equations with respect to transformations makes it possible to work with any convenient transformation of a set of matrices without affecting the validity of any results obtained.

A square matrix is *diagonal* if it has nonvanishing elements only along the principal diagonal ($k = l$). The diagonal elements are then called the *eigenvalues* of the matrix. It is easily seen that the nth power of a diagonal matrix is also diagonal, and has as its eigenvalues the nth powers of the eigenvalues of the original matrix. The matrix A in Eq. (21.17) is said to be *diagonalized* by the matrix S if the matrix A' that results from the transformation is diagonal, so that $A'_{kl} = A'_k \delta_{kl}$. To find A' explicitly, we multiply (21.17) through on the right by S.

$$SA = A'S \qquad (21.18)$$

The set of linear algebraic equations that are obtained by writing out the elements of Eq. (21.18) for a particular row k and all columns l is

$$\sum_m S_{km} A_{ml} = A'_k S_{kl} \qquad \text{or} \qquad \sum_m S_{km}(A_{ml} - A'_k \delta_{ml}) = 0 \qquad (21.19)$$

where A'_k is a particular eigenvalue of A' and the subscript m is summed over from unity to the rank N of the matrix A.

Now (21.19) may be regarded as a set of N homogeneous algebraic equations for the transformation matrix elements S_{km}, where k is fixed. The necessary and sufficient condition that these equations have a solution is that the determinant of their coefficients vanish, or that the determinant of the square matrix $(A_{ml} - A'_k \delta_{ml})$ be zero. This provides a single algebraic equation, called the *secular equation*, which is of order N and has N roots A'_k. Thus the eigenvalues of the diagonal matrix A' resulting from A by transformation are the same no matter how A is diagonalized, except perhaps for the order in which they are arranged; for this reason they are also called the eigenvalues of the original nondiagonal matrix A. A' and A are said to be *degenerate* when two or more eigenvalues are equal.

Matrices of Infinite Rank. The rules (21.2) and (21.3) for addition and multiplication of matrices may be taken over in an obvious way for matrices that have an infinite number of rows and columns, provided that the infinite sum in (21.3) converges. We sometimes deal with matrices that have a nondenumerably infinite number of rows or columns or both; in this case, one or both of the matrix subscripts becomes a continuous variable, and the usual summation over a subscript is replaced by integration over this variable. We do not consider these possibilities in detail here, but simply assume that all reasonable results can be taken over from finite- to infinite-rank matrices without difficulty.[1] The statement that a Hermitian matrix of infinite rank is square means that its rows and columns are labeled in the same way. A unitary matrix of infinite rank need not be square. Its rows and columns can be labeled differently; for example, the number of rows may be denumerably infinite and the number of columns nondenumerably infinite.

We are concerned primarily in quantum mechanics with Hermitian and unitary matrices, mainly of infinite rank. A fundamental theorem

---

[1] A more thorough discussion of this point, and a proof of the following theorem, are given by J. von Neumann, *loc. cit.*

that we shall assume without proof is that any Hermitian matrix can be diagonalized by a unitary transformation; a corollary of this theorem is that the resulting eigenvalues of the Hermitian matrix are unique, except perhaps for the order in which they are arranged.   Starting from this theorem, it is not difficult to show (see Prob. 1) that the necessary and sufficient condition that two Hermitian matrices can be diagonalized by the same unitary transformation is that they *commute* (matrices A and B commute if $AB = BA$).

It also follows from this theorem that the eigenvalues of a Hermitian matrix are real.   If the S and A in (21.17) are unitary and Hermitian, respectively, that equation can be rewritten

$$SAS^* = A' \qquad (21.20)$$

The Hermitian adjoint of Eq. (21.20) is, from (21.14),

$$SAS^* = A'^*$$

Since then $A'^* = A'$, this shows that the Hermitian property is maintained during transformation by a unitary matrix.   If A' is diagonal as well as Hermitian, it follows from (21.13) that its eigenvalues are real. It is easily seen that the converse is also true: a matrix that can be diagonalized by a unitary transformation and has real eigenvalues is Hermitian.

It is important to note with matrices of infinite rank that both of Eqs. (21.11) must be valid in order for A^{-1} to be the inverse of A.   Similarly, both of the latter pair of Eqs. (21.16) must be valid if A is to be unitary.

22. MATRICES IN QUANTUM MECHANICS

The appearance of matrices in quantum mechanics can be connected in a simple way with the solution of the Schrödinger equation (8.2).   In this section we adopt the *Hamiltonian* notation, and justify it in detail in Sec. 23.   We rewrite Eq. (8.2) as

$$Hu_k(\mathbf{r}) = E_k u_k(\mathbf{r}) \qquad (22.1)$$

where the subscript k denotes the different members of the complete orthonormal set of energy eigenfunctions $u_k(\mathbf{r})$ and their corresponding eigenvalues E_k [k specifies the energy, and also distinguishes between degenerate eigenfunctions; it thus includes both E and s of Eq. (10.7)]. The Hamiltonian or energy operator H is given by

$$H = \frac{\mathbf{p}^2}{2m} + V(\mathbf{r}) = -\frac{\hbar^2}{2m}\nabla^2 + V(\mathbf{r}) \qquad (22.2)$$

In accordance with the discussion of Sec. 8, k may be a discrete or a continuous variable, or discrete over part of its range and continuous over the rest.   We shall use the symbol S or S_k to denote a complete summation over the subscript k (the summation includes an integration $\int dk$ over the continuous part of its range).

A Unitary Transformation Matrix.   Suppose that we have a second complete orthonormal set of functions $v_n(\mathbf{r})$, which are not necessarily eigenfunctions of the Schrödinger equation (22.1) with the actual potential energy $V(\mathbf{r})$; they might, for example, be momentum eigenfunctions (11.4) or (11.11), or hydrogen-atom wave functions (16.24) supplemented by continuous-eigenvalue Coulomb-field wave functions like those discussed in Sec. 20.   The v_n can be expanded in terms of the u_k:

$$v_n(\mathbf{r}) = \mathsf{S}_k S_{kn} u_k(\mathbf{r})$$

where it is readily verified from the orthonormality of the u_k that

$$S_{kn} = \int \bar{u}_k(\mathbf{r}) v_n(\mathbf{r}) d\tau$$

Similarly

$$u_k(\mathbf{r}) = \mathsf{S}_n \bar{S}_{kn} v_n(\mathbf{r}) \tag{22.3}$$

We can now see that the matrix of which S_{kn} are the elements is unitary.

$$(SS^*)_{kl} = \mathsf{S}_n S_{kn} \bar{S}_{ln} = \mathsf{S}_n \int \bar{u}_k(\mathbf{r}) v_n(\mathbf{r}) d\tau \int \bar{v}_n(\mathbf{r}') u_l(\mathbf{r}') d\tau'$$
$$= \int\int \bar{u}_k(\mathbf{r}) u_l(\mathbf{r}') \delta(\mathbf{r} - \mathbf{r}') d\tau d\tau' = \int \bar{u}_k(\mathbf{r}) u_l(\mathbf{r}) d\tau \tag{22.4}$$

where use has been made of the closure property that is possessed by any complete orthonormal set of functions such as the $v_n(\mathbf{r})$ [see the discussion of Eq. (10.11)].   The last integral on the right side of (22.4) is a Kronecker δ symbol or a Dirac δ function according as k is one of a discrete or a continuous set of subscripts; in either case, this integral is equivalent to an element of the unit matrix, so that we have shown that $SS^* = \mathbf{1}$.   In similar fashion, it can be established that

$$(S^*S)_{nm} = \mathsf{S}_k \bar{S}_{kn} S_{km} = (\mathbf{1})_{nm}$$

Hamiltonian Matrix.   The functions $v_n(\mathbf{r})$ can be used to calculate a Hamiltonian matrix

$$H_{nm} = \int \bar{v}_n(\mathbf{r}) H v_m(\mathbf{r}) d\tau \tag{22.5}$$

where H is the operator given in (22.2).   We now consider the connection between the Hamiltonian matrix (22.5) in the v_n *representation*, and the energy eigenvalues E_k.

Transformation of H_{nm} by the unitary matrix S gives

$$(SHS^*)_{kl} = \mathsf{S}_{n,m} S_{kn} H_{nm} \bar{S}_{lm}$$
$$= \mathsf{S}_{n,m} \int \bar{u}_k(\mathbf{r}) v_n(\mathbf{r}) d\tau \int \bar{v}_n(\mathbf{r}') H' v_m(\mathbf{r}') d\tau' \int \bar{v}_m(\mathbf{r}'') u_l(\mathbf{r}'') d\tau''$$

where the prime on H indicates that it operates only on the variable $\mathbf{r}'$ to its right. After performing the summation over the subscript m to get $\delta(\mathbf{r}' - \mathbf{r}'')$, it can be seen that

$$\int H'\delta(\mathbf{r}' - \mathbf{r}'')u_l(\mathbf{r}'')d\tau'' = H'\int \delta(\mathbf{r}' - \mathbf{r}'')u_l(\mathbf{r}'')d\tau''$$
$$= H'u_l(\mathbf{r}')$$

On doing the sum over n and dropping the primes, we obtain

$$(SHS^*)_{kl} = \int \bar{u}_k(\mathbf{r})Hu_l(\mathbf{r})d\tau = E_k\delta_{kl} \text{ or } E_k\delta(k - l) \qquad (22.6)$$

which is in diagonal form with the eigenvalues E_k.

Thus the problem of solving the Schrödinger equation is completely equivalent to the problem of diagonalizing the Hamiltonian matrix when it is expressed in some arbitrary representation such as that provided by the functions v_n. The eigenvalues of the Hamiltonian matrix are the energy eigenvalues of the Schrödinger equation, and the unitary transformation matrix S that diagonalizes H serves, through Eq. (22.3), to give the energy eigenfunctions $u_k(\mathbf{r})$ in terms of the arbitrary initial set of functions.

It is interesting to note that S is not necessarily a square matrix. For example, the functions v_n may be the eigenfunctions of a three-dimensional harmonic oscillator, which form a completely discrete set, while the functions u_k may be momentum eigenfunctions, which form a completely continuous set. However the Hamiltonian matrix, in both its diagonal form (22.6) and its nondiagonal form H_{nm}, is square.

Dynamical Variables as Hermitian Matrices. The eigenvalues of the Hamiltonian are found in (22.6) to be the real energy levels E_k. It then follows from Sec. 21 that H is a Hermitian matrix in any representation.

The discussion of Sec. 10 developed the interpretation that the eigenvalues of any operator that represents a dynamical variable are real, since they are the only possible results of precise physical measurement of that variable. Any dynamical variable can be represented as a matrix whose diagonal representation has its eigenvalues along the principal diagonal, and that can be transformed to any other representation by a suitable unitary matrix. Thus any physically measurable dynamical variable can be represented by a Hermitian matrix, and is said to be Hermitian.

Wave Functions as Unitary Matrices. Any complete orthonormal set of functions, such as the $u_k(\mathbf{r})$ or the $v_n(\mathbf{r})$, possesses the closure property

$$\sum_k u_k(\mathbf{r})\bar{u}_k(\mathbf{r}') = \delta(\mathbf{r} - \mathbf{r}') \qquad (22.7)$$

and the orthonormality property

$$\int \bar{u}_k(\mathbf{r}) u_l(\mathbf{r}) d\tau = \delta_{kl} \text{ or } \delta(k - l) \tag{22.8}$$

If now we regard the function $u_k(\mathbf{r})$ as a two-dimensional array of numbers in which the rows are labeled by the position variable $\mathbf{r}$ and the columns by the subscript k, it is equivalent to a matrix $U_{\mathbf{r}k}$. Equation (22.7) is then equivalent to the matrix equation

$$(UU^*)_{\mathbf{rr}'} = \mathbf{S}_k U_{\mathbf{r}k} \bar{U}_{\mathbf{r}'k} = (\mathbf{1})_{\mathbf{rr}'}$$

Similarly, Eq. (22.8) is equivalent to

$$(U^*U)_{kl} = \mathbf{S}_{\mathbf{r}} \bar{U}_{\mathbf{r}k} U_{\mathbf{r}l} = (\mathbf{1})_{kl}$$

Thus U is a unitary matrix.

The r Representation. This suggests that such a unitary matrix be used to effect a transformation. Suppose that we transform the Hamiltonian matrix H_{nm} given in (22.5) by means of the unitary matrix

$$V_{\mathbf{r}n} \equiv v_n(\mathbf{r}).$$

$$\begin{aligned}
(VHV^*)_{\mathbf{rr}'} &= \mathbf{S}_{n,m} V_{\mathbf{r}n} H_{nm} \bar{V}_{\mathbf{r}'m} = \mathbf{S}_{n,m} v_n(\mathbf{r}) H_{nm} \bar{v}_m(\mathbf{r}') \\
&= \mathbf{S}_{n,m} v_n(\mathbf{r}) \int \bar{v}_n(\mathbf{r}'') H'' v_m(\mathbf{r}'') d\tau'' \cdot \bar{v}_m(\mathbf{r}') \\
&= \int \delta(\mathbf{r} - \mathbf{r}'') H'' \delta(\mathbf{r}'' - \mathbf{r}') d\tau'' \\
&= \int \delta(\mathbf{r} - \mathbf{r}'') H' \delta(\mathbf{r}'' - \mathbf{r}') d\tau'' \\
&= H' \int \delta(\mathbf{r} - \mathbf{r}'') \delta(\mathbf{r}'' - \mathbf{r}') d\tau'' \\
&= H' \delta(\mathbf{r} - \mathbf{r}') = H \delta(\mathbf{r} - \mathbf{r}') \tag{22.9}
\end{aligned}$$

The result embodied in (22.9) is the inverse of the definition (22.5). The latter takes a differential operator H and constructs from it a matrix representation, while the former transforms that matrix back into what is effectively the differential operator. However, we now see what was not so obvious from the form (22.2) for H: that a differential operator on the space coordinates can be expressed as a matrix in a representation in which the rows and columns are labeled by the position variables $\mathbf{r}$ and $\mathbf{r}'$. From this point of view, the solution of the Schrödinger differential wave equation (22.1) is equivalent to the diagonalization of the matrix

$$H_{\mathbf{rr}'} = H \delta(\mathbf{r} - \mathbf{r}')$$

just as we saw above that it is equivalent to the diagonalization of the matrix H_{nm}.

The **r** representation is one in which the coordinate **r** is diagonal: $(\mathbf{r})_{\mathbf{r}'\mathbf{r}''} = \mathbf{r}' \delta(\mathbf{r}' - \mathbf{r}'')$. It is worth pointing out explicitly that the Hamiltonian $H_{\mathbf{rr}'}$ in the **r** representation is not diagonal, even though the δ function makes it vanish when **r** differs from $\mathbf{r}'$ by a finite amount. This is because derivatives of the δ function appear, and these have nonvanishing matrix elements infinitesimally removed from the diagonal $\mathbf{r} = \mathbf{r}'$. For example, the matrix $f(\mathbf{r})\delta(\mathbf{r} - \mathbf{r}')$ is diagonal, but the matrix

$$(d/dx)\ \delta(\mathbf{r} - \mathbf{r}')$$

and the matrix $\nabla^2 \delta(\mathbf{r} - \mathbf{r}')$ are not.

A Useful Identity.   If Ω is an operator whose effect on a function $f(\mathbf{r})$ can be represented as

$$\Omega f(\mathbf{r}) = \int \Omega(\mathbf{r},\mathbf{r}')f(\mathbf{r}')d\tau'$$

then we can establish an identity that is sometimes useful:

$$\int \bar{g}(\mathbf{r})[\Omega f(\mathbf{r})]d\tau = \int \overline{[\Omega^* g(\mathbf{r})]}f(\mathbf{r})d\tau \qquad (22.10)$$

If we regard $\Omega(\mathbf{r},\mathbf{r}')$ as a matrix in the $\mathbf{r}$ representation, the Hermitian adjoint of Ω operating on $g(\mathbf{r})$ is

$$\Omega^* g(\mathbf{r}) = \int \overline{\Omega(\mathbf{r}',\mathbf{r})}g(\mathbf{r}')d\tau'$$

from which Eq. (22.10) follows at once.

This identity enables us to transfer operators from one factor of an integrand to another. The partial integrations in Eqs. (7.9), (7.10), and (12.3) are examples of the application of (22.10). In those cases, Ω is a differential operator, and its matrix representation involves derivatives and multiples of the δ function. However, Ω need not be of this specialized type [it might, for example, be an integral operator like the square bracket in Eq. (10.19)], and (22.10) is valid as well for operators that have nonvanishing matrix elements a finite distance from the diagonal.

23. EQUATIONS OF MOTION IN MATRIX FORM

In the preceding section we discussed the principal transformation properties of matrices that represent dynamical variables at a particular instant of time. We now find equations of motion for these variables by computing the time rate of change of their matrix representations. The resulting equations are very similar in form to the classical equations of motion and indicate a general procedure for quantizing any classical system.

Time Rate of Change of a Matrix.   We take as our starting point the time-dependent Schrödinger wave equation (6.16), expressed in terms of a Hamiltonian operator,

$$i\hbar \frac{\partial}{\partial t} \psi(\mathbf{r},t) = H\psi(\mathbf{r},t) \qquad (23.1)$$

where a typical H is that given by Eq. (22.2). A matrix representation for any function F of the dynamical variables can be found in terms of a complete orthonormal set of functions, each of which depends on the time in accordance with (23.1). We call any two of these functions ψ and ϕ, and calculate the time rate of change of a typical matrix element

$$\int \bar\phi F \psi d\tau = \iint \bar\phi(\mathbf{r},t) F(\mathbf{r},\mathbf{r}',t) \psi(\mathbf{r}',t) d\tau d\tau'$$

It is assumed that F is a general operator (not necessarily a differential or multiplicative operator) of the type considered in Eq. (22.10), which may depend explicitly on the time.

Differentiation with respect to t gives

$$\frac{d}{dt} \int \bar\phi F \psi d\tau = \iint \bar\phi(\mathbf{r},t) \left[\frac{\partial}{\partial t} F(\mathbf{r},\mathbf{r}',t) \right] \psi(\mathbf{r}',t) d\tau d\tau'$$
$$+ \iint \bar\phi(\mathbf{r},t) F(\mathbf{r},\mathbf{r}',t) \left[\frac{\partial}{\partial t} \psi(\mathbf{r}',t) \right] d\tau d\tau'$$
$$+ \iint \left[\frac{\partial}{\partial t} \bar\phi(\mathbf{r},t) \right] F(\mathbf{r},\mathbf{r}',t) \psi(\mathbf{r}',t) d\tau d\tau'$$
$$= \int \bar\phi \frac{\partial F}{\partial t} \psi d\tau + \frac{1}{i\hbar} \iint \bar\phi(\mathbf{r},t) F(\mathbf{r},\mathbf{r}',t)[H'\psi(\mathbf{r}',t)] d\tau d\tau'$$
$$- \frac{1}{i\hbar} \iint [H\bar\phi(\mathbf{r},t)] F(\mathbf{r},\mathbf{r}',t) \psi(\mathbf{r}',t) d\tau d\tau'$$

where the first term on the right side is the matrix element of the operator $\partial F/\partial t$, and substitution has been made from Eq. (23.1). We make use of the identity (22.10) to transfer the H (which is Hermitian) from $\bar\phi$ to $F\psi$ in the last term, and obtain the equation

$$\frac{d}{dt} \int \bar\phi F \psi d\tau = \int \bar\phi \frac{\partial F}{\partial t} \psi d\tau + \frac{1}{i\hbar} \int \bar\phi(FH - HF)\psi d\tau$$

This may be written as an equation for matrix elements, since the functions ψ and ϕ are quite arbitrary at any instant of time:

$$\frac{dF}{dt} = \frac{\partial F}{\partial t} + \frac{1}{i\hbar}(FH - HF) \tag{23.2}$$

The left side of (23.2) is the matrix whose elements are the time rate of change of the matrix elements of F, and may be called the total time derivative of the matrix of F. The first term on the right side is the matrix of the partial derivative of F with respect to t, and takes into account the explicit dependence of F on the time. The last term is that part of the time derivative of the F matrix that arises from the change in time of the functions with respect to which the matrix is calculated. Equation

(23.2) is Heisenberg's form of the equation of motion of a dynamical variable.

Classical Lagrangian and Hamiltonian Equations of Motion. In order to bring out the similarity between Eq. (23.2) and the corresponding classical equation, we review briefly the structure of classical Hamiltonian theory. The equations of motion of a conservative dynamical system that has f degrees of freedom may be derived from a *Lagrangian* function $L(q_1, \ldots, q_f, \dot{q}_1, \ldots, \dot{q}_f, t)$ of the coordinates q_i, the velocities $\dot{q}_i \equiv dq_i/dt$, and the time, by means of a variational principle:[1]

$$\delta \int_{t_1}^{t_2} L\, dt = 0, \qquad \delta q_i(t_1) = \delta q_i(t_2) = 0 \tag{23.3}$$

The resulting Lagrangian equations are

$$\frac{d}{dt}\left(\frac{\partial L}{\partial \dot{q}_i}\right) - \frac{\partial L}{\partial q_i} = 0, \qquad i = 1 \cdots f \tag{23.4}$$

If now we define a *momentum canonically conjugate* to q_i as $p_i \equiv \partial L/\partial \dot{q}_i$, and a *Hamiltonian* function of the coordinates and momenta as

$$H(q_1 \cdots q_f, p_1 \cdots p_f, t) = \sum_{i=1}^{f} p_i \dot{q}_i - L \tag{23.5}$$

variation of H leads to the Hamiltonian equations of motion

$$\dot{q}_i = \frac{\partial H}{\partial p_i}, \qquad \dot{p}_i = -\frac{\partial H}{\partial q_i}, \qquad i = 1 \cdots f \tag{23.6}$$

The time dependence of any function of the coordinates, momenta, and the time, calculated along a moving phase point, is

$$\frac{d}{dt} F(q_1 \cdots q_f, p_1 \cdots p_f, t) = \frac{\partial F}{\partial t} + \sum_{i=1}^{f}\left(\frac{\partial F}{\partial q_i}\dot{q}_i + \frac{\partial F}{\partial p_i}\dot{p}_i\right)$$

$$= \frac{\partial F}{\partial t} + \sum_{i=1}^{f}\left(\frac{\partial F}{\partial q_i}\frac{\partial H}{\partial p_i} - \frac{\partial H}{\partial q_i}\frac{\partial F}{\partial p_i}\right)$$

on making use of the Hamiltonian equations (23.6). The *Poisson bracket* $\{A,B\}$ of any two functions of the coordinates and momenta is defined as

$$\{A,B\} \equiv \sum_{i=1}^{f}\left(\frac{\partial A}{\partial q_i}\frac{\partial B}{\partial p_i} - \frac{\partial B}{\partial q_i}\frac{\partial A}{\partial p_i}\right) \tag{23.7}$$

[1] E. T. Whittaker, "Analytical Dynamics," 3d ed., Secs. 99, 109 (Cambridge, London, 1927); H. C. Corben and P. Stehle, "Classical Mechanics," Secs. 26, 63 (Wiley, New York, 1950); H. Goldstein, "Classical Mechanics," Chaps. 2, 7 (Addison-Wesley, Cambridge, Mass., 1950).

In terms of the Poisson bracket, the equation of motion for the function F of the dynamical variables becomes

$$\frac{dF}{dt} = \frac{\partial F}{\partial t} + \{F,H\} \tag{23.8}$$

The left side of Eq. (23.8) is the total time derivative of F along a moving phase point, the first term on the right side takes into account the explicit time dependence of F, and the last term shows the change in F due to the motion of the phase point at which F is evaluated. Thus there is a strong resemblance between Eqs. (23.2) and (23.8); the effect of the moving phase point in the latter corresponds to the effect in the former of the change with time of the functions that specify the matrix representation.

Poisson Brackets and Commutator Brackets. The resemblance between Eqs. (23.2) and (23.8) suggests that the quantum analogues of the classical equations of motion be found in general by substituting the *commutator bracket* divided by $i\hbar$ for the Poisson bracket:

$$\{A,B\} \to \frac{1}{i\hbar}[A,B] \equiv \frac{1}{i\hbar}(AB - BA) \tag{23.9}$$

There are two observations that lend support to this suggestion. The first concerns the classical conditions for a contact transformation from one set of canonical variables q_i,p_i to another Q_i,P_i:[1]

$$\{Q_i,P_j\} = \delta_{ij}, \qquad \{Q_i,Q_j\} = 0, \qquad \{P_i,P_j\} = 0 \tag{23.10}$$

where the Poisson brackets are calculated with respect to the original variables q_i,p_i. Now we saw in Sec. 6 that a successful transition from classical to quantum theory could be made by substituting the differential operator $-i\hbar(\partial/\partial x)$ for p_x, etc. The commutator of x and p_x can then be found by letting it operate on an arbitrary function $g(\mathbf{r})$ of the coordinates.

$$(xp_x - p_x x)g(\mathbf{r}) = -i\hbar x \frac{\partial g}{\partial x} + i\hbar \frac{\partial}{\partial x}(xg) = i\hbar g(\mathbf{r}) \tag{23.11}$$

Since $g(\mathbf{r})$ is arbitrary, this and the other commutators may be written as operator equations

$$xp_x - p_x x = -i\hbar \left(x\frac{\partial}{\partial x} - \frac{\partial}{\partial x}x \right) = i\hbar$$

$$xp_y - p_y x = -i\hbar \left(x\frac{\partial}{\partial y} - \frac{\partial}{\partial y}x \right) = 0$$

$$xy - yx = 0, \qquad p_x p_y - p_y p_x = 0, \qquad \text{etc.}$$

[1] Whittaker, *op. cit.*, pp. 300, 307; Corben and Stehle, *op. cit.*, Chaps. 11–13; Goldstein, *op cit.*, Chap. 8.

These are in agreement with the classical equations (23.10) when the substitution (23.9) is made.

The second observation is that the algebraic properties of the commutator brackets are identical with those of the Poisson brackets. It is readily verified from the definition (23.7) that

$$\{A,B\} = -\{B,A\}, \qquad \{A,c\} = 0, \quad \text{where } c \text{ is a number}$$
$$\{(A_1 + A_2), B\} = \{A_1,B\} + \{A_2,B\} \qquad\qquad (23.12)$$
$$\{A_1 A_2, B\} = \{A_1,B\}A_2 + A_1\{A_2,B\}$$
$$\{A,\{B,C\}\} + \{B,\{C,A\}\} + \{C,\{A,B\}\} = 0$$

The order of possibly noncommuting factors has not been altered. Dirac[1] has shown that the form of the quantum analogue of the Poisson bracket is determined by Eqs. (23.12) to be the right side of (23.9); the constant $\hbar$ is, of course, arbitrary so far as this discussion is concerned (see also Prob. 11).

Quantization of a Classical System. It is plausible on the basis of the preceding discussion to assume that any classical system can be taken over into quantum mechanics by finding the classical Hamiltonian function and equations of motion in terms of some set of canonical variables q_i, p_i, and replacing the Poisson brackets in (23.8) and (23.10) by commutator brackets in accordance with (23.9). The canonical variables are then found to obey the quantum conditions[2]

$$[q_i p_j] = i\hbar\delta_{ij}, \qquad [q_i,q_j] = 0, \qquad [p_i,p_j] = 0 \qquad (23.13)$$

This quantization technique will be found useful in connection with classical wave fields (Chap. XIII) as well as classical particles.

Two precautions are found necessary in applying this technique. First, the coordinates and momenta must be expressed in cartesian coordinates. And second, ambiguities in the order of noncommuting factors are usually resolved by taking a symmetric average of the various possible orders. These precautions are illustrated in the following example.

Motion of a Particle in an Electromagnetic Field. As an example of the foregoing quantization technique, we consider the problem of the motion of a charged mass point in a general external electromagnetic field. The classical Hamiltonian, expressed in terms of the canonical variables $\mathbf{r}, \mathbf{p}$ and the electromagnetic potentials $\mathbf{A}(\mathbf{r},t)$, $\phi(\mathbf{r},t)$, is[3]

$$H = \frac{1}{2m}\left(\mathbf{p} - \frac{e}{c}\mathbf{A}\right)^2 + e\phi \qquad (23.14)$$

---

[1] P. A. M. Dirac, "The Principles of Quantum Mechanics," 3d ed., Sec. 21 (Oxford, New York, 1947).

[2] Note that the derivation of Eq. (12.7) then shows that for any pair of canonical variables $\Delta q_i \cdot \Delta p_i \geq \frac{1}{2}\hbar$.

[3] J. H. Van Vleck, "The Theory of Electric and Magnetic Susceptibilities," pp. **7, 20** (Oxford, New York, 1932). Gaussian units are used in the present book.

where e is the charge on the particle and c is the speed of light; the electric and magnetic field strengths are given in terms of the potentials by

$$\mathbf{E} = -\frac{1}{c}\frac{\partial \mathbf{A}}{\partial t} - \text{grad } \phi, \qquad \mathbf{H} = \text{curl } \mathbf{A} \qquad (23.15)$$

The quantum conditions (23.13) in cartesian coordinates are

$$[x,p_x] = [y,p_y] = [z,p_z] = i\hbar \qquad (23.16)$$

with other pairs of coordinate and momentum components commuting. We now use Eq. (23.2), with the expression (23.14) for H and the relations (23.16), to calculate expressions for the particle velocity $d\mathbf{r}/dt$ and acceleration $d^2\mathbf{r}/dt^2$, for comparison with the corresponding classical expressions.

Evaluation of Commutator Brackets. In order to facilitate evaluation of some of the commutator brackets that arise from substitution into (23.2), we derive a few elementary results. Any two functions of $\mathbf{r}$ commute with each other, since all components of $\mathbf{r}$ commute with each other. It follows from (23.16) that

$$x^2 p_x - p_x x^2 = x(p_x x + i\hbar) - p_x x^2$$
$$= (p_x x + i\hbar)x + i\hbar x - p_x x^2 = 2i\hbar x$$

It is readily shown by induction that

$$x^n p_x - p_x x^n = ni\hbar x^{n-1} \qquad (23.17)$$

It follows from (23.17) that for any function $f(\mathbf{r})$ that can be expressed as a power series in x,y,z, the relation

$$[f(\mathbf{r}),p_x] = f(\mathbf{r})p_x - p_x f(\mathbf{r}) = i\hbar \frac{\partial}{\partial x} f(\mathbf{r}) \qquad (23.18)$$

is valid.[1] Equation (23.18) can also be established for more general functions than power series by making use of the representation of p_x as $-i\hbar(\partial/\partial x)$, as in (23.11); if we operate with the left side of (23.18) on an arbitrary function $g(\mathbf{r})$, we obtain

$$[f(\mathbf{r}),p_x]g(\mathbf{r}) = -i\hbar\left[f(\mathbf{r})\frac{\partial}{\partial x} - \frac{\partial}{\partial x}f(\mathbf{r})\right]g(\mathbf{r}) = g(\mathbf{r})\left[i\hbar\frac{\partial}{\partial x}f(\mathbf{r})\right]$$

which is equivalent to the operator equality (23.18) since $g(\mathbf{r})$ is arbitrary. By repeated application of (23.18) it is easily shown that

$$f(\mathbf{r})p_x^2 - p_x^2 f(\mathbf{r}) = i\hbar\left(p_x \frac{\partial f}{\partial x} + \frac{\partial f}{\partial x} p_x\right) = 2i\hbar \frac{\partial f}{\partial x} p_x + \hbar^2 \frac{\partial^2 f}{\partial x^2} \qquad (23.19)$$

---

[1] This corresponds to the classical relation $\{f(\mathbf{r}),p_x\} = \partial f(\mathbf{r})/\partial x$ [compare with Eq. (23.9)].

Velocity and Acceleration of a Charged Particle. The Hamiltonian (23.14) may now be written, with the help of (23.18),

$$H = \frac{\mathbf{p}^2}{2m} - \frac{e}{2mc}\,(\mathbf{p}\cdot\mathbf{A} + \mathbf{A}\cdot\mathbf{p}) + \frac{e^2}{2mc^2}\,\mathbf{A}^2 + e\phi$$

$$= \frac{\mathbf{p}^2}{2m} - \frac{e}{mc}\,\mathbf{A}\cdot\mathbf{p} + \frac{ie\hbar}{2mc}\,\text{div }\mathbf{A} + \frac{e^2}{2mc^2}\,\mathbf{A}^2 + e\phi \qquad (23.20)$$

The time derivative of a component of $\mathbf{r}$ is then easily shown from (23.2) to be

$$\frac{dx}{dt} = \frac{1}{m}\left(p_x - \frac{e}{c}\,A_x\right) \qquad (23.21)$$

in agreement with the classical relation between the velocity and momentum of a particle in the presence of an electromagnetic field.

The calculation of a component of the acceleration of the particle

$$\frac{d^2x}{dt^2} = \frac{1}{m}\left[\frac{dp_x}{dt} - \frac{e}{c}\frac{dA_x}{dt}\right]$$

$$= \frac{1}{i\hbar m}\,[p_x,H] - \frac{e}{mc}\frac{\partial A_x}{\partial t} - \frac{e}{i\hbar mc}\,[A_x,H]$$

is straightforward, but rather tedious. The result may be written

$$\frac{d^2x}{dt^2} = -\frac{e}{m}\left(\frac{1}{c}\frac{\partial A_x}{\partial t} + \frac{\partial \phi}{\partial x}\right) + \frac{e}{2m^2c}\left[\left(p_y - \frac{e}{c}A_y\right)\left(\frac{\partial A_y}{\partial x} - \frac{\partial A_x}{\partial y}\right)\right.$$

$$+ \left.\left(\frac{\partial A_y}{\partial x} - \frac{\partial A_x}{\partial y}\right)\left(p_y - \frac{e}{c}A_y\right)\right] - \frac{e}{2m^2c}\left[\left(p_z - \frac{e}{c}A_z\right)\left(\frac{\partial A_x}{\partial z} - \frac{\partial A_z}{\partial x}\right)\right.$$

$$+ \left.\left(\frac{\partial A_x}{\partial z} - \frac{\partial A_z}{\partial x}\right)\left(p_z - \frac{e}{c}A_z\right)\right] \qquad (23.22)$$

The Lorentz Force. Equation (23.22), with the similar y- and z-component equations, can be written as a single vector equation for the "force"

$$m\frac{d^2\mathbf{r}}{dt^2} = e\left(-\frac{1}{c}\frac{\partial \mathbf{A}}{\partial t} - \text{grad }\phi\right)$$

$$+ \tfrac{1}{2}\frac{e}{c}\left[\frac{1}{m}\left(\mathbf{p} - \frac{e}{c}\mathbf{A}\right)\times(\text{curl }\mathbf{A}) - (\text{curl }\mathbf{A})\times\frac{1}{m}\left(\mathbf{p} - \frac{e}{c}\mathbf{A}\right)\right]$$

$$= e\mathbf{E} + \tfrac{1}{2}\frac{e}{c}\left(\frac{d\mathbf{r}}{dt}\times\mathbf{H} - \mathbf{H}\times\frac{d\mathbf{r}}{dt}\right) \qquad (23.23)$$

where use has been made of Eqs. (23.15) and (23.21). Equation (23.23) is in agreement with the corresponding classical expression

$$e\mathbf{E} + \frac{e}{c}\,(\mathbf{v}\times\mathbf{H})$$

where $\mathbf{v} = d\mathbf{r}/dt$ is the velocity of the particle, if we take a symmetric average of the two terms $\mathbf{v} \times \mathbf{H}$ and $-\mathbf{H} \times \mathbf{v}$; these are identical classically but differ in quantum mechanics since the $\mathbf{v}$ given by (23.21) does not commute with $\mathbf{H}$.

Equation (23.23) includes a generalization of Ehrenfest's theorem, which was discussed in Sec. 7. If we consider a diagonal element, the left side is the product of the mass and the second time derivative of the expectation value of the position vector of the particle. The right side is the expectation value of the Lorentz force acting on the charge of the particle. Thus (23.23) states that a wave packet moves like a classical particle if it is sufficiently well localized so that the electromagnetic fields change by a negligible amount over its dimensions. This result can, of course, also be obtained by the method of Sec. 7 when, in accordance with (23.1) and (23.20), the Schrödinger wave equation is taken to be

$$i\hbar \frac{\partial \psi}{\partial t} = \left(-\frac{\hbar^2}{2m}\nabla^2 + \frac{ie\hbar}{mc}\mathbf{A}\cdot\mathbf{grad} + \frac{ie\hbar}{2mc}\operatorname{div}\mathbf{A} + \frac{e^2}{2mc^2}\mathbf{A}^2 + e\phi \right)\psi \quad (23.24)$$

Constants of the Motion. Equation (23.2) tells us that if F does not depend explicitly on the time (so that $\partial F/\partial t = 0$), then $dF/dt = 0$ if F commutes with H. In this case, F is said to be a *constant of the motion*. This is usually possible at all times only if H is also constant. If we substitute H for F in (23.2), we see that the constancy of H implies that $\partial H/\partial t = 0$, or that H does not involve the time explicitly. Thus if H is independent of t, a function F of the dynamical variables of the system is a constant if it does not depend on t and commutes with H.

An example of a constant of the motion is any one of the coordinates or momenta of the system whose canonically conjugate momentum or coordinate does not appear explicitly in H. Since the dynamical variable in question commutes with all other variables except its own canonical conjugate, then it commutes with H. Thus if the Hamiltonian for a number of interacting particles does not depend on the position coordinates of the center of mass of the system, the total momentum of the system is a constant of the motion. This is in agreement with the classical result that the total linear momentum of a system of interacting particles is constant if there are no external forces.

In similar fashion, we can make use of the third of Eqs. (14.20) to find the condition for constancy of the angular momentum of a particle. This equation states that the operator that represents the z component of angular momentum is $M_z = i\hbar(\partial/\partial\phi)$, where ϕ is the angular coordinate of rotation about the z axis. Thus, as with (23.11), we have the operator relation

$$\phi M_z - M_z\phi = i\hbar \quad (23.25)$$

and ϕ and M_z may be regarded as canonically conjugate variables. If then H does not depend on the angular coordinates of a particle [for example, if V in Eq. (22.2) depends only on the radial distance r from a fixed center], M_z is a constant of the motion; since there is nothing special about the choice of the z axis, M_x and M_y are also constants. This is in agreement with the classical result that the angular momentum of a particle moving in a central field of force is constant.

The Parity Operator.   Parity was first discussed in Sec. 9, and defined there and in Sec. 14 as the property of an energy eigenfunction that specifies whether it is even or odd with respect to changes of sign of all of the space coordinates. The parity operator P can be introduced in quantum mechanics, even though it has no classical analogue; it is defined as an operator that reflects all coordinates of all particles through the origin:

$$Pf(x_1,y_1,z_1,x_2,y_2,z_2, \ldots ,t)$$
$$= f(-x_1,-y_1,-z_1,-x_2,-y_2,-z_2, \ldots ,t) \quad (23.26)$$

It is evident from (23.26) that P^2 is the unit operator $\mathbf{1}$. Thus if P is diagonalized the square of each of its diagonal elements is unity, and its eigenvalues are ± 1.

If now H is left unchanged by reflection of all coordinates through the origin, P commutes with H and is a constant of the motion. Moreover, it follows from Sec. 21 that P and H can be made diagonal at once. Then the parity of an energy eigenfunction can be well defined (even or odd) and is constant in time.[1]

Energy Representation.   It was shown in Sec. 22 that the set of Schrödinger energy eigenfunctions $u_k(\mathbf{r})$ may be thought of as a unitary matrix that transforms the Hamiltonian operator from the r representation into the diagonal form

$$H_{kl} = E_k \delta_{kl} \text{ or } E_k \delta(k - l)$$

Although the discussion of Sec. 22 is valid for only one instant of time, it can be made valid for all time by using the time-dependent eigenfunctions $u_k(\mathbf{r})e^{-\frac{iE_kt}{\hbar}}$ for the transformation, provided that H is a constant. The matrix representation in which H is diagonal is called the *energy representation*.

---

[1] A particle can also possess an *intrinsic parity*, which is even or odd according as a plus or a minus sign appears in the equation $P\psi(\mathbf{r},t) = \pm\psi(-\mathbf{r},t)$. Note that this extends the range of operation of P to include the wave function itself, not just the space coordinates on which it depends.

The equation of motion (23.2) takes a particularly simple form in this representation, if F does not depend explicitly on the time:

$$\frac{dF_{kl}}{dt} = \frac{1}{i\hbar} (FH - HF)_{kl} = \frac{i}{\hbar} (E_k - E_l)F_{kl} \qquad (23.27)$$

Equation (23.27) can be integrated to give

$$F_{kl}(t) = F^0_{kl}e^{\frac{i(E_k - E_l)t}{\hbar}} \qquad (23.28)$$

where F^0_{kl} is the value of the matrix element at $t = 0$. Thus in the energy representation the off-diagonal matrix elements of any time-independent function of the dynamical variables oscillate in time with frequencies that are related to the energy differences between the stationary states by Bohr's frequency condition (see Sec. 2); the diagonal matrix elements are constant in time.

Virial Theorem. A proof of the virial theorem in quantum mechanics can be given in analogy with the corresponding proof in classical mechanics. In the latter, the starting point is the time average of the time derivative of the quantity $\mathbf{r} \cdot \mathbf{p}$, which is zero for a periodic system. The analogous quantity in quantum mechanics is the time derivative of the expectation value of $\mathbf{r} \cdot \mathbf{p}$, or the diagonal matrix element of the commutator of $\mathbf{r} \cdot \mathbf{p}$ and H in the energy representation, which is also zero.

$$\frac{d}{dt} \langle \mathbf{r} \cdot \mathbf{p} \rangle = \frac{1}{i\hbar} \langle [(\mathbf{r} \cdot \mathbf{p}), H] \rangle = 0$$

$$[(\mathbf{r} \cdot \mathbf{p}), H] = \left[(xp_x + yp_y + zp_z), \frac{p_x^2 + p_y^2 + p_z^2}{2m} + V(x,y,z) \right]$$

$$= \frac{i\hbar}{m} (p_x^2 + p_y^2 + p_z^2) - i\hbar \left(x \frac{\partial V}{\partial x} + y \frac{\partial V}{\partial y} + z \frac{\partial V}{\partial z} \right)$$

$$= 2i\hbar T - i\hbar(\mathbf{r} \cdot \mathbf{grad}\ V)$$

where T is the kinetic energy. We thus conclude that

$$2\langle T \rangle = \langle \mathbf{r} \cdot \mathbf{grad}\ V \rangle \qquad (23.29)$$

Note that it is immaterial whether we start with $\mathbf{r} \cdot \mathbf{p}$ or $\mathbf{p} \cdot \mathbf{r}$, since the difference between them is a constant, and hence commutes with H.

If V is spherically symmetric and proportional to r^n, and the expectation values exist, Eq. (23.29) shows that $2\langle T \rangle = n\langle V \rangle$. The case $n = -1$ is in agreement with the result of Prob. 13, Chap. IV, and the case $n = 2$ is in agreement with the results of Sec. 13.

Dirac's Bra and Ket Notation. A somewhat different notation for states and matrix elements is based on the concept of *bra* and *ket vectors*.[1] A ket vector, or ket, is analogous to the wave function for a state. The symbol $|\rangle$ denotes a group of kets, and the symbol $|m\rangle$ denotes the ket vector that corresponds to the state m of the system. The superposition of two states is represented by a linear combination of the corresponding kets. A bra vector, or bra, is analogous to the complex conjugate of the wave function for a state. The symbol $\langle|$ denotes a group of bras, and the symbol $\langle n|$ denotes the bra vector that corresponds to the state n of the system. The scalar product of a bra and a ket vector corresponds to the integral of the product of the complex conjugate of the wave function for one state and the wave function for another state, and is denoted by $\langle n|m\rangle$. A matrix element like that given in Eq. (22.5) is denoted by $\langle n|H|m\rangle$.

24. ANGULAR MOMENTUM

As an interesting and useful example of the direct treatment of dynamical variables by matrix methods, we now consider the properties of the angular-momentum operator. We work entirely with a representation at a particular instant of time, so that we are not concerned here with the change in time of the resulting angular-momentum matrices. However, if the angular momentum commutes with the Hamiltonian, it is a constant of the motion, and the matrices retain their form for all time. It was shown in Sec. 23 that this is the case if the Hamiltonian is spherically symmetric.

Definition of Angular Momentum. We define the angular momentum **M** of a particle about some point in terms of its displacement **r** from that point and its momentum **p** as in Eq. (14.19)

$$\mathbf{M} = \mathbf{r} \times \mathbf{p} \tag{24.1}$$

We do not now require that **p** be expressible as a differential operator, but rather that the components of **r** and **p** satisfy the commutation relations (23.16). It is then possible to find commutation relations between the components of **M**, that do not involve **r** and **p**.

$$
\begin{aligned}
[M_x, M_y] &= (yp_z - zp_y)(zp_x - xp_z) - (zp_x - xp_z)(yp_z - zp_y) \\
&= yp_x(p_z z - zp_z) + xp_y(zp_z - p_z z) = i\hbar(xp_y - yp_x)
\end{aligned}
$$

[1] Dirac, *op. cit.*, Secs. 5–8.

We thus obtain

$$[M_x, M_y] = i\hbar M_z, \qquad [M_y, M_z] = i\hbar M_x, \qquad [M_z, M_x] = i\hbar M_y \quad (24.2)$$

Equations (24.2) are seen to apply also to the total angular momentum of a system of particles, since the **r** and **p** operators for the individual particles commute with each other and so their angular momenta do also. Now it turns out that the relations (24.2) admit of some matrix representations for **M** that are not compatible with the original definition (24.1). When such a conflict arises, there is in some cases physical reason to regard (24.2) as being more fundamental than (24.1) (see the latter part of this section).

We note that the original definition (24.1) makes **M** Hermitian, since **r** and **p** are Hermitian. This is assumed to be true in general, since the components of **M** can be Hermitian without violating the commutation relations (24.2).

Definition in Terms of Infinitesimal Rotations. The angular momentum can also be defined in a way that permits of generalization to more complicated systems (many interacting particles, spin, fields). We suppose that the system is specified by a Hamiltonian H that is unaffected by rotations R of the coordinate system. For an arbitrary function f, we then have $RHf = HRf$, so that R commutes with H. Thus any rotation R is a constant of the motion, and its constancy is a direct consequence of the invariance of H with respect to rotations. From a physical point of view, the only dynamical variable whose constancy stems from the spherical symmetry of H is the angular momentum. We therefore expect that there is a relation between R and **M**.

Any rotation R can be built up by repeated application of rotations through very small angles about each of the three coordinate axes. The argument of the last paragraph then indicates that each component of **M** is related to an infinitesimal rotation about the corresponding axis. The effect of a rotation about the z axis through an infinitesimal angle ϕ on an arbitrary function f is

$$R_z(\phi)f(x,y,z) = f(x + \phi y,\ y - \phi x,\ z)$$

$$= f(x,y,z) + \phi y\,\frac{\partial f}{\partial x} - \phi x\,\frac{\partial f}{\partial y}$$

$$= \left[1 + \phi\left(y\,\frac{\partial}{\partial x} - x\,\frac{\partial}{\partial y}\right)\right]f(x,y,z)$$

Since f is arbitrary, we can write, with the help of Eq. (24.1),

$$R_z(\phi) = 1 + \frac{\phi}{i\hbar} M_z, \qquad \phi \text{ infinitesimal}$$

This relation is more fundamental than (24.1) and can be used to define $\mathbf{M}$ even when the $\mathbf{r}$ and $\mathbf{p}$ that appear in (24.1) do not exist.

Choice of a Representation. It is apparent from (24.2) that no two of the three components of $\mathbf{M}$ commute with each other, and so it is impossible to find a representation that diagonalizes more than one of them. However, all three components commute with

$$\mathbf{M}^2 = M_x^2 + M_y^2 + M_z^2$$

for example,

$$[M_z, \mathbf{M}^2] = M_z M_x^2 - M_x^2 M_z + M_z M_y^2 - M_y^2 M_z$$
$$= i\hbar(M_x M_y + M_y M_x) - i\hbar(M_y M_x + M_x M_y) = 0$$

Thus it is possible to diagonalize one component of $\mathbf{M}$, say M_z, and $\mathbf{M}^2$ at the same time; we use this to define our representation.

It is then convenient to work with M_z and the non-Hermitian matrix

$$L = M_x + iM_y \qquad (24.3)$$

from which it follows that

$$\mathbf{M}^2 = M_z^2 + \tfrac{1}{2}(LL^* + L^*L) \qquad (24.4)$$

The commutation relations involving L are found from (24.2) to be

$$[\mathbf{M}^2, L] = 0, \qquad [M_z, L] = \hbar L, \qquad [L, L^*] = 2\hbar M_z \qquad (24.5)$$

Our object is to find a representation in which M_z and $\mathbf{M}^2$ are diagonal. The rows and columns of this representation can be labeled by the eigenvalues of these two dynamical variables, and we wish to determine these eigenvalues along with the corresponding matrix for L. The matrices for M_x and M_y are then given by solving (24.3) and its Hermitian adjoint equation:

$$M_x = \tfrac{1}{2}(L^* + L), \qquad M_y = \tfrac{1}{2}i(L^* - L) \qquad (24.6)$$

Relations between Matrix Elements. We label the rows and columns of our representation with a pair of symbols m and j. The eigenvalues of M_z are $m\hbar$, so that m is a dimensionless real number; j is related to the eigenvalues of $\mathbf{M}^2$ in a way that is specified below [see Eq. (24.13)]. Then the first of Eqs. (24.5), written in matrix form, is

$$(\mathbf{M}^2 L)_{m'j', m''j''} - (L\mathbf{M}^2)_{m'j', m''j''} = 0$$

If we work out the matrix products and remember that $\mathbf{M}^2$ is diagonal, this becomes

$$[(\mathbf{M}^2)_{j'} - (\mathbf{M}^2)_{j''}]L_{m'j',m''j''} = 0 \qquad (24.7)$$

where $(\mathbf{M}^2)_{j'}$ is the eigenvalue of $\mathbf{M}^2$ that corresponds to j'. Equation (24.7) tells us that all matrix elements of L vanish except those for which $j' = j''$. Thus we can temporarily ignore j in specifying the L matrix, and remember when we finish that the matrix with which we come out is all for a particular value of j. This may be part of a larger matrix in which j can have various values, but there are no nonvanishing off-diagonal elements of L between the sections of the matrix that correspond to different values of j.

It is therefore sufficient for the present to use only the symbol m to designate rows and columns of L. The second of Eqs. (24.5) then gives

$$(M_z L)_{m',m''} - (LM_z)_{m',m''} = \hbar L_{m',m''}$$

or, since M_z is diagonal with eigenvalues $m\hbar$,

$$(m' - m'')\hbar L_{m',m''} = \hbar L_{m',m''} \qquad (24.8)$$

Thus the only nonvanishing matrix elements of L are those for which $m' = m'' + 1$, and we denote these by

$$L_{m+1,\, m} = \lambda_m \hbar \qquad (24.9)$$

so that λ_m is a dimensionless number that may be complex.

If now we take the mth diagonal element of the third of Eqs. (24.5), we obtain

$$\sum_{m'} (L_{m,m'}L^*_{m',m} - L^*_{m,m'}L_{m',m}) = 2\hbar^2 m$$

Each sum is seen to contain only one nonvanishing term, so that this equation becomes, with the help of (24.9),

$$|\lambda_{m-1}|^2 - |\lambda_m|^2 = 2m \qquad (24.10)$$

Eigenvalues of M_z. Equation (24.10) is a first-order linear difference equation in $|\lambda_m|^2$, and its general solution has one arbitrary constant

$$|\lambda_m|^2 = C - m(m+1) \qquad (24.11)$$

Now $|\lambda_m|^2$ is necessarily positive or zero, and yet the right side of (24.11) evidently attains negative values for sufficiently large positive and negative values of m. This does not cause difficulty if there are two values m_1 and m_2 of m for which $\lambda_m = 0$, and if these two values differ from each other by an integer.   If this is the case, the series of m values in which successive terms differ by unity can terminate at both ends without $|\lambda_m|^2$ becoming negative.   Equation (24.8) can be satisfied at the upper end ($m = m_1$) by having $L_{m_1+1,\ m_1} = 0$ rather than by having an M_z eigenvalue greater than m_1, and (24.8) can be satisfied at the lower end ($m = m_2$) by having $L_{m_2+1,\ m_2} = 0$ rather than by having an M_z eigenvalue less than $m_2 + 1$. $|\lambda_m|^2$ is evidently nonnegative for m values that range from $m_2 + 1$ to m_1, inclusive.

We thus have a finite series of eigenvalues of M_z ranging from m_1 down to $m_2 + 1$ by unit steps, where m_1 and m_2 are the larger and smaller roots of the quadratic equation $C - m(m + 1) = 0$:

$$m_1 = -\tfrac{1}{2} + \tfrac{1}{2}(1 + 4C)^{\frac{1}{2}}, \qquad m_2 = -\tfrac{1}{2} - \tfrac{1}{2}(1 + 4C)^{\frac{1}{2}}$$

We rename m_1 and call it j, in which case $C = j(j + 1)$, and the eigenvalues of M_z range from j to $-j$ by unit steps.   This implies that $2j$ is a positive integer or zero, or that j is restricted to the series of values 0, $\tfrac{1}{2}, 1, \tfrac{3}{2}, \ldots$.

Eigenvalues of M^2; the L Matrix.   Equation (24.11) can now be rewritten in terms of j

$$|\lambda_m|^2 = j(j + 1) - m(m + 1) = (j - m)(j + m + 1) \qquad (24.12)$$

The eigenvalues of M^2 can be found by calculating a diagonal element of (24.4):

$$(M^2)_{mj,mj} = \{m^2 + \tfrac{1}{2}[j(j + 1) - (m - 1)m + j(j + 1) - m(m + 1)]\}\hbar^2$$
$$= j(j + 1)\hbar^2 \qquad\qquad\qquad (24.13)$$

We thus have an infinite number of representations for the matrices M^2, M_z, and L, each of which is characterized by a zero or half-integer value for j and has $2j + 1$ rows and columns.   As expected, the eigenvalues of M^2 are all the same for a particular value of j.   All of these representations may be taken together to form a single representation of infinite rank, although it is often more convenient to consider them separately.

Equation (24.12) leaves the phase of the matrix elements of L arbitrary.   This corresponds to an arbitrariness in the choice of the phase of the angular-momentum eigenfunctions when they are normalized, and is not of physical significance.   We therefore choose all the phases to be zero, and obtain for the nonvanishing matrix elements of L

$$L_{(m+1)j,mj} = [(j - m)(j + m + 1)]^{\frac{1}{2}}\hbar \qquad (24.14)$$

For $j = 0$, M^2 and the components of M are all represented by null matrices of unit rank: (0).   The matrices for the next three values of j, as obtained from Eqs. (24.6), (24.13), and (24.14), are

$$j = \tfrac{1}{2} \qquad M_x = \tfrac{1}{2}\hbar \begin{pmatrix} 0 & 1 \\ 1 & 0 \end{pmatrix}, \qquad M_y = \tfrac{1}{2}\hbar \begin{pmatrix} 0 & -i \\ i & 0 \end{pmatrix}$$

$$M_z = \tfrac{1}{2}\hbar \begin{pmatrix} 1 & 0 \\ 0 & -1 \end{pmatrix}, \qquad \mathbf{M}^2 = \tfrac{3}{4}\hbar^2 \begin{pmatrix} 1 & 0 \\ 0 & 1 \end{pmatrix}$$

$$j = 1 \qquad M_x = \frac{\hbar}{\sqrt{2}} \begin{pmatrix} 0 & 1 & 0 \\ 1 & 0 & 1 \\ 0 & 1 & 0 \end{pmatrix}, \qquad M_y = \frac{\hbar}{\sqrt{2}} \begin{pmatrix} 0 & -i & 0 \\ i & 0 & -i \\ 0 & i & 0 \end{pmatrix}$$

$$M_z = \hbar \begin{pmatrix} 1 & 0 & 0 \\ 0 & 0 & 0 \\ 0 & 0 & -1 \end{pmatrix}, \qquad \mathbf{M}^2 = 2\hbar^2 \begin{pmatrix} 1 & 0 & 0 \\ 0 & 1 & 0 \\ 0 & 0 & 1 \end{pmatrix}$$

$$j = \tfrac{3}{2} \qquad M_x = \tfrac{1}{2}\hbar \begin{pmatrix} 0 & \sqrt{3} & 0 & 0 \\ \sqrt{3} & 0 & 2 & 0 \\ 0 & 2 & 0 & \sqrt{3} \\ 0 & 0 & \sqrt{3} & 0 \end{pmatrix} \qquad (24.15)$$

$$M_y = \tfrac{1}{2}\hbar \begin{pmatrix} 0 & -\sqrt{3}i & 0 & 0 \\ \sqrt{3}i & 0 & -2i & 0 \\ 0 & 2i & 0 & -\sqrt{3}i \\ 0 & 0 & \sqrt{3}i & 0 \end{pmatrix}$$

$$M_z = \tfrac{1}{2}\hbar \begin{pmatrix} 3 & 0 & 0 & 0 \\ 0 & 1 & 0 & 0 \\ 0 & 0 & -1 & 0 \\ 0 & 0 & 0 & -3 \end{pmatrix}, \qquad \mathbf{M}^2 = \tfrac{15}{4}\hbar^2 \begin{pmatrix} 1 & 0 & 0 & 0 \\ 0 & 1 & 0 & 0 \\ 0 & 0 & 1 & 0 \\ 0 & 0 & 0 & 1 \end{pmatrix}$$

Connection with the Spherical Harmonics. Comparison of the foregoing results with those of Sec. 14 suggests a close connection between the matrix representations of the angular momentum for which $j = l$ is an integer, and the spherical harmonics $Y_{lm}(\theta,\phi)$ defined in (14.6). A comparison of Eqs. (14.22) and (14.23) with the $\mathbf{M}^2$ and M_z matrices shows that the corresponding angular-momentum operators of Sec. 14 are simply another representation of the matrices considered in this section. This can also be shown for the L matrix by computing the effect of operation with L on a spherical harmonic. From (14.20) and (24.3), the L operator in polar coordinates is seen to be

$$L = \hbar e^{i\phi} \left(\frac{\partial}{\partial \theta} + i \cot \theta \frac{\partial}{\partial \phi} \right) \qquad (24.16)$$

It is then possible, by making use of the properties of the spherical harmonics discussed in Sec. 14, to show that

$$LY_{lm}(\theta,\phi) = \pm [(l - m)(l + m + 1)]^{\tfrac{1}{2}} \hbar Y_{l, m+1}(\theta,\phi) \qquad (24.17)$$

where the minus sign is for $m \geqq 0$ and the plus sign is for $m < 0$ (the calculation has a somewhat different structure for the two groups of m values). Thus if we set up a matrix to represent the operator L in analogy with Eq. (22.5), we get just the matrix (24.14) with integer j, except for change of some of the signs, which are arbitrary anyhow.

In similar fashion, we can show in analogy with Eqs. (22.7) and (22.8) that $Y_{lm}(\theta,\phi)$ can be regarded as a unitary matrix that transforms from a representation in which the rows and columns are each labeled by the angle variables θ,ϕ to one in which they are labeled by the quantum numbers l,m. The first representation is that which is implicit in the work of Sec. 14, and in which L would be represented as the result of operating with (24.16) on a suitably normalized δ function of the angles. The second representation is that developed in this section, in which L is given by (24.14) except for some sign changes.

Spin Angular Momentum.   It follows from the work of Sec. 14 and of this section that if all of the integer j representations are taken together to form a single representation of infinite rank, the **M** matrices can be expressed by (24.1) in terms of **r** and **p** matrices that satisfy the commutation relations (23.16). This is not true of the half-odd-integer j matrices, which are solutions of Eqs. (24.2) but not of the more restrictive Eqs. (24.1) and (23.16). Thus the matrices for the components of the orbital angular momentum of a particle or a system of particles must have eigenvalues that are integer multiples of $\hbar$, since they must be expressible in terms of coordinates and momenta.

There is nothing to prevent a particle from having an intrinsic angular momentum that is described by Eqs. (24.2) but cannot be expressed in terms of the position and momentum of the particle in accordance with (24.1). The eigenvalues of the components of such an angular momentum could be integers or half odd integers. Moreover, $\mathbf{M}^2$ could have a single eigenvalue corresponding to a single value of j, since $\mathbf{M}^2$ commutes with all three components of **M** and there is no reason why it should not also commute with **r** and **p** [since Eq. (24.1) is not valid in this case]. Thus $\mathbf{M}^2$ could commute with all the dynamical variables that describe the particle, and so could be a constant of the motion under all circumstances; there would then be no objection to equating $\mathbf{M}^2$ to a definite number $j(j+1)\hbar^2$. This is not possible for an orbital angular momentum, since in that case $\mathbf{M}^2$ does not commute with **r** and **p**, and hence is not always a constant.

An intrinsic angular momentum of the type described in the last paragraph is called a *spin angular momentum*. It is found experimentally that electrons, protons, neutrons, and probably also μ mesons each possess a spin angular momentum for which $j = \frac{1}{2}$ and the **M** matrices are given in (24.15) and that π mesons possess a spin angular momentum for which $j = 0$.[1]

Addition of Angular Momenta. It is sometimes of interest to consider the vector sum $\mathbf{M} = \mathbf{M}_1 + \mathbf{M}_2$ of two angular momenta $\mathbf{M}_1$ and $\mathbf{M}_2$ that commute with each other [all components of $\mathbf{M}_1$ commute with all components of $\mathbf{M}_2$, and $\mathbf{M}_1$ and $\mathbf{M}_2$ separately satisfy the commutation relations (24.2)]. These angular momenta could refer to independent particles, or to the spin and orbital angular momenta of the same particle. As pointed out near the beginning of this section, $\mathbf{M}$ obeys the same commutation relations (24.2) as do $\mathbf{M}_1$ and $\mathbf{M}_2$. A representation in which $\mathbf{M}_1^2$, $\mathbf{M}_2^2$, M_{1z}, and M_{2z} are diagonal is easily obtained from the foregoing theory. The rows and columns are labeled by j_1, j_2, m_1, and m_2; the matrices for $\mathbf{M}_1$, for example, have the form (24.15) so far as the indices j_1 and m_1 are concerned, and are unit matrices as regards the indices j_2 and m_2.

It is possible to find a second representation in which $\mathbf{M}_1^2$, $\mathbf{M}_2^2$, $\mathbf{M}^2$, and M_z are diagonal, for which the rows and columns are labeled by j_1, j_2, j, and m [$j(j + 1)\hbar^2$ is an eigenvalue of $\mathbf{M}^2$ and $m\hbar$ is an eigenvalue of M_z]. If j_1 and j_2 are fixed, the first representation has

$$(2j_1 + 1)(2j_2 + 1)$$

rows or columns, and can be specified by products of eigenfunctions of M_{1z} and of M_{2z}, just as the representation (22.6), in which the Hamiltonian is diagonal, is specified by eigenfunctions u_k of the operator H. The second representation, with the same fixed values of j_1 and j_2, must have the same number of rows, since it is specified by eigenfunctions of $\mathbf{M}^2$ and M_z that are linear combinations of the original eigenfunctions. We now find the values of j and m that appear in the second representation.

Eigenvalues of $(\mathbf{M}_1 + \mathbf{M}_2)^2$. Since $M_z = M_{1z} + M_{2z}$, it is apparent that the possible values of m are $m_1 + m_2$. The largest value of m is therefore $j_1 + j_2$, and this occurs only once, when $m_1 = j_1$ and $m_2 = j_2$. This shows that the largest value of j is $j_1 + j_2$, and that there is only one such state. The next largest value of m is $j_1 + j_2 - 1$, and this occurs twice: when $m_1 = j_1$ and $m_2 = j_2 - 1$, and when $m_1 = j_1 - 1$ and $m_2 = j_2$ (provided that neither j_1 nor j_2 is zero). One of the two linearly independent combinations of these two states must be associated with the new state for which $j = j_1 + j_2$, since for that j value there must be m values ranging from $j_1 + j_2$ to $-j_1 - j_2$ by integer steps. The other combination cannot be associated with this or a larger j, since the larger m values that should then also be present actually are not. Therefore the second combination is associated with $j = j_1 + j_2 - 1$. By an

[1] For a discussion of the properties of π and μ mesons, see R. E. Marshak, "Meson Physics," Chaps. 4, 6 (McGraw-Hill, New York, 1952).

extension of this argument we can see that each j value, from $j_1 + j_2$ down to $|j - j_2|$ by integer steps, appears just once, and that with each is associated $2j + 1$ linearly independent combinations of the original eigenfunctions. Thus the number of rows or columns of the second representation is

$$\sum_{j=|j_1-j_2|}^{j_1+j_2} (2j + 1) = (2j_1 + 1)(2j_2 + 1)$$

as expected.

The foregoing result is the same as the addition rule for angular momenta of the old quantum theory: the magnitude of the sum of two angular-momentum vectors can vary from the sum of their magnitudes (parallel case) to the difference of their magnitudes (antiparallel case) by integer steps.

The unitary matrix that transforms from the m_1, m_2 to the j, m representation for fixed values of j_1 and j_2 can be found by matrix methods. Since its structure is rather complicated it is not quoted here.[1]

Problems

1. Assume that any Hermitian matrix can be diagonalized by a unitary matrix. From this, show that the necessary and sufficient condition that two Hermitian matrices can be diagonalized by the same unitary transformation is that they commute.

2. Show that a nonsingular matrix of finite rank must be square.

3. Given two matrices A and B that satisfy the following equations:

$$A^2 = O, \qquad AA^* + A^*A = 1, \qquad B = A^*A$$

where O is the null matrix and 1 is the unit matrix. Show that $B^2 = B$. Find A and B in a representation in which B is diagonal, assuming that it is nondegenerate. Can A be diagonalized in any representation?

4. Given three matrices A, B, and C that satisfy the following equations:

$$A^2 = B^2 = C^2 = 1, \qquad AB + BA = BC + CB = CA + AC = O$$

where 1 is the unit matrix and O is the null matrix. Find all three matrices in a representation in which A is diagonal, assuming that it is nondegenerate.

5. Given three matrices A, B, and C that satisfy the following equations:

$$A^2 = B^2 = C^2 = 1, \qquad BC - CB = iA$$

where 1 is the unit matrix. Show that $AB + BA = AC + CA = O$, where O is the null matrix. Find all three matrices in a representation in which A is diagonal, assuming that it is nondegenerate.

[1] See E. U. Condon and G. H. Shortley, "The Theory of Atomic Spectra," Chap. III, Sec. 14 (Macmillan, New York, 1935); Chap. III also discusses other interesting properties of angular momentum. See also E. Feenberg and G. E. Pake, "Notes on the Quantum Theory of Angular Momentum" (Addison-Wesley, Cambridge, 1953).

6. Make use of the matrix expression (13.18) for x in a representation defined by the harmonic-oscillator wave functions to obtain a similar matrix for x^2, using purely matrix methods. Compare with the answer to Prob. 3, Chap. IV.

7. Use purely matrix methods to show that if $x_{nm} \neq 0$ for a harmonic oscillator, then $E_n - E_m = \pm \hbar (K/\mu)^{\frac{1}{2}}$. Note that for a harmonic oscillator, $H = p^2/2\mu + \frac{1}{2}Kx^2$, $xp - px = i\hbar$.

8. Show by purely matrix methods that if $H = \mathbf{p}^2/2\mu + V(\mathbf{r})$,

$$\sum_n (E_n - E_m)|x_{nm}|^2 = \frac{\hbar^2}{2\mu}$$

where the summation is over all states and x is a cartesian component of $\mathbf{r}$.

9. If $H = p^2/2\mu + V(x)$ for a one-dimensional particle, and $V(x)$ can be expressed as a power series in x, show by purely matrix methods that

$$\frac{dx}{dt} = \frac{p}{\mu}, \qquad \frac{dp}{dt} = -\frac{dV}{dx}$$

What is meant by the operator d/dt in this connection?

10. Transform the Hamiltonian for the harmonic oscillator expressed in the x representation

$$H = -\frac{\hbar^2}{2\mu}\frac{d^2}{dx^2} + \frac{1}{2}Kx^2$$

into the p representation. What are the solutions in the p representation that correspond to the x representation wave functions (13.13)?

11. $A(x,p)$ and $B(x,p)$ can be expressed as power series in x and p, and $[x,p] = i\hbar$. Show by purely matrix methods that

$$\lim_{\hbar \to 0} \frac{1}{i\hbar}[A,B] = \{A,B\}$$

12. Verify Eq. (24.17) by direct operation on the spherical harmonics with the L operator given in Eq. (24.16).

CHAPTER VII

APPROXIMATION METHODS FOR STATIONARY PROBLEMS

In quantum mechanics, as in classical mechanics, there are relatively few systems of physical interest for which the equations of motion are capable of exact solution. Approximation methods are expected to play an important part in virtually all applications of the theory. This enhances rather than diminishes the importance of those problems for which exact solutions can be found, since as was pointed out at the beginning of Chaps. IV and V, exact solutions are often useful as starting points for approximate calculations. In addition, they may also help to establish limits of validity for various approximation methods.

In this chapter and the next we develop several approximation methods and apply them to illustrative problems. It is convenient to divide the methods into two groups according as they deal with stationary states of systems that are represented by eigenfunctions of the energy (considered in this chapter), or with problems in which the Hamiltonian depends on the time (considered in Chap. VIII). In both cases we start with the Schrödinger wave equation, and only occasionally introduce matrix methods or notation.

25. STATIONARY PERTURBATION THEORY

The stationary perturbation theory[1] is concerned with finding the changes in the discrete energy levels and eigenfunctions of a system when a small disturbance is applied. It is assumed from the outset that the Hamiltonian H in the Schrödinger wave equation can be written as the sum of two parts. One of these parts H_0 is of sufficiently simple structure so that its Schrödinger equation can be solved, and the other part H' is small enough so that it can be regarded as a *perturbation* on H_0. It is convenient to retain our old symbols u_n and E_n for the supposedly known normalized eigenfunctions and eigenvalues of the *unperturbed* Hamiltonian H_0, and use ψ and W for the perturbed stationary wave function and energy level:

$$H\psi = W\psi, \qquad H = H_0 + H', \qquad H_0 u_n = E_n u_n \qquad (25.1)$$

Nondegenerate Case. The assumption that H' is small suggests that we expand the perturbed eigenfunction and eigenvalue as power series in

[1] E. Schrödinger, *Ann. d. Physik*, **80**, 437 (1926).

H'. This is most conveniently accomplished in terms of a parameter λ, such that the zero, first, etc., powers of λ correspond to the zero, first, etc., orders of the perturbation calculation. We replace H' by $\lambda H'$, and express ψ and W as power series in λ. We assume that these two series are analytic for λ between zero and one, although this has not been investigated except for a few simple problems.[1] The different orders of the perturbation approximation are then given by the coefficients of corresponding powers of λ. In the final results, λ is set equal to 1.

The perturbed wave function and energy level are written

$$\psi = \psi_0 + \lambda\psi_1 + \lambda^2\psi_2 + \lambda^3\psi_3 + \cdots$$
$$W = W_0 + \lambda W_1 + \lambda^2 W_2 + \lambda^3 W_3 + \cdots \qquad (25.2)$$

and are substituted into the wave equation to give

$$(H_0 + \lambda H')(\psi_0 + \lambda\psi_1 + \cdots)$$
$$= (W_0 + \lambda W_1 + \cdots)(\psi_0 + \lambda\psi_1 + \cdots) \qquad (25.3)$$

Since Eq. (25.3) is supposed to be valid for a continuous range of λ, we can equate the coefficients of equal powers of λ on both sides to obtain a series of equations that represent successively higher orders of the perturbation.

$$H_0\psi_0 = W_0\psi_0$$
$$H_0\psi_1 + H'\psi_0 = W_0\psi_1 + W_1\psi_0$$
$$H_0\psi_2 + H'\psi_1 = W_0\psi_2 + W_1\psi_1 + W_2\psi_0, \text{ etc.} \qquad (25.4)$$

The first of Eqs. (25.4) means that ψ_0 is any one of the unperturbed eigenfunctions, as expected. We therefore put

$$\psi_0 = u_m, \qquad W_0 = E_m \qquad (25.5)$$

This state u_m is assumed to be nondegenerate, although others of the unperturbed eigenfunctions may be degenerate. The case in which the unperturbed state ψ_0 is degenerate is considered later in this section.

First-order Perturbation. It is implicit in the present treatment that the unperturbed state u_m is one of a discrete set (even though the entire set of u's may be partly continuous), since otherwise no interest would attach to the calculation of the perturbed energy. In the next section we consider the perturbation of one of a continuous set of eigenfunctions, in connection with collision problems.

We expand ψ_1 in terms of the u_n

$$\psi_1 = Sa_n^{(1)}u_n \qquad (25.6)$$

[1] For a discussion of this point, see N. Arley and V. Borchsenius, *Acta Math.*, **76**, 261 (1945), especially Part IV.

where S denotes a summation over the discrete set together with an integration over the continuous set of eigenfunctions. Substitution of (25.6) into the second of Eqs. (25.4) gives

$$S a_n^{(1)} H_0 u_n + H' u_m = E_m S a_n^{(1)} u_n + W_1 u_m$$

We replace $H_0 u_n$ by $E_n u_n$ in the first term, multiply by $\bar{u}_k$, and integrate over all space, making use of the orthonormality of the u's:[1]

$$a_k^{(1)}(E_m - E_k) + W_1 \delta_{km} = \int \bar{u}_k H' u_m d\tau \equiv H'_{km} \qquad (25.7)$$

where the integral on the right is the km matrix element of the perturbation energy H' in the representation in which the unperturbed Hamiltonian H_0 is diagonal [see Eq. (22.5)].

If we take $k = m$ in Eq. (25.7), we see that

$$W_1 = H'_{mm} \qquad (25.8)$$

which is the expectation value of H' for the state m. Equation (25.7) also gives

$$a_k^{(1)} = \frac{H'_{km}}{E_m - E_k}, \qquad k \neq m \qquad (25.9)$$

We thus have a solution to first order in H', except that $a_m^{(1)}$ is still undetermined; it is obtained below from the normalization of ψ.

Second-order Perturbation. The solutions to second order in H' are found from the third of Eqs. (25.4) by substituting in

$$\psi_2 = S a_n^{(2)} u_n \qquad (25.10)$$

to give

$$S a_n^{(2)} H_0 u_n + H' S a_n^{(1)} u_n = E_m S a_n^{(2)} u_n + W_1 S a_n^{(1)} u_n + W_2 u_m$$

As before, we replace $H_0 u_n$ by $E_n u_n$ in the first term, multiply by $\bar{u}_k$ and integrate over all space to obtain

$$a_k^{(2)}(E_m - E_k) = S a_n^{(1)} H'_{kn} - W_1 a_k^{(1)} - W_2 \delta_{km} \qquad (25.11)$$

If now we set $k = m$, we see with the help of (25.8) that

$$W_2 = S' a_n^{(1)} H'_{mn} = S' \frac{H'_{mn} H'_{nm}}{E_m - E_n} = S' \frac{|H'_{mn}|^2}{E_m - E_n} \qquad (25.12)$$

where the prime on S denotes the omission of the term $n = m$ from the summation and integration over n. Similarly, if $k \neq m$ in Eq. (25.11),

---

[1] $\int \bar{u}_k u_n d\tau$ is equal to δ_{kn} if either k or n is one of a discrete set, and is equal to $\delta(k - n)$ if both belong to a continuous set; in either case, $S_n f_n \int \bar{u}_k u_n d\tau = f_k$ (see Sec. 10).

we obtain

$$a_k^{(2)} = S' \frac{H'_{kn}H'_{nm}}{(E_m - E_k)(E_m - E_n)} - \frac{H'_{km}H'_{mm}}{(E_m - E_k)^2}$$
$$+ \frac{a_m^{(1)}H'_{km}}{E_m - E_k}, \quad k \neq m \quad (25.13)$$

We thus have a solution to second order in H', except that $a_m^{(2)}$, like $a_m^{(1)}$, is not yet determined.

Normalization of ψ. Since ψ_0 is chosen to be equal to u_m, ψ is already normalized to zero order. If then the normalization integral $\int |\psi|^2 d\tau$ is set equal to unity for all orders of λ, when ψ is given by (25.2), we obtain

$$\int (\psi_0\bar\psi_1 + \bar\psi_0\psi_1)d\tau = 0 \quad \text{in first order}$$
$$\int (\psi_0\bar\psi_2 + \bar\psi_0\psi_2 + |\psi_1|^2)d\tau = 0 \quad \text{in second order}$$

These give at once

$$a_m^{(1)} + \bar a_m^{(1)} = 0, \qquad a_m^{(2)} + \bar a_m^{(2)} + S|a_n^{(1)}|^2 = 0$$

The real parts of $a_m^{(1)}$ and $a_m^{(2)}$ are fixed by these relations, but their imaginary parts are not. The choice of the imaginary parts of these coefficients is equivalent to the choice of a new phase for ψ in each order of the calculation; this in turn affects the phase of the next higher order term in ψ. There is no loss of generality involved in making the simple choice of zero for these imaginary parts, in which case

$$a_m^{(1)} = 0, \qquad a_m^{(2)} = -\tfrac12 S|a_n^{(1)}|^2$$

Note that the perturbed energies are independent of this choice.[1]

The energy and wave function to second order in H' are then (setting $\lambda = 1$)

$$W = E_m + H'_{mm} + S'_n \frac{|H'_{mn}|^2}{E_m - E_n}$$
$$\psi = u_m + S'_k \frac{H'_{km}u_k}{E_m - E_k} + S'_k \left\{ \left[S'_n \frac{H'_{kn}H'_{nm}}{(E_m - E_k)(E_m - E_n)} \right.\right.$$
$$\left.\left. - \frac{H'_{km}H'_{mm}}{(E_m - E_k)^2} \right] u_k - \tfrac12 \frac{|H'_{km}|^2}{(E_m - E_k)^2} u_m \right\} \quad (25.14)$$

It follows from Eqs. (25.8) and (25.12) that the calculation of W to a given order in H' requires knowledge of ψ only to the next lower order.

Perturbation of an Oscillator. As a simple example of the application of the first- and second-order perturbation theory to a nondegenerate state, we consider the perturbation of the mth energy level of the linear

[1] See also S. T. Epstein, *Am. J. Phys.*, **22**, 613 (1954).

harmonic oscillator of Sec. 13 by an additional energy $H' = \frac{1}{2}bx^2$. The unperturbed Hamiltonian is $H_0 = p^2/2\mu + \frac{1}{2}Kx^2$ (the mass is denoted by μ to avoid confusion with the quantum number m); the unperturbed eigenfunctions $u_m(x)$ given by Eq. (13.13) correspond to the eigenvalues $E_m = (m + \frac{1}{2})\hbar(K/\mu)^{\frac{1}{2}}$, where $m = 0, 1, 2, \ldots$. This example is evidently a trivial one since the perturbed eigenfunctions and eigenvalues are given simply by replacing K by $K + b$ in $u_m(x)$ and E_m; it is nevertheless instructive.

We require the matrix elements of x^2 between various pairs of harmonic-oscillator wave functions. These may be obtained with the help of the generating function (13.10) for the Hermite polynomials, as in Prob. 3 of Chap. IV, or more simply by matrix multiplication using the definition (21.3) and the expressions for x_{nm} given in Eq. (13.18). We readily obtain

$$(x^2)_{nm} = \sum_k x_{nk}x_{km} = \begin{cases} (2\alpha^2)^{-1}[(m+1)(m+2)]^{\frac{1}{2}}, & n = m+2 \\ (2\alpha^2)^{-1}(2m+1), & n = m \\ (2\alpha^2)^{-1}[m(m-1)]^{\frac{1}{2}}, & n = m-2 \\ 0, & \text{otherwise} \end{cases} \quad (25.15)$$

where $\alpha = (\mu K/\hbar^2)^{\frac{1}{4}}$. Substitution into the first of Eqs. (25.14) then gives for the energy to second order

$$W = (m + \tfrac{1}{2})\hbar \left(\frac{K}{\mu}\right)^{\frac{1}{2}} \left[1 + \frac{b}{2K} - \frac{b^2}{8K^2}\right]$$

in agreement with the expansion of $(m + \frac{1}{2})\hbar[(K + b)/\mu]^{\frac{1}{2}}$ to second order in b.

Degenerate Case. We now show that the foregoing treatment is incomplete when the unperturbed state m is degenerate. We suppose first that there is a state k that is degenerate with and orthogonal to the state m ($E_k = E_m$, $\int \bar{u}_k u_m d\tau = 0$). Then Eq. (25.7) tells us that $H'_{km} = 0$. Thus the first-order perturbation theory developed above is satisfactory only if H'_{km} actually is zero.

If now $H'_{km} = 0$ and we suppose in addition that $H'_{kk} = H'_{mm}$, Eq. (25.11) tells us that

$$\underset{n \neq k, m}{S} a_n^{(1)} H'_{kn} = \underset{n \neq k, m}{S} \frac{H'_{kn} H'_{nm}}{E_m - E_n} = 0$$

In this case the degeneracy between the states k and m is not removed in first order, since the first-order perturbed energies for the two states ($E_k + H'_{kk}$ and $E_m + H'_{mm}$) are equal. Then the second-order perturbation theory developed above is satisfactory in general only if there exist no states n that connect the states k and m through the perturbation; i.e., only if either or both of H'_{kn} and H'_{nm} are zero for all n.

We can summarize the situation by saying that the foregoing perturbation theory fails in first order if there is degeneracy of the unperturbed
state in zero order and the perturbation energy H' connects the degenerate
states in first order.   Similarly, the theory fails in second order if there is
degeneracy of the unperturbed state in first order and the perturbation
energy connects the degenerate states in second order (through one or
more other states).

Removal of Degeneracy in First Order.   Let us suppose that the
perturbation removes the degeneracy of the unperturbed state m in some
order.   This means that there are at least two exact eigenfunctions of the
Hamiltonian $H = H_0 + \lambda H'$ that have eigenvalues that are different
when $\lambda \neq 0$ and become equal when λ is made to vanish.   Now we
assumed earlier that the eigenfunctions are continuous analytic functions
of λ as $\lambda \to 0$; thus each of the eigenfunctions that are nondegenerate
when $\lambda \neq 0$, approaches a definite linear combination of the degenerate
unperturbed eigenfunctions when $\lambda = 0$.   If these linear combinations
are not the same as the unperturbed eigenfunctions on which the calculation is based, the expansions (25.2) are not valid for $\lambda = 0$, and the
method developed above breaks down.

It now becomes clear that we may treat degenerate unperturbed
states by perturbation theory, if we first perform an exact diagonalization
of as much of the perturbation matrix H'_{nl} as is necessary to remove the
degeneracy.   This is equivalent to finding the linear combinations of the
unperturbed eigenfunctions that fit on continuously to the exact perturbed eigenfunctions when λ is made different from zero.   For example,
suppose that only the unperturbed state k is degenerate with m, and
$H'_{km} = H'_{mk} \neq 0$.   In this case we need only diagonalize the submatrix

$$\begin{pmatrix} H'_{mm} & H'_{mk} \\ H'_{km} & H'_{kk} \end{pmatrix} \tag{25.16}$$

in order to remove the degeneracy (in this case it is removed in first
order) and find the correct linear combination of u_m and u_k that can be
used for higher order perturbation calculations.   An explicit example of
this type of situation is given below.

Removal of Degeneracy in Second Order.   It may, however, happen
that $H'_{km} = 0$ and $H'_{kk} = H'_{mm}$, so that the degeneracy is not removed in
first order.   A direct but unnecessarily complicated procedure then consists in diagonalizing the submatrix of the entire Hamiltonian that
includes the rows and columns labeled by all subscripts n for which either
H'_{mn} or H'_{kn} is different from zero.   Rows and columns of this matrix can
be rearranged to bring together any ones that are desired.   For example,
when there are two such subscripts n and l, we can diagonalize

$$\begin{pmatrix} E_m + H'_{mm} & 0 & H'_{mn} & H'_{ml} \\ 0 & E_m + H'_{mm} & H'_{kn} & H'_{kl} \\ H'_{nm} & H'_{nk} & E_n + H'_{nn} & H'_{nl} \\ H'_{lm} & H'_{lk} & H'_{ln} & E_l + H'_{ll} \end{pmatrix} \qquad (25.17)$$

to remove the degeneracy in second order.

A less direct but analytically simpler procedure consists in expanding the exact eigenfunctions in powers of λ as in (25.2), (25.6), and (25.10).[1] Because of the degeneracy, however, we now include both u_m and u_k in the zero-order term.

$$\psi_m = a_m u_m + a_k u_k + \mathbf{S}'(\lambda a_l^{(1)} + \lambda^2 a_l^{(2)}) u_l$$
$$\psi_k = b_m u_m + b_k u_k + \mathbf{S}'(\lambda b_l^{(1)} + \lambda^2 b_l^{(2)}) u_l$$
$$\psi_n = u_n + \mathbf{S}_{l \neq n}(\lambda a_{nl}^{(1)} + \lambda^2 a_{nl}^{(2)}) u_l, \qquad n \neq m,k$$

where the prime on $\mathbf{S}$ indicates that $l \neq m,k$. Substitution of the first of these into the wave equation $(H_0 + \lambda H')\psi_m = W_m \psi_m$, where

$$W_m = E_m + \lambda W_m^{(1)} + \lambda^2 W_m^{(2)},$$

gives to second order in λ

$$\lambda a_m H' u_m + \lambda a_k H' u_k + \mathbf{S}'(\lambda a_l^{(1)} E_l u_l + \lambda^2 a_l^{(2)} E_l u_l + \lambda^2 a_l^{(1)} H' u_l)$$
$$= (\lambda W_m^{(1)} + \lambda^2 W_m^{(2)})(a_m u_m + a_k u_k)$$
$$+ \mathbf{S}'(\lambda a_l^{(1)} E_m u_l + \lambda^2 a_l^{(2)} E_m u_l + \lambda^2 a_l^{(1)} W_m^{(1)} u_l) \qquad (25.18)$$

We now multiply (25.18) through on the left by $\bar{u}_m$ and integrate to obtain

$$\lambda a_m H'_{mm} + \mathbf{S}' \lambda^2 a_l^{(1)} H'_{ml} = \lambda W_m^{(1)} a_m + \lambda^2 W_m^{(2)} a_m \qquad (25.19)$$

since $H'_{mk} = 0$. Similarly, Eq. (25.18) can be multiplied by $\bar{u}_k$ and by $\bar{u}_n$ $(n \neq m,k)$, and integrated in each case to give

$$\lambda a_k H'_{kk} + \mathbf{S}' \lambda^2 a_l^{(1)} H'_{kl} = \lambda W_m^{(1)} a_k + \lambda^2 W_m^{(2)} a_k \qquad (25.20)$$

$$\lambda a_m H'_{nm} + \lambda a_k H'_{nk} + \lambda a_n^{(1)} E_n + \lambda^2 a_n^{(2)} E_n + \mathbf{S}' \lambda^2 a_l^{(1)} H'_{nl}$$
$$= \lambda a_n^{(1)} E_m + \lambda^2 a_n^{(2)} E_m + \lambda^2 a_n^{(2)} W_m^{(1)} \qquad (25.21)$$

The first-order terms in (25.19) and (25.20) give the expected result

$$W_m^{(1)} = H'_{mm} = H'_{kk}$$

[1] J. H. Van Vleck, *Phys. Rev.*, **33,** 467 (1929), Sec. 4.

The second-order terms give

$$\mathsf{S}'a_l^{(1)}H'_{ml} = W_m^{(2)}a_m$$
$$\mathsf{S}'a_l^{(1)}H'_{kl} = W_m^{(2)}a_k \tag{25.22}$$

The first-order terms in (25.21) give an expression for $a_l^{(1)}$, where $l = n \ne m,k$:

$$a_l^{(1)}(E_m - E_l) = a_m H'_{lm} + a_k H'_{lk} \tag{25.23}$$

Substitution of (25.23) into (25.22) gives a pair of homogeneous algebraic equations for a_m and a_k. These equations have a nonvanishing solution if and only if the determinant of the coefficients of a_m and a_k is zero [see the discussion of Eq. (21.19)]:

$$\begin{vmatrix} \mathsf{S}' \dfrac{H'_{ml}H'_{lm}}{E_m - E_l} - W_m^{(2)} & \mathsf{S}' \dfrac{H'_{ml}H'_{lk}}{E_m - E_l} \\[2mm] \mathsf{S}' \dfrac{H'_{kl}H'_{lm}}{E_m - E_l} & \mathsf{S}' \dfrac{H'_{kl}H'_{lk}}{E_m - E_l} - W_m^{(2)} \end{vmatrix} = 0 \tag{25.24}$$

The secular equation (25.24) is of second order in this case, while the similar equation resulting from (25.17) is of fourth order. It is apparent that this procedure always yields lower order secular equations than exact diagonalization.

Equation (25.24) would also have been obtained if we had started from the equation for ψ_k rather than ψ_m. The two roots of (25.24) are $W_m^{(2)}$ and $W_k^{(2)}$, and the two pairs of solutions of (25.22) are a_m, a_k and b_m, b_k. We thus obtain perturbed energy levels in which the degeneracy has been removed in second order, and also find the correct linear combinations of the unperturbed degenerate wave functions u_m and u_k.

First-order Stark Effect in Hydrogen. As an example, we now consider the first-order change in the energy levels of a hydrogen atom due to an external electric field of strength E directed along the positive z axis (*Stark effect*). H_0 is the unperturbed Hamiltonian for a hydrogen atom, which from (16.5) and (22.2) is

$$H_0 = -\frac{\hbar^2}{2\mu}\nabla^2 - \frac{e^2}{r}$$

where μ is the reduced mass (16.4). H' is the extra energy of the nucleus and electron due to the external field and is readily shown to be

$$H' = -e\mathsf{E}z = -e\mathsf{E}r\cos\theta \tag{25.25}$$

where the polar axis is in the direction of positive z.

The discussion of Sec. 14 showed that the wave functions for any spherically symmetric potential energy, when expressed in spherical harmonics, have even parity when the azimuthal quantum number l is even, and odd parity when l is odd. Now the perturbation (25.25) is an odd operator, since it changes sign when the coordinates are reflected through the origin. Thus the only matrix elements of H' that fail to vanish are those for unperturbed states that have opposite parities; in particular, all diagonal elements of H' for the unperturbed hydrogen-atom wave functions given in (16.24) are zero. This shows that a nondegenerate state, such as the ground state ($n = 1$) of hydrogen, has no first-order Stark effect.

The first excited state ($n = 2$) of hydrogen is fourfold degenerate; the quantum numbers l and m have the values (0,0), (1,0), (1,1), (1,−1). We now show quite generally that nonvanishing off-diagonal matrix elements of H' exist only for states that have the same quantum number m. It is apparent from (23.16) that z commutes with the z component of angular momentum $M_z = xp_y - yp_x$, so that $[M_z, H'] = 0$. The ks matrix element of this commutator in a representation in which M_z is diagonal is $(m_k - m_s)\hbar H'_{ks} = 0$, so that $H'_{ks} = 0$ unless $m_k = m_s$. Thus only the first two of the above four degenerate unperturbed states need be considered in calculating the first-order Stark effect of the first excited state of hydrogen.

Perturbed Energy Levels. The perturbation submatrix that has to be diagonalized is of the form (25.16), where $H'_{mm} = H'_{kk} = 0$, and

$$H'_{km} = -e\mathsf{E} \int \bar{u}_{210}(\mathbf{r}) r \cos \theta \, u_{200}(\mathbf{r}) \, d\tau$$

$$= -\frac{e\mathsf{E}}{16a_0{}^4} \int_0^\infty \int_{-1}^1 r^4 \left(2 - \frac{r}{a_0}\right) e^{-r/a_0} w^2 \, dw dr$$

$$= 3e\mathsf{E}a_0,$$

where $w = \cos \theta$, and use has been made of (16.24). We now wish to transform this two-row submatrix of H' from the representation in terms of u_{200} and u_{210} to a representation in which it is diagonal and has the eigenvalues W_1 and W_2.

We follow the notation of Eqs. (22.3) and (22.5). The wave functions are $v_1 = u_{200}$, $v_2 = u_{210}$ for the nondiagonal representation, and $\bar{S}_{11}v_1 + \bar{S}_{12}v_2$, $\bar{S}_{21}v_1 + \bar{S}_{22}v_2$ for the diagonal representation. Then in accordance with the discussion of Eq. (21.19), the eigenvalues of H' are the two roots of the determinantal or secular equation

$$\begin{vmatrix} H'_{11} - W_i & H'_{12} \\ H'_{12} & H'_{22} - W_i \end{vmatrix} = \begin{vmatrix} -W_i & 3e\mathsf{E}a_0 \\ 3e\mathsf{E}a_0 & -W_i \end{vmatrix} = 0, \qquad i = 1,2$$

These are easily found to be $W_1 = 3e\mathsf{E}a_0$, $W_2 = -3e\mathsf{E}a_0$. The transformation matrix S can be found by writing out the matrix equation

$$SH' = WS, \qquad W = \begin{pmatrix} W_1 & 0 \\ 0 & W_2 \end{pmatrix}$$

together with the unitary conditions on S. The result contains arbitrary phase factors, which may be chosen equal to zero, in which case

$$S = 2^{-\frac{1}{2}} \begin{pmatrix} 1 & 1 \\ 1 & -1 \end{pmatrix}$$

Thus two of the four degenerate states for $n = 2$ are unaffected by the electric field to first order, and the other two form linear combinations $2^{-\frac{1}{2}}(u_{200} + u_{210})$ with extra energy $3e\mathsf{E}a_0$ in the electric field, and

$$2^{-\frac{1}{2}}(u_{200} - u_{210})$$

with extra energy $-3e\mathsf{E}a_0$. This means that the hydrogen atom in this unperturbed state behaves as though it has a permanent electric-dipole moment of magnitude $3ea_0$, which can be oriented in three different ways: one state parallel to the external electric field, one state antiparallel to the field, and two states with zero component along the field.

Occurrence of Permanent Electric-dipole Moments. As remarked above, a permanent electric-dipole moment (energy change proportional to E) can appear in hydrogen only when the unperturbed state is degenerate, whereas an induced electric-dipole moment (energy change proportional to E^2) can appear in any state (see Probs. 1 and 12). We now show that the first conclusion is generally valid for any system that is described by a Hamiltonian that is unaffected by reflection of the coordinates of all particles through the origin. It follows from the discussion of Eq. (23.26) that a nondegenerate state of such a system has definite parity (even or odd). Then since the electric-dipole-moment operator is odd, its expectation value is zero. All the interactions between particles thus far encountered in physical theory lead to Hamiltonian functions that are unchanged by reflection. Since the ground states of all atoms and nuclei are very likely to be nondegenerate,[1] it is to be expected that an atom or a

---

[1] Apart from degeneracy due to the orientation of the total angular momentum of the system in space, which cannot give rise to an electric-dipole moment because all these degenerate states have the same parity, degeneracy either is associated with some special symmetry property of the system (such as the separability of the hydrogen-atom wave equation in spherical and parabolic coordinates) that is unlikely to occur for many-particle systems, or is accidental and hence very improbable on statistical

nucleus in its ground state will not possess a permanent electric-dipole moment, and none has ever been found experimentally. An extension of the foregoing argument leads to the expectation that an atom or a nucleus can possess electric charge, electric-quadrupole moment, magnetic-dipole moment, etc., but not magnetic pole, electric-dipole moment, magnetic-quadrupole moment, etc. (see also Prob. 21, Chap. XI).

26. THE BORN APPROXIMATION

In the preceding section we considered the perturbation of those energy eigenvalues, and the corresponding eigenfunctions, which are part of a discrete set. Here we are concerned with the perturbation of one of a continuous set of eigenfunctions. As in Chap. V, such eigenfunctions are of interest in connection with the theory of collisions. The object of the calculation is not to determine an energy eigenvalue, which in this case can be fixed in advance, but to find the perturbed eigenfunction and its relation to the scattering cross section. To simplify matters, we restrict our attention to those cases in which the entire potential energy of interaction between the colliding particles is regarded as a perturbation, and carry the calculation only to first order. As we shall see, this *Born approximation*[1] is best applied when the kinetic energy of the colliding particles is large in comparison with the interaction energy. It therefore supplements the method of partial waves (Sec. 19), which is most useful when the bombarding energy is small.

Perturbation Approximation. We wish to solve the wave equation for the relative motion, Eq. (18.8),

$$-\frac{\hbar^2}{2\mu}\nabla^2 u + V(\mathbf{r})u = Eu, \quad \mu = \frac{m_1 m_2}{m_1 + m_2} \tag{26.1}$$

and obtain an asymptotic form like that given by Eq. (18.10),

$$u(r,\theta,\phi) \xrightarrow[r\to\infty]{} e^{ikz} + r^{-1}f(\theta,\phi)e^{ikr}, \quad E = \frac{\hbar^2 k^2}{2\mu} \tag{26.2}$$

We adopt the perturbation approach of Sec. 25, and put

$$u(\mathbf{r}) = e^{ikz} + v(\mathbf{r}), \tag{26.3}$$

---

grounds. In some molecules, however, there is a group of nearly degenerate states between which matrix elements of the electric-dipole operator exist; if these energy levels are closely spaced in comparison with either the thermal energy of the molecule or the energy associated with the applied electric field, they give rise to a permanent electric-dipole moment [see J. H. Van Vleck, "The Theory of Electric and Magnetic Susceptibilities," p. 154 (footnote 28), Secs. 48, 70 (Oxford, New York, 1932)].

[1] M. Born, *Zeits. f. Physik*, **38**, 803 (1926).

where the scattered wave $v(\mathbf{r})$ is to be a small addition to the unperturbed plane wave solution e^{ikz}. The term $v(\mathbf{r})$ will be found only to first order in the scattering potential $V(\mathbf{r})$; the Born approximation becomes quite arduous when carried to higher orders.

Substitution of (26.3) into (26.1) gives

$$(-\nabla^2 - k^2)v = -U(\mathbf{r})e^{ikz} - U(\mathbf{r})v, \qquad U(\mathbf{r}) = \frac{2\mu}{\hbar^2} V(\mathbf{r}) \qquad (26.4)$$

Our assumption that $v(\mathbf{r})$ is small in comparison with e^{ikz}, or the roughly equivalent assumption that $U(\mathbf{r})$ is small in comparison with k^2, leads us to neglect the second term on the right side of Eq. (26.4). We therefore have to solve the inhomogeneous wave equation

$$(-\nabla^2 - k^2)v(\mathbf{r}) = -U(\mathbf{r})e^{ikz} \qquad (26.5)$$

where the right side is known. A sufficient criterion for the validity of our solution is

$$|v(\mathbf{r})| \ll |e^{ikz}| = 1, \qquad \text{for all } \mathbf{r} \qquad (26.6)$$

This condition, while always sufficient, is in some cases more stringent than is necessary for the Born approximation to provide useful results.

Green's Function. Rather than discuss Eq. (26.5) as a special case, we indicate a method of solution of the more general inhomogeneous partial differential equation

$$(\Omega - \omega_0)v(\mathbf{r}) = F(\mathbf{r}) \qquad (26.7)$$

Here Ω is a Hermitian operator that defines a complete orthonormal set of eigenfunctions $u_\omega(\mathbf{r})$ with real eigenvalues ω, and $F(\mathbf{r})$ is a known function of $\mathbf{r}$.

$$\begin{aligned}\Omega u_\omega(\mathbf{r}) &= \omega u_\omega(\mathbf{r}) \\ \int \bar{u}_{\omega'}(\mathbf{r})u_\omega(\mathbf{r})d\tau &= \delta(\omega - \omega') \\ \int \bar{u}_\omega(\mathbf{r})u_\omega(\mathbf{r}')d\omega &= \delta(\mathbf{r} - \mathbf{r}')\end{aligned} \qquad (26.8)$$

It is assumed for definiteness that the eigenvalues ω form a continuous set. Equation (26.7) can be solved by expanding $v(\mathbf{r})$ in terms of u_ω.

$$v(\mathbf{r}) = \int A_\omega u_\omega(\mathbf{r})d\omega \qquad (26.9)$$

Substitution into (26.7) gives

$$\int A_\omega(\omega - \omega_0)u_\omega(\mathbf{r})d\omega = F(\mathbf{r})$$

If we multiply this equation by $\bar{u}_{\omega'}(\mathbf{r})$ and integrate over $\mathbf{r}$, we obtain

$$A_{\omega'} = \frac{\int \bar{u}_{\omega'}(\mathbf{r})F(\mathbf{r})d\tau}{\omega' - \omega_0}$$

Thus the solution of (26.7) can be written

$$v(\mathbf{r}) = \int G_{\omega_0}(\mathbf{r},\mathbf{r}')F(\mathbf{r}')d\tau' \tag{26.10}$$

where the function

$$G_{\omega_0}(\mathbf{r},\mathbf{r}') = \int \frac{u_\omega(\mathbf{r})\bar{u}_\omega(\mathbf{r}')}{\omega - \omega_0}\, d\omega \tag{26.11}$$

is called the *Green's function* for the operator Ω and the number ω_0.[1]

Green's Function for a Free Particle. The Green's function (26.11) can be evaluated without great difficulty when the operator Ω is the Hamiltonian for a free particle. A suitably normalized eigenfunction of $-\nabla^2$ corresponding to the eigenvalue k'^2 is from (11.11)

$$u_{\mathbf{k}'}(\mathbf{r}) = (2\pi)^{-\frac{3}{2}} \exp i\mathbf{k}' \cdot \mathbf{r}$$

where $\mathbf{k}'$ is any vector of magnitude k'. Thus the Green's function is

$$G_k(\mathbf{r},\mathbf{r}') = (2\pi)^{-3} \int \frac{\exp(i\mathbf{k}' \cdot \mathbf{r}) \exp(-i\mathbf{k}' \cdot \mathbf{r}')}{k'^2 - k^2}\, d\tau_{k'} \tag{26.12}$$

We perform the $\mathbf{k}'$ integration in spherical polar coordinates with the polar axis in the direction of the vector $\varrho \equiv \mathbf{r} - \mathbf{r}'$.

$$\begin{aligned} G_k(\mathbf{r},\mathbf{r}') &= (2\pi)^{-3} \int_0^\infty \int_0^\pi \int_0^{2\pi} \frac{e^{ik'\rho \cos\theta}}{k'^2 - k^2} k'^2 dk' \sin\theta d\theta d\phi \\ &= (2\pi^2\rho)^{-1} \int_0^\infty \frac{\sin k'\rho}{k'^2 - k^2} k' dk' \\ &= (4\pi^2\rho)^{-1} \int_{-\infty}^\infty \frac{\kappa \sin\kappa}{\kappa^2 - \sigma^2}\, d\kappa \end{aligned} \tag{26.13}$$

where $\sigma \equiv k\rho = k|\mathbf{r} - \mathbf{r}'|$ is a positive number.

The singularities in the integrand of (26.13) at $\kappa = \pm\sigma$ can be discussed in terms of the corresponding singularity of the expansion coefficient A_ω in (26.9) at $\omega = \omega_0$. The behavior of A_ω at $\omega = \omega_0$ cannot be found from Eq. (26.7) alone, since to any solution $v(\mathbf{r})$ of the inhomogeneous equation can be added a solution $u_{\omega_0}(\mathbf{r})$ of the corresponding homogeneous equation. The addition that is to be made can be determined only from the boundary conditions that are imposed on $v(\mathbf{r})$. In similar fashion, the contribution to the integral in (26.13) from the infinitesimal neighborhood of the points $\kappa = \pm\sigma$ can be determined only from comparison of Eqs. (26.3) and (26.2), which shows that we want only those solutions $v(\mathbf{r})$ that have the asymptotic form $r^{-1}f(\theta,\phi)e^{ikr}$. From the relation (26.10) between $v(\mathbf{r})$ and $G_k(\mathbf{r},\mathbf{r}')$, we see that we must evaluate the integral in (26.13) so that it approaches $e^{i\sigma}$ when σ is large.

---

[1] For a fuller discussion of Green's functions, see P. M. Morse and H. Feshbach, "Methods of Theoretical Physics," Chap. 7 (McGraw-Hill, New York, 1953).

Explicit Evaluation. The contribution to this integral from the infinitesimal neighborhood of the points $\kappa = \pm\sigma$ can be adjusted by regarding it as a contour integral in the complex κ plane. The main path of integration is along the real axis, and we now show that the choice of the contour near the two singularities determines the dependence of the integral on σ.

Suppose that we choose the contour as shown in Fig. 21(a). The integral in (26.13) can be written

$$(2i)^{-1} \int \frac{\kappa e^{i\kappa}}{(\kappa - \sigma)(\kappa + \sigma)} \, d\kappa - (2i)^{-1} \int \frac{\kappa e^{-i\kappa}}{(\kappa - \sigma)(\kappa + \sigma)} \, d\kappa \qquad (26.14)$$

The first integral can be evaluated by closing the contour with an infinite

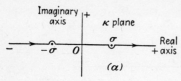

(a)

semicircle C in the positive imaginary half plane as in Fig. 21(b), since the exponential becomes vanishingly small there and contributes nothing to the integral. Then the value of the first integral is $2\pi i$ times the residue of the integrand at the only pole ($\kappa = \sigma$) that lies within the contour: $\pi i e^{i\sigma}$.

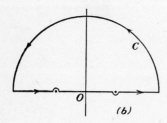

(b)

The second integral in (26.14) can be evaluated by closing the contour with an infinite semicircle C' in the negative imaginary half plane as in Fig 21c. It is equal to $-2\pi i$ times the residue at the only pole ($\kappa = -\sigma$) that lies within the contour: $-\pi i e^{i\sigma}$. Thus the entire expression (26.14) is equal to $\pi e^{i\sigma}$. It is not difficult to see that the choice of any contour other than that of Fig. 21(a) would have given a term $e^{-i\sigma}$ in addition to or in place of the term $e^{i\sigma}$. Such a term in G corresponds to an incoming wave in $v(\mathbf{r})$, and is ruled out because of the asymptotic form (26.2) of the desired solution.

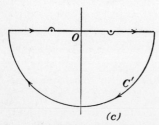

(c)

Fig. 21. Contours for the evaluation of the integral in Eq. (26.13).

Substitution into Eq. (26.13) shows that the Green's function for a free particle (represented by the operator $-\nabla^2$) is

$$G_k(\mathbf{r},\mathbf{r}') = (4\pi|\mathbf{r} - \mathbf{r}'|)^{-1} \exp ik|\mathbf{r} - \mathbf{r}'| \qquad (26.15)$$

Scattering Cross Section. From Eqs. (26.3), (26.5), (26.10), and (26.15) we obtain an approximate solution of the wave equation (26.1)

$$u(\mathbf{r}) = e^{ikz} - (4\pi)^{-1}\int|\mathbf{r} - \mathbf{r}'|^{-1}\,e^{ik|\mathbf{r}-\mathbf{r}'|}e^{ikz'}U(\mathbf{r}')d\tau' \qquad (26.16)$$

The second term in (26.16) has the form of a superposition of waves scattered from all points $\mathbf{r}'$ with amplitudes proportional to the product of the incident wave amplitude and the scattering potential at those points.

We assume that $U(\mathbf{r}')$ falls off rapidly enough for large r' so that there is an asymptotic region in which r is large in comparison with those values of r' for which there is a significant contribution to the integrand. We can then put

$$|\mathbf{r} - \mathbf{r}'| \xrightarrow[r\to\infty]{} r - wr', \qquad |\mathbf{r} - \mathbf{r}'|^{-1} \xrightarrow[r\to\infty]{} \frac{1}{r} + \frac{wr'}{r^2}$$

where w is the cosine of the angle between the vectors $\mathbf{r}$ and $\mathbf{r}'$. Thus the asymptotic form of (26.16) is

$$u(\mathbf{r}) \xrightarrow[r\to\infty]{} e^{ikz} - (4\pi r)^{-1}e^{ikr}\int U(\mathbf{r}')e^{ik(z'-wr')}d\tau' \qquad (26.17)$$

Comparison of (26.2) and (26.17) shows that the scattered amplitude is

$$\begin{aligned} f(\theta,\phi) &= -(4\pi)^{-1}\int U(\mathbf{r}')e^{ik(z'-wr')}d\tau' \\ &= -(4\pi)^{-1}\int U(\mathbf{r}')\,\exp i\mathbf{K}\cdot\mathbf{r}'d\tau' \end{aligned} \qquad (26.18)$$

Here we define a vector $\mathbf{K} = \mathbf{k}_0 - \mathbf{k}$, where $\mathbf{k}_0$ is the vector of magnitude k that has the direction of the incident beam (polar axis), and $\mathbf{k}$ is the vector of magnitude k that has the direction of the polar angles (θ,ϕ) of the point at which the scattered amplitude is measured. Figure 22 shows these three vectors; the magnitude of $\mathbf{K}$ is evidently $2k\sin\frac{1}{2}\theta$. Its physical significance is that $\hbar\mathbf{K}$ is the momentum transferred from the incident particle to the scattering potential during the collision. Thus if a Fourier integral analysis of the scattering potential into harmonic space waves is made, it is

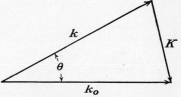

Fig. 22.   Relation between the propagation vectors $\mathbf{k}_0$ for the incident particle, $\mathbf{k}$ for the scattered particle, and the angle of scattering θ. The momentum transfer in the collision is $\hbar\mathbf{K}$, which has the magnitude $2\hbar k\sin\frac{1}{2}\theta$.

apparent from the second integral in (26.18) that the scattered amplitude in a particular direction is proportional to the Fourier component of the scattering potential that corresponds to the momentum change of the particle during the collision.

The differential scattering cross section is given by Eq. (18.11):

$$\sigma(\theta,\phi) = |f(\theta,\phi)|^2 \qquad (26.19)$$

In the event that $U(\mathbf{r}) = U(r)$ is spherically symmetric, the integrals over the polar angles of $\mathbf{r}'$ in (26.18) can be evaluated by taking the direction of $\mathbf{K}$ as the polar axis. Then

$$f(\theta) = -K^{-1} \int_0^\infty r' \sin Kr'\, U(r')dr' \qquad (26.20)$$

As expected, the scattered amplitude is independent of the angle ϕ. It is interesting to note from (26.19) and (26.20) that the amount of scattering depends on the bombarding speed v and the scattering angle θ only through the combination $K \propto v \sin \tfrac{1}{2}\theta$.

Perturbation Treatment of Partial Waves. When $U(r)$ is spherically symmetric, the wave equation (26.1) can be separated in spherical coordinates, as was done in Sec. 19, and solved approximately by a perturbation method. The radial wave equation for the lth partial wave is

$$\frac{1}{r^2} \frac{d}{dr}\left(r^2 \frac{dR_l}{dr}\right) + \left[k^2 - \frac{l(l+1)}{r^2} - U(r)\right] R_l = 0 \qquad (26.21)$$

As with Eq. (26.3), we put $R_l(r) = j_l(kr) + \chi_l(r)$, where $j_l(kr)$ given by Eq. (15.5) is the unperturbed solution. The approximate equation for χ_l is found from (26.21) to be

$$\frac{1}{r^2} \frac{d}{dr}\left(r^2 \frac{d\chi_l}{dr}\right) + \left[k^2 - \frac{l(l+1)}{r^2}\right] \chi_l = U(r)j_l(kr) \qquad (26.22)$$

where a term $U(r)\chi_l(r)$ has been neglected.

Like Eq. (26.5), Eq. (26.22) is an inhomogeneous differential equation of which the right side is known. The solution can be expressed in terms of a Green's function $G(r,r')$, in analogy with Eq. (26.10):

$$\chi_l(r) = \int_0^\infty G(r,r')U(r')j_l(kr')r'^2 dr' \qquad (26.23)$$

The requirements on $G(r,r')$ are that it be regular at $r = 0$, so that $\chi_l(r)$ will be regular there, and that it satisfy the equation

$$\frac{1}{r^2} \frac{d}{dr}\left[r^2 \frac{dG(r,r')}{dr}\right] + \left[k^2 - \frac{l(l+1)}{r^2}\right] G(r,r') = \frac{\delta(r-r')}{r'^2} \qquad (26.24)$$

Substitution of (26.23) into (26.22) then shows that the latter is satisfied.

In dealing with a total differential equation like (26.24), it is often less convenient to use the general form (26.11), which worked well in the three-dimensional case, than it is to proceed in the following way: We note that $G(r,r')$ is a solution of the free-particle radial equation [right side of (26.24) equal to zero] except at the point $r = r'$. If then $G(r,r')$ is a particular free-particle solution for $r < r'$ and another free-particle solution for $r > r'$, this requirement has been met. If in addition the two solutions have the same value but different slopes at $r = r'$, then the derivative of the discontinuous slope that arises from the left side of (26.24) will give a multiple of a δ function at $r = r'$. Since $G(r,r')$ must be regular at $r = 0$, the solution for $r < r'$ is taken to be $j_l(kr)$. It can be shown in this way that the form of the Green's function is

$$G(r,r') = kj_l(kr_<)n_l(kr_>) \tag{26.25}$$

where $r_<$ is the lesser of r and r', and $r_>$ is the greater of r and r'. It is apparent that this function is regular at $r = 0$ and satisfies Eq. (26.24) except perhaps at $r = r'$. In order to investigate the point $r = r'$, we substitute (26.25) into (26.24) and integrate both sides of the equation with respect to r over an infinitesimal region that contains the point r'. The right side is then $1/r'^2$, and the second term on the left side vanishes in the infinitesimal limit. The first term on the left side is

$$\lim_{\epsilon \to 0} \int_{r'-\epsilon}^{r'+\epsilon} \frac{1}{r^2} \frac{d}{dr}\left[r^2 \frac{dG(r,r')}{dr}\right] dr = \frac{1}{r'^2} \lim_{\epsilon \to 0}\left[r^2 \frac{dG(r,r')}{dr}\right]\Bigg|_{r'-\epsilon}^{r'+\epsilon}$$
$$= k^2[j_l(kr')n_l'(kr') - j_l'(kr')n_l(kr')]$$

From the last of Eqs. (15.9), the square bracket on the right side is equal to $(kr')^{-2}$. It follows then that $G(r,r')$ defined by (26.25) is actually the required Green's function.

Phase Shifts. Substitution of (26.25) into (26.23) gives

$$\chi_l(r) = k \int_0^\infty j_l(kr_<)n_l(kr_>)U(r')j_l(kr')r'^2dr'$$
$$\xrightarrow[r \to \infty]{} kn_l(kr) \int_0^\infty j_l^2(kr')U(r')r'^2dr' \tag{26.26}$$

Now the phase shift δ_l is defined in terms of the asymptotic form of $R_l(r)$ by Eq. (19.7)

$$R_l(r) \xrightarrow[r \to \infty]{} \text{constant } [j_l(kr) - \tan \delta_l n_l(kr)]$$

Comparison with the asymptotic form of $R_l(r) \cong j_l(kr) + \chi_l(r)$, obtained from (26.26), shows that

$$\tan \delta_l \cong -k \int_0^\infty j_l^2(kr')U(r')r'^2dr' \tag{26.27}$$

Equation (26.27) is the perturbation or Born approximation expression for the phase shifts. If all these δ_l are small, they can be substituted into Eq. (19.11) for $f(\theta)$ with the approximation $e^{2i\delta_l} - 1 \cong 2i\delta_l$, in which case

$$f(\theta) \cong k^{-1} \sum_{l=0}^\infty (2l + 1)\delta_l P_l(\cos \theta)$$
$$\cong -\int_0^\infty r^2 U(r)\left[\sum_{l=0}^\infty (2l + 1)j_l^2(kr)P_l(\cos \theta)\right] dr \tag{26.28}$$

The summation in brackets can be shown[1] to be equal to $\sin Kr/Kr$, where $K = 2k \sin \frac{1}{2}\theta$, so that (26.28) is equal to the Born approximation amplitude (26.20), as expected.

[1] G. N. Watson, "Theory of Bessel Functions," 2d ed., p. 366 (Macmillan, New York, 1945).

The foregoing perturbation treatment of partial waves is of practical interest since it has been found in some cases that substitution of the approximate phase shifts (26.27) into the exact expression (19.11) for the scattered amplitude results in an improvement on the Born approximation amplitude (26.20) when the δ_l are not all small in comparison with unity. In general, it is much easier to evaluate the integral in (26.27) than to find the phase shift exactly from a solution of the radial wave

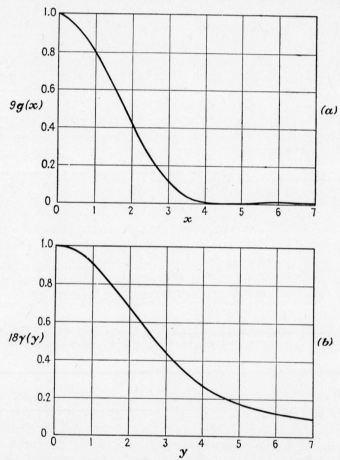

FIG. 23. (a) Angle distribution function for scattering by a square-well potential, as given by Eq. (26.29); (b) total cross section function given by Eq. (26.30).

equation. Also, the Born approximation amplitude (26.20) can be used as a device for summing the partial wave series for large l where the δ_l are small; changes can then be made in the low terms of the series.

Scattering by a Square Well Potential. As a first example of the application of the Born approximation result (26.20), we consider the scattering by a square well potential: $V(r) = -V_0$, $r < a$, $V(r) = 0$, $r > a$. Substitution into (26.20) gives

$$f(\theta) = \frac{2\mu V_0}{\hbar^2 K^3} (\sin Ka - Ka \cos Ka), \quad K = 2k \sin \tfrac{1}{2}\theta$$

Thus the differential scattering cross section is

$$\sigma(\theta) = \left(\frac{2\mu V_0 a^3}{\hbar^2}\right)^2 g(2ka \sin \tfrac{1}{2}\theta), \qquad g(x) \equiv \frac{(\sin x - x \cos x)^2}{x^6} \qquad (26.29)$$

The function $g(x)/g(0) = 9g(x)$ is plotted in Fig. 23a. At high energies ($ka \gg 1$), the scattering shows a strong maximum in the forward direction so that most of the scattered particles are in a cone whose angular opening is of order $1/ka$.

The total cross section is most easily evaluated by changing the variable of integration from θ to $x = Ka = 2ka \sin \tfrac{1}{2}\theta$, in which case $\sin \theta d\theta$ is replaced by $xdx/(ka)^2$. Equation (26.29) then gives

$$
\begin{aligned}
\sigma &= \left(\frac{2\mu V_0 a^3}{\hbar^2}\right)^2 \frac{2\pi}{(ka)^2} \int_0^{2ka} g(x)xdx \\
&= \frac{32\pi\mu^2 V_0^2 a^6}{\hbar^4} \gamma(2ka) \\
\gamma(y) &\equiv \frac{1}{y^2} \int_0^y \frac{(\sin x - x \cos x)^2}{x^5} dx \\
&= \frac{1}{4y^2}\left(1 - \frac{1}{y^2} + \frac{\sin 2y}{y^3} - \frac{\sin^2 y}{y^4}\right)
\end{aligned}
\qquad (26.30)
$$

Since $\gamma(0) = \tfrac{1}{18}$ and $\gamma(y)$ approaches $1/4y^2$ as y becomes large, the total cross section is $16\pi\mu^2 V_0^2 a^6/9\hbar^4$ in the limit $ka \ll 1$ and becomes

$$\frac{\pi\mu V_0^2 a^4}{\hbar^2 E}$$

when the bombarding energy E measured in the center-of-mass system is large. The function $\gamma(y)/\gamma(0) = 18\gamma(y)$ is plotted in Fig. 23b.

Validity of the Born Approximation. A convenient criterion for the validity of the Born approximation as applied to the foregoing problem can be set up by using Eq. (26.6) and assuming that $v(\mathbf{r})$ is largest at the center of the scattering potential. This condition is probably sufficient, but may be more stringent than is actually required; for example, the small-angle scattering (small momentum transfer) may be given correctly when the large-angle scattering is not. From (26.16), our criterion is that

$$|v(0)| = \frac{\mu}{\hbar^2} \left| \int_0^\infty \int_{-1}^1 e^{ikr(1+w)} V(r) r \, dr \, dw \right|$$

$$= \frac{\mu}{\hbar^2 k} \left| \int_0^\infty (e^{2ikr} - 1) V(r) \, dr \right|$$

$$= \frac{\mu V_0}{2\hbar^2 k^2} \left| e^{2ika} - 2ika - 1 \right|$$

$$= \frac{\mu V_0}{2\hbar^2 k^2} (y^2 - 2y \sin y + 2 - 2 \cos y)^{\frac{1}{2}} \ll 1, \quad y \equiv 2ka \quad (26.31)$$

In the low-energy limit ($ka \ll 1$), (26.31) becomes $\mu V_0 a^2 / \hbar^2 \ll 1$, while in the high-energy limit ($ka \gg 1$) it becomes

$$\frac{\mu V_0 a}{\hbar^2 k} = \frac{V_0 a}{\hbar v} \ll 1,$$

where v is the speed of the incident particle. If the square well potential is about "strong" enough to bind a particle (as shown in Sec. 15, this requires that $\mu V_0 a^2 / \hbar^2 \approx 1$), the Born approximation may therefore be used for the computation of the scattering only when $ka \gg 1$. Thus the Born approximation supplements the method of partial waves (Sec. 19), which is most useful when ka is less than or of order unity.

The qualitative features of the results obtained here and above for a square well potential apply to any potential that possesses a well-defined range.

Scattering by a Screened Coulomb Field. As a second example of the application of the Born approximation, we consider the elastic scattering of an electron by a neutral atom that is represented by a simple form of screened Coulomb potential: $V(r) = -(Ze^2/r)e^{-\frac{r}{a}}$. This potential energy behaves like the nuclear Coulomb potential for atomic number Z when r is small, and falls off rapidly when r is large in comparison with the "radius" a of the atomic electron cloud that screens the nucleus. The Thomas-Fermi statistical theory of the atom (see Sec. 38) shows that for moderately heavy atoms, a is roughly equal to $\hbar^2/me^2 Z^{\frac{1}{3}}$, where m is the electron mass.[1]

Substitution of this potential into (26.20) gives

$$f(\theta) = \frac{2mZe^2}{\hbar^2 K} \int_0^\infty \sin Kr \, e^{-\frac{r}{a}} dr = \frac{2mZe^2}{\hbar^2(K^2 + a^{-2})}, \quad K = 2k \sin \tfrac{1}{2}\theta \quad (26.32)$$

---

[1] For a discussion of the scattering by a Thomas-Fermi atom, see N. F. Mott and H. S. W. Massey, "The Theory of Atomic Collisions," 2d ed., Chap. IX, Sec. 4.1 (Oxford, New York, 1949).

This gives a cross section in agreement with the Rutherford result (20.11) when the momentum transfer is large enough so that $1/a^2$ can be neglected in comparison with K^2 in the denominator; in the analogous classical situation, the particle passes close to the nucleus, so that the screening electrons are relatively ineffective.   Equation (26.32), unlike the Rutherford result, yields a finite cross section at vanishingly small angles; the analogous classical particles pass far from the nucleus and are well screened from it by the atomic electrons.   The total cross section is

$$\sigma = \int_0^{2k} |f|^2 \frac{2\pi K dK}{k^2} = \frac{16\pi m^2 Z^2 e^4 a^4}{\hbar^4 (4k^2 a^2 + 1)}$$

With the above Thomas-Fermi expression for a, this becomes $4\pi Z^{\frac{4}{3}}/k^2$ at high energies ($ka \gg 1$), which agrees in order of magnitude with the result of a numerical integration[1] of the scattering produced by the Thomas-Fermi potential.

The criterion (26.31) for the validity of the Born approximation becomes

$$\frac{2mZe^2}{\hbar^2 k} \left| \int_0^\infty \sin x \, e^{ix - \frac{x}{ka}} \frac{dx}{x} \right| \ll 1$$

where x replaces kr as the variable of integration.   For $ka \ll 1$, this becomes $2mZe^2 a/\hbar^2 \ll 1$, which with the above approximate expression for a is equivalent to $Z^{\frac{2}{3}} \ll 1$; thus the Born approximation cannot be used for the scattering of slow electrons by atoms.   For $ka \gg 1$, the criterion becomes $(Ze^2/\hbar v) \ln ka \ll 1$.   Since it turns out that this result is substantially unaffected by relativity theory the approximation becomes poor for the heavier elements, where

$$\frac{Ze^2}{\hbar c} = \frac{Z}{137}$$

becomes comparable with unity.

It is interesting to note the close correspondence between the various results for the square well potential and for the screened Coulomb field when a is chosen the same in the two cases and $V_0 \approx Ze^2/a$.

27. THE VARIATION METHOD

The variation method was first used for the approximate determination of the lowest or ground-state energy level of a system and within the last several years has been applied to collision problems.   In the energy-level case, which we consider first, it can be used when there is no closely related problem that is capable of exact solution, so that the perturbation

---

[1] E. C. Bullard and H. S. W. Massey, *Proc. Camb. Phil. Soc.*, **26**, 556 (1930).

method is inapplicable. The variation method can also be applied to systems that are described by a nonseparable Schrödinger equation, in which case numerical solutions are extremely arduous and the WKB method (Sec. 28) cannot be used. The application to collision theory is taken up in the latter part of this section.

Expectation Value of the Energy. It was shown in Sec. 10 that if an arbitrary normalized function ψ is expanded in energy eigenfunctions

$$\psi = \sum_E A_E u_E, \quad \text{where} \quad H u_E = E u_E \quad (27.1)$$

and the u_E form a complete orthonormal set, then the expectation value of H for the function ψ is given by

$$\langle H \rangle = \int \bar{\psi} H \psi \, d\tau = \sum_E E |A_E|^2 \quad (27.2)$$

where the integration is extended over the entire range of all the coordinates of the system. It is assumed for convenience in Eqs. (27.1) and (27.2) that the energy eigenvalues are all discrete; this can be accomplished by enclosing the system in a box (Sec. 10), or else the summation can be replaced by the symbol S (Sec. 22).

A useful inequality can be derived from Eq. (27.2) by replacing each eigenvalue E in the summation on the right side by the lowest eigenvalue E_0:

$$\langle H \rangle \geqq \sum_E E_0 |A_E|^2 = E_0 \sum_E |A_E|^2 \quad (27.3)$$

Since $\sum_E |A_E|^2 = 1$ for a normalized function ψ, as was shown in Sec. 10, (27.3) yields the inequality

$$E_0 \leqq \int \bar{\psi} H \psi \, d\tau \quad (27.4)$$

In the event that ψ is not normalized, (27.4) evidently can be rewritten as

$$E_0 \leqq \frac{\int \bar{\psi} H \psi \, d\tau}{\int |\psi|^2 \, d\tau} \quad (27.5)$$

The variation method[1] consists in evaluating the integrals on the right side of (27.4) or (27.5) with a *trial function* ψ that depends on a number of parameters, and varying these parameters until the expectation value of the energy is a minimum. The result is an upper limit for the ground-state energy of the system, which is likely to be close if the

---

[1] The method was originally applied by Lord Rayleigh in 1873 to the computation of the vibration frequencies of mechanical systems—"Theory of Sound," 2d rev. ed., vol. 1, Sec. 88 (Macmillan, London, 1937; reprinted by Dover, New York). See also Morse and Feshbach, *op. cit.*, Sec. 9.4.

form of the trial function resembles that of the eigenfunction (see Prob. 9). Thus it is important to make use of any available information or physical intuition in choosing the trial function.[1]

Application to Excited States. The variation method can also be used to obtain an upper limit for one of the higher energy levels if the trial function is orthogonal to the eigenfunctions of all the lower states. Suppose that the energy levels are arranged in an ascending series: $E_0, E_1, E_2, \ldots$. Then if ψ is orthogonal to u_{E_i} for $i = 0, 1, \ldots, n$, it is easily seen from (27.1) that the corresponding expansion coefficients A_{E_i} are all zero. An inequality can be derived from (27.2) by replacing each eigenvalue E in the summation on the right by E_{n+1}, with the result that the expectation value of the energy is an upper limit on this eigenvalue.

The trial function $\psi - u_{E_0} \int \bar{u}_{E_0} \psi d\tau$ is evidently orthogonal to u_{E_0}, so that if the lowest eigenfunction is known either from an exact solution or to a sufficiently good approximation from a variation calculation, an upper limit for the energy of the first excited state can be computed. Trial functions that are orthogonal to any number of known eigenfunctions are easily found in this way.

It is sometimes possible to divide the energy eigenfunctions into groups such that any member of one group is orthogonal to any member of any other group. Suppose that there is a Hermitian operator F that commutes with H $(FH - HF = 0)$; then from a theorem of Sec. 21, F and H can be diagonalized simultaneously and have common eigenfunctions. Now any two eigenfunctions of F that correspond to different eigenvalues are orthogonal to each other.[2] Thus a trial function that is constructed entirely from eigenfunctions of F that correspond to a given eigenvalue is orthogonal to all other eigenfunctions that correspond to different eigenvalues of F, and will provide an upper limit for the lowest energy eigenvalue that is associated with this eigenvalue of F. The foregoing results are useful when the operator F is one whose eigenfunctions are easily recognizable by some simple property, such as, for example, the symmetry in case F is the angular momentum or the parity. Then a trial function with angular dependence corresponding to a particular angular momentum, or with a particular parity, can easily be written down, and gives an upper limit for the lowest energy level that has this angular momentum or parity.

---

[1] For an extension of this method that gives both upper and lower limits, see T. Kato, *Jour. Phys. Soc. Japan*, **4**, 334 (1949), and G. Temple, *Proc. Roy. Soc. (London)*, **A211**, 204 (1952).

[2] This is shown explicitly in Eq. (10.4) for the energy operator, and the proof given there is easily extended to any Hermitian operator.

Ground State of Helium. As a first example, we use the variation method with a simple trial function to obtain an upper limit for the energy of the ground state of the helium atom. The helium atom consists of a nucleus of charge $+2e$ surrounded by two electrons; from Eq. (16.1) we find that its Hamiltonian is (neglecting the motion of the nucleus)

$$H = -\frac{\hbar^2}{2m}\left(\nabla_1^2 + \nabla_2^2\right) - 2e^2\left(\frac{1}{r_1} + \frac{1}{r_2}\right) + \frac{e^2}{r_{12}} \qquad (27.6)$$

where $\mathbf{r}_1$ and $\mathbf{r}_2$ are the position vectors of the two electrons with respect to the nucleus as origin, and $r_{12} = |\mathbf{r}_1 - \mathbf{r}_2|$ is the distance between the two electrons.

If the interaction energy e^2/r_{12} between the two electrons were not present, the ground-state eigenfunction of H would be the product of two normalized hydrogenic wave functions $u_{100}(\mathbf{r}_1)u_{100}(\mathbf{r}_2)$ given in Eq. (16.24):

$$\psi(\mathbf{r}_1,\mathbf{r}_2) = \frac{Z^3}{\pi a_0^3}\,e^{-\left(\frac{Z}{a_0}\right)(r_1+r_2)} \qquad (27.7)$$

with $Z = 2$. We shall use (27.7) as a trial function, and permit Z to be the variation parameter so that it is not necessarily equal to 2.

It follows from Prob. 13, Chap. IV, that the expectation values of the kinetic and potential energies for the ground state of a hydrogen atom are $e^2/2a_0$ and $-e^2/a_0$, respectively; the corresponding hydrogen wave function is $(\pi a_0^3)^{-\frac{1}{2}} e^{-\frac{r}{a_0}}$. The expectation value of either of the kinetic energy operators in (27.6) for the function (27.7) is obtained most easily by noting that operation with the Laplacian gives a result that is inversely proportional to the square of the length scale of the wave function; since the scale of (27.7) is smaller than that of the hydrogen wave function by a factor of Z, the expectation value of each of the kinetic energy operators is $e^2Z^2/2a_0$. Similarly, the factors $1/r$ make the expectation values of the nuclear potential energy operators inversely proportional to the length scale; there is also an additional factor 2 from the nuclear charge, so that each one is $-2e^2Z/a_0$.

Electron Interaction Energy. The expectation value of the interaction energy between the electrons is

$$\iint \bar{\psi}(\mathbf{r}_1,\mathbf{r}_2)\frac{e^2}{r_{12}}\,\psi(\mathbf{r}_1,\mathbf{r}_2)d\tau_1 d\tau_2$$

$$= \left(\frac{Z^3}{\pi a_0^3}\right)^2 e^2 \iint \frac{1}{r_{12}}\,e^{-\left(\frac{2Z}{a_0}\right)(r_1+r_2)}d\tau_1 d\tau_2 \qquad (27.8)$$

This integral is most easily evaluated by regarding it as the mutual electrostatic energy of two overlapping, spherically symmetric, charge distributions, in which case simplifications from the theory of electrostatics can be introduced.

A more general way of performing the integration, which can also be used for wave functions that are not spherically symmetric, consists in expanding $1/r_{12}$ in spherical harmonics.

$$\frac{1}{r_{12}} = \frac{1}{r_1} \sum_{l=0}^{\infty} \left(\frac{r_2}{r_1}\right)^l P_l(\cos\theta), \qquad r_1 > r_2$$

$$= \frac{1}{r_2} \sum_{l=0}^{\infty} \left(\frac{r_1}{r_2}\right)^l P_l(\cos\theta), \qquad r_1 < r_2 \qquad (27.9)$$

where θ is the angle between $\mathbf{r}_1$ and $\mathbf{r}_2$, $\cos\theta = \cos\theta_1 \cos\theta_2 + \sin\theta_1 \cdot \sin\theta_2 \cos(\phi_1 - \phi_2)$, and θ_1, ϕ_1 and θ_2, ϕ_2 are the polar angles of the vectors $\mathbf{r}_1$ and $\mathbf{r}_2$, respectively.[1] It can be shown[2] that $P_l(\cos\theta) = P_l(\cos\theta_1)P_l(\cos\theta_2)$

$$+ 2 \sum_{m=1}^{l} \frac{(l-m)!}{(l+m)!} P_l^m(\cos\theta_1)P_l^m(\cos\theta_2)\cos m(\phi_1 - \phi_2) \qquad (27.10)$$

When (27.9) and (27.10) are substituted into (27.8) and use is made of the orthogonality of the spherical harmonics, the integration over the polar angles of $\mathbf{r}_1$ causes all terms to vanish except that for which l and m are zero. The integral on the right side of (27.8) becomes

$$(4\pi)^2 \int_0^{\infty} \left[\int_0^{r_1} \frac{1}{r_1} e^{-\frac{2Z}{a_0}(r_1+r_2)} r_2^2 dr_2 + \int_{r_1}^{\infty} \frac{1}{r_2} e^{-\frac{2Z}{a_0}(r_1+r_2)} r_2^2 dr_2 \right] r_1^2 dr_1$$

which can be evaluated as $5\pi^2 a_0^5/8Z^5$. Thus the electron interaction energy has the expectation value $5e^2Z/8a_0$.

Variation of the Parameter Z. We now have the result that the expectation value of the Hamiltonian (27.6) for the trial function (27.7) is

$$\langle H \rangle = \frac{e^2 Z^2}{a_0} - \frac{4e^2 Z}{a_0} + \frac{5e^2 Z}{8a_0} = \frac{e^2}{a_0}(Z^2 - \tfrac{27}{8}Z)$$

---

[1] Equations (27.9) follow at once from the generating function (14.10) for the Legendre polynomials; the expression for $\cos\theta$ is simply obtained from the scalar product of the vectors $\mathbf{r}_1$ and $\mathbf{r}_2$ in rectangular coordinates.

[2] E. T. Whittaker and G. N. Watson, "A Course of Modern Analysis," 4th ed., p. 328 (Cambridge, London, 1935).

Differentiation with respect to Z shows that this is a minimum when $Z = \frac{27}{16} = 1.69$. Thus the lowest upper limit for the ground-state energy of the helium atom obtainable with this trial function is

$$-(\tfrac{27}{16})^2 \frac{e^2}{a_0} = -2.85 \frac{e^2}{a_0}$$

The experimental value for the energy required to just remove both electrons from a helium atom is $2.904e^2/a_0$, so that our limit is about 1.9 per cent high. The most careful variation calculation of the ground-state energy of helium gives a result in excellent agreement with experiment,[1] and provides an important verification of the theory of quantum mechanics.

The result that hydrogenic wave functions give the best energy value when $Z = \frac{27}{16}$ rather than 2 indicates that each electron screens the

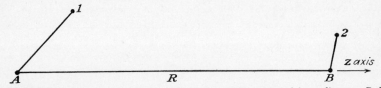

FIG. 24.   Two hydrogen atoms, with nuclei at A and B separated by a distance R, have electrons at 1 and 2; their interaction is given by H' in Eq. (27.11).

nucleus from the other electron, the effective nuclear charge being reduced by $\frac{5}{16}$ of an electronic charge.

If the electron interaction term e^2/r_{12} is regarded as a perturbation, the first-order perturbation energy is given by $\langle H \rangle$ with $Z = 2$ and is $-2.75e^2/a_0$, which is 5.3 per cent above the experimental value. It is apparent that, in general, the first-order perturbation calculation is equivalent to a nonoptimal variation calculation.

van der Waals Interaction.   As our second example of the application of the variation method, we calculate the van der Waals (long-range) interaction between two hydrogen atoms in their ground states. It is convenient to consider this problem first by means of the perturbation theory, since it is then easier to see that the leading term in the energy at great separation distances varies inversely as the sixth power of this distance. Also, it turns out that the perturbation theory and the variation method provide opposite limits for the coefficient of this term.

[1] E. A. Hylleraas, *Zeits. f. Physik*, **65**, 209 (1930).   J. Sucher and H. M. Foley, *Phys. Rev.*, **95**, 966 (1954), discuss a number of corrections and give references to more recent work.

We assume that the nuclei of the two hydrogen atoms, A and B, are fixed in space a distance R apart, and that the z axis is chosen parallel to the line through A and B. Then if $\mathbf{r}_1$ is the vector displacement of electron 1 from nucleus A and $\mathbf{r}_2$ is the vector displacement of electron 2 from nucleus B (see Fig. 24), the Hamiltonian for the two electrons can be written

$$H = H_0 + H'$$

$$H_0 = -\frac{\hbar^2}{2m}(\nabla_1^2 + \nabla_2^2) - \frac{e^2}{r_1} - \frac{e^2}{r_2}$$

$$H' = \frac{e^2}{R} + \frac{e^2}{r_{12}} - \frac{e^2}{r_{1B}} - \frac{e^2}{r_{2A}}$$

$$(27.11)$$

The unperturbed Hamiltonian H_0 has the solution

$$u_0(\mathbf{r}_1,\mathbf{r}_2) = u_{100}(\mathbf{r}_1)u_{100}(\mathbf{r}_2)$$

for two noninteracting hydrogen atoms in their ground states. We regard the interaction terms H' as a perturbation; this is equivalent to assuming that $R \gg a_0$.

Since we are interested in the leading term in the interaction energy when R is large, we expand H' in powers of $1/R$ and keep the lowest terms.

$$H' = \frac{e^2}{R}\left\{1 + \left[1 + \frac{2(z_2 - z_1)}{R} + \frac{(x_2 - x_1)^2 + (y_2 - y_1)^2 + (z_2 - z_1)^2}{R^2}\right]^{-\frac{1}{2}}\right.$$

$$\left. - \left(1 - \frac{2z_1}{R} + \frac{r_1^2}{R^2}\right)^{-\frac{1}{2}} - \left(1 + \frac{2z_2}{R} + \frac{r_2^2}{R^2}\right)^{-\frac{1}{2}}\right\}$$

$$\cong \frac{e^2}{R^3}(x_1 x_2 + y_1 y_2 - 2z_1 z_2) \qquad (27.12)$$

The last term is the interaction energy of two electric dipoles that correspond to the instantaneous configurations of the two atoms.[1]

It is apparent at once that the expectation value of the leading term in H' for the state $u_0(\mathbf{r}_1,\mathbf{r}_2)$ is zero, since u_0 is an even function of $\mathbf{r}_1$ and $\mathbf{r}_2$ and H' is an odd function of $\mathbf{r}_1$ and $\mathbf{r}_2$ separately. It can also be shown that all the neglected higher terms in H' have zero expectation value for u_0, since these terms can be expressed as spherical harmonics of order different from zero. Thus the leading term in the interaction energy is the second-order perturbation of the dipole-dipole term, which is proportional to H'^2 and hence varies like $1/R^6$.

---

[1] The neglected terms in the expansion (27.12) that vary like $1/R^4$ are the dipole-quadrupole interaction; the $1/R^5$ terms are the quadrupole-quadrupole interaction, etc.

Perturbation Calculation. From Eq. (25.12), the second-order change in the energy of the two hydrogen atoms is

$$W(R) = S' \frac{|H'_{0n}|^2}{E_0 - E_n} \qquad (27.13)$$

where the index n refers to all states of the pair of unperturbed hydrogen atoms (including dissociated states), and the ground state u_0 is excluded from the summation and integration that is denoted by S'. It is apparent that $W(R)$ is negative, since $E_0 < E_n$ and the numerator of each term in (27.13) is positive. We thus conclude that the interaction is attractive and proportional to $1/R^6$, when R is large; both these conclusions can be shown to be valid for any pair of atoms that are in nondegenerate, spherically symmetric ground states.

We can obtain an upper limit on the positive quantity $-W(R)$ by replacing each E_n in (27.13) by the energy E_{n*} of the lowest excited state of the two hydrogen atoms for which H'_{0n*} is different from zero. Then the denominator can be taken outside of the summation, which can be evaluated as a matrix product

$$S'|H'_{0n}|^2 = S' H'_{0n} H'_{n0} = S H'_{0n} H'_{n0} - H'^2_{00} = (H'^2)_{00} - H'^2_{00}$$

Since we have seen that $H'_{00} = 0$, we have that

$$-W(R) \leqq \frac{(H'^2)_{00}}{E_{n*} - E_0} \qquad (27.14)$$

The state $n*$ is that in which *both* atoms are excited to states of principal quantum number 2, so that $E_0 = -2(e^2/2a_0)$, $E_{n*} = -2(e^2/8a_0)$, and $E_{n*} - E_0 = 3e^2/4a_0$. From (27.12) we have

$$H'^2 = \frac{e^4}{R^6} (x_1^2 x_2^2 + y_1^2 y_2^2 + 4z_1^2 z_2^2 + 2x_1 x_2 y_1 y_2 - \cdots) \qquad (27.15)$$

The expectation value of the cross-product terms like $x_1 x_2 y_1 y_2$ is zero since these terms are odd functions of one of the cartesian components of $\mathbf{r}_1$ or $\mathbf{r}_2$. The first three terms in the parenthesis of (27.15) are each the product of two identical factors that are equal to

$$\int x^2 |u_{100}(\mathbf{r})|^2 d\tau = \tfrac{1}{3} \int r^2 |u_{100}(\mathbf{r})|^2 d\tau$$

$$= \frac{1}{3\pi a_0^3} \int_0^\infty r^2 e^{-\frac{2r}{a_0}} 4\pi r^2 dr = a_0^2$$

so that $(H'^2)_{00} = 6e^4a_0^4/R^6$. Substitution into (27.14) gives

$$W(R) \geqq - \frac{8e^2a_0^5}{R^6} \qquad (27.16)$$

Variation Calculation. An upper limit on $W(R)$ can always be obtained by the variation method. It is apparent, however, that some judgment must be used in the choice of the trial function ψ; thus if ψ does not depend on R, the dependence of the expectation value of the energy on R will be like that of H', that is, $1/R^3$. An upper limit with this R dependence is of no value to us, since what we really want to determine is a limit on the coefficient of the $1/R^6$ interaction. A useful choice for ψ will be one in which there is a term proportional to H', since there will then be terms in the expectation value that are proportional to H'^2 and hence vary like $1/R^6$.

We choose for the trial function

$$\psi(\mathbf{r}_1,\mathbf{r}_2) = u_{100}(\mathbf{r}_1)u_{100}(\mathbf{r}_2)(1 + AH')$$

where A is to be the variation parameter. Since this ψ is not normalized, we use (27.5) rather than (27.4) and obtain

$$E_0 + W(R) \leqq \frac{\iint u_0(1 + AH')(H_0 + H')u_0(1 + AH')d\tau_1 d\tau_2}{\iint u_0^2(1 + AH')^2 d\tau_1 d\tau_2} \qquad (27.17)$$

where again u_0 is the product of the ground-state hydrogen wave functions, and A is assumed to be real. The right side of (27.17) can be written

$$\frac{E_0 + 2A(H'^2)_{00} + A^2(H'H_0H')_{00}}{1 + A^2(H'^2)_{00}} \qquad (27.18)$$

since u_0 is a normalized eigenfunction of H_0 with the eigenvalue

$$E_0 = - \frac{e^2}{a_0},$$

and $H'_{00} = (H'^3)_{00} = 0$. It is easily seen that $(H'H_0H')_{00}$ is a sum of squares of factors of the form $\int u_{100}(\mathbf{r}) \, x \, H_0 \, x \, u_{100}(\mathbf{r})d\tau$; this can be shown by direct computation to be zero.

Since we are interested only in terms of order H'^2, we expand the denominator of (27.18):

$$[E_0 + 2A(H'^2)_{00}][1 + A^2(H'^2)_{00}]^{-1} \cong E_0 + (H'^2)_{00}(2A - E_0A^2) \qquad (27.19)$$

If we remember that E_0 is negative, we find that (27.19) has a minimum with respect to variation of A when $A = 1/E_0$, in which case (27.17) becomes

$$E_0 + W(R) \leqq E_0 + \frac{(H'^2)_{00}}{E_0} = E_0 - \frac{6e^2 a_0^5}{R^6} \qquad (27.20)$$

Thus in (27.16) and (27.20) we have both upper and lower limits on the interaction energy

$$-\frac{8e^2 a_0^5}{R^6} \leqq W(R) \leqq -\frac{6e^2 a_0^5}{R^6}$$

More careful variation calculations have shown that the numerical coefficient in $W(R)$ is very nearly 6.50.[1]

Integral Equation for Collision Problem.   The remainder of this section deals with the application of the variation method to collision theory. It is assumed that the scattering potential is spherically symmetric, so that a separation into partial waves can be made as in Sec. 19.[2]   The differential cross section can be calculated from Eq. (19.12) once the phase shifts δ_l are known.   These are defined by Eq. (19.7) in terms of the asymptotic form of the radial wave function

$$R_l(r) = j_l(kr) + \chi_l(r) \xrightarrow[r \to \infty]{} j_l(kr) - \tan \delta_l n_l(kr) \qquad (27.21)$$

Substitution into the radial wave equation (26.21) shows that χ_l satisfies the equation

$$\frac{1}{r^2} \frac{d}{dr} \left(r^2 \frac{d\chi_l}{dr} \right) + \left[k^2 - \frac{l(l+1)}{r^2} \right] \chi_l = U(r) R_l(r) \qquad (27.22)$$

exactly, unlike Eq. (26.22), which is only satisfied approximately for a potential that can be treated as a perturbation.   The solution in terms of a Green's function can still be used, however.   In analogy with Eq. (26.23), χ_l is given by

$$\chi_l(r) = \int_0^\infty G(r,r') U(r') R_l(r') r'^2 dr' \qquad (27.23)$$

where $G(r,r')$ is defined by Eq. (26.25).

[1] See L. Pauling and E. B. Wilson, Jr., "Introduction to Quantum Mechanics," Sec. 47a (McGraw-Hill, New York, 1935).

[2] L. Hulthén, *Dixième Congrès des Mathématiciens Scandinaves*, Copenhagen, p. 201 (1946), and earlier papers cited there; J. Schwinger, *Phys. Rev.*, **72**, 742 (1947), **78**, 135 (1950).   The present treatment is based on unpublished lectures of Schwinger (1947); see also F. Rohrlich and J. Eisenstein, *Phys. Rev.*, **75**, 705 (1949), and J. M. Blatt and J. D. Jackson, *Phys. Rev.*, **76**, 18 (1949).   For a discussion of the unseparated case and additional references, see E. Gerjuoy and D. S. Saxon, *Phys. Rev.*, **94**, 478 (1954). See also Morse and Feshbach, *op. cit.*, Sec. 9.4.

Substitution of (27.23) into (27.21) yields an integral equation for the radial wave function $R_l(r)$

$$R_l(r) = j_l(kr) + \int_0^\infty G(r,r')U(r')R_l(r')r'^2 dr' \qquad (27.24)$$

This equation is completely equivalent to the differential equation (26.21) but is more convenient to use as a starting point for a variation calculation. Comparison of the asymptotic form of (27.24) with (27.21) shows that the phase shift is given by

$$\tan \delta_l = -k \int_0^\infty j_l(kr')U(r')R_l(r')r'^2 dr' \qquad (27.25)$$

This equation is valid only if $R_l(r)$ is so normalized as to have the asymptotic form indicated in (27.21). Equation (27.25) is exact. It may be approximated by replacing $R_l(r)$ by $j_l(kr)$ in its right side, to obtain the Born approximation expression (26.27).

Variation Principle for the Phase Shift. It seems at first that Eq. (27.25) is not very useful, since the phase shift is expressed in terms of the radial wave function, which cannot be known unless the phase shift is also known. However, one might hope to improve upon the Born approximation by making a better guess as to the form of $R_l(r)$ than the simple choice $j_l(kr)$. In cases of practical interest, there is a rather well-defined region in which $U(r)$ is appreciably different from zero, so it would seem that R_l need be guessed only within this potential range. Unfortunately, Eq. (27.25) is correct only if R_l is properly normalized, in accordance with the asymptotic form of (27.21), so that in actuality R_l must be known asymptotically as well as within the potential. Further, (27.25) does not possess the stationary property of the right side of (27.4) or (27.5); these have minimum values for the correct eigenfunction, so that a first-order error in the trial function produces only a second-order error in the energy eigenvalue (see Prob. 9).

It would be desirable, then, to rewrite Eq. (27.25) so that it retains the property that R_l need be known only within the potential, but in such a way that the normalization of R_l is unimportant and that $\tan \delta_l$ is stationary with respect to variations of R_l. The first of these three objectives is accomplished if R_l always appears in an integrand multiplied by $U(r)$. The second objective is accomplished if $\tan \delta_l$ can be made a factor in an equation that is homogeneous in R_l. The only other equation available to help in the rewriting is (27.24). If now we multiply both sides of (27.25) by the integral on its right side, the left side is of first degree and the right side of second degree in R_l. The left side can then be made of second degree by substituting for $j_l(kr)$ from Eq. (27.24), after which a homogeneous equation is obtained.   The result is

$$\tan \delta_l \left[\int_0^\infty R_l^2(r) U(r) r^2 dr \right.$$

$$\left. - \int_0^\infty \int_0^\infty R_l(r) U(r) G(r,r') U(r') R_l(r') r^2 r'^2 dr dr' \right]$$

$$= -k \left[\int_0^\infty j_l(kr) U(r) R_l(r) r^2 dr \right]^2 \quad (27.26)$$

Equation (27.26) is an expression for the phase shift that requires knowledge of R_l only within the potential and in which the normalization of R_l does not enter.   The stationary property can now be investigated by making a small arbitrary variation of R_l from its correct form and seeing if the resulting first-order variation in $\tan \delta_l$ is zero.   Suppose that an arbitrary variation of R_l is applied to an integral $I = \int_0^\infty f(r) R_l(r) dr$.

The variation can be built up by combining independent variations at each point r, each of which can be represented by a Dirac δ function. This is equivalent to replacing $R_l(r)$ by $R_l(r) + \delta R_l(r_0) \delta(r - r_0)$, and changes I into $I + f(r_0) \delta R_l(r_0)$.   Thus, dropping the subscript,

$$\delta I = f(r) \delta R_l(r)$$

is the variation in I produced by a variation in R_l at the point r.

Application of this procedure to Eq. (27.26) yields

$$\delta (\tan \delta_l) \left[\int_0^\infty R_l^2(r) U(r) r^2 dr \right.$$

$$\left. - \int_0^\infty \int_0^\infty R_l(r) U(r) G(r,r') U(r') R_l(r') r^2 r'^2 dr dr' \right]$$

$$+ \tan \delta_l \left[2 R_l(r) U(r) r^2 \delta R_l(r) \right.$$

$$\left. - 2 U(r) r^2 \delta R_l(r) \int_0^\infty G(r,r') U(r') R_l(r') r'^2 dr' \right]$$

$$= -2 k j_l(kr) U(r) r^2 \delta R_l(r) \int_0^\infty j_l(kr') U(r') R_l(r') r'^2 dr'$$

The second square bracket on the left side may be rewritten with the help of (27.24) as

$$2 j_l(kr) U(r) r^2 \delta R_l(r)$$

and the right side becomes, after substitution from (27.25),

$$+2 \tan \delta_l j_l(kr) U(r) r^2 \delta R_l(r)$$

These two terms cancel, so that $\delta(\tan \delta_l) = 0$, and (27.26) possesses the stationary property.

Equation (27.26) can be rewritten with substitution of a trial function $u(r)$ for the correct wave function $R_l(r)$

$$k \cot \delta_l \cong \frac{\int_0^\infty \int_0^\infty u(r)U(r)G(r,r')U(r')u(r')r^2r'^2 dr dr' - \int_0^\infty u^2(r)U(r)r^2 dr}{\left[\int_0^\infty j_l(kr)U(r)u(r)r^2 dr\right]^2} \quad (27.27)$$

and provides a variation principle for calculation of the phase shift δ_l. While (27.27) is stationary for the correct wave function, it is in general neither a maximum nor a minimum, so that one cannot set a limit on the phase shift in this way.

Zero Angular Momentum. When $l = 0$, it is convenient to replace the trial function $u(r)$ by $v(r) = ru(r)$. The Green's function in this case is $G(r,r') = -(krr')^{-1} \sin kr_< \cos kr_>$. Equation (27.27) then becomes

$$k \cot \delta_0 \cong$$
$$-\frac{k^{-1}\int_0^\infty v(r)U(r)\left[\cos kr \int_0^r \sin kr' U(r')v(r') dr' + \sin kr \int_r^\infty \cos kr' U(r')v(r') dr'\right] dr + \int_0^\infty v^2(r)U(r) dr}{k^{-2}\left[\int_0^\infty \sin kr U(r)v(r) dr\right]^2} \quad (27.28)$$

As a simple example of the application of Eq. (27.28), we consider its limiting form when k becomes zero. The variation principle for the zero-energy phase shift is

$$(k \cot \delta_0)_0 \cong$$
$$-\frac{\int_0^\infty v(r)U(r)\left[\int_0^r r'U(r')v(r') dr' + r\int_r^\infty U(r')v(r') dr'\right] dr + \int_0^\infty v^2(r)U(r) dr}{\left[\int_0^\infty rU(r)v(r) dr\right]^2} \quad (27.29)$$

To test this expression, we consider a uniform potential of magnitude U and radius a (square well or square barrier), and assume the simple trial function $u(r) = $ constant or $v(r) = r$. We do not make explicit use of the stationary property of (27.29), since this would require that the form of $v(r)$ be varied; rather we use it implicitly in the sense that it increases our confidence in the reliability of the estimate that is obtained. The result is $(k \cot \delta_0)_0 = -[(3/Ua^3) + (6/5a)]$. For the same quantity, the Born approximation formula (26.27) gives $-(3/Ua^3)$. The exact result, obtained as in Sec. 19, is $-[(3/Ua^3) + (6/5a)] + $ higher order terms in Ua^2. Thus the Born approximation is correct for very weak scattering potentials, as expected, and the variation method in addition gives correctly the next term in an expansion in powers of the potential. A similar behavior is found when terms of order k^2a^2 are included (low incident energy; see Prob. 16).

28. THE WKB APPROXIMATION

In the development of quantum mechanics, the Bohr-Sommerfeld quantization rules of the old quantum theory (Sec. 2) occupy a position intermediate between classical and quantum mechanics. It is interesting that there is a method for the approximate treatment of the Schrödinger wave equation that shows its connection with the quantization rules. It is based on an expansion of the wave function in powers of $\hbar$, which, while of a semiconvergent or asymptotic character, is nevertheless also useful for the approximate solution of quantum-mechanical problems in appropriate cases. This method is called the *Wentzel-Kramers-Brillouin* or *WKB approximation*, although the general mathematical technique had been used earlier by Liouville, Rayleigh, and Jeffreys.[1] It is applicable to situations in which the wave equation can be separated into one or more total differential equations, each of which involves a single independent variable.

Classical Limit. A solution $\psi(\mathbf{r},t)$ of the Schrödinger wave equation (6.16)

$$i\hbar \frac{\partial \psi}{\partial t} = -\frac{\hbar^2}{2\mu} \nabla^2 \psi + V(\mathbf{r})\psi$$

can be written in the form

$$\psi(\mathbf{r},t) = A \exp \frac{iW(\mathbf{r},t)}{\hbar}$$

in which case W satisfies the equation

$$\frac{\partial W}{\partial t} + \frac{1}{2\mu} (\mathbf{grad}\ W)^2 + V - \frac{i\hbar}{2\mu} \nabla^2 W = 0 \qquad (28.1)$$

---

[1] It is sometimes called the *BWK method*, the *classical approximation*, or the *phase integral method*. For the original work, see J. Liouville, *J. de Math.*, **2**, 16, 418 (1837); Lord Rayleigh, *Proc. Roy. Soc.* **A86**, 207 (1912); H. Jeffreys, *Proc. London Math. Soc.* (2), **23**, 428 (1923); G. Wentzel, *Zeits. f. Physik.*, **38**, 518 (1926); H. A. Kramers, *Zeits. f. Physik.*, **39**, 828 (1926); L. Brillouin, *Comptes Rendus*, **183**, 24 (1926). For more recent developments, see E. C. Kemble, "The Fundamental Principles of Quantum Mechanics," Sec. 21 (McGraw-Hill, New York, 1937); R. E. Langer, *Phys. Rev.*, **51**, 669 (1937); W. H. Furry, *Phys. Rev.*, **71**, 360 (1947); S. C. Miller, Jr., and R. H. Good, Jr., *Phys. Rev.*, **91**, 174 (1953). The treatment of this section resembles most closely those of Kramers and Langer.

In the classical limit $(\hbar \to 0)$, Eq. (28.1) is the same as Hamilton's partial differential equation for the principal function W:[1]

$$\frac{\partial W}{\partial t} + H(\mathbf{r},\mathbf{p}) = 0, \qquad \mathbf{p} = \mathbf{grad}\ W$$

Since the momentum of the particle is the gradient of W, the possible trajectories are orthogonal to the surfaces of constant W and hence, in the classical limit, to the surfaces of constant phase of the wave function ψ. Thus in this limit the rays associated with ψ (orthogonal trajectories to the surfaces of constant phase) are the possible paths of the classical particle.

If ψ is an energy eigenfunction $u(\mathbf{r})e^{-\frac{iEt}{\hbar}}$, W can be written

$$W(\mathbf{r},t) = S(\mathbf{r}) - Et$$

In this case, we have that

$$u(\mathbf{r}) = A \exp \frac{iS(\mathbf{r})}{\hbar}, \qquad \frac{1}{2\mu}(\mathbf{grad}\ S)^2 - [E - V(\mathbf{r})] - \frac{i\hbar}{2\mu}\nabla^2 S = 0 \quad (28.2)$$

The WKB method obtains the first two terms (one term beyond the classical expression) of an expansion of S in powers of $\hbar$, in the one-dimensional case.

Approximate Solutions. The basic equation that we consider is written in one of the forms

$$\frac{d^2u}{dx^2} + k^2(x)u = 0, \qquad\qquad k^2 > 0 \qquad (28.3)$$

$$\frac{d^2u}{dx^2} - \kappa^2(x)u = 0, \qquad\qquad \kappa^2 > 0 \qquad (28.4)$$

so that k and κ are always real. These are equivalent to the one-dimensional wave equation (8.5), if we put

$$k(x) = +\frac{1}{\hbar}\{2\mu[E - V(x)]\}^{\frac{1}{2}} \quad \text{when } V(x) < E$$
$$\kappa(x) = +\frac{1}{\hbar}\{2\mu[V(x) - E]\}^{\frac{1}{2}} \quad \text{when } V(x) > E$$
$$(28.5)$$

---

[1] E. T. Whittaker, "Analytical Dynamics," 3d ed., Sec. 142 (Cambridge, London, 1927); H. Goldstein, "Classical Mechanics," Sec. 9-1 (Addison-Wesley, Cambridge, Mass., 1950).

Equations (28.3) and (28.4) are also equivalent to the radial wave equation (19.2) if x is replaced by r, $V(r)$ is replaced by

$$V(r) + \frac{\hbar^2 l(l+1)}{2\mu r^2},$$

and u is equal to r times the radial wave function.

We restrict our attention for the present to Eq. (28.3); we shall be able to generalize the resulting expression for $u(x)$ to obtain solutions of (28.4). We put

$$u(x) = A e^{\frac{iS(x)}{\hbar}}$$

which on substitution into (28.3) gives the one-dimensional form of (28.2)

$$i\hbar S'' - S'^2 + \hbar^2 k^2 = 0 \tag{28.6}$$

where primes denote differentiation with respect to x.

We substitute an expansion of S in powers of $\hbar$ into (28.6) and equate equal powers of $\hbar$.

$$S = S_0 + \hbar S_1 + \cdots$$
$$-S_0'^2 + 2\mu(E - V) = 0$$
$$iS_0'' - 2S_0'S_1' = 0, \text{ etc.}$$

Integration of these equations gives

$$S_0(x) = \pm\hbar \int^x k(x')dx', \qquad S_1(x) = \tfrac{1}{2}i \ln k(x),$$

where arbitrary constants of integration that can be absorbed in the coefficient A have been omitted. We thus obtain to this order of approximation

$$u(x) = Ak^{-\frac{1}{2}} \exp\left(\pm i \int^x k\,dx\right), \qquad V < E \tag{28.7}$$

In similar fashion, the approximate solution of (28.4) is

$$u(x) = B\kappa^{-\frac{1}{2}} \exp\left(\pm \int^x \kappa\,dx\right), \qquad V > E \tag{28.8}$$

Asymptotic Nature of the Solutions. The accuracy of these WKB solutions can be gauged by comparing the magnitudes of the successive terms S_0 and $\hbar S_1$ in the series for S. Since S_0 is a monotonic increasing function of x so long as k does not vanish, the ratio $\frac{\hbar S_1}{S_0}$ is small if $\frac{\hbar S_1'}{S_0'}$ is small. We thus expect (28.7) to be useful in that part of the domain of x where

$$\left|\frac{\hbar S_1'}{S_0'}\right| = \left|\frac{k'}{2k^2}\right| \ll 1 \tag{28.9}$$

Now the local de Broglie wave length λ is $2\pi/k$, so that (28.9) can be written

$$\frac{\lambda}{4\pi} \left| \frac{dk}{dx} \right| \ll k$$

which means that the fractional change in k (or in the wave length) in the distance $\lambda/4\pi$ is small compared to unity. Thus the WKB solutions are useful when the potential energy changes so slowly that the momentum of the particle is sensibly constant over many wave lengths.

The same criterion is obtained for (28.8) if we now mean by the "wave length" the distance in which the magnitude of u changes by a factor $e^{2\pi}$.

It is apparent that the condition (28.9) is violated near the turning points of the classical motion, where $V(x) = E$, k and κ are zero, and the "wave length" is infinite. Thus the solutions (28.7) and (28.8) are asymptotically valid in the sense that they can be used several wave lengths from the nearest turning point if, as is usually the case, the wave length is there slowly varying.

The asymptotic solutions are of little use to us unless we know how to connect an oscillating solution like (28.7) to an exponential solution like (28.8) across a turning point. It is only in this way, for example, that we can apply boundary conditions and obtain energy eigenvalues. The derivation of such *connection formulas*, which we consider next, is the central problem of the WKB approximation.

Solution near a Turning Point. The wave equations (28.3) and (28.4) are regular at a turning point, so that there is a solution that is analytic there and has asymptotic forms like (28.7) and (28.8). Such a solution usually cannot be written down in closed form. The wave equation can, however, be modified slightly so that an exact solution that has the desired asymptotic forms can be obtained.

We can without loss of generality take the origin of x at a particular turning point; we also assume for the moment that $V(x) < E$ to the right of the turning point (positive x), and put $\xi(x) \equiv \int_0^x k\,dx$. Now if $k^2(x) = Cx^n$, where C is a positive constant, Eq. (28.3) is known to have the solutions

$$u(x) = A\,\xi^{\frac{1}{2}}k^{-\frac{1}{2}}J_{\pm m}(\xi), \qquad m = \frac{1}{n+2} \qquad (28.10)$$

where J is a Bessel function; this can be verified by direct substitution. The asymptotic form of J is such (see below) that (28.10) agrees asymptotically with (28.7).

We therefore try to retain this form by rewriting (28.3) with an additional term $\theta(x)$:

$$\frac{d^2u}{dx^2} + (k^2 - \theta)u = 0 \tag{28.11}$$

Substitution of (28.10) into (28.11) shows that the new equation is satisfied if we define θ as

$$\theta(x) \equiv \frac{3k'^2}{4k^2} - \frac{k''}{2k} + (m^2 - \tfrac{1}{4}) \frac{k^2}{\xi^2} \tag{28.12}$$

We expand k^2 as a power series in x:

$$k^2(x) = Cx^n(1 + ax + bx^2 + \cdots)$$

in which case θ can also be expanded in a series. The $1/x^2$ and $1/x$ terms vanish, and the leading term is independent of x.

$$\theta(x) \xrightarrow[x \to 0]{} \frac{3(n+5)a^2}{2(n+4)(n+6)} - \frac{3b}{n+6} \tag{28.13}$$

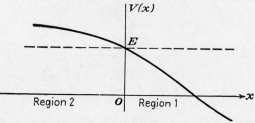

Fig. 25.   A typical linear turning point, where $V(x) = E$ at $x = 0$; in region 1, $E > V(x)$, and in region 2, $E < V(x)$.

We can now see that (28.11) is a good approximation to the actual wave equation (28.3). The similarity in structure between each of the three terms in (28.12) and the asymptotic accuracy criterion (28.9) indicates that $\theta \ll k^2$ in the asymptotic region if the WKB method can be used at all. At and near the turning point, θ is not negligible in comparison with k^2, since θ is a constant and k^2 vanishes at $x = 0$. However, (28.13) shows that $\theta(0)$ is quite small, being of second order in the deviation of k^2 from the simple form Cx^n. Thus for potential functions $V(x)$ that are slowly varying, (28.10) is expected to be a good approximation to the actual solution of equation (28.3).

Linear Turning Point. We now specialize to the situation of greatest physical interest, in which $n = 1$. A typical linear turning point is shown in Fig. 25; Eq. (28.3) is used in region 1 ($x > 0$), and Eq. (28.4) in region 2 ($x < 0$). We put $\xi_1 \equiv \int_0^x k\,dx$, $\xi_2 \equiv \int_x^0 \kappa\,dx$, so that both ξ_1 and ξ_2 increase as x moves away from the turning point; this makes it easy to generalize the results to situations in which the regions 1 and 2 are interchanged. The two independent solutions in each of the two regions are

$$u_1^{\pm}(x) = A_{\pm}\xi_1^{\frac{1}{2}}k^{-\frac{1}{2}}J_{\pm\frac{1}{3}}(\xi_1)$$
$$u_2^{\pm}(x) = B_{\pm}\xi_2^{\frac{1}{2}}\kappa^{-\frac{1}{2}}I_{\pm\frac{1}{3}}(\xi_2)$$

$$(28.14)$$

It is evident that we must replace J by I, the Bessel function of imaginary argument, in region 2.

We require the leading terms of the power series expansions and of the asymptotic expansions for these functions:[1]

$$J_{\pm\frac{1}{3}}(\xi_1) \xrightarrow[x\to 0]{} \frac{(\frac{1}{2}\xi_1)^{\pm\frac{1}{3}}}{\Gamma(1 \pm \frac{1}{3})}$$

$$\xrightarrow[x\to\infty]{} (\tfrac{1}{2}\pi\xi_1)^{-\frac{1}{2}}\cos\left(\xi_1 \mp \frac{\pi}{6} - \frac{\pi}{4}\right)$$

$$(28.15)$$

$$I_{\pm\frac{1}{3}}(\xi_2) \xrightarrow[x\to 0]{} \frac{(\frac{1}{2}\xi_2)^{\pm\frac{1}{3}}}{\Gamma(1 \pm \frac{1}{3})}$$

$$\xrightarrow[x\to\infty]{} (2\pi\xi_2)^{-\frac{1}{2}}[e^{\xi_2} + e^{-\xi_2} \cdot e^{-(\frac{1}{2}\pm\frac{1}{3})\pi i}]$$

It is important to note that the term $e^{-\xi_2}$ in the asymptotic expansion for I can be retained only when a combination of solutions $I_{\pm\frac{1}{3}}$ is chosen such that the coefficient of e^{ξ_2} is zero. This is because other terms in the asymptotic expansion, such as e^{ξ_2}/ξ_2, have been neglected, and these are of larger order of magnitude than $e^{-\xi_2}$. The asymptotic nature of the WKB approximation is such that if the term that increases exponentially away from the turning point is present, it is impossible to say whether or not the decreasing exponential term is also there.

Connection at the Turning Point. The leading term in k^2 at $x = 0$ is Cx, so that $k \cong cx^{\frac{1}{2}}$, $\kappa \cong c|x|^{\frac{1}{2}}$, $\xi_1 \cong (2c/3)x^{\frac{3}{2}}$, $\xi_2 \cong (2c/3)|x|^{\frac{3}{2}}$, where $c = +C^{\frac{1}{2}}$. Then from (28.14) and (28.15) we obtain the behavior of the u's near $x = 0$

$$u_1^+ \cong A_+ \frac{(\frac{2}{3})^{\frac{1}{2}}(\frac{1}{3}c)^{\frac{1}{3}}}{\Gamma(\frac{4}{3})}x, \qquad u_1^- \cong A_- \frac{(\frac{2}{3})^{\frac{1}{2}}(\frac{1}{3}c)^{-\frac{1}{3}}}{\Gamma(\frac{2}{3})}$$

$$u_2^+ \cong B_+ \frac{(\frac{2}{3})^{\frac{1}{2}}(\frac{1}{3}c)^{\frac{1}{3}}}{\Gamma(\frac{4}{3})}|x|, \qquad u_2^- \cong B_- \frac{(\frac{2}{3})^{\frac{1}{2}}(\frac{1}{3}c)^{-\frac{1}{3}}}{\Gamma(\frac{2}{3})}$$

It is apparent then that u_1^+ joins smoothly on to u_2^+ if $B_+ = -A_+$, and that u_1^- joins smoothly on to u_2^- if $B_- = A_-$.

These relations between the coefficients can be used to obtain asymptotic forms like (28.7) and (28.8) for the two independent solutions u^+ and u^- in the two regions (the arbitrary multiplying constants $A_{\pm}$ are omitted).

---

[1] Whittaker and Watson, *op. cit.*, Chap. 17.

$$u^+ \xrightarrow[x \to +\infty]{} (\tfrac{1}{2}\pi k)^{-\frac{1}{2}} \cos\left(\xi_1 - \frac{5\pi}{12}\right)$$

$$\xrightarrow[x \to -\infty]{} -(2\pi\kappa)^{-\frac{1}{2}}(e^{\xi_2} + e^{-\xi_2 - \frac{5\pi i}{6}})$$

$$u^- \xrightarrow[x \to +\infty]{} (\tfrac{1}{2}\pi k)^{-\frac{1}{2}} \cos\left(\xi_1 - \frac{\pi}{12}\right)$$

$$\xrightarrow[x \to -\infty]{} (2\pi\kappa)^{-\frac{1}{2}}(e^{\xi_2} + e^{-\xi_2 - \frac{\pi i}{6}})$$

(28.16)

The asymptotic forms of any linear combination of u^+ and u^- can be found from Eqs. (28.16).

Asymptotic Connection Formulas. Convenient connection formulas between the asymptotic WKB solutions in the two regions can be obtained by choosing suitable linear combinations of u^+ and u^-. Thus the combination $u^+ + u^-$ contains only the decreasing exponential, and yields the first connection formula

$$\tfrac{1}{2}\kappa^{-\frac{1}{2}}e^{-\xi_2} \to k^{-\frac{1}{2}} \cos(\xi_1 - \tfrac{1}{4}\pi) \qquad (28.17)$$

The arrow in (28.17) implies that the asymptotic solution in region 2 that appears on the left goes into the asymptotic solution in region 1 that appears on the right, but that the converse is not necessarily true. This is because a small error in the phase of the cosine introduces the dominant increasing exponential in region 2.[1]

Another linear combination of u^+ and u^- can be found that gives the second connection formula

$$\sin\eta\,\kappa^{-\frac{1}{2}}e^{\xi_2} \leftarrow k^{-\frac{1}{2}} \cos(\xi_1 - \tfrac{1}{4}\pi + \eta) \qquad (28.18)$$

where η is appreciably different from zero or an integer multiple of π. The arrow in (28.18) appears since the neglected decreasing exponential in region 2 alters the phase of the cosine in region 1 by an indeterminate amount if the connection is reversed.

Energy Levels of a Potential Well. We now give a simple example of the application of the WKB approximation that serves as a derivation of one of the Bohr-Sommerfeld quantization rules. We wish to find the energy levels of a particle moving in the one-dimensional potential well

[1] The converse of (28.17) can be used in the following sense: If some parameter in the solution (such as the energy E) is varied continuously so that the phase of the cosine in region 1 passes through the value $-\tfrac{1}{4}\pi$, the increasing exponential in region 2 disappears for some indeterminate value of the phase close to $-\tfrac{1}{4}\pi$ and leaves only the decreasing exponential. This result is useful, for example, in treating the resonance scattering of alpha particles by a heavy nucleus.

shown in Fig. 26. For any assumed energy level E, there are supposed to be just two turning points of the classical motion such that

$$V(x_1) = V(x_2) = E$$

The regions $x < x_1$ and $x > x_2$ are Type 2 regions in which we know that u decreases away from the turning points in order to satisfy the boundary conditions at $\pm \infty$. Thus we have only the decreasing exponential WKB solution in these regions.

The connection formula (28.17) can be applied at the turning point x_1, which separates a Type 2 region from the Type 1 region $x_1 < x < x_2$.

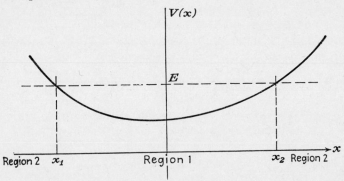

FIG. 26. Application of the WKB method to a potential trough; linear turning points occur at x_1 and x_2.

The only change is that the lower limit on the ξ_1 integral is changed from 0 to x_1, so that the solution to the right of the turning point is

$$k^{-\frac{1}{2}} \cos \left(\int_{x_1}^{x} k\,dx - \tfrac{1}{4}\pi \right) \tag{28.19}$$

apart from an arbitrary multiplying constant. The same connection formula can also be applied at x_2 by reversing the direction of the x axis and changing the fixed limit on the ξ integrals from 0 to x_2; the arrow in (28.17) still means that we go from a region 2 solution to a region 1 solution, but now the latter is to the left of the turning point and the former is to the right. We redefine $\xi_1 = \int_{x}^{x_2} k\,dx$, $\xi_2 = \int_{x_2}^{x} \kappa\,dx$ so that they still increase going away from the turning point, in which case (28.17) can be used without any modification. The solution to the left of this turning point is then $k^{-\frac{1}{2}} \cos \left(\int_{x}^{x_2} k\,dx - \tfrac{1}{4}\pi \right)$, which can be written

$$k^{-\frac{1}{2}} \cos \left(\int_{x_1}^{x} k\,dx - \tfrac{1}{4}\pi - \eta \right), \quad \eta \equiv \int_{x_1}^{x_2} k\,dx - \tfrac{1}{2}\pi \tag{28.20}$$

As was the case in the qualitative discussion of discrete energy eigenvalues in Sec. 8, we obtain the energy levels of this system by requiring that the two solutions (28.19) and (28.20) join together smoothly in the interior of region 1. This evidently requires that η be zero or a positive integer multiple of π, since $\int_{x_1}^{x_2} k\,dx$ is necessarily positive. We can write the determining equation for the eigenvalues as

$$\int_{x_1}^{x_2} k\,dx = (n + \tfrac{1}{2})\pi, \quad n = 0, 1, 2, \ldots \quad (28.21)$$

Equation (28.21) is to be used for values of n up to the point at which E becomes so large that one or both of the turning points disappears.

A Quantization Rule. The expression (28.5) for k can be substituted into (28.21) to give one of the Bohr-Somerfeld quantization rules of the old quantum theory

$$2\int_{x_1}^{x_2} \{2\mu[E - V(x)]\}^{\frac{1}{2}}dx = (n + \tfrac{1}{2})h \quad (28.22)$$

The left side of (28.22) is the integral around a complete cycle of the motion (from x_1 to x_2 and back to x_1) of the momentum $[2\mu(E - V)]^{\frac{1}{2}}$. The right side is the quantum value of the phase integral, with half-integer rather than integer quantum numbers.

It is easily seen from the form of the solution (28.20) that n is the number of nodes of the WKB wave function between the turning points. Since it is basic to the WKB method that we can develop asymptotic solutions like (28.7) only several wave lengths from each turning point, the approximation should be good only if the turning points are several wave lengths apart, or if n is large in comparison with unity. This confirms the earlier view that the WKB method is a semiclassical approximation, since it is expected to be most useful in the nearly classical limit of large quantum numbers.

Actually, the WKB approximation also gives quite good results for the low quantum states of many systems. For example, if we apply (28.22) to the harmonic oscillator $V(x) = \tfrac{1}{2}Kx^2$, it is known from the old quantum theory that the correct energy levels are obtained for all quantum numbers.

Special Boundary Conditions. The boundary condition to be applied to a WKB solution at a perfectly rigid wall (V changes discontinuously to $+\infty$ at $x = x_0$) is that the wave function vanishes there. Thus if k (for a region of Type 1) is slowly varying up to x_0 and other turning points are remote, the asymptotic solution can be used and has the form

$$k^{-\frac{1}{2}}\sin\left(\int_{x_0}^{x} k\,dx\right).$$

Similarly, for a finite potential step that is far from other turning points, the asymptotic WKB solutions can be used up to the point of discontinuity of V if k or κ is slowly varying. Then the magnitudes and slopes of the solutions on the two sides can be matched at this point.

As pointed out after Eq. (28.5), the WKB method can be applied to the radial wave equation for a spherically symmetric potential. When $l = 0$, the radial wave function must be finite at $r = 0$, and so u must vanish there. If k or κ is slowly varying there, the asymptotic solutions can be used; for example, if $E - V(r)$ is positive, finite, and slowly varying at and near $r = 0$, the solution is $k^{-\frac{1}{2}} \sin\left(\int_0^r k\,dr\right)$. When the effective potential energy is infinite at $r = 0$, either because V itself is infinite or because of the centrifugal-force contribution for $l \neq 0$, the situation is more complicated and requires further investigation.

Problems

1. A one-dimensional harmonic oscillator of charge e is perturbed by an electric field of strength E in the positive x direction. Calculate the change in each energy level to second order in the perturbation. Show that this problem can be solved exactly, and compare the result with the perturbation approximation.

2. A one-dimensional harmonic oscillator is perturbed by an extra potential energy bx^3. Calculate the change in each energy level to second order in the perturbation.

3. Find the first-order Stark effect for a hydrogen atom in the state $n = 3$.

4. A system that has three unperturbed states can be represented by the perturbed Hamiltonian matrix

$$\begin{pmatrix} E_1 & 0 & a \\ 0 & E_1 & b \\ \bar{a} & \bar{b} & E_2 \end{pmatrix}$$

where $E_2 > E_1$. Use the second-order nondegenerate perturbation theory to find the perturbed eigenvalues. Then diagonalize the matrix to find the exact eigenvalues. Finally, use the second-order degenerate perturbation theory. Compare the three results obtained.

5. Show that the total scattering cross section by a potential that falls off at great distances like r^{-n} is finite if and only if $n > 2$, (a) by means of the Born approximation formula (26.20), and (b) by means of the Born approximation expression for the phase shifts (26.27) (see footnote 1, page 78).

6. Find the differential scattering cross section for a potential $V(r) = -V_0 e^{-\frac{r}{a}}$, using the Born approximation. What is the validity criterion in this case, and under what circumstances is it satisfied?

7. In a particular scattering problem in which the potential is spherically symmetric, the phase shift δ_0 is large and can be computed exactly, but all the other phase shifts are small. Derive an expression for the differential scattering cross section with the help of the Born approximation, in which all the phase shifts are taken into account.

8. Use the Born approximation to discuss qualitatively the scattering by a crystal lattice of identical atoms.

9. A trial function ψ differs from an eigenfunction u_E by a small amount, so that $\psi = u_E + \epsilon\psi_1$, where u_E and ψ_1 are normalized and $\epsilon \ll 1$. Show that $\langle H \rangle$ differs from E only by terms of order ϵ^2.

10. If the first $n - 1$ eigenfunctions of a particular Hamiltonian are known, write down a formal expression for a variation-method trial function that could be used to get an upper limit on the nth energy level.

11. Find the next terms (of order R^{-4}) in the expansion of Eq. (27.12). Show that their diagonal matrix element for the unperturbed ground state vanishes, so that there is no inverse fourth power contribution to the van der Waals interaction.

12. Use the first nonvanishing term in the series (27.13) to get a lower limit for $-W(R)$. Compare with that obtained from the variation calculation.

13. Use the combination of perturbation and variation methods employed in Sec. 27 in connection with the van der Waals interaction to obtain limits on the electric susceptibility of a hydrogen atom in its ground state. The electric susceptibility is the ratio of the induced electric-dipole moment to the applied electric field, or is the negative of the second derivative of the perturbed energy with respect to the electric field at zero applied field.

14. A particle of mass m is bound by the potential of Prob. 6, where $\hbar^2/mV_0a^2 = \frac{3}{4}$. Use the variation method with a trial function $e^{-\alpha r}$ to get a good limit on the lowest energy eigenvalue.

15. Make use of Eqs. (27.24) and (27.25) to obtain the second Born approximation expression for $\tan \delta_l$. What does this give for the zero-energy phase shift in a uniform potential when $l = 0$?

16. Retain the terms of order k^2 on the right side of Eq. (27.28), and use the resulting variation principle with $v(r) = r$ to calculate $k \cot \delta_0$ for a uniform potential. Compare with the first Born approximation when calculated through terms of order k^2, and with the exact result.

17. Use Eq. (27.29) with $v(r) = r$ to calculate $(k \cot \delta_0)_0$ for the exponential potential of Prob. 6. Compare with the first Born approximation.

18. Show that the WKB approximation gives the correct energy eigenvalues for all states of the harmonic oscillator.

19. Apply the WKB method to the one-dimensional motion of a particle of mass m in a potential that equals $-V_0$ at $x = 0$, changes linearly with x until it vanishes at $x = \pm a$, and is zero for $|x| > a$. Find all the bound energy levels obtained in this approximation if $mV_0a^2/\hbar^2 = 40$.

20. Use the WKB approximation to show that an attractive three-dimensional potential that falls off like r^{-n} for large r has an infinite number of bound states if $n \leqq 2$.

21. Discuss the connection between the WKB approximation and the penetration through "opaque" potential barriers; the barriers are to be like that considered in Sec. 17, although not necessarily square.

CHAPTER VIII

APPROXIMATION METHODS FOR TIME-DEPENDENT PROBLEMS

It is generally impossible to obtain exact solutions of the Schrödinger equation when the Hamiltonian depends on the time. The three approximation methods that we consider in this chapter all start from the assumption that there is a time-independent Hamiltonian that approximates the actual Hamiltonian in some sense, for which the Schrödinger equation can be solved. The time-dependent part of the actual Hamiltonian may be small compared to the stationary part, in which case a perturbation method can be used. Or there may be time-dependent parameters in the actual Hamiltonian that change very slowly (*adiabatic approximation*) or very rapidly (*sudden approximation*) in comparison with the periods of the approximate stationary solutions.

29. TIME-DEPENDENT PERTURBATION THEORY

The perturbation theory of a system for which the Hamiltonian depends on the time[1] is sometimes called the *method of variation of constants*. It starts from the assumption of Sec. 25 that

$$H = H_0 + H', \qquad H_0 u_n = E_n u_n \qquad (29.1)$$

where the unperturbed Hamiltonian H_0 can be solved for its normalized eigenfunctions u_n and its energy eigenvalues E_n, and the perturbation H' is small. Since H' now depends on the time, stationary solutions of the actual Schrödinger equation do not exist, and we must work with the time-dependent equation

$$i\hbar \frac{\partial \psi}{\partial t} = H\psi \qquad (29.2)$$

Expansion in Unperturbed Eigenfunctions. Our procedure is to express ψ as an expansion in the eigenfunctions $u_n e^{-\frac{iE_n t}{\hbar}}$ of the unperturbed time-dependent wave equation, where the expansion coefficients evidently depend on the time.

$$\psi = \mathsf{S} a_n(t) u_n e^{-\frac{iE_n t}{\hbar}} \qquad (29.3)$$

---

[1] P. A. M. Dirac, *Proc. Roy. Soc.*, **A112**, 661 (1926); **A114**, 243 (1927).

S denotes a summation over the discrete set together with an integration over the continuous set of eigenfunctions. Substitution of (29.3) into (29.2) gives

$$S i\hbar \dot{a}_n u_n e^{-\frac{iE_n t}{\hbar}} + S a_n E_n u_n e^{-\frac{iE_n t}{\hbar}} = S a_n (H_0 + H') u_n e^{-\frac{iE_n t}{\hbar}}$$

where the dot denotes differentiation with respect to the time.

We replace $H_0 u_n$ by $E_n u_n$ on the right side, multiply through on the left by $\bar{u}_k$, and integrate over all space, making use of the orthonormality of the u's

$$i\hbar \dot{a}_k e^{-\frac{iE_k t}{\hbar}} = S a_n e^{-\frac{iE_n t}{\hbar}} \int \bar{u}_k H' u_n d\tau$$

The integral on the right is the matrix element H'_{kn} of the perturbation. We define the Bohr (angular) frequency

$$\omega_{kn} \equiv \frac{E_k - E_n}{\hbar} \tag{29.4}$$

and obtain

$$\dot{a}_k = (i\hbar)^{-1} S H'_{kn} a_n e^{i\omega_{kn} t} \tag{29.5}$$

The group of Eqs. (29.5) for all k's is exactly equivalent to the Schrödinger equation (29.2); the amplitude a_n of a particular unperturbed eigenfunction u_n in the expansion of ψ has replaced the amplitude ψ at a particular point in space. Because of the choice of the representation, which is determined by the eigenfunctions of the unperturbed Hamiltonian, H_0 does not appear explicitly in (29.5).

The perturbation approximation consists in replacing H' by $\lambda H'$ in (29.1) and (29.5), and expressing the a's as power series in λ:

$$a_n = a_n^{(0)} + \lambda a_n^{(1)} + \lambda^2 a_n^{(2)} + \cdots \tag{29.6}$$

As in Sec. 25, we assume that these series are analytic for λ between 0 and 1. We can therefore substitute (29.6) into (29.5), equate coefficients of equal powers of λ, and set $\lambda = 1$ in the final results. The substitution yields the set of equations

$$\dot{a}_k^{(0)} = 0; \qquad \dot{a}_k^{(s+1)} = (i\hbar)^{-1} S H'_{kn} a_n^{(s)} e^{i\omega_{kn} t}, \quad s = 0, 1, 2, \ldots \tag{29.7}$$

These can in principle be integrated successively to obtain approximate solutions to any desired order in the perturbation.

First-order Perturbation. The first of Eqs. (29.7) shows that the zero-order coefficients $a_k^{(0)}$ are constant in time. Their values are the initial conditions of the problem, which specify the state of the system before the perturbation is applied. We assume throughout this section that all except one of the $a_k^{(0)}$ are zero, so that the system is in a definite unperturbed energy state when the perturbation is applied.[1] The results that we shall obtain can easily be generalized to situations in which more than one of the zero-order coefficients is different from zero.

We thus put $a_k^{(0)} = \delta_{km}$ or $\delta(k - m)$, according as the state m is one of a discrete or a continuous set. Integration of the first-order equation gives

$$a_k^{(1)}(t) = (i\hbar)^{-1} \int_{-\infty}^{t} H'_{km}(t')e^{i\omega_{km}t'}dt' \qquad (29.8)$$

where the constant of integration is taken to be zero in order that $a_k^{(1)}$ be zero at $t = -\infty$ (before the perturbation is applied). If H' is of finite duration, the amplitude of a state u_k ($k \neq m$) after the perturbation has disappeared is proportional to the time Fourier component of the matrix element of the perturbation between this state and the initial state, that corresponds to the angular frequency ω_{km} given in (29.4). This result is analogous to that obtained for the scattered amplitude in the Born approximation [see the discussion of Eq. (26.18)].

Equation (29.8) takes a particularly simple form if the perturbation H' is independent of the time except for being turned on at one time and off at a later time. We call these two times 0 and t, respectively, and obtain for the first-order amplitudes at the time t (these are also the amplitudes at any subsequent time)

$$a_k^{(1)}(t) = -\frac{H'_{km}}{\hbar} \frac{e^{i\omega_{km}t} - 1}{\omega_{km}} \qquad (29.9)$$

Thus the probability of finding the system in the state k at t is

$$|a_k^{(1)}(t)|^2 = \frac{4|H'_{km}|^2 \sin^2 \frac{1}{2}\omega_{km}t}{\hbar^2\omega_{km}^2}$$

The factor $\sin^2 \frac{1}{2}\omega_{km}t/\omega_{km}^2$ is plotted in Fig. 27 as a function of ω_{km}.

Physical Interpretation. The height of the main peak in Fig. 27 increases in proportion to t^2, while its breadth decreases inversely as t, so that the area under the curve is proportional to t. Thus if there is a group of states k that have energies nearly equal to that of the initial state m, and for which H'_{km} is roughly independent of k, the probability of finding the system in one or another of these states is proportional to t. This is the physically interesting situation, since what we wish to calculate eventually is a *transition probability per unit time w*, and this implies that

---

[1] This need not conflict with the uncertainty relation (3.3), since the infinite lapse of time prior to the application of the perturbation makes it possible to determine the original energy of the system with arbitrarily great precision.

the probability that a transition has taken place when the perturbation has been on for a time t is proportional to t.[1]

It follows that a definite value of w exists only when the final state k is one of a continuous or nearly continuous set of states. The spread in energy of the final states to which transitions occur, shown in Fig. 27

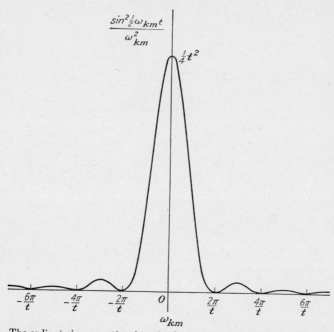

Fig. 27. The ordinate is proportional to the first-order perturbation probability of finding a system in a state that has an energy different from that of the initial state by $\hbar\omega_{km}$; the scales for ordinate and abscissa depend on the duration t of the perturbation in the manner indicated.

$(E_k = E_m + \hbar\omega_{km})$, is connected with the uncertainty relation (3.3) for energy and time in the following way. We can regard the perturbation H' as a device that measures the energy of the system (which is not necessarily its initial energy since the system is disturbed) by transferring it to one of the states k. The time available for the measurement is t, so that the uncertainty in energy predicted by (3.3) is of order $\hbar/t$, in agreement with the breadth of the main peak in Fig. 27. It is interesting

---

[1] We assume that the total transition probability to all states k is small enough in comparison with unity so that the initial state m is not significantly depleted. This is equivalent to the original assumption that the perturbation is small, which means that for times t of physical interest, there is little change in the initial state. There can still be an effect of observable magnitude if a large number of independent systems receive identical treatment.

to note that conservation of energy, suitably modified by the uncertainty principle, is an automatic consequence of the calculation and does not have to be inserted as a separate assumption.

Transition Probability. In order to obtain an explicit expression for w, it is convenient to assume that the system is contained in a large cubical box of dimensions L that has periodic boundary conditions at its walls (Sec. 10). Then the eigenfunctions u_n form a discrete set and can be normalized to unity in the volume L^3. We now consider a particular group of final states k that have nearly the same energy as the initial state m and for which the matrix element H'_{km} of the perturbation is a slowly varying function of k. We define a density of final states $\rho(k)$ such that $\rho(k)dE_k$ is the number of such states in the energy range dE_k, and assume that $\rho(k)$ is also a slowly varying function of k.

The transition probability per unit time to one or another of this group of states can then be written

$$w = t^{-1} \sum_k |a_k^{(1)}(t)|^2 = t^{-1} \int |a_k^{(1)}(t)|^2 \rho(k)dE_k \qquad (29.10)$$

when the box L is large enough so that the summation over k can be replaced by the integration over E_k. Since H'_{km} and $\rho(k)$ are slowly varying and most of the contribution to the integral comes from a narrow range of energy about $E_k = E_m$, they can be taken outside of the integral, and (29.10) can be rewritten as

$$w = \frac{1}{t} \frac{4|H'_{km}|^2}{\hbar} \rho(k) \int_{-\infty}^{\infty} \frac{\sin^2 \frac{1}{2}\omega_{km}t}{\omega_{km}^2} d\omega_{km} \qquad (29.11)$$

where the index k now refers to a typical one of the group of states having about the energy E_m. The integral in (29.11) is $\frac{1}{2}t \int_{-\infty}^{\infty} x^{-2} \sin^2 x dx = \frac{1}{2}\pi t$, so that we finally obtain

$$w = \frac{2\pi}{\hbar} \rho(k)|H'_{km}|^2 \qquad (29.12)$$

which is independent of t, as expected.

There may be several different groups of final states k, all of which have about the energy E_m but for which the perturbation matrix elements H'_{km} and the densities of states $\rho(k)$, while nearly constant within a group, differ from one group to another. Then (29.12) gives the transitions per unit time to a particular group; similar expressions of the same form give the rates of transition to other groups.

Scattering Cross Section. As a first application of Eq. (29.12), we calculate w when the initial and final states are free-particle momentum eigenfunctions (plane waves) and the perturbation is a potential energy $V(\mathbf{r})$. The result can be interpreted in terms of an elastic scattering cross section, and then agrees with the Born approximation result (Sec. 26), as expected. We take for the initial and final states

$$u_m(\mathbf{r}) = L^{-\frac{3}{2}} \exp i\mathbf{k}_0 \cdot \mathbf{r}, \qquad u_k(\mathbf{r}) = L^{-\frac{3}{2}} \exp i\mathbf{k} \cdot \mathbf{r}$$

where $\mathbf{k}_0$ and $\mathbf{k}$ are the initial and final propagation vectors, respectively. Thus the perturbation matrix element is

$$H'_{km} = L^{-3}\int \exp(-i\mathbf{k} \cdot \mathbf{r})V(\mathbf{r}) \exp(i\mathbf{k}_0 \cdot \mathbf{r})d\tau$$
$$= L^{-3}\int V(\mathbf{r}) \exp(i\mathbf{K} \cdot \mathbf{r})d\tau \quad (29.13)$$

where $\mathbf{K} = \mathbf{k}_0 - \mathbf{k}$.

The density of final states can be found from the permitted values of $\mathbf{k}$ in a box: $k_x = 2\pi n_x/L$, etc., where the n's are positive or negative integers or zero. Thus there are $(L/2\pi)^3 dk_x dk_y dk_z$ states in the range $dk_x dk_y dk_z$ of propagation vector. Now there are many different final states $\mathbf{k}$ with the same energy, corresponding to different directions of $\mathbf{k}$ with a given magnitude. The matrix element (29.13) usually depends on the direction of $\mathbf{k}$, so that we have to consider only a small range of directions at a time. We therefore ask for the rate of transition into an infinitesimal element of solid angle $\sin \theta d\theta d\phi$ about some direction that is specified by the polar angles θ, ϕ. Then $\rho(k)dE_k$ is equal to the number of states in the range $d\tau_k$ given by the above solid angle element and the magnitude element dk that corresponds to the energy element dE_k.

$$\rho(k)dE_k = \left(\frac{L}{2\pi}\right)^3 k^2 dk \sin \theta d\theta d\phi$$

Since $E_k = \hbar^2 k^2/2\mu$, $dE_k/dk = \hbar^2 k/\mu$, and we obtain for $\rho(k)$

$$\rho(k) = \frac{\mu L^3}{8\pi^3\hbar^2} k \sin \theta d\theta d\phi \quad (29.14)$$

The value of w obtained in this way is the number of particles scattered into the element of solid angle per unit time when there is one incident particle in the volume L^3. This is an incident flux of v/L^3 particles per unit area and time, where $v = \hbar k/\mu$ is the speed of the incident or scattered particle (since energy is conserved). Since the differential scattering cross section is defined as the scattering per unit incident flux, we have that

$$\sigma(\theta,\phi) \sin \theta d\theta d\phi = \frac{\mu L^3}{\hbar k} w \quad (29.15)$$

Substitution of (29.12), (29.13), and (29.14) into (29.15) gives

$$\sigma(\theta,\phi) = \left(\frac{\mu}{2\pi\hbar^2}\right)^2 \left|\int V(\mathbf{r}) \exp{(i\mathbf{K}\cdot\mathbf{r})d\tau}\right|^2 \qquad (29.16)$$

This agrees with the Born approximation result (26.18) and (26.19), and has the same range of validity.

Harmonic Perturbation.   Another situation for which Eq. (29.8) assumes a simple form occurs when the perturbation depends harmonically on the time, except for being turned on at zero time and off at time t. If we put $H'_{km}(t') = H'^0_{km} \sin \omega t'$, the first-order amplitudes at time t are

$$a_k^{(1)}(t) = -\frac{H'^0_{km}}{2i\hbar}\left[\frac{e^{i(\omega_{km}+\omega)t} - 1}{\omega_{km} + \omega} - \frac{e^{i(\omega_{km}-\omega)t} - 1}{\omega_{km} - \omega}\right] \qquad (29.17)$$

The probability of finding the system in the state k is appreciable only when the denominator of one or the other of the two terms in (29.17) is practically zero.   Thus there is no interference between the two terms, and the perturbation can produce transitions for which $\omega_{km} \cong \pm\omega$ if the corresponding matrix element does not vanish.   The energy-conservation condition $E_k \cong E_m$ obtained earlier is now replaced by the condition

$$E_k \cong E_m \pm \hbar\omega \qquad (29.18)$$

Equation (29.18) suggests that the first-order effect of a perturbation that varies harmonically in the time with angular frequency ω is to transfer to or receive from the system on which it acts an amount of energy $\hbar\omega$.   This concept will be used for a qualitative treatment of radiation processes in Chap. X.

Second-order Perturbation.   The series of equations (29.7) can readily be solved to second order for a perturbation that is constant in time. We take the equation with $s = 1$, and substitute from (29.9) on the right side.

$$\dot{a}_k^{(2)} = \frac{i}{\hbar^2} \mathbf{S} \frac{H'_{kn}H'_{nm}}{\omega_{nm}}\left(e^{i\omega_{km}t} - e^{i\omega_{kn}t}\right)$$

Integration of this equation subject to the initial condition $a_k^{(2)}(0) = 0$ gives for the second-order amplitudes at time t

$$a_k^{(2)}(t) = \hbar^{-2}\mathbf{S}\frac{H'_{kn}H'_{nm}}{\omega_{nm}}\left[\frac{e^{i\omega_{km}t} - 1}{\omega_{km}} - \frac{e^{i\omega_{kn}t} - 1}{\omega_{kn}}\right] \qquad (29.19)$$

Equation (29.19) indicates that transitions for which the probability increases linearly with the time can occur either for $\omega_{km} \cong 0$ or $\omega_{kn} \cong 0$. While the first type of transition conserves energy between the initial state m and the final state k, the second need not. It is not difficult to see that the second bracket term arises from the 1 in the numerator of (29.9), which in turn comes from the initial condition at zero time. This initial condition means that the perturbation is turned on suddenly; thus the mathematical formulation suggests that the second-order transitions that do not conserve energy are caused by the sudden turning on of the perturbation. This is in agreement with Eqs. (29.8) and (29.17), which show that a perturbation that has nonzero frequency Fourier components can give up energy to or absorb energy from the system that it perturbs. In the case we are now considering, these Fourier components are not marked enough to produce in first order a transition probability that is proportional to the time, but they do in second order.

In most practical problems, the sudden turning on of the perturbation is introduced as a mathematical artifice that simplifies the calculation. Actually, in such cases, the perturbation either is always present, or is turned on very slowly, and we are concerned with transitions that conserve energy between initial and final states. Problems that can be treated by the sudden approximation (see end of Sec. 31) are an exception; there energy need not be conserved. Throughout this section and the next, we assume that only transitions that conserve the energy actually occur ($\omega_{km} \cong 0$).

Suppose now that the perturbation produces no transitions in first order; this means that there are no states n that conserve energy ($\omega_{nm} \cong 0$) for which the matrix element $H'_{nm} \neq 0$. Since $\omega_{km} \cong 0$, this means also that $H'_{nm} = 0$ whenever $\omega_{kn} \cong 0$. In this case, the second term in the bracket of (29.19) is never appreciable. The calculation of w is carried through as before, except that $a_k^{(2)}$ replaces $a_k^{(1)}$; thus (29.12) can be used if the matrix element H'_{km} is replaced by the second-order matrix element

$$ S \frac{H'_{kn} H'_{nm}}{E_m - E_n} \tag{29.20} $$

Effect of First-order Transitions. In the event that transitions can occur in first order, but they are not to the state in which we are interested, we can proceed as follows. It is still true that the second term in the bracket of (29.19) is negligible for states n that have energies appreciably different from E_k (or E_m), since then ω_{kn} is large. However, there may now be states n for which E_n, E_m, and E_k are all close together and neither H'_{kn} nor H'_{nm} is zero. The second bracket term cannot be ignored, for without it the summation or integration over n would have a singularity when ω_{nm} is zero. It is not difficult to see that for any value of ω_{km} (zero or otherwise), the entire bracket is proportional to ω_{nm} (which is equal to $\omega_{km} - \omega_{kn}$) when ω_{nm} is small; this cancels out the ω_{nm}

in the denominator, and makes the summand or integrand finite where $\omega_{nm} = 0$.[1]

We now show how an explicit evaluation of (29.19) is obtained in this case if S can be represented by an integral over E_n or ω_{nm}. We divide the integral into parts according as $|\omega_{nm}|$ is large or is not large in comparison with $1/t$. In the first region, the second bracket term in (29.19) can be neglected, since $|\omega_{kn}| = |\omega_{km} - \omega_{nm}|$ is also large in comparison with $1/t$ ($\omega_{km} \cong 0$ means that $\omega_{km}t$ is not large in comparison with unity). We thus obtain for this part of the integral

$$\frac{e^{i\omega_{km}t} - 1}{\omega_{km}} \int' \frac{H'_{kn}H'_{nm}}{\omega_{nm}} \rho(n)\hbar d\omega_{nm} \qquad (29.21)$$

Here $\rho(n)dE_n$ is the number of states of the particular group n under consideration in the energy range dE_n; the prime on the integral implies that the region $-c/t \leq \omega_{nm} \leq c/t$ is excluded from the integration, where c is a constant number that is large in comparison with unity. If there are two or more distinct groups of states n for which the matrix elements or densities of states differ, a further summation over these different groups must eventually be carried out.

In the second region, where $|\omega_{nm}| \leq c/t$, we assume that t is large enough so that $H'_{kn}H'_{nm}\rho(n)$ can be regarded as a constant, taken outside of the integral, and evaluated at $\omega_{nm} = 0$. We must now use both terms in the bracket of (29.19) in order that the integrand be finite. This part of the integral is then

$$[\hbar H'_{kn}H'_{nm}\rho(n)]_{\omega_{nm}=0} \cdot \int_{-\frac{c}{t}}^{\frac{c}{t}} \left[\frac{e^{i\omega_{km}t} - 1}{\omega_{km}} - \frac{e^{i(\omega_{km}-\omega_{nm})t} - 1}{\omega_{km} - \omega_{nm}} \right] \frac{d\omega_{nm}}{\omega_{nm}} \qquad (29.22)$$

The integral that appears in (29.22) can be evaluated by considering the contour in the complex ω_{nm} plane shown in Fig. 28, which contains no poles of the integrand. Thus the integral over the closed contour is zero, and the integral in (29.22) is equal to the integral around the semi-circle of radius c/t taken in the counterclockwise direction. The magnitude of ω_{nm} is great enough over this semicircle so that the contribution

---

[1] This result follows quite generally from the structure of the whole perturbation calculation, since there is no way in which a singularity can appear. Thus if the perturbation is turned on slowly rather than suddenly, so that the energy-conservation difficulties mentioned above do not occur, the second bracket term of (29.19) has a more complicated form but still cancels out the singularity at $\omega_{nm} = 0$. This can be verified by direct calculation.

of the second term in the integrand can be neglected in comparison with the first. The integral in (29.22) is then easily evaluated and becomes

$$\pi i \, \frac{e^{i\omega_{km}t} - 1}{\omega_{km}} \tag{29.23}$$

For large t, the prime on the integral in (29.21) is equivalent to taking its principal value.[1] Thus if we substitute (29.23) into (29.22) and add the result to (29.21), we obtain an expression like (29.21) except that the primed integral is replaced by the principal value of the integral plus πi times the residue of the integrand at the pole $\omega_{nm} = 0$. This is equivalent to evaluating the integral along a contour in the complex ω_{nm} plane

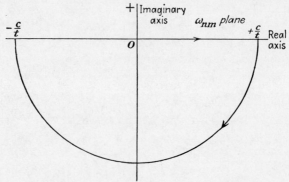

Fig. 28.   Contour for the evaluation of the integral in Eq. (29.22).

that passes along the real axis from $-\infty$ to ∞ except for passing beneath the origin. We thus obtain finally

$$a_k^{(2)}(t) = \frac{e^{i\omega_{km}t} - 1}{\hbar\omega_{km}} \int_C \frac{H'_{kn}H'_{nm}}{E_n - E_m} \, \rho(n)dE_n \tag{29.24}$$

where the contour C is over the real axis of E_n except for passing under the pole of the integrand at $E_n = E_m$. Equation (29.24) is to be used in place of (29.19) whenever S can be represented by $\int\rho(n)dE_n$. Comparison of Eqs. (29.24) and (29.9) shows that we can use the expression (29.12) for w if we replace the matrix element H'_{km} by the integral in (29.24), which we sometimes call the second-order matrix element. An example of this is given in the next section.

Intermediate States. We see that the time-dependent perturbation theory gives a result in first order if there is a nonvanishing matrix

---

[1] E. T. Whittaker and G. N. Watson, "A Course of Modern Analysis," 4th ed., pp. 75, 117 (Cambridge, London, 1935).

element of H' that connects the initial state m and the final state k. If $H'_{km} = 0$, but there are one or more states n for which neither H'_{nm} nor H'_{kn} is zero, the transition occurs in second order.

It is then convenient to think of one of the states n as an *intermediate state:* the perturbation transfers the system from m to k in two steps, through a state n. Energy need not be conserved for an intermediate state, since it has only a transient existence and according to the uncertainty relation (3.3) it is impossible to determine the energy of such a short-lived state with any precision. If some of the intermediate states do conserve energy, the summation (29.20) over these states must be interpreted in accordance with the integral in (29.24).

In some cases, a perturbation can produce a particular transition only through two or more different intermediate states; this corresponds to a third or higher order of the perturbation calculation. If the perturbation is small, it usually happens that the result of a calculation to the lowest order in which the transition occurs gives a useful result, while higher order calculations do not improve on this and may even be quite misleading.

30. INELASTIC COLLISIONS

The expression for the scattering cross section given in the preceding section is easily generalized to a description of inelastic collisions, in which internal as well as kinetic energy can be transferred between the colliding systems. In this section we apply the result to two problems that are typical of first-order and of second-order processes.[1] The latter calculation is of unusual theoretical interest, for it shows explicitly how a particle that is described entirely in terms of a plane wave (momentum eigenfunction) can produce a sharp track in a Wilson cloud chamber.

Expression for the Cross Section. The expression (29.12) for the rate of transition w is applicable to inelastic collisions if the matrix element is defined accordingly. We consider here the collision of a fast electron with a hydrogen atom in its ground state, and wish to calculate the cross section for scattering of the electron through a definite angle accompanied by excitation of the hydrogen atom to a definite state. We leave out of consideration the possibility that the incident electron changes places with the atomic electron; such exchange collisions will be taken up in Chap. IX.

---

[1] The examples considered in this section can also be treated by an extension of the Born approximation; such an extension to first-order rearrangement collisions is given in Sec. 34. For the treatment of second-order processes, it is more convenient to work with the method of variation of constants.

The unperturbed Hamiltonian is the sum of the kinetic energy of the incident electron and the Hamiltonian for the hydrogen atom:

$$H_0 = -\frac{\hbar^2}{2m}\nabla_1^2 - \frac{\hbar^2}{2m}\nabla_2^2 - \frac{e^2}{r_2} \tag{30.1}$$

where $\mathbf{r}_1$ and $\mathbf{r}_2$ are the coordinates of the incident and atomic electrons, respectively, referred to the atomic nucleus, which is massive enough so that its motion can be neglected. The perturbation is the electrostatic energy of interaction between the incident electron and the electron and nucleus of the atom

$$H' = \frac{e^2}{r_{12}} - \frac{e^2}{r_1} \tag{30.2}$$

The unperturbed wave functions are eigenfunctions of (30.1), which we choose to be

$$\begin{matrix} L^{-\frac{3}{2}}\exp\left(i\mathbf{k}_0\cdot\mathbf{r}_1\right)u_{100}(\mathbf{r}_2) & \text{initial state} \\ L^{-\frac{3}{2}}\exp\left(i\mathbf{k}\cdot\mathbf{r}_1\right)u_{200}(\mathbf{r}_2) & \text{final state} \end{matrix} \tag{30.3}$$

In spectroscopic notation, this corresponds to a $1S \rightarrow 2S$ transition of the atom. The magnitude of the propagation vector of the electron after the collision is fixed by conservation of energy

$$k^2 = k_0^2 - \frac{2m}{\hbar^2}\frac{3e^2}{8a_0} \tag{30.4}$$

Equations (30.2), (30.3), and (30.4) specify the matrix element that appears in (29.12).

$$H'_{21} = L^{-3}\int\int\exp\left(i\mathbf{K}\cdot\mathbf{r}_1\right)\bar{u}_{200}(\mathbf{r}_2)\left(\frac{e^2}{r_{12}} - \frac{e^2}{r_1}\right)u_{100}(\mathbf{r}_2)d\tau_1 d\tau_2,$$
$$\mathbf{K} = \mathbf{k}_0 - \mathbf{k} \quad (30.5)$$

The differential cross section can be obtained from w as in the preceding section. It must be remembered, however, that k appears in the expression (29.14) for the density of final states, whereas the initial speed $v_0 = \hbar k_0/m$ appears in the expression for the incident particle flux. Thus the cross section is

$$\sigma(\theta) = \frac{k}{k_0}\left(\frac{m}{2\pi\hbar^2}\right)^2 L^6|H'_{21}|^2 \tag{30.6}$$

where θ is the angle between the vectors $\mathbf{k}$ and $\mathbf{k}_0$.

Evaluation of the Matrix Element. It is apparent from the structure of the matrix element (30.5) that the term e^2/r_1 in the integrand contributes nothing because of the orthogonality of u_{100} and u_{200}. This is to be expected physically, since interaction between the incident electron and the nucleus cannot produce excitation of the atomic electron.

The integration of the remaining term over $\mathbf{r}_1$ can be carried out by transforming the volume element from $d\tau_1 d\tau_2$ to $d\tau_\rho d\tau_2$, where $\varrho = \mathbf{r}_1 - \mathbf{r}_2$; the Jacobian of the transformation is easily seen to be unity. We can then write

$$\int \frac{\exp i\mathbf{K} \cdot \mathbf{r}_1}{r_{12}} d\tau_1 = \exp(i\mathbf{K} \cdot \mathbf{r}_2) \int \frac{\exp i\mathbf{K} \cdot \varrho}{\rho} d\tau_\rho$$

$$= 2\pi \exp(i\mathbf{K} \cdot \mathbf{r}_2) \int_0^\infty \int_{-1}^1 e^{iK\rho w} \rho \, d\rho \, dw$$

$$= \frac{4\pi}{K} \exp(i\mathbf{K} \cdot \mathbf{r}_2) \int_0^\infty \sin K\rho \, d\rho$$

where we have taken the polar axis of ϱ along the vector $\mathbf{K}$ and put w for the cosine of the angle between ϱ and $\mathbf{K}$. The last integral is not strictly convergent, but can be evaluated by inserting an integrating factor $e^{-\alpha\rho}$ into the integrand and subsequently taking the limit $\alpha \to 0$. The justification for this is that the integration over $\mathbf{r}_2$ in (30.5), if performed first, gives a result that falls off like $1/r_1^2$ and hence like $1/\rho^2$ for large ρ,[1] so that for large ρ, the integrand here behaves like $\sin K\rho/\rho$ and the integral converges. We thus obtain

$$\int \frac{\exp i\mathbf{K} \cdot \mathbf{r}_1}{r_{12}} d\tau_1 = \frac{4\pi}{K} \exp(i\mathbf{K} \cdot \mathbf{r}_2) \lim_{\alpha \to 0} \int_0^\infty \sin K\rho \, e^{-\alpha\rho} d\rho$$

$$= \frac{4\pi}{K} \exp(i\mathbf{K} \cdot \mathbf{r}_2) \lim_{\alpha \to 0} \left(\frac{K}{\alpha^2 + K^2} \right) = \frac{4\pi}{K^2} \exp i\mathbf{K} \cdot \mathbf{r}_2 \quad (30.7)$$

Substitution of Eq. (30.7) and the expressions following Eq. (16.24) for the hydrogen wave functions into (30.5), gives an integral over $\mathbf{r}_2$ that can be evaluated as

$$H'_{21} = L^{-3} \frac{16 \sqrt{2}\pi a_0^2 e^2}{(K^2 a_0^2 + \frac{9}{4})^3}, \qquad a_0 = \frac{\hbar^2}{me^2}$$

Differential and Total Cross Sections.   The differential cross section for this collision thus becomes

$$\sigma(\theta) = \frac{k}{k_0} \frac{128 a_0^2}{(K^2 a_0^2 + \frac{9}{4})^6} \tag{30.8}$$

where

$$K^2 = k_0^2 + k^2 - 2k_0 k \cos \theta$$
$$= (2k_0 \sin \tfrac{1}{2}\theta)^2 - (k_0 - k)(k_0 + k - 2k_0 \cos \theta)$$

---

[1] The leading term in $1/r_{12}$ when $r_1 \gg r_2$ is $1/r_1$, and the integral of this over $\mathbf{r}_2$ vanishes because of the orthogonality of u_{100} and u_{200}.

Now the perturbation calculation is best when $k_0 a_0 \gg 1$, in which case k is close to k_0 and we can rewrite (30.4).

$$(k_0 - k)(k_0 + k) = \frac{2m}{\hbar^2}\frac{3e^2}{8a_0} = \frac{3}{4a_0^2}$$

$$k_0 + k \cong 2k_0, \qquad k_0 - k \cong \frac{3}{8k_0 a_0^2} \tag{30.9}$$

With the help of (30.9), the expression for K^2 in this high-energy limit becomes

$$K^2 \cong \left(4k_0^2 - \frac{3}{2a_0^2}\right)\sin^2 \tfrac{1}{2}\theta \cong (2k_0 \sin \tfrac{1}{2}\theta)^2$$

Then according to (30.8), most of the scattering occurs for $Ka_0 \lesssim 1$, which is equivalent to $\theta \lesssim 1/k_0 a_0$. Beyond this, $\sigma(\theta)$ falls off with increasing angle approximately like $\operatorname{cosec}^{12} \tfrac{1}{2}\theta$. This is a much more rapid decrease with angle than the $\operatorname{cosec}^4 \tfrac{1}{2}\theta$ dependence (26.32) obtained for elastic scattering by an atom, and is characteristic of inelastic processes.

The total cross section is found by making use of the exact expression for K^2 to replace the element of solid angle $2\pi\sin \theta d\theta$ by $2\pi K dK/k_0 k$, with limits $k_0 - k$ and $k_0 + k$. Then the integral of (30.8) can be obtained explicitly. However, the discussion of the last paragraph shows that at high energies most of the contribution to the integral comes from near its lower limit, and in accordance with (30.9)

$$(k_0 - k)^2 a_0^2 \cong \frac{9}{64k_0^2 a_0^2} \ll \frac{9}{4}$$

We thus obtain the leading term in the total cross section at high energies by taking the limits 0 and ∞ for K:

$$\sigma \cong \frac{128\pi}{5k_0^2}\left(\frac{2}{3}\right)^{10} \tag{30.10}$$

Cross sections for elastic and other inelastic collisions with hydrogen may be obtained by replacing u_{200} in the matrix element (30.5) by the appropriate final-state wave function, and modifying (30.4) accordingly. The total elastic cross section at high energies turns out to be $7\pi/3k_0^2$, which is about five times as large as (30.10). Excitation to the states that have $n = 2$, $l = 1$ ($1S \to 2P$ transitions) is most easily calculated by choosing the three final states ($m = 0$, ± 1) with their polar axis along the momentum transfer vector $\mathbf{K}$. Then the factors $e^{\pm i\phi}$ that appear in the wave functions for $m = \pm 1$ make these matrix elements vanish and only the state (210) is excited. This corresponds physically to the inability of the incident electron, whose momentum loss is along **K,** to exert a torque on the atomic electron about this axis. The high-energy cross section for this process turns out to be

$$\sigma \cong \frac{576\pi}{k_0^2} \left(\frac{2}{3}\right)^{12} \ln (4k_0a_0) \qquad (30.11)$$

The appearance of the logarithmic factor in Eq. (30.11) derives from an extra factor $1/K^2$ in the differential cross section. Thus in comparison with the $1S \rightarrow 2S$ scattering, the $1S \rightarrow 2P$ differential scattering is more pronounced at small angles and the total scattering decreases less rapidly with increasing energy at high energies.

Production of a Cloud-chamber Track. It seems surprising at first that a fast electron, which we can assume possesses a definite momentum (magnitude and direction) and hence cannot be localized in space, can produce a sharp track in a cloud chamber. This phenomenon may be considered from various points of view. In accordance with Ehrenfest's theorem (Sec. 7), we can represent the electron by a wave packet whose center of gravity moves like a classical particle. If the wave length is short enough, the packet can be quite small without spreading rapidly, and will then interact only with atoms that lie close to the path of its center. This implies that the electron is represented by a superposition of plane waves and hence has an uncertainty in its momentum that enables its position to be sufficiently well defined.

Another approach consists in describing the electron by a single plane wave, and regarding its interaction with the first atom that it excites or ionizes as a position measurement that carries with it an uncertainty of the order of the atomic size. Thereafter, the electron is represented by a packet, like that described in the last paragraph, which is well localized if the first atom is large in comparison with the wave length.

We consider here in detail a description in which the electron and the atoms of the cloud-chamber gas are treated as parts of a single system, so that we do not have to regard an atomic interaction as a position determination that changes the structure of the electron's wave function.[1] To simplify matters, we assume that there are just two atoms present in their ground states, and that their nuclei are far from each other and are fixed in space. We then calculate the cross section for a process in which both atoms are excited and the electron is scattered inelastically. For ɛ fast incident electron, the perturbation theory can be used, and the process is of second order. The calculation is interesting both because

---

[1] See also W. Heisenberg, "The Physical Principles of the Quantum Theory," p. 66 (University of Chicago Press, Chicago, 1930).

of the answer obtained and because it provides an instructive application of the second-order perturbation theory developed in Sec. 29.

The result of the calculation is that the cross section is very small unless the momentum vector of the incident electron is nearly parallel to the line that joins the two nuclei, and unless also the incident and final electron momenta are nearly parallel. These three directions can have an angular spread in radians that is of the order of the ratio of the wave length of the electron to the size of the atom. This is analogous to the result obtained above for the inelastic collision of a fast electron with a hydrogen atom: the angular spread of the scattered electron was found to be roughly $1/k_0 a_0$. It is also in agreement with the wave-packet description of the process, since a localization of the electron by an atomic size a in a direction transverse to its motion produces an uncertainty in the transverse momentum component of amount $\hbar/a$ and an angular spread of order $\hbar/ap \cong 1/k_0 a$.

Formulation of the Problem. The nucleus of the first atom can without loss of generality be placed at the origin, and that of the second atom at the point $\mathbf{R}$. The two atoms are assumed to be far enough apart so that the interaction between them can be neglected. The unperturbed Hamiltonian is then the sum of the kinetic energy of the incident electron and the unperturbed Hamiltonians of the two atoms. The perturbation is the sum of the interaction H_1' between the incident electron and the first atom, and the interaction H_2' between the electron and the second atom. In the initial state, both atoms are in their ground states u_0 with energies ϵ_0, and the incident electron has the propagation vector $\mathbf{k}_0$. In the final state, the first atom is in the state u_n with energy ϵ_n, the second is in the state u_m with energy ϵ_m, and the propagation vector of the electron is $\mathbf{k}_{nm}$.

It is apparent that the transition in which we are interested cannot occur in first order. It can occur in second order, and there are two groups of intermediate states. In the first group, the first atom is in the state u_n, the second in the state u_0, and the incident electron has some propagation vector $\mathbf{k}_{n0}$. In the second group, the first atom is in the state u_0, the second in the state u_m, and the propagation vector of the electron is called $\mathbf{k}_{0m}$. Thus the second-order matrix element (29.20) is

$$\sum_{\mathbf{k}_{n0}} \frac{(H_2')_{nm,n0}(H_1')_{n0,00}}{E_{00} - E_{n0}} + \sum_{\mathbf{k}_{0m}} \frac{(H_1')_{nm,0m}(H_2')_{0m,00}}{E_{00} - E_{0m}} \qquad (30.12)$$

$$E_{00} = 2\epsilon_0 + \frac{\hbar^2 k_0^2}{2m}, \qquad E_{n0} = \epsilon_n + \epsilon_0 + \frac{\hbar^2 k_{n0}^2}{2m}$$

$$E_{0m} = \epsilon_0 + \epsilon_m + \frac{\hbar^2 k_{0m}^2}{2m}$$

We evaluate only the first sum in (30.12) explicitly and indicate the changes that are to be made in the result to obtain the second sum. The matrix elements that appear there are

$$(H_2')_{nm,n0}$$
$$= L^{-3}\iint \bar{u}_m(2)\exp(-i\mathbf{k}_{nm}\cdot\mathbf{r})H_2'(2,\mathbf{r})u_0(2)\exp(i\mathbf{k}_{n0}\cdot\mathbf{r})d\tau_2 d\tau \qquad (30.13)$$
$$(H_1')_{n0,00}$$
$$= L^{-3}\iint \bar{u}_n(1)\exp(-i\mathbf{k}_{n0}\cdot\mathbf{r}')H_1'(1,\mathbf{r}')u_0(1)\exp(i\mathbf{k}_0\cdot\mathbf{r}')d\tau_1 d\tau'$$

Here 1 and 2 denote all the internal coordinates of the first and second atoms, respectively, and $d\tau_1$ and $d\tau_2$ are the corresponding elements of integration; $\mathbf{r}$ and $\mathbf{r}'$ are variables of integration with volume elements $d\tau$ and $d\tau'$, both of which specify the position of the incident electron with respect to the origin. An integral over 1 has been performed in the first of Eqs. (30.13) to give unity, and a similar integral over 2 has been performed in the second equation.

Evaluation of the k Sum. When the matrix elements (30.13) are substituted into the first sum of (30.12) and the sum and integrals are interchanged, we must evaluate

$$\sum_{\mathbf{k}_{n0}} \frac{\exp i\mathbf{k}_{n0}\cdot(\mathbf{r}-\mathbf{r}')}{k_{n0}^2 - \kappa^2}, \qquad \kappa^2 \equiv k_0^2 - \frac{2m}{\hbar^2}(\epsilon_n - \epsilon_0) \qquad (30.14)$$

For a box of sufficiently large dimensions L, we can replace the summation in (30.14) by an integration:

$$\left(\frac{L}{2\pi}\right)^3 \int \frac{\exp i\mathbf{k}_{n0}\cdot(\mathbf{r}-\mathbf{r}')}{k_{n0}^2 - \kappa^2} d\tau_{k_{n0}} \qquad (30.15)$$

The integral in (30.15) has the form of that which appeared in the Green's function (26.12) for a free particle. Thus the only new problem presented by the evaluation of (30.15) is the determination of the contour that takes proper account of the singularity of the integrand at $k_{n0} = \kappa$. This singularity is of the type discussed near the end of the last section and arises from the possibility of first-order transitions in which just one of the atoms is excited. Equation (29.24) shows that the proper contour to use for the integral over the magnitude k_{n0} of the vector $\mathbf{k}_{n0}$ is one that goes from 0 to $+\infty$ by passing under the real axis at the pole κ. After the angular integrations are performed, the integrand is even in k_{n0}, and this contour can be reflected in the origin. The resulting contour, which extends from $-\infty$ to $+\infty$, is exactly the same as that used in the evaluation of (26.13) and shown in Fig. 21a. We therefore obtain from the earlier work an explicit expression for the summation (30.14):

$$\frac{L^3}{4\pi|\mathbf{r}-\mathbf{r}'|}\exp i\kappa|\mathbf{r}-\mathbf{r}'| \qquad (30.16)$$

Second-order Matrix Element.   It is convenient to rewrite the matrix elements (30.13) in terms of new functions

$$F_m(\mathbf{r} - \mathbf{R}) = \int \bar{u}_m(2)H_2'(2,\mathbf{r})u_0(2)d\tau_2$$
$$F_n(\mathbf{r}') = \int \bar{u}_n(1)H_1'(1,\mathbf{r}')u_0(1)d\tau_1$$

These functions are very small except when their arguments differ from zero by distances of the order of the size of the atom.   We put

$$\mathbf{r}'' = \mathbf{r} - \mathbf{R},$$

so that practically all the contribution to the first summation of (30.12) comes from small values of r' and r''.   We can then approximate

$$|\mathbf{r} - \mathbf{r}'| = |\mathbf{R} + \mathbf{r}'' - \mathbf{r}'| \cong R + \frac{\mathbf{R} \cdot \mathbf{r}''}{R} - \frac{\mathbf{R} \cdot \mathbf{r}'}{R}$$
$$|\mathbf{r} - \mathbf{r}'|^{-1} \cong R^{-1}$$

to obtain the leading terms in (30.16) for large R.   The first summation of (30.12) then becomes, to this approximation,

$$-\frac{2m}{\hbar^2} \frac{1}{4\pi L^3} \frac{\exp i(\boldsymbol{\kappa} - \mathbf{k}_{nm}) \cdot \mathbf{R}}{R} \int F_n(\mathbf{r}')[\exp i(\mathbf{k}_0 - \boldsymbol{\kappa}) \cdot \mathbf{r}']d\tau'$$
$$\cdot \int F_m(\mathbf{r}'')[\exp i(\boldsymbol{\kappa} - \mathbf{k}_{nm}) \cdot \mathbf{r}'']d\tau''   \quad (30.17)$$

where $\boldsymbol{\kappa}$ is a vector of magnitude κ given by (30.14), that has the direction of $\mathbf{R}$.

In similar fashion, the second summation of (30.12) becomes

$$-\frac{2m}{\hbar^2} \frac{1}{4\pi L^3} \frac{\exp i(\boldsymbol{\kappa}' + \mathbf{k}_0) \cdot \mathbf{R}}{R} \int F_n(\mathbf{r}')[\exp -i(\boldsymbol{\kappa}' + \mathbf{k}_{nm}) \cdot \mathbf{r}']d\tau'$$
$$\cdot \int F_m(\mathbf{r}'')[\exp i(\mathbf{k}_0 + \boldsymbol{\kappa}') \cdot \mathbf{r}'']d\tau''   \quad (30.18)$$

where $\boldsymbol{\kappa}'$ is a vector in the direction of $\mathbf{R}$ whose magnitude is given by (30.14) with ϵ_n replaced by ϵ_m.

The differential cross section is obtained by substituting the sum of (30.17) and (30.18) for H_{21}' in (30.6), and replacing k by k_{nm}.   Conservation of energy requires that

$$k_{nm}^2 = k_0^2 - \frac{2m}{\hbar^2}(\epsilon_n + \epsilon_m - 2\epsilon_0)$$

Discussion of the Cross Section.   The integrals that appear in (30.17) and (30.18) have the characteristic structure associated with the perturbation treatment of collision problems.   They are very small unless the propagation vector that appears in the exponent of the integrand has a magnitude that is of order $1/a$ or less, where a is a typical linear dimension of the atom (F significantly different from zero). It follows that (30.17) is significant only when the vectors $\mathbf{k}_0$, $\mathbf{\kappa}$, and $\mathbf{k}_{nm}$ are nearly equal in magnitude and direction. Because of the assumption that the incident electron is fast, the magnitudes are very nearly equal in any event. Then the cross section is appreciable only when the vectors $\mathbf{R}$ and $\mathbf{k}_{nm}$ are nearly parallel to $\mathbf{k}_0$. The permitted angular deviation from parallelism is easily seen to be of order $1/k_0 a$.

In similar fashion, it follows that (30.18) is significant only when $\mathbf{\kappa}'$, and hence $\mathbf{R}$, is nearly antiparallel to both $\mathbf{k}_0$ and $\mathbf{k}_{nm}$, in which case the latter two vectors are nearly parallel to each other.

The two terms together show that excitation of both atoms occurs with appreciable probability only when the line joining the two atoms is nearly parallel to the direction of the incident electron. It is apparent also that the cross section falls off inversely as the square of the distance R between the two atoms, as would be expected.

31. ADIABATIC AND SUDDEN APPROXIMATIONS

In this section we develop approximation methods that involve the rate of change of the Hamiltonian, rather than the magnitude of the time-dependent part of the Hamiltonian. If the Hamiltonian changes very slowly with the time, we expect to be able to approximate solutions of the Schrödinger equation by means of stationary energy eigenfunctions of the instantaneous Hamiltonian, so that a particular eigenfunction at one time goes over continuously into the corresponding eigenfunction at a later time (adiabatic approximation). If the Hamiltonian changes from one steady form to another over a very short time interval, we expect that the wave function does not change much, although the expansion of this function in eigenfunctions of the initial and final Hamiltonians may be quite different (sudden approximation). We determine here to what extent both of these types of approximation are valid.

Expansion in Instantaneous Energy Eigenfunctions. We consider first the adiabatic approximation, and wish to solve the Schrödinger equation

$$i\hbar \frac{\partial \psi}{\partial t} = H(t)\psi \tag{31.1}$$

when $H(t)$ varies slowly with the time.[1] The solutions of the energy eigenvalue equation at each instant of time are assumed to be known.

$$H(t)u_n(t) = E_n(t)u_n(t) \tag{31.2}$$

---

[1] M. Born and V. Fock, *Zeits. f. Physik*, **51**, 165 (1928); P. Güttinger, *Zeits. f. Physik*, **73**, 169 (1931).

We assume also that the u_n are orthonormal, nondegenerate, and discrete; their phases are fixed below.

Suppose that the wave function is known at zero time; at later times we put

$$\psi = \sum_n a_n(t)u_n(t) \exp\left[-\frac{i}{\hbar}\int_0^t E_n(t')dt'\right] \qquad (31.3)$$

Substitution of (31.3) into (31.1) gives

$$i\hbar \sum_n \left(\dot{a}_n u_n + a_n \frac{\partial u_n}{\partial t} - \frac{i}{\hbar} a_n u_n E_n\right) \exp\left[-\frac{i}{\hbar}\int_0^t E_n(t')dt'\right]$$

$$= H\sum_n a_n u_n \exp\left[-\frac{i}{\hbar}\int_0^t E_n(t')dt'\right]$$

Since $Hu_n = E_n u_n$ from (31.2), the last term on the left side cancels the right side. Multiplying through on the left by $\bar{u}_k$ and integrating over all the coordinates of the system ($\int d\tau$), we obtain

$$\dot{a}_k = -\sum_n a_n \exp\left[\frac{i}{\hbar}\int_0^t (E_k - E_n)dt'\right] \cdot \int \bar{u}_k \frac{\partial u_n}{\partial t} d\tau \qquad (31.4)$$

We now seek an expression for the integral on the right side of Eq. (31.4) that is easier to interpret in physical terms. Differentiation of (31.2) with respect to t gives

$$\frac{\partial H}{\partial t} u_n + H\frac{\partial u_n}{\partial t} = \frac{\partial E_n}{\partial t} u_n + E_n \frac{\partial u_n}{\partial t}$$

Multiplying through on the left by $\bar{u}_k$ and integrating over the coordinates gives

$$\int \bar{u}_k \frac{\partial H}{\partial t} u_n d\tau + \int \bar{u}_k H \frac{\partial u_n}{\partial t} d\tau = E_n \int \bar{u}_k \frac{\partial u_n}{\partial t} d\tau, \quad k \neq n \quad (31.5)$$

We make use of Eq. (22.10) to rewrite the second integral on the left side of Eq. (31.5), and remember that H is Hermitian.

$$\int \bar{u}_k H \frac{\partial u_n}{\partial t} d\tau = \int (H\bar{u}_k)\frac{\partial u_n}{\partial t} d\tau = E_k \int \bar{u}_k \frac{\partial u_n}{\partial t} d\tau$$

Substitution into (31.5) gives an expression for the integral on the right side of (31.4)

$$\int \bar{u}_k \frac{\partial u_n}{\partial t} d\tau = -\frac{\int \bar{u}_k \left(\frac{\partial H}{\partial t}\right) u_n d\tau}{E_k - E_n}, \qquad n \neq k \qquad (31.6)$$

Choice of Phases. In order to rewrite Eq. (31.4) along the lines indicated in the last paragraph, we must have an expression for

$$\int \bar{u}_n \frac{\partial u_n}{\partial t} d\tau$$

We now show that this integral is pure imaginary, and that a proper choice of the dependence of the phase of u_n on t makes it zero. Differentiation of the normalization integral for u_n gives

$$0 = \frac{d}{dt} \int \bar{u}_n u_n d\tau = \int \frac{\partial \bar{u}_n}{\partial t} u_n d\tau + \int \bar{u}_n \frac{\partial u_n}{\partial t} d\tau$$

Since the two integrals on the right are complex conjugates of each other, each must be pure imaginary: $\int \bar{u}_n (\partial u_n / \partial t) d\tau = i\alpha(t)$.

We now change the phase of u_n by an amount $\gamma(t)$, which is permissible since the phases of the eigenfunctions are arbitrary at each instant of time. For the new eigenfunction $u_n' \equiv u_n e^{i\gamma(t)}$,

$$\int \bar{u}_n' \frac{\partial u_n'}{\partial t} d\tau = \int \bar{u}_n e^{-i\gamma} \frac{\partial}{\partial t} (u_n e^{i\gamma}) d\tau = i\alpha(t) + i\frac{d}{dt}\gamma(t) \qquad (31.7)$$

Thus the choice $\gamma(t) = -\int_0^t \alpha(t') dt'$ for the phase makes the integral on the left side of (31.7) vanish. In what follows, we assume that u_n' has been substituted for u_n, with a consequent change in Eqs. (31.6), and omit the primes.

We adopt our earlier notation $\hbar\omega_{kn} = E_k - E_n$, and substitute (31.6) into (31.4):

$$\dot{a}_k = \sum_n' \frac{a_n}{\hbar\omega_{kn}} \left[\exp\left(i \int_0^t \omega_{kn} dt' \right) \right] \left(\frac{\partial H}{\partial t} \right)_{kn} \qquad (31.8)$$

where the prime on the summation indicates that the term $n = k$ is excluded from the summation. The last term on the right side of Eq. (31.8) is the kn matrix element of $\partial H/\partial t$.

Adiabatic Approximation. The group of Eqs. (31.8) for all k's is exactly equivalent to the Schrödinger equation (31.1). We now estimate the order of magnitude of a_k by assuming that all the quantities $(a_n, \omega_{kn}, u_n, \partial H/\partial t)$ that appear on the right side of (31.8) are constant in time. If further we assume that the system is in the state m at $t = 0$, we can put $a_n = \delta_{nm}$. We thus obtain

$$\dot{a}_k \cong \frac{1}{\hbar\omega_{km}} \left(\frac{\partial H}{\partial t} \right)_{km} e^{i\omega_{km}t}, \qquad\qquad k \neq m$$

which is readily integrated to give

$$a_k(t) \cong \frac{1}{i\hbar\omega_{km}^2} \left(\frac{\partial H}{\partial t}\right)_{km} (e^{i\omega_{km}t} - 1), \qquad k \neq m \qquad (31.9)$$

With the above approximations, Eq. (31.9) shows that the probability amplitude for a state other than the initial state oscillates in time and has no steady change over long periods of time even though H changes by a finite amount. If the change in H during the Bohr period for the transition $m \to k$ is small in comparison with the energy difference between these two states, the transition is unlikely to occur. The change in amplitude of the state k after a long time is of the order of the ratio of these two energies.

$$|a_k| \sim \left|\frac{(1/\omega_{km})(\partial H/\partial t)}{E_k - E_m}\right| \qquad (31.10)$$

Connection with Perturbation Theory. An exceptional situation arises when the Hamiltonian oscillates in time with a frequency nearly equal to one of the transition frequencies, say ω_{km}. This is a case of resonance, and we expect from the discussion of Sec. 29 that even a very small change in H can produce appreciable changes in the amplitude a_k over long periods of time, so that (31.10) is not valid. It is then no longer permissible to assume that the time dependence of $\partial H/\partial t$ can be neglected, and the passage from (31.8) to (31.9) is not justified.

In order to consider this case more carefully, we assume that only a small part of H oscillates in time with an angular frequency ω that is close to ω_{km}:

$$H = H_0 + H' \sin \omega t, \qquad \frac{\partial H}{\partial t} = \omega H' \cos \omega t$$

where H' is small in comparison with H_0 and both of these are constant in time. If then the dependence of a_n, ω_{kn}, and u_n on time is neglected and we put $a_n = \delta_{nm}$ as before, Eq. (31.8) becomes

$$\dot{a}_k \cong \frac{\omega H'_{km} \cos \omega t}{\hbar\omega_{km}} e^{i\omega_{km}t}$$

$$= \frac{\omega H'_{km}}{2\hbar\omega_{km}} [e^{i(\omega_{km}+\omega)t} + e^{i(\omega_{km}-\omega)t}]$$

This is readily integrated to give

$$a_k(t) \cong \frac{\omega H'_{km}}{2i\hbar\omega_{km}} \left[\frac{e^{i(\omega_{km}+\omega)t} - 1}{\omega_{km} + \omega} + \frac{e^{i(\omega_{km}-\omega)t} - 1}{\omega_{km} - \omega}\right] \qquad (31.11)$$

This shows that the adiabatic approximation (31.10) breaks down for $\omega_{km} \cong \pm\omega$, since then (31.11) increases steadily with the time. If ω_{km} is close to $+\omega$, the first bracket term can be neglected and we can replace ω/ω_{km} outside the bracket by $+1$; if ω_{km} is close to $-\omega$, the second bracket term can be neglected and we can replace ω/ω_{km} by -1. In both cases, we see that (31.11) agrees with the perturbation-theory result given in Eq. (29.17).

Discontinuous Change in H. As an introduction to the sudden approximation, we consider first a situation in which the Hamiltonian changes discontinuously from one form that is constant in time to another. Suppose that $H = H_0$ for $t < 0$ and $H = H_1$ for $t > 0$, where

$$H_0 u_n = E_n u_n, \qquad H_1 v_m = E_m v_m$$

and the u's and v's are complete orthonormal sets of functions that are not necessarily discrete. The general solutions can be written

$$\psi = \mathsf{S} a_n u_n e^{-\frac{iE_n t}{\hbar}} \qquad t < 0$$

$$\psi = \mathsf{S} b_m v_m e^{-\frac{iE_m t}{\hbar}} \qquad t > 0$$

$$(31.12)$$

where the a's and b's are independent of the time.

Since the wave equation (31.1) is of first order in the time, the wave function at all points in space must be a continuous function of the time at $t = 0$, although its time derivative is not. The b's are then readily expressed in terms of the a's by equating the two solutions (31.12) at $t = 0$, multiplying by a particular $\bar{v}$, and integrating over the coordinates:

$$b_m = \mathsf{S} a_n \int \bar{v}_m u_n d\tau \qquad (31.13)$$

The appearance of final states m that need not have the same energy as an initial state is a consequence of the non-zero frequency Fourier components into which the suddenly changing Hamiltonian can be resolved (see Sec. 29).

Sudden Approximation. The sudden approximation consists in using Eqs.(31.13) when the change in the Hamiltonian occupies a very short but finite interval of time t_0. In order to make an estimate of the error introduced in b_m, we consider a problem that, while somewhat artificial, can easily be solved formally. Suppose that $H = H_0$ for $t < 0$, $H = H_1$ for $t > t_0$, and $H = H_i$ for $0 < t < t_0$. The intermediate Hamiltonian, which is assumed to be constant in time, has a complete orthonormal set of energy eigenfunctions:

$$H_i w_k = E_k w_k$$

The true solution can be expanded in terms of the w's with constant coefficients:

$$\psi = \mathsf{S} c_k w_k e^{-\frac{iE_k t}{\hbar}} \qquad 0 < t < t_0$$

The continuity condition at $t = 0$ gives

$$c_k = \mathbf{S}_n a_n \int \bar{w}_k u_n d\tau \qquad (31.14)$$

In similar fashion, the continuity condition at $t = t_0$ gives, with the help of (31.14),

$$b_m = \mathbf{S}_k c_k \int \bar{v}'_m w'_k d\tau' \cdot e^{-\frac{i(E_k - E_m)t_0}{\hbar}}$$

$$= \mathbf{S}_k \mathbf{S}_n a_n \int \bar{w}_m u_n d\tau \int \bar{v}'_m w'_k d\tau \cdot e^{-\frac{i(E_k - E_m)t_0}{\hbar}}$$

$$= \mathbf{S}_n a_n \int\int \bar{v}'_m \left[\mathbf{S}_k w'_k \bar{w}_k e^{-\frac{i(E_k - E_m)t_0}{\hbar}} \right] u_n d\tau d\tau' \qquad (31.15)$$

where the primes denote a different set of coordinate variables of integration. The closure relation (10.11) shows that the bracket in the last term of (31.15) becomes a product of δ functions of the differences between primed and unprimed coordinates when $t_0 = 0$, in which case the expression for b_m agrees with (31.13), as it should.

The difference between the exact expression (31.15) for b_m and the approximate expression (31.13) is measured by the difference between $\exp[-i(E_k - E_m)t_0/\hbar]$ and unity. This is small if t_0 is small in comparison with all the periods $h/(E_k - E_m)$ that correspond to the eigenfunctions k and m that appear when H changes.

A useful validity criterion is that t_0 be small in comparison with the periods associated with the initial motion, since new states of motion that have very much shorter periods (high energies) are excited with relatively small amplitudes. When the sudden approximation is useful, the error in b_m (and hence in ψ) is of the order of the ratio of t_0 to a typical initial period.

Transient Disturbance. An interesting special case of (31.15) is that in which initial and final Hamiltonians are the same ($H_1 = H_0$, $v_m = u_m$) and the system is initially in a particular state n. Then if t_0 is short enough to satisfy the validity criterion of the last paragraph, we can expand the exponential in the last member of (31.15) and retain only the first two terms.

$$b_m \cong \int\int \bar{u}'_m \mathbf{S}_k w'_k \bar{w}_k \left[1 - \frac{it_0}{\hbar}(E_k - E_m) \right] u_n d\tau d\tau'$$

$$= \int\int \bar{u}'_m \mathbf{S}_k w'_k \bar{w}_k \left[1 - \frac{it_0}{\hbar}(H_i - E_m) \right] u_n d\tau d\tau'$$

With the help of the closure relation, the orthogonality of u_m and u_n when $m \neq n$, the substitution $E_m \bar{u}_m = H_0 \bar{u}_m$, and Eq. (22.10), this can be reduced to

$$b_m \cong -\frac{it_0}{\hbar} \int \bar{u}_m(H_i - H_0)u_n d\tau, \quad m \neq n \quad (31.16)$$

Equation (31.16) can be generalized to a situation in which H_i depends on the time; in this case a result that is also correct to first order in t_0 is obtained by replacing $H_i t_0$ by $\int_0^{t_0} H_i dt$.

It should be noted that the expression (31.16) for b_m can be useful even when $H_i - H_0$ is not small in comparison with H_0, provided that the general criterion for the validity of the sudden approximation is satisfied (t_0 sufficiently small). On the other hand, the perturbation theory (Sec. 29) is useful when a small time-dependent addition to the Hamiltonian is applied for a long time.

Disturbance of an Oscillator. As a simple example of the application of the approximation methods developed in this section, we consider a linear harmonic oscillator in which the position of the equilibrium point $a(t)$ depends on the time. The Hamiltonian for this system is

$$H(t) = -\frac{\hbar^2}{2m}\frac{\partial^2}{\partial x^2} + \tfrac{1}{2}K[x - a(t)]^2$$

The instantaneous energy eigenfunctions are the harmonic-oscillator wave functions (13.13) centered at the point $a(t)$, and the energy levels are unchanged:

$$u_n(x) = N_n H_n[\alpha(x - a)]e^{-\frac{1}{2}\alpha^2(x-a)^2}, \quad E_n = (n + \tfrac{1}{2})\hbar\omega_c$$

We suppose first that the equilibrium point moves slowly, and investigate the circumstances under which the adiabatic approximation is applicable. If the oscillator is initially in its ground state ($n = 0$), the time derivative of the Hamiltonian $\partial H/\partial t = -K(x - a)\dot{a}$ has a non-vanishing matrix element only with the first excited state. With the help of (13.18) this is found to be

$$\left(\frac{\partial H}{\partial t}\right)_{10} = -\frac{K\dot{a}}{\alpha\sqrt{2}} = -K\dot{a}(\tfrac{1}{2}\hbar)^{\frac{1}{2}}(Km)^{-\frac{1}{4}}$$

Substitution into (31.9) shows that the coefficient of the time-dependent factor in the amplitude of the first excited state has the magnitude

$$\frac{K\dot{a}}{\hbar\omega_c^2}\frac{(\tfrac{1}{2}\hbar)^{\frac{1}{2}}}{(Km)^{\frac{1}{4}}} = \frac{\dot{a}}{(2\hbar\omega_c/m)^{\frac{1}{2}}}$$

This expression may be interpreted physically by noting that the denominator is of the order of the maximum speed of a hypothetical classical oscillator that has the zero-point energy. Thus the adiabatic approximation is good if the equilibrium point moves slowly in comparison with the classical-oscillator speed.   It is easily seen that for the nth excited state, the equilibrium-point speed must be small in comparison with $1/n$ times the corresponding classical-oscillator speed.

The sudden approximation can be applied to an oscillator in its ground state when the time required to move the equilibrium point from one steady position to another is small in comparison with $1/\omega_c$.   If this point is displaced a distance a in the positive direction along the line of motion, application of (31.13) shows that the probability amplitude for the nth state after the displacement is

$$\frac{\alpha^{\frac{1}{2}}}{\pi}\int_{-\infty}^{\infty}\bar{u}_n(x-a)e^{-\frac{1}{2}\alpha^2x^2}dx = \frac{\alpha^{\frac{1}{2}}}{\pi^{\frac{1}{2}}}\int_{-\infty}^{\infty}\bar{u}_n(x)e^{-\frac{1}{2}\alpha^2(x+a)^2}dx$$

This integral is identical with the expression for A_n in Eq. (13.21), except for the sign of a, and has already been evaluated with the help of the generating function (13.10) for the Hermite polynomials.   The earlier discussion (Sec. 13) shows that the states most likely to be excited are those that have a classical amplitude of oscillation that is of the order of the displacement a; this is in agreement with the corresponding classical result.

Problems

1. A hydrogen atom in its ground state is placed between the plates of a condenser. A voltage pulse is applied to the condenser so as to produce a homogeneous electric field that has the time dependence: $\mathsf{E} = 0, t < 0; \mathsf{E} = \mathsf{E}_0 e^{-\frac{t}{\tau}}, t > 0$.   Find the first-order probability that the atom is in the 2S state (200) after a long time.   What is the corresponding probability that it is in one of the 2P states?

2. An alternating voltage of angular frequency $\omega > me^4/2\hbar^3$ is applied to the condenser of Prob. 1.   What is the probability per unit time for the hydrogen atom to make a transition from its normal state to an ionized state?   Assume, only for the purpose of this problem, that the electronic wave function for the ionized state can be represented by a plane wave.

3. Extend Eq. (29.20) to the case in which a transition can occur only in third order of the perturbation.   Assume that none of the intermediate states has the same energy as the initial and final states.

4. Use the perturbation theory to calculate the differential collision cross section for the $1S \rightarrow 2S$ excitation of a hydrogen atom.   Integrate this to obtain the total cross section, and show that it becomes the expression given in Sec. 30 at high bombarding energy.

5. Use the perturbation theory to calculate the differential collision cross section for the $1S \rightarrow 2P$ excitation of a hydrogen atom.   Show that the total cross section becomes the expression given in Eq. (30.11) at high bombarding energy.

6. Discuss the statement that appears at the end of the next to the last paragraph of Sec. 31.   In particular, show physically why it need not be a sufficient condition for the applicability of the adiabatic approximation that the equilibrium-point speed be small in comparison with the corresponding classical-oscillator speed.

7. Under what circumstances is $\psi(t) = [\exp(-iHt/\hbar)]\psi(0)$ a valid representation of the solution ψ at time t in terms of the Hamiltonian H and the solution at time zero? Show that, in general, the operator Ht in the exponent cannot be replaced by $\int_0^t H dt'$. Show, however, that $H_i t_0$ in Eq. (31.16) can be replaced by $\int_0^{t_0} H_i dt$ to first order in t_0.

8. A hydrogen nucleus of mass 3 is radioactive, and changes into a helium nucleus of mass 3 with the emission of an electron that has not more than about 17,000 electron-volts energy. Show that the sudden approximation can be applied to the extra-nuclear electron that is initially present in the hydrogen atom, and is superior to the other approximation methods that might be used. Calculate the numerical values of the probabilities that the resulting helium ion is found in its $1S$, $2S$, and $2P$ states if the hydrogen atom is initially in its $1S$ state. Give a qualitative discussion of the energy balance in this process.

CHAPTER IX

IDENTICAL PARTICLES AND SPIN

The quantum-mechanical theory of particles presented thus far is deficient in three respects. First, whenever two or more particles are described at once, like the electron and proton of the hydrogen atom (Sec. 16) or the incident and atomic electrons in an inelastic collision (Sec. 30), it is assumed that the particles can be distinguished from each other. This is a valid assumption in the first example, since electrons and protons possess quite different masses and electrical charges. In the second example, however, there is no observable difference between the incident and atomic electrons, and the consequences of this *identity* should appear in the formalism. The second defect of the theory is the omission of an intrinsic *spin angular momentum*, or *spin*, actually possessed by some of the particles found in nature.[1] Third, no mention has as yet been made of the special theory of relativity, which is expected to affect the theoretical description of particles that move with speeds close to that of light.

The ways in which the first two of these defects can be remedied are described in this chapter, and illustrative examples are discussed. Relativistic effects are taken up in Chap. XII.

32. IDENTICAL PARTICLES

Identical particles cannot be distinguished by means of any inherent property, since otherwise they would not be identical in all respects. In classical mechanics, the existence of sharply definable trajectories for individual particles makes it possible in principle to distinguish between particles that are identical except for their paths, since each particle can be followed during the course of an experiment. In quantum mechanics, the finite size and the spreading of the wave packets that can describe individual particles often make it impossible to distinguish between identical particles because of their positions, especially if they interact with each other to an appreciable extent. This is true of the electrons in a single atom, where we have seen that the description in terms of moving wave packets breaks down completely. However, the electrons of different atoms that are well separated from each other may, to good

---

[1] Spin was first discovered in connection with electrons, by G. E. Uhlenbeck and S. Goudsmit, *Naturwiss.*, **13**, 953 (1925); *Nature*, **117**, 264 (1926).

approximation, be regarded as distinguishable. This section considers some of the effects of identity on the quantum-mechanical treatment of systems of two or more particles. Other effects that involve the spin explicitly will be taken up in the remainder of this chapter.

Physical Meaning of Identity. The impossibility in principle of dis-- tinguishing between identical particles in most quantum-mechanical problems can lead to effects that have no classical analogue. As an example, we compare the elastic collision of two identical particles that have a particular interaction between them, with the collision of two different particles that have the same interaction between them.

In a classical treatment, there is no difference of principle between the results of these two experiments, since it is possible to distinguish between the incident and struck particles in the first case as well as in the second. In practice, however, this distinction would usually be made only in the second experiment. Thus, according to classical mechanics, the meas- ured differential cross section in the first experiment is equal to the sum of the corresponding cross sections measured for the incident and struck particles in the second experiment. In the corresponding quantum- mechanical situation, the identical particles in the first experiment cannot be distinguished by means of their trajectories, since they cannot be well localized without interfering with the scattering process. Thus the dis- tinction between incident and struck particles has no physical significance, and the simple connection between the results of the two experiments that is found in the classical case need not exist.

We use the word *identical* to describe particles that can be sub- stituted for each other under the most general possible circumstances with no change in the physical situation. Identical particles can in some cases be distinguished from each other, as when their wave packets do not overlap. Another case, discussed more fully in Sec. 33, arises when each of the particles possesses an intrinsic spin angular momentum, which is a constant of the motion in a particular collision. Then since the component of the spin along some axis is assumed not to change dur- ing this collision, the particles can be distinguished if they have different spin components. Results of this kind must, of course, be a consequence of the formalism that we now set up.

Symmetric and Antisymmetric Wave Functions. The Schrödinger wave equation for n identical particles is

$$i\hbar \frac{\partial}{\partial t} \psi (1,2, \ldots ,n; t) = H(1,2, \ldots ,n)\psi(1,2, \ldots ,n; t) \quad (32.1)$$

where each of the numbers represents all the coordinates (positional and spin) of one of the particles. The Hamiltonian H is symmetrical in its arguments, since the identity of the particles means that they can be substituted for each other without changing H.

There are two kinds of solutions ψ of Eq. (32.1) that possess symmetry properties of particular interest. A wave function is *symmetric* if the interchange of any pair of particles among its arguments leaves the wave function unchanged. A wave function is *antisymmetric* if the interchange of any pair of particles changes the sign of ψ. We now show that the symmetry character of a wave function does not change in time. If ψ_S is symmetric at a particular time t, then $H\psi_S$ is also symmetric, and (32.1) states that $\partial\psi_S/\partial t$ is symmetric. Since ψ_S and its time derivative are symmetric at time t, ψ_S at an infinitesimally later time $t + dt$ is given by $\psi_S + (\partial\psi_S/\partial t)dt$, and is also symmetric. Such a step-by-step integration of the wave equation can, in principle, be continued for arbitrarily large time intervals, and ψ_S is seen to remain symmetric always. In similar fashion, if ψ_A is antisymmetric at any time, $H\psi_A$ and hence $\partial\psi_A/\partial t$ are antisymmetric, and integration of the wave equation shows that ψ_A is always antisymmetric.

The foregoing proof is not altered if H and ψ have as their arguments the coordinates of two or more different groups of identical particles; thus a wave function that is initially set up to be symmetric or antisymmetric in the coordinates of each identical-particle group always retains this character. This makes it possible for the different groups of identical particles found in nature to have definite symmetry characters, and this is actually found to be the case. Electrons, protons, and neutrons are the only material particles for which the experimental evidence is unambiguous, and each of these kinds of particles is described by antisymmetric wave functions.

Construction from Unsymmetrized Functions. We now show how ψ_S or ψ_A can be constructed from a general unsymmetrized solution ψ of Eq. (32.1). If the arguments of ψ are permuted in any way, the resulting function is a solution of (32.1). That this is true follows from the observation that the same permutation applied throughout Eq. (32.1) does not impair its validity, since it corresponds simply to a relabeling of the particles; then since H is symmetric, the permuted H is the same as the original H, and the resulting equation is the same as (32.1) for the permuted ψ. In this way $n!$ solutions can be obtained from any one solution, each of which corresponds to one of the $n!$ permutations of the n arguments of ψ. It is evident that any linear combination of these functions is also a solution of the wave equation (32.1).

The sum of all these functions that are linearly independent is a symmetric (unnormalized) wave function ψ_S, since the interchange of any pair of particles changes any one of the component functions into another of them and the latter into the former, leaving the entire wave function unchanged. An antisymmetric unnormalized wave function can be constructed by adding together all the permuted functions that arise from the original solution by means of an even number of interchanges of pairs of particles, and subtracting the sum of all the permuted functions that arise by means of an odd number of interchanges of pairs of particles in the original solution. It is apparent that a nonvanishing antisymmetric wave function cannot be formed from a solution that is unaltered by the interchange of any pair of particles.

In the event that the Hamiltonian does not involve the time, stationary solutions $\psi(1,2, \ldots ,n; t) = u(1,2, \ldots ,n)e^{-\frac{iEt}{\hbar}}$ can be found, where

$$[H(1,2, \ldots ,n) - E]u(1,2, \ldots ,n) = 0$$

The earlier discussion shows that the solutions derived from any u by means of permutations of its arguments are degenerate with the original u; this is called *exchange degeneracy*. When $n = 2$, the $2! = 2$ permutations result in $u(1,2)$ and $u(2,1)$; the symmetric and antisymmetric combinations are obtained by taking the upper and lower sign, respectively, in

$$u(1,2) \pm u(2,1) \tag{32.2}$$

When $n = 3$, the $3! = 6$ permutations yield $u(1,2,3)$, $u(2,1,3)$, $u(3,2,1)$, $u(1,3,2)$, $u(2,3,1)$, and $u(3,1,2)$; the symmetric and antisymmetric combinations are

$$[u(1,2,3) + u(2,3,1) + u(3,1,2)]$$
$$\pm [u(2,1,3) + u(1,3,2) + u(3,2,1)] \tag{32.3}$$

with the upper and lower sign, respectively.

All the energy eigenfunctions that are exchange degenerate with $u(1,2)$ can be formed from the two solutions (32.2). When $n = 3$, however, there are four linearly independent eigenfunctions that cannot be formed from the two functions (32.3). These additional solutions, which always appear when $n > 2$, can be chosen so as to possess permanent symmetry characters that resemble but are somewhat more complicated than those of the symmetric and antisymmetric solutions. However, they do not appear to describe particles found in nature.

Distinguishability of Identical Particles. It is to be expected that the result of an experiment is independent of the symmetry character of the wave function if the coordinates of the particles do not overlap. This corresponds to a situation in which the particles can be distinguished by means of their positions (or their spin components) even though they are identical. Such a situation implies, in the case of two particles, that the wave function $u(1,2)$ is different from zero only when the coordinate 1 is in some region A, the coordinate 2 is in a region B, and A and B have no common domain.

The coordinate probability density associated with the wave function $u(1,2)$ is $|u(1,2)|^2$, and the densities associated with the symmetrized wave functions (32.3) are

$$|u(1,2) \pm u(2,1)|^2 = |u(1,2)|^2 + |u(2,1)|^2 \pm 2Re[u(1,2)\bar{u}(2,1)] \quad (32.4)$$

where Re denotes the real part of the expression in brackets. If now $u(1,2)$ vanishes whenever 1 is not in A and 2 is not in B, and A and B do not overlap, the bracket term is zero everywhere, and (32.4) becomes $|u(1,2)|^2 + |u(2,1)|^2$.

Thus the density associated with either of the symmetrized wave functions (32.2) is the sum of the densities associated with $u(1,2)$ and $u(2,1)$ separately. This is precisely the result that will be obtained if the particles are not identical but no attempt is made to distinguish between them in performing the experiment. Thus the interference effects between exchange-degenerate wave functions, represented by the bracket term in (32.4), disappear when the coordinates of the particles do not overlap.

The Exclusion Principle. In many problems, a useful zero-order approximation can be obtained by neglecting the interactions between the particles that make up the system under consideration. The approximate (unperturbed) Hamiltonian is the sum of equal Hamiltonian functions for the separate particles

$$H_0(1,2, \ldots, n) = H_0'(1) + H_0'(2) + \cdots + H_0'(n) \quad (32.5)$$

and the approximate energy eigenfunction is a product of one-particle eigenfunctions of H_0'

$$u(1,2, \ldots, n) = v_\alpha(1)v_\beta(2) \ldots v_\nu(n)$$
$$E = E_\alpha + E_\beta + \cdots + E_\nu \quad (32.6)$$
$$H_0'(1)v_\alpha(1) = E_\alpha v_\alpha(1), \text{ etc.}$$

If the particles are electrons, an antisymmetric wave function must be constructed from the u given by (32.6). This is most easily expressed as a determinant of the v's:

$$u_A(1,2, \ldots n) = \begin{vmatrix} v_\alpha(1) & v_\alpha(2) & \cdots & v_\alpha(n) \\ v_\beta(1) & v_\beta(2) & \cdots & v_\beta(n) \\ \cdots & \cdots & \cdots & \cdots \\ \cdots & \cdots & \cdots & \cdots \\ v_\nu(1) & v_\nu(2) & \cdots & v_\nu(n) \end{vmatrix} \quad (32.7)$$

The (unnormalized) u_A given in (32.7) is clearly an antisymmetric solution of the approximate wave equation $(H_0 - E)u_A = 0$.

Equation (32.7) has the interesting property that it vanishes if two or more of the v's are the same. This is a special case of the general result stated earlier that an antisymmetric wave function cannot be constructed from a solution that is unaltered by the interchange of any pair of particles. Thus the approximate Hamiltonian H_0 has no solutions for which there is more than one electron in any one of the states $\alpha, \beta, \ldots, \nu$. This result is known as the *exclusion principle* and was first postulated by Pauli[1] as an explanation of the periodic system of the chemical elements (see Sec. 38).

Connection with Statistical Mechanics. The unsymmetrized zero-order solution given in Eq. (32.6) can be used to construct a symmetric as well as an antisymmetric wave function. Such a symmetric (unnormalized) function is easily seen to be the sum of all different permutations of the numbers $1, 2, \ldots, n$ among the one-particle eigenfunctions $v_\alpha, v_\beta, \ldots, v_\nu$. This wave function is unique, and can be specified simply by stating how many particles are in each of the states $\alpha, \beta, \ldots$. In the same way, an antisymmetric wave function can be specified by stating how many particles are in each state. The fundamental statistical difference between particles that are described by antisymmetric and by symmetric wave functions is that the number of the former type that can occupy any state is limited to 0 or 1, whereas any number $(0, 1, 2, \ldots)$ of the latter type of particles can occupy any state.

The treatment of aggregates of large numbers of noninteracting (or weakly interacting) particles for which the states can be enumerated in these two ways forms the subject matter of quantum *statistical mechanics*. Particles that are described by antisymmetric wave functions are said to obey *Fermi-Dirac statistics*, and particles that are described by symmetric wave functions obey *Einstein-Bose statistics*.[2]

Of the material particles whose statistics are definitely known, electrons, protons, and neutrons obey Fermi-Dirac statistics, and π mesons obey Einstein-Bose statistics.[3] Also, light quanta, or photons, in so far as they can be treated as particles, obey Einstein-Bose statistics even though they cannot usefully be described by means of wave functions. Further, aggregates of particles that are sufficiently tightly bound so that they can be regarded as "particles" are described either by symmetric or by antisymmetric wave functions.

For example, the nucleus of a helium atom is made up of two protons, two neutrons, and an indeterminate number of π mesons, which are strongly bound together. If we consider a number of helium nuclei that

[1] W. Pauli, *Zeits. f. Physik*, **31**, 765 (1925).

[2] See, for example, R. C. Tolman, "The Principles of Statistical Mechanics," Chap. X (Oxford, New York, 1938).

[3] R. E. Marshak, "Meson Physics," Chap. 4 (McGraw-Hill, New York, 1952).

interact with each other weakly enough so that the changes in the internal motions of the nuclei can be neglected, we can see that the motions of the centers of gravity of the nuclei can be described approximately by a symmetric wave function.   The interchange of a pair of helium nuclei can be thought of as the resultant of the interchanges of two pairs of protons, two pairs of neutrons, and a number of pairs of π mesons.   Since the actual wave function is antisymmetric in all the protons and in all the neutrons, the resultant of the first four interchanges leaves the approximate wave function unchanged; the symmetry of the wave function in the π mesons is such that the latter interchanges also have no effect.   By an extension of this argument, we see that weakly interacting "particles" (nuclei, atoms, or molecules) obey Einstein-Bose statistics when each of them consists of an even total number of electrons, protons, and neutrons, and obey Fermi-Dirac statistics when each consists of an odd total number of these particles.[1]

Collisions of Identical Particles.   When the only forces acting on two particles result from their mutual interaction, the over-all motion can be separated into motion of the center of mass of the two particles and motion of the particles relative to each other, as discussed in Secs. 16 and 18.   It is apparent that an interchange of two identical particles does not affect the position vector of the center of mass [which is $\frac{1}{2}(\mathbf{r}_1 + \mathbf{r}_2)$ since the particles have equal masses], but changes the sign of the relative position vector $\mathbf{r}$ ($= \mathbf{r}_1 - \mathbf{r}_2$).   We postpone consideration of the spins of the particles until the next section, and see now what effect symmetry or antisymmetry of the space part of the wave function has on the elastic scattering of a particle by another that is identical with it.

The asymptotic form of the unsymmetrized scattering wave function in the center-of-mass coordinate system is given by Eq. (18.10).

$$u(\mathbf{r}) \xrightarrow[r \to \infty]{} e^{ikz} + r^{-1}f(\theta,\phi)e^{ikr} \qquad (32.8)$$

where r,θ,ϕ are the polar coordinates of the relative position vector $\mathbf{r}$. Since the polar coordinates of the vector $-\mathbf{r}$ are r, $\pi - \theta$, $\phi + \pi$, the asymptotic forms of the symmetric and antisymmetric wave functions formed from (32.8) are given by

$$(e^{ikz} \pm e^{-ikz}) + [f(\theta,\phi) \pm f(\pi - \theta,\ \phi + \pi)]r^{-1}e^{ikr} \qquad (32.9)$$

with upper and lower signs, respectively.

From the discussion of Sec. 18, it follows that the differential scattering cross section in the center-of-mass coordinate system is the square of the magnitude of the bracket term in (32.9):

$$\sigma(\theta,\phi) = |f(\theta,\phi)|^2 + |f(\pi - \theta,\ \phi + \pi)|^2$$
$$\pm 2Re[f(\theta,\phi)\bar{f}(\pi - \theta,\ \phi + \pi)] \quad (32.10)$$

[1] A more rigorous treatment that leads to the same conclusion has been given by P. Ehrenfest and J. R. Oppenheimer, *Phys. Rev.*, **37**, 333 (1931).

The normalization adopted here can be justified by noticing that in the classical limit, where the identical particles are distinguishable and the last (interference) term in Eq. (32.10) drops out, $\sigma(\theta,\phi)$ becomes just the sum of the differential cross sections for observation of the incident particle ($|f(\theta,\phi)|^2$) and of the struck particle ($|f(\pi - \theta, \phi + \pi)|^2$), as it should.

In the usual case, for which f is independent of ϕ, it is apparent that the scattering per unit solid angle is symmetrical about $\theta = 90°$ in the center-of-mass coordinate system. It is easily seen from Eq. (18.7) with $\gamma = 1$ that the scattering per unit angle (not per unit solid angle) in the laboratory coordinate system

$$\sigma_0(\theta_0) \sin \theta_0 = 4 \cos \theta_0 \sin \theta_0 \, \{ |f(2\theta_0)|^2$$
$$+ |f(\pi - 2\theta_0)|^2 \pm 2Re[f(2\theta_0)\bar{f}(\pi - 2\theta_0)]\}$$

is symmetrical about $\theta_0 = 45°$.

33. SPIN ANGULAR MOMENTUM

The treatment of identical particles presented in the preceding section must now be supplemented by inclusion of the spin angular momenta of the particles. It was shown in Sec. 24 that the operator **M,** which has the properties associated with an angular momentum, can be represented by matrices in an infinite number of ways. For each representation, M^2 and one component of **M,** say M_z, can be diagonalized; their eigenvalues are $j(j + 1)\hbar^2$ and the series $j\hbar$, $(j - 1)\hbar$, . . . , $-j\hbar$, respectively, where $2j$ is zero or a positive integer. If the expression for **M** in terms of the position and momentum of a particle ($\mathbf{r} \times \mathbf{p}$) is abandoned, then M^2 can commute with the Hamiltonian for that particle. In this case, M^2, and hence j, is a constant of the motion and characterizes the particle for all time; the corresponding intrinsic angular momentum is called the *spin* of the particle. We shall replace **M** by **S** and j by s in dealing with the spin.

Connection between Spin and Statistics. As remarked in Sec. 24, electrons, protons, and neutrons have $s = \frac{1}{2}$, and π mesons have $s = 0$. Aggregates of particles that are sufficiently tightly bound can be regarded as "particles," and can be characterized by definite magnitudes of their total internal angular momenta, so long as their internal motions and the relative spin orientations of their component particles are not significantly affected by the interactions between aggregates. This is exactly analogous to the situation with regard to the statistics obeyed by the aggregates, discussed in the preceding section.

The treatment of the addition of angular momenta, presented at the end of Sec. 24, can be generalized to give the possible magnitudes of the total internal angular momentum, which we call the *spin*, of any aggregate of fundamental particles. If the aggregate consists of n particles, each of which has $s = \frac{1}{2}$, and any number of particles with $s = 0$, and if the internal orbital angular momentum of these particles is ignored, the total s can be any integer from 0 to $\frac{1}{2}n$ if n is even, or can vary by integer steps from $\frac{1}{2}$ to $\frac{1}{2}n$ if n is odd. The total orbital-angular-momentum quantum number can be shown to be an integer or zero in general;[1] its inclusion extends the maximum value of s for the aggregate, but does not alter the conclusion that s is zero or an integer if n is even, and is half an odd integer if n is odd.

We see then that for the known fundamental particles and for aggregates of them that have a definite spin, there is a unique connection between the spin and the statistics. Particles or aggregates that have zero or integer spin are described by symmetric wave functions and obey Einstein-Bose statistics, and particles or aggregates that have half-odd-integer spin are described by antisymmetric wave functions and obey Fermi-Dirac statistics. There is some theoretical reason, based on relativistic quantum mechanics,[2] to believe that this connection also holds for other fundamental particles whose existence is suspected but whose spin and statistics have not yet been determined (other mesons and neutrinos).

Spin Matrices and Eigenfunctions. The spin can be included in the formalism developed in Sec. 32 by having each of the numbers $1, 2, \ldots, n$ that appear as the arguments of ψ and u represent a spin coordinate as well as the three space coordinates of that particle. The spin coordinate differs from the space coordinates in that it takes on only $2s + 1$ values for a particle (or aggregate) of spin s, instead of the infinite number of values that are taken on by each space coordinate. Thus the "spin space" consists of a finite number of points. The spin wave function of a single particle is completely determined by the specification of $2s + 1$ numbers, whereas the space wave function involves the specification of a continuously infinite set of numbers (which is equivalent to a continuous function of the space coordinates).[3]

A convenient set of orthonormal one-particle spin functions is provided by the normalized eigenfunctions of the $\mathbf{M}^2$ and M_z matrices given in equations (24.15). These eigenfunctions are $(2s + 1)$-row, one-column matrices that have zeros in all positions except one. For example, if $s = \frac{3}{2}$, the four spin eigenfunctions are easily seen to be

---

[1] The work of Secs. 14 and 24 shows that this is true for noninteracting particles that move in central force fields, and the result turns out not to be affected by particle interactions.

[2] W. Pauli, *Phys. Rev.*, **58**, 716 (1940).

[3] If the space and spin motions are closely enough coupled together, the space wave function may depend on the spin coordinate, so that $2s + 1$ space functions are required.

$$v(\tfrac{3}{2}) = \begin{pmatrix}1\\0\\0\\0\end{pmatrix}, \quad v(\tfrac{1}{2}) = \begin{pmatrix}0\\1\\0\\0\end{pmatrix}, \quad v(-\tfrac{1}{2}) = \begin{pmatrix}0\\0\\1\\0\end{pmatrix}, \quad v(-\tfrac{3}{2}) = \begin{pmatrix}0\\0\\0\\1\end{pmatrix} \quad (33.1)$$

and correspond to S_z eigenvalues of $\tfrac{3}{2}\hbar$, $\tfrac{1}{2}\hbar$, $-\tfrac{1}{2}\hbar$, and $-\tfrac{3}{2}\hbar$, respectively. The orthonormality is demonstrated by multiplying the Hermitian adjoint of one spin function into itself or another function

$$(0\ 1\ 0\ 0)\begin{pmatrix}0\\1\\0\\0\end{pmatrix} = 1, \qquad (0\ 1\ 0\ 0)\begin{pmatrix}0\\0\\1\\0\end{pmatrix} = 0, \text{ etc.}$$

with the help of the usual rule for matrix multiplication.

Symmetric or antisymmetric many-particle wave functions can be constructed from unsymmetrized solutions that include the spin by following the procedure outlined in the preceding section. It is sometimes convenient to choose the unsymmetrized solutions to be eigenfunctions of the square of the magnitude of the total spin of the identical particles $(\mathbf{S}_1 + \mathbf{S}_2 + \cdots + \mathbf{S}_n)^2$ and of the z component of this total spin $S_{1z} + S_{2z} + \cdots + S_{nz}$. These quantities are constants of the motion if the Hamiltonian does not contain interaction terms between the spins and other angular momenta. In addition, such functions are often useful as zero-order wave functions when the spin interactions are weak enough to be regarded as a perturbation. There is no loss of generality in choosing the unsymmetrized solutions in this way, since in the absence of spin interactions any solution can be expressed as a linear combination of total-spin eigenfunctions.

Collisions of Identical Particles. The effect of spin on the collision of two identical particles (or aggregates) can now be taken into account if the interaction between the particles does not involve the spin. Since each particle has $2s + 1$ spin eigenfunctions, there are altogether $(2s + 1)^2$ independent spin functions for the pair, each of which is a product of one-particle spin functions.

Any $(2s + 1)^2$ linearly independent combinations of these products can be used in place of them. These are conveniently divided into three classes. The first class consists of products of one-particle functions in which both particles are in the same spin state with S_z value $m\hbar$:

$$v_1(m)v_2(m), \qquad -s \leqq m \leqq s$$

where the subscript specifies which of the particles is in each state; there are evidently $2s + 1$ such states. The second class consists of sums of products

$$v_1(m')v_2(m'') + v_1(m'')v_2(m'), \qquad m' \neq m''$$

There are $s(2s + 1)$ of these states. The third class consists of differences of products

$$v_1(m')v_2(m'') - v_1(m'')v_2(m'), \qquad m' \neq m''$$

Again there are $s(2s + 1)$ of these.

The first two classes are clearly symmetric in an interchange of the spin coordinates of the two particles, and the third class is antisymmetric in such an interchange. Thus the total of $(2s + 1)^2$ states can be divided into $(s + 1)(2s + 1)$ symmetric and $s(2s + 1)$ antisymmetric states. Associated with the symmetric spin states must be a symmetric space state if s is an integer (symmetric total wave function), and an antisymmetric space state if s is half an odd integer (antisymmetric total wave function). Similarly, the antisymmetric spin states multiply antisymmetric space states if $2s$ is even, and multiply symmetric states if $2s$ is odd. We see then that if all the spin states are equally likely to appear in a collision,[1] a fraction $(s + 1)/(2s + 1)$ of the collisions will be described by the wave function (32.9) with the upper sign, and a fraction $s/(2s + 1)$ will be described by (32.9) with the lower sign, if $2s$ is even.

This and the similar result for $2s$ odd can be summarized by rewriting Eq. (32.10)

$$\sigma(\theta) = |f(\theta)|^2 + |f(\pi - \theta)|^2 + \frac{(-1)^{2s}}{2s + 1} 2Re[f(\theta)\bar{f}(\pi - \theta)] \qquad (33.2)$$

where f is assumed to be independent of ϕ.

Equation (33.2) can also be derived by making use of the earlier observation that particles that have different spin components are distinguishable, in which case the interference term in (32.10) disappears. This occurs in a fraction $2s/(2s + 1)$ of the collisions. In the remaining fraction $1/(2s + 1)$ of the collisions, the particles have the same spin component, and the symmetric or antisymmetric space state (upper or lower sign in the interference term) must be used according as $2s$ is even or odd.

Electron Spin Functions. In the remainder of this chapter we consider only electron spin functions ($s = \frac{1}{2}$). The spin matrices are given by the first line of Eq. (24.15), and may be written as $\mathbf{S} = \frac{1}{2}\hbar\boldsymbol{\sigma}$, where

$$\sigma_x = \begin{pmatrix} 0 & 1 \\ 1 & 0 \end{pmatrix}, \qquad \sigma_y = \begin{pmatrix} 0 & -i \\ i & 0 \end{pmatrix}, \qquad \sigma_z = \begin{pmatrix} 1 & 0 \\ 0 & -1 \end{pmatrix} \qquad (33.3)$$

[1] See footnote 1, page 242.

are called the *Pauli spin matrices.*[1] The normalized eigenfunctions of S_z may be written in analogy with Eqs. (33.1) as

$$v(\tfrac{1}{2}) = \begin{pmatrix} 1 \\ 0 \end{pmatrix}, \qquad v(-\tfrac{1}{2}) = \begin{pmatrix} 0 \\ 1 \end{pmatrix} \tag{33.4}$$

and have eigenvalues $\tfrac{1}{2}\hbar$ and $-\tfrac{1}{2}\hbar$, respectively; they are both eigenfunctions of S^2 with the same eigenvalue $\tfrac{3}{4}\hbar^2$.

Since we shall have occasion to write down products of spin functions for different electrons, it is convenient to abbreviate the notation as follows:

$$v_1(\tfrac{1}{2})v_2(-\tfrac{1}{2})v_3(\tfrac{1}{2})v_4(\tfrac{1}{2}) = (+-++), \text{ etc.}$$

where the first particle has the eigenvalue $\tfrac{1}{2}\hbar$ for S_{1z}, the second has the eigenvalue $-\tfrac{1}{2}\hbar$ for S_{2z}, etc. S_1 has no effect on the spin functions of any but the first particle.

The following operational rules are easily obtained from (33.3) and (33.4):

$$\begin{array}{lll} \sigma_x(+) = (-), & \sigma_y(+) = \;\;\;i(-), & \sigma_z(+) = \;\;\;\;(+) \\ \sigma_x(-) = (+), & \sigma_y(-) = -i(+), & \sigma_z(-) = -(-) \end{array} \tag{33.5}$$

There are four linearly independent spin functions for a pair of electrons: $(++)$, $(+-)$, $(-+)$, $(--)$. These are orthonormal, since the one-particle spin functions (33.4) are orthonormal. As remarked earlier, it is often convenient to regroup these functions into combinations that are eigenfunctions of $(S_1 + S_2)^2$ and $S_{1z} + S_{2z}$. It can be verified with the help of (33.5) that the following four combinations are orthonormal and have the indicated eigenvalues:

	$(S_1 + S_2)^2$	$S_{1z} + S_{2z}$	
$(++)$	$2\hbar^2$	$\hbar$	
$2^{-\frac{1}{2}}[(+-) + (-+)]$	$2\hbar^2$	0	(33.6)
$(--)$	$2\hbar^2$	$-\hbar$	
$2^{-\frac{1}{2}}[(+-) - (-+)]$	0	0	

It is interesting to note that the first three of the two-particle spin functions (33.6) together behave in all respects like a single "particle" of spin $s = 1$, and the last of the spin functions (33.6) behaves like a single "particle" of spin $s = 0$.[2] Not only do they have the proper eigenvalues of the square of the magnitude of the total spin and the z component of the total spin, but the result of operating on the triplet spin function with the x or y components of the total spin is in agreement

[1] W. Pauli, *Zeits. f Physik*, **43**, 601 (1927).

[2] The first three states are called a *triplet* and the last a *singlet*. In the old quantum theory, the triplet corresponds to parallel electron spins and the singlet to antiparallel spins.

with the corresponding matrices in the second line of Eq. (24.15). This provides an example of the addition of angular momenta; according to Sec. 24, the combination of two systems of angular momenta $\frac{1}{2}$ results in a system of angular momentum either 1 or 0.

The Helium Atom. The ground state of the helium atom was considered from the point of view of the variation method in Sec. 27. We now consider the ground and first excited states of helium with the help of the somewhat simpler first-order perturbation theory of Sec. 25; the symmetry effects of the spins of the two electrons are taken into account, although spin-dependent forces are neglected. We use products of hydrogenic wave functions u_{nlm} (with $Z = 2$) as the unperturbed eigenfunctions of the problem, and are interested in classifying the states according to symmetry and spin properties rather than in obtaining accurate energy levels.

In spectroscopic notation, the ground state of helium is the $1s^2$ state: both electrons are in the hydrogenic state u_{100}. Since this space state is symmetric, the spin state that multiplies it must be the antisymmetric singlet given as the last of the functions (33.6), for which the total spin is zero.

The space part of the first excited state of helium is eightfold degenerate in the zero-order approximation. The spectroscopic configurations are $1s2s$ and $1s2p$. Apart from electron exchange, the first state is nondegenerate and the second is triply degenerate (because of the three $2p$ states); the exchange degeneracy doubles the number of states, since either electron can occupy the $1s$ state and the other the $2s$ or $2p$ state. In order to simplify matters, we consider here only the doubly (exchange) degenerate $1s2s$ state; it is not difficult to show that the $1s2p$ states can be treated separately (see Prob. 7).

The perturbation energy is the electrostatic repulsion between the electrons e^2/r_{12}, and the unperturbed states are $u_{100}(\mathbf{r}_1)u_{200}(\mathbf{r}_2)$ and $u_{100}(\mathbf{r}_2)u_{200}(\mathbf{r}_1)$. The spin need not be considered explicitly at this point since the spin-dependent forces are neglected; appropriate spin functions will be multiplied in later to make the entire wave function antisymmetric. The matrix of the perturbation for these two states has the structure of (25.16) and can be written

$$\begin{pmatrix} J & K \\ K & J \end{pmatrix} \tag{33.7}$$

where

$$
\begin{aligned}
J &= \int\int \bar{u}_{100}(\mathbf{r}_1)\bar{u}_{200}(\mathbf{r}_2)\,\frac{e^2}{r_{12}}\,u_{100}(\mathbf{r}_1)u_{200}(\mathbf{r}_2)d\tau_1 d\tau_2 \\
K &= \int\int \bar{u}_{100}(\mathbf{r}_1)\bar{u}_{200}(\mathbf{r}_2)\,\frac{e^2}{r_{12}}\,u_{100}(\mathbf{r}_2)u_{200}(\mathbf{r}_1)d\tau_1 d\tau_2
\end{aligned}
\tag{33.8}
$$

J is often called the *direct* or *Coulomb energy*, and K the *exchange energy*.

Application of the diagonalization technique of Sec. 25 (see the treatment of the first-order Stark effect in hydrogen) shows that the eigenvalues of the perturbation (33.7) are $J + K$ and $J - K$; they correspond to the normalized eigenfunctions $2^{-\frac{1}{2}}[u_{100}(\mathbf{r}_1)u_{200}(\mathbf{r}_2) + u_{100}(\mathbf{r}_2)u_{200}(\mathbf{r}_1)]$ and $2^{-\frac{1}{2}}[u_{100}(\mathbf{r}_1)u_{200}(\mathbf{r}_2) - u_{100}(\mathbf{r}_2)u_{200}(\mathbf{r}_1)]$, respectively. Since the first of these is a symmetric space function, it must be multiplied by the antisymmetric singlet spin function. Similarly the second, which is an antisymmetric space function, must be multiplied by one of the symmetric spin functions that make up the triplet in (33.6). Since K turns out to be positive, the singlet spin state has a substantially higher energy than the triplet spin states. This is not due to a spin-dependent interaction, but to a coupling between the spins and the electrostatic interaction that is introduced by the exclusion principle (use of antisymmetric wave functions).

Spin Functions for Three Electrons. In the treatment of exchange scattering from helium that is given in the next section, we shall require eigenfunctions of the total spin of three electrons that are analogous to those given in Eqs. (33.6) for two electrons. We can regard three electrons as $1 + 2$ electrons, in the sense that we can combine an electron ($s = \frac{1}{2}$) with the triplet two-electron function ($s = 1$) and with the singlet function ($s = 0$). In the first case, the results on addition of angular momenta, given in Sec. 24, show that we should get two groups of spin functions for the three electrons that correspond to $s = \frac{1}{2}$ and $s = \frac{3}{2}$; in the second case we should get a single group of three-electron spin functions that correspond to $s = \frac{1}{2}$. We thus expect one *quartet* group of spin states ($s = \frac{3}{2}$) and two distinct *doublet* groups of spin states ($s = \frac{1}{2}$), or a total of $4 + 2 + 2 = 8$ individual three-electron spin states. These must of course be expressible as linear combinations of the $2^3 = 8$ products of one-electron spin functions.

It is not difficult to show that the following eight combinations are orthonormal and have the indicated eigenvalues:

	$(\mathbf{S}_1 + \mathbf{S}_2 + \mathbf{S}_3)^2$	$S_{1z} + S_{2z} + S_{3z}$
$(+++)$	$\frac{15}{4}\hbar^2$	$\frac{3}{2}\hbar$
$3^{-\frac{1}{2}}[(++-) + (+-+) + (-++)]$	$\frac{15}{4}\hbar^2$	$\frac{1}{2}\hbar$
$3^{-\frac{1}{2}}[(--+) + (-+-) + (+--)]$	$\frac{15}{4}\hbar^2$	$-\frac{1}{2}\hbar$
$(---)$	$\frac{15}{4}\hbar^2$	$-\frac{3}{2}\hbar$
$6^{-\frac{1}{2}}[(++-) + (+-+) - 2(-++)]$	$\frac{3}{4}\hbar^2$	$\frac{1}{2}\hbar$
$6^{-\frac{1}{2}}[(--+) + (-+-) - 2(+--)]$	$\frac{3}{4}\hbar^2$	$-\frac{1}{2}\hbar$
$2^{-\frac{1}{2}}[(++-) - (+-+)]$	$\frac{3}{4}\hbar^2$	$\frac{1}{2}\hbar$
$2^{-\frac{1}{2}}[(--+) - (-+-)]$	$\frac{3}{4}\hbar^2$	$-\frac{1}{2}\hbar$

$$(33.9)$$

The first four (quartet) states are symmetric in the interchange of any pair of particles. The division of the four doublet states into two pairs is arbitrary, and is done here in such a way as to make the first pair of doublet states symmetric in the interchange of particles 2 and 3, and the second doublet pair antisymmetric in 2 and 3. As they are written, the doublets have no symmetry with respect to interchanges of the other pairs of particles.

34. REARRANGEMENT COLLISIONS

Cross sections for elastic and inelastic collisions of electrons with hydrogen atoms were calculated in Sec. 30 by means of perturbation theory, under the assumption that exchange of the incident and atomic electrons can be neglected. In this section, we consider the effects of electron exchange taken together with spin and the exclusion principle, but continue to use perturbation theory, which is most useful for high-energy collisions.[1] We first consider a general *rearrangement collision* by means of the Born approximation of Sec. 26, then show the connection between this method and the time-dependent perturbation theory of Sec. 29, and finally apply the theory to exchange collisions of electrons with hydrogen and helium atoms.

Notation for Rearrangement Collisions. A general binary rearrangement collision can be described as an event in which a system A in state m collides with a system B in state n, and systems C in state s and D in state t emerge. It is assumed that the same particles make up the systems A,B as make up the systems C,D (no particles appear or disappear and no photons are involved), although the particles are rearranged during the collision. We use the letters A,B,C,D to denote all the internal coordinates (including spins) of the respective systems, $\mathbf{r}_{ab}$ and $\mathbf{r}_{cd}$ to denote the vectors that connect the centers of mass of the systems A,B and C,D, respectively, and $M_{ab} = \dfrac{M_a M_b}{M_a + M_b}$ and $M_{cd} = \dfrac{M_c M_d}{M_c + M_d}$ to denote the reduced masses associated with the relative motion before and after the collision. The entire calculation is performed in the center-of-mass system; the transformation to the laboratory system can be effected by means of the general results of Sec. 18.

It was shown in Sec. 32 that a calculation of this type can be carried through as though the particles are distinguishable. At the end, a linear combination of the exchange-degenerate wave functions is formed that has the proper symmetry in each group of identical particles. The symmetrization will be left for the specific examples given near the end of this section. For the general problem considered here, we obtain only an approximate unsymmetrized wave function.

---

[1] For a discussion of other methods applicable to lower energy collisions, see N. F. Mott and H. S. W. Massey, "The Theory of Atomic Collisions," 2d ed., Chaps. X and XI (Oxford, New York, 1949).

We wish to solve the wave equation

$$(H - E)\psi = 0 \tag{34.1}$$

where the Hamiltonian can be written in either of two ways:

$$H = H_{ab} + H'_{ab} = H_{cd} + H'_{cd} \tag{34.2}$$

The unperturbed Hamiltonians for the initial and final systems are

$$H_{ab} = H_a + H_b + T_{ab}, \qquad T_{ab} = -\frac{\hbar^2}{2M_{ab}}\nabla^2_{ab}$$
$$H_{cd} = H_c + H_d + T_{cd}, \qquad T_{cd} = -\frac{\hbar^2}{2M_{cd}}\nabla^2_{cd} \tag{34.3}$$

where the T's represent the kinetic energy operators for the relative motions in the center-of-mass system. The unperturbed states of the initial and final systems are (known) solutions of the wave equations

$$(H_a - E_{am})u_{am}(A) = 0, \qquad (H_b - E_{bn})u_{bn}(B) = 0$$
$$(H_c - E_{cs})u_{cs}(C) = 0, \qquad (H_d - E_{dt})u_{dt}(D) = 0 \tag{34.4}$$

The interaction terms H'_{ab} and H'_{cd} are regarded as small perturbations.

It is always possible to expand the exact solution in the complete orthonormal set of functions $u_{cs}(C)u_{dt}(D)$, where the expansion coefficients are functions of the relative coordinate $\mathbf{r}_{cd}$:

$$\psi = \sum_{s,t} u_{cs}(C)u_{dt}(D)v_{st}(\mathbf{r}_{cd}) \tag{34.5}$$

Our problem consists in finding approximate expressions for the functions $v_{st}(\mathbf{r}_{cd})$ that correspond to internal final states s and t for the systems C and D, and that arise from the unperturbed initial state

$$\psi_0 = u_{am}(A)u_{bn}(B)\exp(i\mathbf{k}_0 \cdot \mathbf{r}_{ab})$$
$$k_0^2 = \frac{2M_{ab}}{\hbar^2}(E - E_{am} - E_{bn}) \tag{34.6}$$

Use of the Born Approximation. Substitution of ψ from Eq. (34.5) into the wave equation (34.1) yields, with the help of (34.2), (34.3), and (34.4)

$$\sum_{s,t} u_{cs}(C)u_{dt}(D)(T_{cd} + E_{cs} + E_{dt} - E)v_{st}(\mathbf{r}_{cd}) = -H'_{cd}\psi \tag{34.7}$$

If now Eq. (34.7) is multiplied through on the left by $\bar{u}_{cs'}(C)\bar{u}_{dt'}(D)$ and integrated over all the coordinates of C and D, the orthonormality of the u's causes all the terms on the left side to vanish except that for which $s = s'$ and $t = t'$. We drop the primes and write this as

$$(T_{cd} + E_{cs} + E_{dt} - E)v_{st}(\mathbf{r}_{cd}) = -\iint \bar{u}_{cs}(C)\bar{u}_{dt}(D)H'_{cd}\psi d\tau_c d\tau_d \tag{34.8}$$

Equation (34.8) can be written in a form that is analogous to Eq. (26.4):

$$(-\nabla_{cd}^2 - k^2)v_{st}(\mathbf{r}_{cd}) = -\frac{2M_{cd}}{\hbar^2} \int \int \bar{u}_{cs}(C)\bar{u}_{dt}(D)H'_{cd}\psi d\tau_c d\tau_d$$

$$k^2 = \frac{2M_{cd}}{\hbar^2}(E - E_{cs} - E_{dt}) \tag{34.9}$$

Equation (34.9) with all s and t represents a sequence of exact equations that can in principle be solved for the functions v_{st}. This situation is similar to that encountered in Eq. (26.4), where we obtained an approximate solution by replacing the exact by the unperturbed solution on the right side. We now obtain an approximate solution of (34.9) by replacing ψ by the ψ_0 given in (34.6); then the right side is known, and the inhomogeneous equation is readily solved for v_{st} by means of an appropriate Green's function. The substitution of ψ_0 for ψ is equivalent to the assumption that there is very little interaction between the unperturbed initial systems A and B. This implies not only that the transition $A,B \rightarrow C,D$ has a small probability, but also that ψ_0 is a good approximation to the actual wave function even when the two systems A and B are close together or overlap. In practical cases, it is difficult to set up a workable criterion for the validity of this approximation, although useful results are likely to be obtained when E is large in comparison with all the interaction energies that appear in H'_{ab}.

With the help of the Green's function (26.15), the solution of the inhomogeneous equation (34.9), with ψ replaced by ψ_0, becomes

$$v_{st}(\mathbf{r}'_{cd}) = -\frac{M_{cd}}{2\pi\hbar^2} \int \int \int |\mathbf{r}'_{cd} - \mathbf{r}_{cd}|^{-1} [\exp (ik|\mathbf{r}'_{cd} - \mathbf{r}_{cd}|)]$$

$$\cdot \bar{u}_{cs}(C)\bar{u}_{dt}(D)H'_{cd}u_{am}(A)u_{bn}(B)[\exp (i\mathbf{k}_0 \cdot \mathbf{r}_{ab})]d\tau_c d\tau_d d\tau_{cd} \tag{34.10}$$

The integration in (34.10) is over all the unprimed coordinates; the element of integration can be represented either as $d\tau_c d\tau_d d\tau_{cd}$ or as $d\tau_a d\tau_b d\tau_{ab}$, and is abbreviated in what follows as $d\tau$.

The asymptotic form of (34.10) when systems C and D are well separated is

$$v_{st}(\mathbf{r}'_{cd}) \xrightarrow[r'_{cd} \to \infty]{} g_{st}(\theta,\phi)r'^{-1}_{cd}e^{ikr'_{cd}}$$

$$g_{st}(\theta,\phi) = -\frac{M_{cd}}{2\pi\hbar^2} \int \bar{u}_{cs}(C)\bar{u}_{dt}(D)[\exp (-i\mathbf{k} \cdot \mathbf{r}_{cd})]$$

$$\cdot H'_{cd}u_{am}(A)u_{bn}(B)[\exp (i\mathbf{k}_0 \cdot \mathbf{r}_{ab})]d\tau \tag{34.11}$$

Here, θ and ϕ are the polar angles of the vector $\mathbf{r}'_{cd}$, and $\mathbf{k}$ is a vector that has this direction and the magnitude given by Eq. (34.9). Equation (34.6) is normalized so that the incident flux of systems A and B is the initial relative speed $v_0 = \hbar k_0/M_{ab}$, and Eqs. (34.5) and (34.11) are normalized so that the radial outgoing flux of systems C and D per unit solid angle is $v|g_{st}(\theta,\phi)|^2$, where the final relative speed $v = \hbar k/M_{cd}$. Thus the differential cross section for the collision $A,B \rightarrow C,D$ is

$$\sigma_{st}(\theta,\phi) = \frac{v}{v_0}\,|g_{st}(\theta,\phi)|^2 \qquad (34.12)$$

Lack of Orthogonality of Initial and Final States. There is an arbitrariness in the expression (34.12) for the cross section that arises from the fact that the wave function ψ_0 for the initial state is not in general orthogonal to the function $\psi_f = u_{cs}(C)u_{dt}(D)\,\exp\,(i\mathbf{k}\cdot\mathbf{r}_{cd})$, the complex conjugate of which also appears in the expression for $g_{st}(\theta,\phi)$. ψ_f may be said to describe a final state in which the systems C and D are observed to be moving in the direction θ,ϕ. Since the initial and final wave functions are eigenfunctions of different unperturbed Hamiltonians H_{ab} and H_{cd}, respectively, they are not expected to be orthogonal to each other. If they are not orthogonal, the addition of a constant potential energy (which corresponds to zero force) to H'_{cd} alters the expression for $g_{st}(\theta,\phi)$; such a change in H'_{cd} could be made by adding an arbitrary constant multiple of ψ to both sides of Eq. (34.7), thus also changing the magnitude of E. We avoid this arbitrariness by defining H'_{cd} as the energy of interaction between systems C and D that vanishes as r_{cd} becomes infinite; the additive constant is then fixed uniquely. A similar definition is made for H'_{ab}.

It is interesting to note that H'_{ab} can be used in place of H'_{cd} in the integral for $g_{st}\,(\theta,\phi)$. This integral is $\int\bar\psi_f H'_{cd}\psi_0 d\tau$; with the help of Eq. (22.10) it can be transformed as follows:

$$\int\bar\psi_f H'_{cd}\psi_0 d\tau = \int\overline{(H'_{cd}\psi_f)}\psi_0 d\tau$$

$$= \int\overline{[(H - H_{cd})\psi_f]}\psi_0 d\tau = \int\bar\psi_f H\psi_0 d\tau - E\int\bar\psi_f\psi_0 d\tau$$

where we have made use of the relation $H_{cd}\psi_f = E\psi_f$. In similar fashion, $\int\bar\psi_f H'_{ab}\psi_0 d\tau$ can be shown to be equal to the last expression by making use of the relation $H_{ab}\psi_0 = E\psi_0$. Thus so long as ψ_0 and ψ_f are exact solutions for the unperturbed Hamiltonians H_{ab} and H_{cd}, respectively, we see that

$$\int\bar\psi_f H'_{cd}\psi_0 d\tau = \int\bar\psi_f H'_{ab}\psi_0 d\tau \qquad (34.13)$$

Equation (34.13) has, for example, the consequence that $g_{st}(\theta,\phi) = 0$ if $H'_{ab} = 0$, even if H'_{cd} is not zero and the initial and final states are not orthogonal. This result is to be expected, since if $H'_{ab} = 0$, there is no interaction between the colliding systems A and B and the transition does not occur.

Connection with Time-dependent Perturbation Theory. It is also possible to derive Eq. (34.12) by the method of variation of constants

(Sec. 29). We expand the wave function ψ in unperturbed final-state wave functions $\psi_f = u_{cs}(C)u_{dt}(D)\exp(i\mathbf{k} \cdot \mathbf{r}_{cd})$, where the subscript f stands for the states s and t of systems C and D and for the relative propagation vector $\mathbf{k}$:

$$\psi = \sum_f a_f(t)\psi_f e^{-\frac{iE_f t}{\hbar}} \tag{34.14}$$

The time-dependent wave equation is

$$i\hbar \frac{\partial \psi}{\partial t} = H\psi = (H_{cd} + H'_{cd})\psi \tag{34.15}$$

Substitution of (34.14) into (34.15) gives

$$i\hbar \sum_f \dot{a}_f \psi_f e^{-\frac{iE_f t}{\hbar}} = \sum_f a_f H'_{cd} \psi_f e^{-\frac{iE_f t}{\hbar}} \tag{34.16}$$

where use is made of the relation $(H_{cd} - E_f)\psi_f = 0$. Equation (34.16) can be simplified by multiplying through on the left by $\bar{\psi}_{f'}$ and integrating over all the coordinates; since the ψ_f are orthonormal, we obtain

$$i\hbar \dot{a}_{f'} = \sum_f a_f \int \bar{\psi}_{f'} H'_{cd} \psi_f d\tau \cdot e^{\frac{i(E_{f'} - E_f)t}{\hbar}} \tag{34.17}$$

The system of Eqs. (34.17) is exact. We now make two approximations, which together are equivalent to the Born approximation substitution of ψ_0 for ψ on the right side of Eq. (34.9). First, we assume that the perturbation H'_{cd} is small; because of Eq. (34.13), this is equivalent for our purpose to the Born approximation assumption that H'_{ab} is small. Then we can insert the unperturbed amplitudes $a_f^{(0)}$ on the right side of (34.17), and calculate the first-order perturbed amplitudes $a_{f'}^{(1)}$ on the left side. Second, we assume that the initial state $\psi_0 e^{-\frac{iEt}{\hbar}}$ can be expanded in terms of only those (degenerate) ψ_f whose energies E_f are equal to the initial energy E. This assumes that ψ_0 is an eigenfunction of the final unperturbed Hamiltonian H_{cd}, which is equal to $H_{ab} + H'_{ab} - H'_{cd}$; since ψ_0 is actually an eigenfunction of H_{ab}, this also is equivalent to the assumption that the perturbations H'_{ab} and H'_{cd} are small.

We can then replace E_f by E in the time factor on the right side of Eq. (34.17) and take this factor outside of the summation over f. The unperturbed amplitudes $a_f^{(0)}$ are defined by $\psi_0 = \sum_f a_f^{(0)} \psi_f$, which gives

$$a_f^{(0)} = \int \bar{\psi}_f \psi_0 d\tau \tag{34.18}$$

With the help of (34.18), the summation over f can be rewritten

$$\sum_f \int \psi_{f'} H_{cd}' \psi_f d\tau \int \psi_f \psi_0 d\tau = \int \psi_{f'} H_{cd}' \psi_0 d\tau$$

where use has been made of the closure relation for the complete orthonormal set of functions ψ_f. Thus Eq. (34.17) becomes, to first order,

$$i\hbar \dot{a}_{f'}^{(1)} = \int \psi_{f'} H_{cd}' \psi_0 d\tau \cdot e^{\frac{i(E_{f'}-E)t}{\hbar}} \tag{34.19}$$

Equation (34.19) can be handled in precisely the same way as Eq. (29.7), and yields the differential collision cross section (34.12).

Exchange Collisions of Electrons with Hydrogen. As a simple first example of a rearrangement collision in which effects of identity and spin appear, we consider the elastic scattering of an electron from a hydrogen atom. In a problem of this type, we must know the asymptotic forms of the unsymmetrized wave function for all permutations of identical particles.[1] A wave function that has the proper symmetry character can then be constructed by the methods outlined in Sec. 32. We first obtain the asymptotic form of the wave function when the incident electron is scattered and when the incident electron exchanges with the atomic electron, to the accuracy of the Born approximation; spin-dependent interactions are neglected.

The incident and atomic electrons are denoted by 1 and 2, respectively, in the unsymmetrized wave function. The asymptotic form of the stationary wave function $\psi(\mathbf{r}_1,\mathbf{r}_2)$ that corresponds to nonexchange elastic scattering with the total energy E is a product of the ground-state hydrogen wave function $u_{100}(\mathbf{r}_2)$ for electron 2, and an incident-plane plus outgoing-scattered wave for electron 1:

$$\psi(\mathbf{r}_1,\mathbf{r}_2) \xrightarrow[r_1 \to \infty]{} [\exp(i\mathbf{k}_0 \cdot \mathbf{r}_1) + r_1^{-1} e^{ik_0 r_1} f(\theta_1)] u_{100}(\mathbf{r}_2)$$
$$\frac{\hbar^2 k_0^2}{2m} = E + \frac{me^4}{2\hbar^2} \tag{34.20}$$

The work of Secs. 26 and 30 shows that the scattered amplitude has the form

$$f(\theta_1) = -\frac{m}{2\pi\hbar^2} \int\int [\exp(-i\mathbf{k} \cdot \mathbf{r}_1)] \bar{u}_{100}(\mathbf{r}_2) \left(\frac{e^2}{r_{12}} - \frac{e^2}{r_1}\right)$$
$$\cdot (\exp i\mathbf{k}_0 \cdot \mathbf{r}_1) u_{100}(\mathbf{r}_2) d\tau_1 d\tau_2 \tag{34.21}$$

where $\mathbf{k}$ is a vector of magnitude k_0 that has the direction θ_1 (f does not depend on the other polar angle ϕ_1).

J. R. Oppenheimer, *Phys. Rev.*, **32**, 361 (1928).

The asymptotic form of $\psi(\mathbf{r}_1,\mathbf{r}_2)$ that corresponds to elastic exchange scattering is a product of the ground-state hydrogen wave function $u_{100}(\mathbf{r}_1)$ for electron 1, and an outgoing scattered wave for electron 2.

$$\psi(\mathbf{r}_1,\mathbf{r}_2) \xrightarrow[r_2 \to \infty]{} r_2^{-1}e^{ik_0r_2}g(\theta_2)u_{100}(\mathbf{r}_1) \tag{34.22}$$

There is no plane wave in this case, since electron 2 is not incident on the atom. In accordance with Eq. (34.11), the exchange scattered amplitude is

$$g(\theta_2) = -\frac{m}{2\pi\hbar^2} \int \int [\exp(-i\mathbf{k} \cdot \mathbf{r}_2)]\bar{u}_{100}(\mathbf{r}_1) \left(\frac{e^2}{r_{12}} - \frac{e^2}{r_2}\right)$$
$$\cdot (\exp i\mathbf{k}_0 \cdot \mathbf{r}_1)u_{100}(\mathbf{r}_2)d\tau_1 d\tau_2 \tag{34.23}$$

where $\mathbf{k}$ has the magnitude k_0 and is in the direction θ_2.

We must now form an antisymmetric wave function from products of $\psi(\mathbf{r}_1,\mathbf{r}_2)$ and appropriate spin functions. The spin functions can be taken to be the set of four given after Eq. (33.5); however, it is simpler to make use of the four symmetrized combinations (33.6). The spin of the incident electron is not assumed to have any definite relation to the spin of the atomic electron. In this case we can use either of these sets of spin functions, calculate the scattering with each of the four spin states of a set, and then average the results with equal weights for each state.[1] The first three of the spin functions (33.6) are symmetric, and must be multiplied by the antisymmetric space function $\psi(\mathbf{r}_1,\mathbf{r}_2) - \psi(\mathbf{r}_2,\mathbf{r}_1)$; the fourth spin function is antisymmetric, and must be multiplied by

$$\psi(\mathbf{r}_1,\mathbf{r}_2) + \psi(\mathbf{r}_2,\mathbf{r}_1).$$

Differential Cross Section. The asymptotic forms of the symmetrized space functions for large values of one of the electron coordinates, say r_1, are obtained from (34.20) and (34.22).

---

[1] This is a consequence of the fundamental hypothesis of quantum statistical mechanics; see, for example, R. C. Tolman, "The Principles of Statistical Mechanics," Sec. 84 (Oxford, New York, 1938). It can be shown that either of two complete orthonormal sets of wave functions can be used in such a statistical calculation (in the present problem, the two sets are complete so far as the spins of two electrons are concerned). The two sets, say v_n and u_k, were shown in Sec. 22 to be connected by a unitary transformation: $v_n = \sum_k S_{kn}u_k$, where S is a unitary matrix. Then

$$\sum_n |v_n|^2 = \sum_{n,k,k'} S_{kn}\bar{S}_{k'n}u_k\bar{u}_{k'} = \sum_{k,k'} \delta_{kk'}u_k\bar{u}_{k'} = \sum_k |u_k|^2$$

Since the probability of observing a given event (such as the scattering in a particular direction) is proportional to the square of a wave function, the same average result is obtained from a statistical mixture of either set of wave functions.

$\psi(\mathbf{r}_1,\mathbf{r}_2) \pm \psi(\mathbf{r}_2,\mathbf{r}_1)$

$$\underset{r_1 \to \infty}{\longrightarrow} [\exp(i\mathbf{k}_0 \cdot \mathbf{r}_1) + r_1^{-1}e^{ik_0r_1}f(\theta_1) \pm r^{-1}e^{ik_0r_1}g(\theta_1)]u_{100}(\mathbf{r}_2) \quad (34.24)$$

The first two terms in the bracket on the right side of (34.24) come from the first term on the left side, and the third term on the right side comes from the second term on the left side. The differential cross section must be computed with the upper sign in one quarter of the collisions, and with the lower sign in three quarters of the cases. We thus obtain

$$\sigma(\theta) = \tfrac{1}{4}|f(\theta) + g(\theta)|^2 + \tfrac{3}{4}|f(\theta) - g(\theta)|^2 \quad (34.25)$$

Equation (34.25) can also be derived without explicit reference to the spin wave functions, as was Eq. (33.2), by making use of the earlier observation that particles that have different spin components are distinguishable. In half the collisions, the electrons have different spin components, and the cross section is just the sum $|f(\theta)|^2 + |g(\theta)|^2$ of the direct and exchange cross sections; in the other half, the electrons are indistinguishable, and the antisymmetric space function must be used. We thus obtain

$$\sigma(\theta) = \tfrac{1}{2}(|f(\theta)|^2 + |g(\theta)|^2) + \tfrac{1}{2}|f(\theta) - g(\theta)|^2$$

which is easily seen to be the same as (34.25).

An integral of the form $\int (\exp i\mathbf{k} \cdot \mathbf{r})F(\mathbf{r})d\tau$ is small if $ka \gg 1$, where it is assumed that F is a smooth function of $\mathbf{r}$ that becomes small for $r > a$. Since both the $\mathbf{r}_1$ and $\mathbf{r}_2$ integrals in (34.23) are of this type, we expect g to be quite small in comparison with f for $ka_0 \gg 1$. This is the situation in which the Born approximation is most applicable, so that the corrections due to exchange are expected to be fairly small for the cross sections calculated in Sec. 30.

Exchange Collisions with Helium. In dealing with the elastic scattering of an electron from a helium atom in its ground state, it is convenient to work with the space and spin wave functions together. According to the discussion of Sec. 33, the two electrons in the helium atom are in a symmetric space state and an antisymmetric (singlet) spin state. Thus if the incident electron is denoted by 1 and the atomic electrons by 2 and 3, the unperturbed wave function is $(\exp i\mathbf{k}_0 \cdot \mathbf{r}_1)u_0(\mathbf{r}_2,\mathbf{r}_3)v(1,2,3)$, where u_0 is the symmetric space function for the normal state, and $v(1,2,3)$ is a spin function that is antisymmetric in 2 and 3. The eight spin functions for three electrons are grouped in (33.9) according to symmetry in 2 and 3; it is apparent that $v(1,2,3)$ must be one of the last doublet pair given there.

The asymptotic forms of the first-order perturbed wave function including spin are found to be

$$\psi(1,2,3) \xrightarrow[r_1\to\infty]{} [(\exp i\mathbf{k}_0\cdot\mathbf{r}_1) + r_1^{-1}f(\theta_1)]u_0(\mathbf{r}_2,\mathbf{r}_3)v(1,2,3)$$

$$\xrightarrow[r_2\to\infty]{} r_2^{-1}g'(\theta_2)u_0(\mathbf{r}_3,\mathbf{r}_1)v(2,3,1) \qquad (34.26)$$

$$\xrightarrow[r_3\to\infty]{} r_3^{-1}g'(\theta_3)u_0(\mathbf{r}_1,\mathbf{r}_2)v(3,1,2)$$

where there is antisymmetry only in electrons 2 and 3.   Here

$$f(\theta_1) = -\frac{m}{2\pi\hbar^2} \int\int\int [\exp(-i\mathbf{k}\cdot\mathbf{r}_1)]\bar{u}_0(\mathbf{r}_2,\mathbf{r}_3)$$

$$\cdot\left(\frac{e^2}{r_{12}} + \frac{e^2}{r_{13}} - \frac{2e^2}{r_1}\right)(\exp i\mathbf{k}_0\cdot\mathbf{r}_1)u_0(\mathbf{r}_2,\mathbf{r}_3)d\tau_1 d\tau_2 d\tau_3$$

and a spin term $v^*(1,2,3)v(1,2,3) = 1$ has been omitted.   Also

$$g'(\theta_2) = g(\theta_2)v^*(2,3,1)v(1,2,3),$$

$$g(\theta_2) = -\frac{m}{2\pi\hbar^2} \int\int\int [\exp(-i\mathbf{k}\cdot\mathbf{r}_2)]\bar{u}_0(\mathbf{r}_3,\mathbf{r}_1) \qquad (34.27)$$

$$\cdot\left(\frac{e^2}{r_{12}} + \frac{e^2}{r_{23}} - \frac{2e^2}{r_2}\right)(\exp i\mathbf{k}_0\cdot\mathbf{r}_1)u_0(\mathbf{r}_2,\mathbf{r}_3)d\tau_1 d\tau_2 d\tau_3$$

with a similar expression for $g'(\theta_3)$.   The product of spin functions in (34.27) is readily evaluated by making use of the one-electron functions (33.4) and remembering that v^* is the Hermitian adjoint of v.   We take for $v(1,2,3)$ the next to the last spin function of (33.9), and obtain

$$v^*(2,3,1)v(1,2,3) = 2^{-\frac{1}{2}}[(-++)^* - (++-)^*]$$

$$\cdot 2^{-\frac{1}{2}}[(++-) - (+-+)] = -\tfrac{1}{2} \qquad (34.28)$$

The completely antisymmetric wave function derived from $\psi(1,2,3)$ is given in Eq. (32.3) with the lower sign.   Since ψ is already antisymmetric in its last two arguments, it is apparent that the second bracket terms in (32.3) duplicate the first bracket terms.   The asymptotic form of the wave function for large values of one of the electron coordinates, say r_1, is then obtained from (34.26) and (34.28):

$$\psi(1,2,3) + \psi(2,3,1) + \psi(3,1,2) \xrightarrow[r_1\to\infty]{}$$

$$\{(\exp i\mathbf{k}_0\cdot\mathbf{r}_1) + r_1^{-1}e^{ik_0r_1}[f(\theta_1) - \tfrac{1}{2}g(\theta_1) - \tfrac{1}{2}g(\theta_1)]\}u_0(\mathbf{r}_2,\mathbf{r}_3)v(1,2,3) \quad (34.29)$$

The differential cross section obtained from (34.29) is

$$\sigma(\theta) = |f(\theta) - g(\theta)|^2 \qquad (34.30)$$

Like Eqs. (33.2) and (34.25), Eq. (34.30) can be derived without explicit reference to the spin functions.   Since the two atomic electrons must have antiparallel spins (singlet state) in order for the helium atom to be in its ground state, the spin component of the incident electron is the same as that of one of the atomic electrons and different from that of the other. It cannot exchange with the latter in an elastic collision, since then both the resulting atomic electrons would be in the same spin state and the exclusion principle would force the atom into an excited state. Thus it can only exchange with the electron with which it is indistinguishable, so that the antisymmetric combination of direct (f) and exchange (g) amplitudes must be used; this gives Eq. (34.30).

In the absence of spin-dependent interactions, the excitation of a triplet state of helium by electron impact can be accomplished only by exchange between the incident electron and one of the atomic electrons. In this case, there is no direct (f) amplitude, and hence no interference between direct and exchange amplitudes.

Problems

1. Show that the antisymmetric wave function given in Eq. (32.7) vanishes if there is an identical linear relation between the functions $v_\alpha, v_\beta, \ldots, v_\nu$.

2. Show that if a wave function $u(1,2, \ldots n)$ is an energy eigenfunction of a symmetric Hamiltonian that corresponds to a nondegenerate eigenvalue, it is either symmetric or antisymmetric. Show this first for $n = 2$, then for $n = 3$, and then indicate how the proof can be extended to arbitrary n.

3. Verify that the spin wave functions given in Eq. (33.6) are eigenfunctions of $(\mathbf{S}_1 + \mathbf{S}_2)^2$ and $S_{1z} + S_{2z}$ with the indicated eigenvalues. Show also that the result of operating on these functions with the x and y components of the total spin is in agreement with the appropriate matrices given in Eqs. (24.15).

4. Carry through the calculations of Prob. 3 for the spin functions given in Eq. (33.9).

5. Find the eigenfunctions of the square of the magnitude of the total spin and the z component of the total spin of four electrons, and show that they can be grouped into one quintet, three triplet, and two singlet states. (*Hint:* Start with the triplet and singlet spin functions for two pairs of two electrons, and make use of the matrices (24.15) together with the corresponding set for $j = 2$.)

6. Use Eq. (33.2) to write down an expression for the scattering of protons in the center-of-mass coordinate system, assuming that the Coulomb interaction extends in to $r = 0$. Discuss the classical limit of the cross section ($\hbar \to 0$), particularly in the neighborhood of $\theta = 90°$, and show that the interference term drops out if the average scattering over an arbitrarily small but finite range of angle is computed.

7. Show that the $1s2p$ configurations in helium can be treated separately from the $1s2s$ configurations so far as the first-order energy-level calculation of Sec. 33 is concerned.

8. What would be the unperturbed ground-state wave functions of helium if each electron had spin angular momentum $\hbar$ and obeyed Einstein-Bose statistics?

9. Write down the unperturbed ground-state wave function for a neutral lithium atom.

10. Show by direct calculation that Eq. (34.25) is obtained if the incident and atomic electrons are assumed to be described by the four spin wave functions $(++)$, $(+-)$, $(-+)$, and $(--)$, rather than by the triplet and singlet combinations (see footnote 1, page 242).

CHAPTER X

SEMICLASSICAL TREATMENT OF RADIATION

No account has thus far been given in this book of the interaction between material particles and electromagnetic radiation. As would be expected, a treatment that is consistent with the foregoing theory of material particles requires that quantum equations of motion of the electromagnetic field be found that are analogous to Maxwell's equations. Indeed, it is only in this way that Planck's original quantum hypothesis can be fitted into a general theoretical framework. The development of the elements of a quantum theory of radiation will be postponed until Chap. XIV. In the present chapter we treat the electromagnetic field classically and the particles with which the field interacts by quantum mechanics. Such a semiclassical treatment is bound to be incomplete and not wholly satisfactory, although it is simpler in principle than the quantum electrodynamics presented in Chap. XIV. We shall find that it is possible in this approximate way to give a plausible and correct account of the influence of an external radiation field on a system of particles (absorption and induced emission), but not of the influence of the particles on the field (spontaneous emission). Nevertheless, the results of the classical treatment of the latter phenomenon can be converted to quantum theory in a correct, if not very convincing, manner. Some simple applications of the theory are given in Sec. 37.

35. ABSORPTION AND INDUCED EMISSION

The Schrödinger wave equation for the motion of a particle of mass m and charge e in an electromagnetic field described by the potentials $\mathbf{A}, \phi$, with an additional potential energy V, is obtained by adding a term $V\psi$ to the right side of Eq. (23.24).

$$i\hbar \frac{\partial \psi}{\partial t} = \left[-\frac{\hbar^2}{2m} \nabla^2 + \frac{ie\hbar}{mc} \mathbf{A} \cdot \mathbf{grad} + \frac{ie\hbar}{2mc} (\text{div } \mathbf{A}) \right.$$
$$\left. + \frac{e^2}{2mc^2} \mathbf{A}^2 + e\phi + V \right]\psi \quad (35.1)$$

We regard V as the potential energy that binds the particle (of electrostatic origin if the particle is an electron); $\mathbf{A}, \phi$ represent an electromagnetic field that is weak enough so that those terms can be regarded as a perturbation. Our object is to calculate the probabilities of transitions between stationary states of the particle in the potential energy V, that are produced by the field. We first discuss some properties of the field and its plane wave solutions.

Maxwell's Equations. Maxwell's equations of motion for the electromagnetic field are, in Gaussian units,

$$\text{curl } \mathbf{E} + \frac{1}{c}\frac{\partial \mathbf{H}}{\partial t} = 0, \qquad \text{curl } \mathbf{H} - \frac{1}{c}\frac{\partial \mathbf{E}}{\partial t} = \frac{4\pi}{c}\mathbf{J}$$
$$\text{div } \mathbf{E} = 4\pi\rho, \qquad \text{div } \mathbf{H} = 0 \tag{35.2}$$

If the divergence of the second of these equations is combined with the time derivative of the third, we obtain the equation of continuity for the electric charge and current densities ρ and $\mathbf{J}$

$$\text{div } \mathbf{J} + \frac{\partial \rho}{\partial t} = 0 \tag{35.3}$$

The electric and magnetic field strengths can be expressed in terms of the potentials by Eqs. (23.15):

$$\mathbf{E} = -\frac{1}{c}\frac{\partial \mathbf{A}}{\partial t} - \text{grad } \phi, \qquad \mathbf{H} = \text{curl } \mathbf{A} \tag{35.4}$$

which cause the first and fourth of Eqs. (35.2) to be satisfied identically. The potentials are not defined uniquely by Eqs. (35.4), since any $\mathbf{A}, \phi$ that give the correct $\mathbf{E}$ and $\mathbf{H}$ can evidently be replaced by new potentials $\mathbf{A}', \phi'$ without altering the field strengths, where

$$\mathbf{A}' = \mathbf{A} + \text{grad } \chi, \qquad \phi' = \phi - \frac{1}{c}\frac{\partial \chi}{\partial t} \tag{35.5}$$

and χ is an arbitrary function of $\mathbf{r}$ and t (see also Prob. 3).

Substitution of (35.4) into the second and third of Eqs. (35.2) gives

$$\text{curl curl } \mathbf{A} + \frac{1}{c^2}\frac{\partial^2 \mathbf{A}}{\partial t^2} + \frac{1}{c}\text{grad }\frac{\partial \phi}{\partial t} = \frac{4\pi}{c}\mathbf{J}$$
$$\frac{1}{c}\frac{\partial}{\partial t}\text{div } \mathbf{A} + \nabla^2\phi = -4\pi\rho \tag{35.6}$$

If the vector $\mathbf{A}$ is written in rectangular coordinates, we can put

$$\text{curl curl } \mathbf{A} = \text{grad (div } \mathbf{A}) - \nabla^2\mathbf{A},$$

where the last term is the vector whose components are the Laplacians of the components of $\mathbf{A}$. We can therefore simplify Eqs. (35.6) by making a *gauge transformation* (35.5) from $\mathbf{A}, \phi$ to $\mathbf{A}', \phi'$ such that the new potentials satisfy the *Lorentz condition:*

$$\text{div } \mathbf{A}' + \frac{1}{c} \frac{\partial \phi'}{\partial t} = 0 \tag{35.7}$$

The gauge function χ then satisfies the equation

$$\nabla^2 \chi - \frac{1}{c^2} \frac{\partial^2 \chi}{\partial t^2} = -\left(\text{div } \mathbf{A} + \frac{1}{c} \frac{\partial \phi}{\partial t} \right) \tag{35.8}$$

Equations (35.6) then become

$$\nabla^2 \mathbf{A}' - \frac{1}{c^2} \frac{\partial^2 \mathbf{A}'}{\partial t^2} = -\frac{4\pi}{c} \mathbf{J}$$
$$\nabla^2 \phi' - \frac{1}{c^2} \frac{\partial^2 \phi'}{\partial t^2} = -4\pi\rho \tag{35.9}$$

Plane Electromagnetic Waves. If $\mathbf{J} = 0$ and $\rho = 0$ (completely empty space), it can be shown that it is possible to choose the gauge function so that div $\mathbf{A}' = 0$ and $\phi' = 0$ for all $\mathbf{r}$ and t, without loss of generality (see Prob. 1). Then transverse plane wave solutions can be found for $\mathbf{A}'$, and hence also for $\mathbf{E}$ and $\mathbf{H}$. We drop the primes and have in this case

$$\nabla^2 \mathbf{A} - \frac{1}{c^2} \frac{\partial^2 \mathbf{A}}{\partial t^2} = 0, \qquad \text{div } \mathbf{A} = 0 \tag{35.10}$$

A typical plane wave solution of (35.10) is one that represents a real potential with the propagation vector $\mathbf{k}$ and the real polarization vector $|\mathbf{A}_0|$:

$$\mathbf{A}(\mathbf{r},t) = 2|\mathbf{A}_0| \cos (\mathbf{k} \cdot \mathbf{r} - \omega t + \alpha)$$
$$= \mathbf{A}_0[\exp i(\mathbf{k} \cdot \mathbf{r} - \omega t)] + \text{c.c.} \tag{35.11}$$

Here "c.c." denotes the complex conjugate of the term that precedes it, and the constant complex vector $\mathbf{A}_0$ is defined to be $|\mathbf{A}_0|e^{i\alpha}$. The first of Eqs. (35.10) is satisfied if $\omega = kc$, where k is the magnitude of $\mathbf{k}$, and the second is satisfied if $\mathbf{A}_0$ is perpendicular to $\mathbf{k}$.

The electric and magnetic fields associated with the vector potential (35.11) are

$$\mathbf{E} = -2k|\mathbf{A}_0| \sin (\mathbf{k} \cdot \mathbf{r} - \omega t + \alpha)$$
$$\mathbf{H} = -2\mathbf{k} \times |\mathbf{A}_0| \sin (\mathbf{k} \cdot \mathbf{r} - \omega t + \alpha)$$

The *Poynting vector* $(c/4\pi)\mathbf{E} \times \mathbf{H}$ is evidently in the direction of $\mathbf{k}$; its magnitude averaged over a period $2\pi/\omega$ of the oscillation is

$$\frac{\omega^2}{2\pi c} |\mathbf{A}_0|^2 \tag{35.12}$$

where $|A_0|^2$ is equal to the scalar product of $|A_0|$ with itself ($|A_0| \cdot |A_0|$) or the scalar product of A_0 and its complex conjugate ($A_0 \cdot \overline{A}_0$). The quantity (35.12) is the intensity associated with the plane wave (35.11).

Use of Perturbation Theory. We now return to Eq. (35.1), and use it to calculate the probability of a transition between stationary states that is produced by the vector potential (35.11), which is regarded as a small perturbation. The third term (div A) and fifth term (ϕ) on the right side of (35.1) are now zero. The ratios of the second to the first term and the fourth to the second term on the right side of (35.1) are of order eA/cp, where p is the momentum of the particle. The magnitude of this quantity is estimated in a practical case in Prob. 2, and is so small that the perturbation approximation is justified. Thus to the first order of perturbation theory, we can neglect the term $e^2A^2/2mc^2$, and rewrite Eq. (35.1)

$$i\hbar \frac{\partial \psi}{\partial t} = (H_0 + H')\psi$$

$$H_0 = -\frac{\hbar^2}{2m} \nabla^2 + V(\mathbf{r}), \qquad H' = \frac{ie\hbar}{mc} \mathbf{A} \cdot \mathbf{grad} \tag{35.13}$$

We proceed as in Sec. 29, and expand ψ in stationary eigenfunctions $u_k(\mathbf{r})$ of the unperturbed Hamiltonian H_0 with time-dependent coefficients $a_k(t)$. If the system is initially in the state n and the perturbation is turned on at $t = 0$, the first-order amplitudes at time t are given by an expression similar to (29.17).

$$a_k^{(1)}(t) = -\frac{H'^0_{kn}}{\hbar} \frac{e^{i(\omega_{kn}-\omega)t} - 1}{\omega_{kn} - \omega} - \frac{H''^0_{kn}}{\hbar} \frac{e^{i(\omega_{kn}+\omega)t} - 1}{\omega_{kn} + \omega}$$

$$H'^0_{kn} = \frac{ie\hbar}{mc} \int \bar{u}_k(\exp i\mathbf{k} \cdot \mathbf{r})A_0 \cdot \mathbf{grad} \ u_n d\tau \tag{35.14}$$

$$H''^0_{kn} = \frac{ie\hbar}{mc} \int \bar{u}_k[\exp (-i\mathbf{k} \cdot \mathbf{r})]\overline{A}_0 \cdot \mathbf{grad} \ u_n d\tau$$

As discussed in Sec. 29, the probability of finding the system in the state k is appreciable only when the denominator of one or the other of the two terms in (35.14) is practically zero. There is no interference between the two terms: the first is important when $E_k \cong E_n + \hbar\omega$, and the second is important when $E_k \cong E_n - \hbar\omega$. Thus the probability of finding the system in a state k that has an energy higher than the initial state by about $\hbar\omega$ is proportional to $|H'^0_{kn}|^2$, and the probability of finding the system in a state k' that has a correspondingly lower energy is proportional to $|H''^0_{k'n}|^2$.

Transition Probability. The discussion of Sec. 29 shows that the transition probability per unit time is independent of the time only if the final state can be any of a very closely spaced or continuously distributed group. The need for a group of final states arises from the dependence of the probability $|a_k^{(1)}(t)|^2$ on the energy, which is shown in Fig. 27; it is the area under this curve, not the ordinate at a particular abscissa, that is proportional to t.

In the same way, a constant transition probability per unit time is obtained in the present problem if the incident radiation is monochromatic (definite value of ω) and transitions can occur to any of a group of closely spaced or continuously distributed final states. The result is Eq. (29.12) with either $H_{kn}^{\prime 0}$ or $H_{k'n}^{\prime\prime 0}$ substituted for H_{km}'. However, the computation of a transition probability between two discrete states is often of interest. In this case, the transition probability per unit time is not constant in time, if the incident radiation is strictly monochromatic, and depends markedly on the difference between ω and

$$|\omega_{kn}| = |E_k - E_n|/\hbar.$$

What we do in this case is to assume that the radiation covers a spread of frequencies with no phase relations between the different frequency components, so that the radiation can be characterized by an intensity per unit frequency range that is constant in the neighborhood of $|\omega_{kn}|$.[1]

The probability of finding the system in the final state is then proportional to $|H_{kn}^{\prime 0}|^2$ or $|H_{k'n}^{\prime\prime 0}|^2$, which in turn is proportional to $|\mathbf{A}_0|^2$ and hence to the intensity. If the intensity in the small angular frequency range $\Delta\omega$ is $I(\omega)\Delta\omega$, Eq. (35.12) tells us that we can put

$$|\mathbf{A}_0|^2 = \frac{2\pi c}{\omega^2} I(\omega)\Delta\omega \tag{35.15}$$

where $\mathbf{A}_0$ is the vector potential amplitude that characterizes the frequency range $\Delta\omega$. The probability that a transition in which the system is left in a higher energy state ($E_k \cong E_n + \hbar\omega$) has taken place at the time t is then

$$
\begin{aligned}
|a_k^{(1)}(t)|^2 &= \sum_\omega \frac{4|H_{kn}^{\prime 0}|^2 \sin^2 \frac{1}{2}(\omega_{kn} - \omega)t}{\hbar^2(\omega_{kn} - \omega)^2} \\
&= \sum_\omega \frac{8\pi e^2}{m^2 c\omega^2} I(\omega)\Delta\omega \left| \int \bar{u}_k(\exp i\mathbf{k}\cdot\mathbf{r})\operatorname{grad}_A u_n d\tau \right|^2
\end{aligned}
$$

$$\cdot \frac{\sin^2 \frac{1}{2}(\omega_{kn} - \omega)t}{(\omega_{kn} - \omega)^2} \tag{35.16}$$

[1] For a discussion of the situation in which the intensity is not constant near $|\omega_{kn}|$, see W. Heitler, "The Quantum Theory of Radiation," 3d ed., Sec. 20 (Oxford, New York, 1954).

where grad_A is the component of the gradient operator along the polarization vector $\mathbf{A}_0$. The contributions to the probability from various frequency ranges are additive, since there are no phase relations between the radiation components of different frequencies.

Each frequency range $\Delta\omega$ in (35.16) can be made infinitesimally small, and the summation replaced by an integration. Since the time factor has a sharp maximum at $\omega = \omega_{kn}$, the other factors that involve ω can be taken outside the integral and the limits on ω extended to $\pm\infty$, as was done in going from Eq. (29.10) to (29.11). Thus the transition probability per unit time for an upward transition becomes

$$\frac{1}{t}\left|a_k^{(1)}(t)\right|^2 = \frac{8\pi e^2}{m^2 c \omega_{kn}^2}\, I(\omega_{kn})\left|\int \bar{u}_k(\exp i\mathbf{k}\cdot\mathbf{r})\,\text{grad}_A\, u_n d\tau\right|^2$$

$$\cdot \int_{-\infty}^{\infty} \frac{\sin^2 \frac{1}{2}(\omega_{kn} - \omega)t}{t(\omega_{kn} - \omega)^2}\, d\omega$$

$$= \frac{4\pi^2 e^2}{m^2 c \omega_{kn}^2}\, I(\omega_{kn})\left|\int \bar{u}_k(\exp i\mathbf{k}\cdot\mathbf{r})\,\text{grad}_A\, u_n d\tau\right|^2 \qquad (35.17)$$

where the magnitude of $\mathbf{k}$ is now ω_{kn}/c. An expression very similar to (35.17) is obtained for the probability per unit time of a downward transition $(E_{k'} \cong E_n - \hbar\omega)$:

$$\frac{4\pi^2 e^2}{m^2 c \omega_{nk'}^2}\, I(\omega_{nk'})\left|\int \bar{u}_{k'}[\exp (-i\mathbf{k}\cdot\mathbf{r})]\,\text{grad}_A\, u_n d\tau\right|^2 \qquad (35.18)$$

In this case the magnitude of $\mathbf{k}$ is $\omega_{nk'}/c$.

Interpretation in Terms of Absorption and Emission. Equations (35.17) and (35.18) give probabilities per unit time for transitions of the particle between stationary states under the influence of a classical radiation field. These expressions can now be interpreted in terms of absorption and emission of quanta of electromagnetic radiation. It is necessary to assume that such quanta exist and provide the energy units of the radiation field, and that energy is conserved between field and particle. The particle gains the amount of energy $E_k - E_n$ in an upward transition under the influence of radiation of angular frequency ω_{kn}. The quantum energy of this radiation is $\hbar\omega_{kn} = E_k - E_n$, so that it is reasonable to associate with the upward transition of the particle the *absorption* of one quantum from the radiation field.

In similar fashion the downward transition is associated with the emission of one quantum whose energy corresponds to the frequency of the radiation field. In accordance with Eq. (35.18), the emission probability is proportional to the intensity of the radiation present. This process is therefore referred to as *induced emission*.

It is sometimes convenient to rewrite Eq. (35.18) in terms of the reverse transition to that which appears in (35.17). Equation (35.17) describes the transition from an initial lower state n to a final upper state k; (35.18) can be made to describe the transition from an initial upper state k to a final lower state n, if n is replaced by k and k' by n. Then (35.18) becomes

$$\frac{4\pi^2 e^2}{m^2 c \omega_{kn}^2} I(\omega_{kn}) \left| \int \bar{u}_n [\exp(-i\mathbf{k} \cdot \mathbf{r})] \operatorname{grad}_A u_k d\tau \right|^2 \qquad (35.19)$$

We can now show that the integral in (35.19) is just minus the complex conjugate of the integral in (35.17). By means of a partial integration, or with the help of Eq. (22.10), the integral in (35.19) is seen to be equal to[1]

$$-\int u_k \operatorname{grad}_A [\bar{u}_n \exp(-i\mathbf{k} \cdot \mathbf{r})] d\tau$$

Since only the component of the gradient along the polarization vector $\mathbf{A}_0$ appears, and this direction is perpendicular to the propagation vector $\mathbf{k}$, the operator grad_A does not affect $\exp(-i\mathbf{k} \cdot \mathbf{r})$. Thus the integral in (35.19) is equal to

$$-\int u_k [\exp(-i\mathbf{k} \cdot \mathbf{r})] \operatorname{grad}_A \bar{u}_n d\tau$$

and the square of its magnitude is equal to the square of the magnitude of the integral that appears in (35.17).

Since (35.17) and (35.19) are the same, the probabilities of reverse transitions between any pair of states under the influence of the same radiation field are equal.

Electric-dipole Transitions. In most cases of practical interest, the wave length of the radiation is many times greater than the linear dimensions of the wave functions that describe the motion of the particle. This means that the quantity $\mathbf{k} \cdot \mathbf{r}$ that appears in the exponential in the integral of (35.17) is small in comparison with unity wherever u_n and u_k are large enough to give an appreciable contribution to the integral. A good approximation is then obtained by replacing $\exp i\mathbf{k} \cdot \mathbf{r}$ by 1.

The resulting integral can be simplified by expressing it as a matrix element of the momentum of the particle

$$\int \bar{u}_k \operatorname{grad}_A u_n d\tau = \frac{i}{\hbar} \int \bar{u}_k p_A u_n d\tau = \frac{i}{\hbar} (p_A)_{kn}$$

where p_A is the component of the particle momentum $\mathbf{p}$ along the direction of polarization of the incident radiation. The matrix theory of Sec.

---

[1] In using Eq. (22.10), it must be remembered that the operator i **grad,** not the operator **grad,** is Hermitian.

23 shows that the momentum matrix of the unperturbed particle is given by $\mathbf{p} = m(d\mathbf{r}/dt)$.   Thus from Eq. (23.27)

$$\frac{1}{m} (\mathbf{p})_{kn} = \frac{d}{dt} (\mathbf{r})_{kn} = \frac{i}{\hbar} (E_k - E_n)(\mathbf{r})_{kn} = i\omega_{kn}(\mathbf{r})_{kn}$$

The integral in Eq. (35.17) becomes, in this approximation,

$$\int \bar{u}_k \operatorname{grad}_A u_n d\tau = -\frac{m}{\hbar} \omega_{kn}(r_A)_{kn} = -\frac{m}{\hbar} \omega_{kn} \int \bar{u}_k r_A u_n d\tau \quad (35.20)$$

where r_A is the component of $\mathbf{r}$ along the direction of polarization.   Equation (35.20) can, of course, also be derived without recourse to matrix methods (see Prob. 3).

Transitions for which the probability can be computed by substitution of (35.20) into (35.17) are called *electric-dipole transitions*, since only the matrix element of the electric-dipole moment $e\mathbf{r}$ of the particle is involved.[1]   The transition probabilities per unit time for absorption and induced emission then become, in the dipole approximation,

$$\frac{4\pi^2 e^2}{\hbar^2 c} I(\omega_{kn})|(r_A)_{kn}|^2 \quad (35.21)$$

It is convenient to denote by $(\mathbf{r})_{kn}$ the vector whose cartesian components are the kn matrix elements of x, y, and z, and to put

$$|(\mathbf{r})_{kn}|^2 = (\mathbf{r})_{kn} \cdot \overline{(\mathbf{r})_{kn}} \quad (35.22)$$

which is the scalar product of $(\mathbf{r})_{kn}$ and its complex conjugate.   The reason for doing this is that there are usually pairs of states k and n for which $|(\mathbf{r})_{kn}|^2$ is the same, but for which the vector $(\mathbf{r})_{kn}$ has various orientations in space.[2]   Then if Θ is the angle between $(\mathbf{r})_{kn}$ and the direction of polarization of the incident radiation, $|(\mathbf{r})_{kn}|^2 \cos^2 \Theta$ can be substituted for $|(r_A)_{kn}|^2$ in Eq. (35.21), and an average performed over Θ.   The average of (35.21) for such pairs of states is then

$$\frac{4\pi^2 e^2}{3\hbar^2 c} I(\omega_{kn})|(\mathbf{r})_{kn}|^2 \quad (35.23)$$

Forbidden Transitions.   It may happen that the dipole matrix element $(\mathbf{r})_{kn}$ is zero for particular states k and n.   In that case the approxi-

---

[1] The quantity $e\mathbf{r}$ is the electric-dipole moment of the particle of charge e with respect to an arbitrarily placed origin; the addition of a constant vector (corresponding to a shift in the origin) to $\mathbf{r}$ does not affect the matrix element (35.20), since u_k and u_n are orthogonal.

[2] For example, if the particle moves in a spherically symmetric potential $V(r)$, the state k can have $l = 0$, and the states n can have $l = 1$ and three values $(0, \pm 1)$ for the magnetic quantum number m.

mate replacement of exp $i\mathbf{k} \cdot \mathbf{r}$ by 1 in the integral of (35.17) is not justified. The exponential can be expanded in a power series

$$\exp i\mathbf{k} \cdot \mathbf{r} = 1 + i\mathbf{k} \cdot \mathbf{r} + \frac{1}{2!}(i\mathbf{k} \cdot \mathbf{r})^2 + \cdots$$

or in a series of spherical harmonics like (19.9)

$$\exp i\mathbf{k} \cdot \mathbf{r} = j_0(kr) + 3ij_1(kr)P_1(\cos \theta) - 5j_2(kr)P_2(\cos \theta) + \cdots$$

where θ is the angle between $\mathbf{k}$ and $\mathbf{r}$. The second series is more convenient than the first if, as is usually the case, the wave functions u_k and u_n can be expressed in terms of spherical harmonics.

With either series, the dominant factor in the nth term is proportional to $(kr)^n$ if $kr \ll 1$ [see the first of Eqs. (15.7)]. Thus if the dipole matrix element vanishes but the next term of each series does not, the transition matrix element is reduced by a factor that has the order of magnitude ka, where the linear dimensions of the particle wave functions are of order a. A transition of this type is called a *forbidden transition*, since its probability is reduced by a factor $(ka)^2$ with respect to dipole or *allowed transitions*, and usually $ka \ll 1$. Successive terms in the series can be interpreted in terms of electric-dipole, -quadrupole, etc., transitions, and involve successively higher powers of ka.

If both the states u_k and u_n are spherically symmetric, the integral $\int \bar{u}_k (\exp i\mathbf{k} \cdot \mathbf{r}) \operatorname{grad}_A u_n d\tau$ is identically zero. This can be seen by choosing cartesian coordinates for performing the integration such that the x axis is along the direction of polarization. Then $\operatorname{grad}_A u_n$ is an odd function of x, whereas u_k is an even function of x, and $\exp i\mathbf{k} \cdot \mathbf{r} = e^{i(k_y y + k_z z)}$ is also even in x, since the vector $\mathbf{k}$ is perpendicular to the direction of polarization and hence is in the yz plane. Thus the integrand is an odd function of x and the integral in (35.17) vanishes. The transition between these states is said to be *strictly forbidden*, since the first-order probability given by (35.17) is zero. It is still possible for transitions to be produced by higher orders of the perturbation H' given in Eq. (35.13); in such a calculation, the previously neglected term $e^2A^2/2mc^2$ must be included in H'. However, it can be shown with the help of quantum electrodynamics that such higher order transitions involve more than one quantum, and hence are not simple emission or absorption processes in which the quantum energy is equal to the energy difference between the unperturbed states k and n of the particle.

36. SPONTANEOUS EMISSION

A classical charged oscillator can absorb energy from a radiation field or give energy up to it, depending on the phase relation between the field and the oscillator. These effects are analogous to the absorption and induced emission of the last section. A classical oscillator also emits radiation spontaneously, whether or not an external radiation field is present. In this section, we calculate the electromagnetic radiation from a classical oscillating charge-current distribution in the absence of external fields, and somewhat arbitrarily rewrite the formulas in terms of quantum matrix elements to obtain a probability for *spontaneous emission*. The results are then verified by comparison with Planck's expression for the distribution of thermal radiation in a cavity.

Classical Radiation Field. A charge-current distribution can be completely specified by the current density $\mathbf{J}$, since $\mathbf{J}$ determines the charge density ρ through the equation of continuity (35.3). In similar fashion, the electromagnetic fields in empty space, away from charges and currents, can be completely specified by either $\mathbf{E}$ or $\mathbf{H}$, because of the connections (35.2) between them. Now a wave equation for $\mathbf{H}$ is readily obtained by taking the **curl** of the first of Eqs. (35.9).

$$\nabla^2 \mathbf{H} - \frac{1}{c^2} \frac{\partial^2}{\partial t^2} \mathbf{H} = -\frac{4\pi}{c} \operatorname{curl} \mathbf{J}. \tag{36.1}$$

Thus $\mathbf{H}$ can be obtained in terms of $\mathbf{J}$ alone, whereas the similar equation for $\mathbf{E}$ involves both $\mathbf{J}$ and ρ (although ρ can, of course, be eliminated). We proceed by solving Eq. (36.1) for $\mathbf{H}$ when the three cartesian components of $\mathbf{J}$ vary harmonically in time with the same angular frequency ω but not necessarily with the same phase:

$$\begin{aligned} J_x(\mathbf{r},t) &= 2|J_x(\mathbf{r})| \cos (\omega t - \eta_x) = J_x(\mathbf{r})e^{-i\omega t} + \text{c.c.} \\ J_x(\mathbf{r}) &= |J_x(\mathbf{r})|e^{i\eta_x} \end{aligned} \tag{36.2}$$

with similar expressions for the y and z components. We are interested only in the steady-state solutions for $\mathbf{E}$ and $\mathbf{H}$ that have the same frequency ω

$$\begin{aligned} E_x(\mathbf{r},t) &= 2|E_x(\mathbf{r})| \cos (\omega t - \xi_x) = E_x(\mathbf{r})e^{-i\omega t} + \text{c.c.} \\ H_x(\mathbf{r},t) &= 2|H_x(\mathbf{r})| \cos (\omega t - \zeta_x) = H_x(\mathbf{r})e^{-i\omega t} + \text{c.c.} \\ E_x(\mathbf{r}) &= |E_x(\mathbf{r})|e^{i\xi_x}, \qquad H_x(\mathbf{r}) = |H_x(\mathbf{r})|e^{i\zeta_x} \end{aligned} \tag{36.3}$$

again with similar expressions for the y and z components. From the second of Eqs. (35.2), $\mathbf{E}$ is given in terms of $\mathbf{H}$ in empty space by

$$\mathbf{E}(\mathbf{r}) = \frac{ic}{\omega} \operatorname{curl} \mathbf{H}(\mathbf{r}) \tag{36.4}$$

With substitutions from (36.2) and (36.3), Eq. (36.1) becomes

$$(\nabla^2 + k^2)\mathbf{H}(\mathbf{r}) = -\frac{4\pi}{c} \operatorname{curl} \mathbf{J}(\mathbf{r}), \qquad k = \frac{\omega}{c} \tag{36.5}$$

This is an inhomogeneous equation of the type (26.5); its solution can be expressed in terms of the Green's function (26.15), and is

$$\mathbf{H}(\mathbf{r}) = \frac{1}{c} \int \frac{\text{curl } \mathbf{J}(\mathbf{r}')}{|\mathbf{r} - \mathbf{r}'|} \left[\exp\left(ik|\mathbf{r} - \mathbf{r}'|\right)\right] d\tau' \qquad (36.6)$$

Equation (36.6) is the *retarded* solution of (36.5); for large r, this solution is an outgoing wave that varies with r and t like $r^{-1} e^{i(kr-\omega t)} +$ c.c., so that the field produced by a current element occurs at a later time and hence is retarded with respect to the current element.

Asymptotic Form. We are interested in the energy and angular momentum carried away by the field. As shown below, the energy can be found from the leading terms in the asymptotic expression for the field at very large r, which vary as $1/r$; the angular momentum requires in addition some terms that vary as $1/r^2$. The r-dependent part of the integrand of (36.6) can be expanded in powers of $1/r$

$$\frac{\exp\left(ik|\mathbf{r} - \mathbf{r}'|\right)}{|\mathbf{r} - \mathbf{r}'|} \xrightarrow[r \to \infty]{} \frac{1}{r}\left(1 + \frac{r' \cos\theta + \frac{1}{2}ikr'^2 \sin^2\theta}{r}\right) e^{ik(r - r' \cos\theta)} \qquad (36.7)$$

where θ is the angle between $\mathbf{r}'$ and $\mathbf{r}$. Substitution of (36.7) into (36.6) gives, together with (36.4), a complete specification of the asymptotic electromagnetic field through terms of order $1/r^2$.

Radiated Energy. The Poynting vector, which is the energy-flux vector, is equal to $(c/4\pi)[\mathbf{E}(\mathbf{r},t) \times \mathbf{H}(\mathbf{r},t)]$. From (36.3), we see that its time average $\mathbf{P}(\mathbf{r})$ over a period of the oscillation has as a typical component

$$P_z(\mathbf{r}) = \frac{c}{\pi}\{|\mathbf{E}_x(\mathbf{r})| \, |\mathbf{H}_y(\mathbf{r})|[\cos\left(\omega t - \xi_x\right) \cos\left(\omega t - \zeta_y\right)]_{\text{time avg.}}$$

$$- |\mathbf{E}_y(\mathbf{r})| \, |\mathbf{H}_x(\mathbf{r})|[\cos\left(\omega t - \xi_y\right) \cos\left(\omega t - \zeta_x\right)]_{\text{time avg.}}\}$$

$$= \frac{c}{2\pi}\{|\mathbf{E}_x(\mathbf{r})| \, |\mathbf{H}_y(\mathbf{r})| \cos\left(\xi_x - \zeta_y\right) - |\mathbf{E}_y(\mathbf{r})| \, |\mathbf{H}_x(\mathbf{r})| \cos\left(\xi_y - \zeta_x\right)\}$$

This and the other two components can be put in the form

$$\mathbf{P}(\mathbf{r}) = \frac{c}{2\pi} \, Re[\mathbf{E}(\mathbf{r}) \times \overline{\mathbf{H}(\mathbf{r})}] \qquad (36.8)$$

where Re denotes the real part of the expression that follows. Now we are interested only in those terms in the energy flux that fall off as $1/r^2$, since only these correspond to radiated energy; we therefore require only the terms of order $1/r$ in $\mathbf{E}$ and $\mathbf{H}$.

It is convenient in writing down explicit expressions for the fields to choose cartesian axes such that the z axis is along the vector $\mathbf{r}$, which goes from the center of the charge-current distribution to the point at which the field is measured. Equations (36.4), (36.6), and (36.7) then give, to order $1/r$ (where now $r = z$),

$$\mathsf{H}_x \to -\frac{ik}{rc}e^{ikr}\int J_y(\mathbf{r}')e^{-ikz'}d\tau'$$

$$\mathsf{H}_y \to \frac{ik}{rc}e^{ikr}\int J_x(\mathbf{r}')e^{-ikz'}d\tau'$$

$$\mathsf{H}_z \to 0$$

$$\mathsf{E}_x \to \frac{ik}{rc}e^{ikr}\int J_x(\mathbf{r}')e^{-ikz'}d\tau' \qquad (36.9)$$

$$\mathsf{E}_y \to \frac{ik}{rc}e^{ikr}\int J_y(\mathbf{r}')e^{-ikz'}d\tau'$$

$$\mathsf{E}_z \to 0$$

Partial integration has been used to get rid of the derivatives of $\mathbf{J}$ in the integrand of H. Equations (36.9) show that the asymptotic fields are transverse to the direction of propagation. They also relate the polarization of the emitted radiation to the current distribution, and show that only the component of the current perpendicular to the direction of propagation contributes to the radiated energy. Substitution into (36.8) gives

$$P_z = \frac{k^2}{2\pi r^2 c}\left(\left|\int J_x e^{-ikz'}d\tau'\right|^2 + \left|\int J_y e^{-ikz'}d\tau'\right|^2\right) \qquad (36.10)$$

Equation (36.10) can be generalized to give the average energy flux in the direction of a vector $\mathbf{k}$

$$\frac{k^2}{2\pi r^2 c}\left|\int J_{\perp\mathbf{k}}(\mathbf{r}')[\exp{(-i\mathbf{k}\cdot\mathbf{r}')}]d\tau'\right|^2 \qquad (36.11)$$

where $J_{\perp\mathbf{k}}$ is the component of $\mathbf{J}$ perpendicular to $\mathbf{k}$.

Dipole Radiation. Equation (36.11) is an exact expression for the energy radiated by the classical current distribution (36.2). As in Sec. 35, the electric-dipole approximation is obtained in the long-wave-length limit by assuming that $kr' \ll 1$ and replacing $\exp{(-i\mathbf{k}\cdot\mathbf{r}')}$ by 1 in the integrand. The energy flux is then

$$\frac{k^2}{2\pi r^2 c}\left|\int J_{\perp\mathbf{k}}(\mathbf{r}')d\tau'\right|^2 \qquad (36.12)$$

From Eqs. (36.9) with the same approximation, it is apparent that the polarization (direction of the electric field) of the radiation is determined by the total current vector $\mathbf{J}_0 \equiv \int\mathbf{J}(\mathbf{r}')d\tau'$. The radiation is linearly polarized if $\mathbf{J}_0$ has only one component in the plane perpendicular to the direction of propagation, circularly polarized if $\mathbf{J}_0$ has two equal components in this plane that are perpendicular to each other and 90° out of phase (so that one component is i times the other), etc.

If $\mathbf{J}_0$ has only one component, the angular distribution of the radiation can be found by replacing $|\int J_{\perp\mathbf{k}}(\mathbf{r}')d\tau'|^2$ in (36.12) by

$$(\mathbf{J}_0 \cdot \bar{\mathbf{J}}_0) \sin^2 \theta = |\mathbf{J}_0|^2 \sin^2 \theta$$

where θ is the angle between $\mathbf{J}_0$ and $\mathbf{k}$, and $|\mathbf{J}_0|^2$ is an abbreviation for the scalar product of $\mathbf{J}_0$ and its complex conjugate. The total power radiated is then the integral of (36.12) over the surface of a sphere of radius r

$$\frac{4k^2}{3c}|\mathbf{J}_0|^2 \tag{36.13}$$

Equation (36.13) is also valid if $\mathbf{J}_0$ has more than one component, and these do not necessarily have the same phase (see Prob. 11).

Angular Momentum. The angular momentum radiated per unit time is equal to the torque exerted on a large, perfectly absorbing sphere that is centered at the charge-current distribution that constitutes the source of radiation. The average energy flux is $\mathbf{P}$, so that the (directed) energy density is $(1/c)\mathbf{P}$ and the momentum density is $(1/c^2)\mathbf{P}$. Since the radiation travels outward with speed c, the torque exerted on a perfectly absorbing differential element of area, dA, that is perpendicular to $\mathbf{r}$ is cdA times the vector product of $\mathbf{r}$ and the momentum density: $(dA/c)(\mathbf{r} \times \mathbf{P})$. Integration of this quantity over the sphere of radius r gives the angular momentum radiated by the source per unit time. Thus only the components of $\mathbf{P}$ tangential to the sphere are involved: in the notation of Eqs. (36.9), these are P_x and P_y, since the z axis is along $\mathbf{r}$.

If E_z and H_z were zero, the tangential components P_x and P_y would also be zero, and no angular momentum would be radiated. The third and sixth of Eqs. (36.9) imply only that the z (radial) components of the field are of smaller order than $1/r$; actually they are of order $1/r^2$. This means that P_x and P_y fall off as $1/r^3$ for large r. Then since $\mathbf{r} \times \mathbf{P}$ appears in the expression for the angular momentum, and the area of the absorbing sphere is proportional to r^2, the total angular momentum absorbed by a large sphere is independent of r.

We require the $1/r^2$ terms in E_z and H_z, but not in the other field components.

$$\mathsf{H}_z \to \frac{ik}{r^2c}e^{ikr}\int [y'J_x(\mathbf{r}') - x'J_y(\mathbf{r}')]e^{-ikz'}d\tau'$$

$$\mathsf{E}_z \to \frac{1}{r^2c}e^{ikr}\int [2J_z(\mathbf{r}') + ikx'J_x(\mathbf{r}') + iky'J_y(\mathbf{r}')]e^{-ikz'}d\tau' \tag{36.14}$$

Equations (36.9) and (36.14) are sufficient for an exact calculation of the radiated angular momentum.[1]

Dipole Case. The expressions for P_x and P_y are simplified by the dipole approximation since only the terms of lowest order in kr' need be retained in (36.9) and (36.14). It is easy to see that the leading term in P_x, for example, is $-(c/2\pi)Re(\mathsf{E}_z\overline{\mathsf{H}}_y)$ and not $(c/2\pi)Re(\mathsf{E}_y\overline{\mathsf{H}}_z)$. We obtain to lowest order in kr'

$$P_x = \frac{k}{\pi r^3 c} Re\left(i \int J_z d\tau' \int \bar{J}_x d\tau' \right)$$

$$P_y = \frac{k}{\pi r^3 c} Re\left(i \int J_z d\tau' \int \bar{J}_y d\tau' \right) \tag{36.15}$$

Equations (36.15) refer to axes fixed with respect to the element dA of absorbing area at $\mathbf{r}$. They must now be rewritten in terms of general

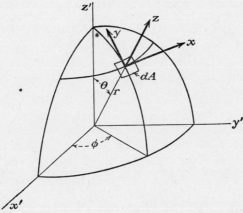

Fig. 29.   Relation between the unprimed coordinate system of Eqs. (36.15) and the primed coordinate system of Eq. (36.16).

cartesian coordinates, in order that the angular-momentum component about a particular axis fixed in space can be found. This is analogous to the rewriting of the energy-flux expression (36.10) in the general form (36.11), but is somewhat more complicated. To accomplish this, we choose new cartesian coordinates x',y',z' that are fixed in space. With respect to these, the orientation of the old axes depends on $\mathbf{r}$ in the following way (see Fig. 29): the z axis is in the direction of $\mathbf{r}$ and has the polar angles θ,ϕ with respect to the new axes, the y axis is perpendicular to $\mathbf{r}$ and in the plane of $\mathbf{r}$ and z', and the x axis is perpendicular to the plane of $\mathbf{r}$ and z'. If now we wish to calculate the contribution to the z' component of angular momentum from absorption by the element of area

$$dA = r^2 \sin \theta d\theta d\phi$$

[1] For a more general discussion, see J. M. Blatt and V. F. Weisskopf, "Theoretical Nuclear Physics," Appendix B (Wiley, New York, 1952).

at **r**, we need only P_x given in (36.15). This can be rewritten in terms of the components of the total current vector $\mathbf{J}_0$ along the new axes as

$$P_x = \frac{k}{\pi r^3 c} Re[i(J_{0x'} \sin \theta \cos \phi + J_{0y'} \sin \theta \sin \phi + J_{0z'} \cos \theta)$$
$$\cdot (\bar{J}_{0y'} \cos \phi - \bar{J}_{0x'} \sin \phi)] \quad (36.16)$$

The moment arm about the z' axis associated with P_x is $r \sin \theta$, so that the differential element of angular-momentum component is

$$dM_{z'} = \frac{1}{c} r \sin \theta \, P_x r^2 \sin \theta d\theta d\phi \quad (36.17)$$

Substitution of (36.16) into (36.17) and integration over the polar angles gives

$$M_{z'} = \frac{4ik}{3c^2} (J_{0x'}\bar{J}_{0y'} - J_{0y'}\bar{J}_{0x'}) \quad (36.18)$$

It is apparent from Eq. (36.18) that the radiation of a particular component of angular momentum depends only on the perpendicular components of $\mathbf{J}_0$. Moreover, there must be two such perpendicular components that are out of phase with each other, for if $J_{0x'}$ and $J_{0y'}$ are both real or have the same phase, the parenthesis in (36.18) is zero. Thus a linear dipole ($\mathbf{J}_0$ entirely in one direction) radiates no angular momentum. The maximum angular momentum for a given value of $|\mathbf{J}_0|^2$ is radiated when $\mathbf{J}_0$ has two equal perpendicular components that are 90° out of phase with each other and the third perpendicular component is zero. If the nonvanishing components are along x' and y' we can put $J_{0y'} = iJ_{0x'}$; Eq. (36.18) then becomes

$$M_{z'} = \frac{8k}{3c^2} |J_{0x'}|^2 = \frac{4k}{3c^2} |\mathbf{J}_0|^2 \quad (36.19)$$

and the other two components of **M** are zero.

Comparison of Eqs. (36.13) and (36.19) shows that the maximum angular momentum radiated per unit time by an oscillating electric dipole is $1/kc = 1/\omega$ times the energy radiated per unit time. If this relation is taken over into quantum theory, it shows that a quantum of energy, $\hbar\omega$, radiated by an electric dipole carries with it an amount of angular momentum that does not exceed $\hbar$.

Conversion from Classical to Quantum Theory. We now convert the classical expression (36.13) for the power radiated by an electric dipole, to quantum theory. This requires that we find a quantum analogue for the total current vector $\mathbf{J}_0$ and associate the radiated power with a transition probability between states of the particle that is doing the radiating.

We want to replace $\mathbf{J}$ by a current density that is associated with an initial upper state u_k and a final lower state u_n, since energy is radiated during the transition from k to n. It is natural to represent the current density as the product of a charge density and a velocity, and to take for the velocity the momentum operator divided by the mass: $-(i\hbar/m)$ **grad**. The charge density for a stationary state is expected to be the charge of the particle times its position probability density: $e|\psi|^2$. However, we are concerned here with a transition between states, so we replace this by $e\bar{u}_n u_k$. The way in which the **grad** that appears in the velocity operates on the wave functions that appear in the charge density is determined by arguments of the type presented in Sec. 7 [see Eq. (7.3)]. We thus arrive at a quantity to substitute for the classical current density:

$$\mathbf{J}(\mathbf{r}) \rightarrow -\frac{ie\hbar}{m}\,\bar{u}_n(\mathbf{r})\,\mathbf{grad}\,u_k(\mathbf{r}) \tag{36.20}$$

We assume that (36.20) can be substituted into all the foregoing classical expressions to give quantum results.[1]

Integration of (36.20) over the coordinates gives the total current vector

$$\mathbf{J}_0 = -\frac{ie\hbar}{m}\int \bar{u}_n\,\mathbf{grad}\,u_k d\tau = -ie\omega_{nk}\int \bar{u}_n \mathbf{r} u_k d\tau = ie\omega_{kn}\overline{(\mathbf{r})_{kn}} \tag{36.21}$$

with the help of equation (35.20). Substitution of (36.21) into (36.13) then gives the radiated power. We interpret this power as the product of the spontaneous rate of transition from k to n, and the quantum energy $\hbar\omega_{kn} = \hbar(E_k - E_n)$ given off in each transition. The transition probability per unit time for spontaneous emission then becomes

$$\frac{4e^2 k^2 \omega_{kn}}{3\hbar c}\,|(\mathbf{r})_{kn}|^2 = \frac{4e^2 \omega_{kn}{}^3}{3\hbar c^3}\,|(\mathbf{r})_{kn}|^2 \tag{36.22}$$

where use has been made of the relation $\omega_{kn} = kc$.

Planck Distribution Formula. The transition from the classical expression (36.13) to the quantum expression (36.22) can claim only a moderate amount of plausibility. The correctness of the latter result can however be verified by showing that Planck's formula for the spectral distribution of thermal radiation in a cavity follows from (36.22) and (35.23). This is the way in which the relation between the probabilities

[1] The exponential that appears in (36.11), for example, can be placed either before or after the **grad** operator, since only the component of **grad** that is perpendicular to **k** enters in.

for absorption, induced emission, and spontaneous emission was first obtained.[1]

We assume that the walls of the cavity contain particles of charge e and mass m, each of which is bound by a potential V of the type that appears in (35.1). When these particles are in equilibrium with thermal radiation at the absolute temperature T, there must be as many quanta of each frequency emitted as absorbed per unit time. The rate of emission of quanta of frequency ω_{kn} is the sum of (35.23) and (36.22), multiplied by the number of particles that are in the upper state k. The rate of absorption of these quanta is the product of (35.23) and the number of particles in the lower state n. Now from statistical mechanics,[2] the equilibrium ratio of the number of particles in the upper state to the number in the lower state is given by $e^{-(E_k - E_n)/\kappa T}$, where κ is Boltzmann's constant. We thus obtain, on dropping the subscripts from ω_{kn},

$$\varrho^{-\frac{\hbar\omega}{\kappa T}} \left[\frac{4\pi^2 e^2}{3\hbar^2 c} I(\omega) |(\mathbf{r})_{kn}|^2 + \frac{4e^2\omega^3}{3\hbar c^3} |(\mathbf{r})_{kn}|^2 \right] = \frac{4\pi^2 e^2}{3\hbar^2 c} I(\omega) |(\mathbf{r}_{kn})|^2$$

This is readily solved for $I(\omega)$ to give

$$I(\omega) = \frac{\hbar\omega^3}{\pi^2 c^2 (e^{\frac{\hbar\omega}{\kappa T}} - 1)} \tag{36.23}$$

It is interesting to note that the parameters e, m, and $(\mathbf{r})_{kn}$ of the particle that emits and absorbs the radiation drop out of the expression for $I(\omega)$. The agreement between Eq. (36.23) and the Planck distribution formula provides a verification of the ratio of (35.23) to (36.22), and hence shows that the latter expression is correct if the former is.

Line Breadth. A classical oscillator that radiates electromagnetic waves loses energy, so that the amplitude of its oscillation decreases in time. Thus the electromagnetic fields given off by it have a damped sinusoidal time dependence: $e^{-\frac{1}{2}\gamma t} \cos (\omega_0 t + \alpha)$. The Fourier analysis of these fields gives the frequency spectrum of the radiation from the oscillator. The radiated intensity per unit frequency range at the angular frequency ω is proportional to

$$\frac{1}{(\omega - \omega_0)^2 + \frac{1}{4}\gamma^2} \tag{36.24}$$

---

[1] A. Einstein, *Phys. Zeits.*, **18**, 121 (1917). Einstein's A coefficient is just (36.22), and his B coefficient is (35.23) divided by the energy density of radiation $I(\omega_{kn})/c$ (this is expressed in terms of the angular frequency ω_{kn} rather than the circular frequency $\omega_{kn}/2\pi$).

[2] See, for example, R. C. Tolman, "The Principles of Statistical Mechanics," Chap. IV (Oxford, New York, 1938).

According to (36.24), the intensity of the emitted spectral line has half its maximum value when $\omega = \omega_0 \pm \frac{1}{2}\gamma$. The quantity γ is called the *natural line breadth*, and in cases of practical interest is small in comparison with ω_0.

The line breadth is evidently twice the initial fractional rate of decrease of the amplitude of the classical oscillator, or is equal to the initial fractional rate of decrease of the oscillator's energy. It is plausible to associate the rate of decrease of the energy of the classical oscillator with the rate of decrease of the probability of finding the corresponding quantum system in its initial upper state. If this is done, the quantum analogue of the classical natural line breadth γ is the initial transition probability per unit time for spontaneous emission given in (36.22).[1]

The foregoing relation between transition probability and line breadth can be arrived at in a qualitative but more general way by means of the uncertainty relation (3.3). The reciprocal of the transition probability per unit time is of the order of magnitude of the time that the quantum system stays in its upper state. Thus a determination of the energy of the upper state cannot occupy a time that is of larger order of magnitude than the lifetime $1/\gamma$ of this state. According to (3.3), this means that the energy cannot be determined with an accuracy much greater than $\hbar$ divided by the lifetime, or $\hbar\gamma$. If the energy of the upper state is uncertain by this amount, the frequency of the emitted line will be uncertain (broadened) by γ. In general, a quantum energy level is broadened by any process that shortens its lifetime: the level is perfectly sharp only if the lifetime of the state is infinite (true stationary energy eigenfunction).

A qualitative idea of the natural breadth of electric-dipole lines emitted by a quantum system can be obtained by rewriting the expression (36.22) for γ in the form

$$\frac{\gamma}{\omega_{kn}} = \frac{4}{3}\frac{e^2}{\hbar c}k^2|(\mathbf{r})_{kn}|^2$$

The factor $e^2/\hbar c$ is a dimensionless constant that is very nearly equal to $\frac{1}{137}$ if e is the electronic charge,[2] and the factor $k^2|(\mathbf{r})_{kn}|^2$ has already been assumed small in comparison with unity in arriving at the dipole approximation. Thus the ratio of line breadth to angular frequency is expected to be quite small (it is of the order of 10^{-6} for typical atomic dipole lines).

37. SOME APPLICATIONS OF RADIATION THEORY

The semiclassical radiation theory developed earlier in this chapter is applied in this section first to the determination of the conditions for

---

[1] For further discussion of line breadth, see Heitler, *op. cit.*, Sec. 18.

[2] This is the *fine-structure constant* that appears in the theory of the fine structure of atomic energy levels (see Chap. XII).

allowed transitions, and next to the theory of the Cerenkov effect.   The latter is of some practical interest and also shows how to calculate the radiation from a current distribution that does not depend harmonically on the time.   Finally, the theory of the photoelectric effect is discussed.

Selection Rules for a Single Particle.   The discussion of forbidden transitions at the end of Sec. 35 shows that the probabilities for absorption and induced emission are reduced by a factor of at least $(ka)^2$ with respect to allowed transitions if the dipole matrix element $(\mathbf{r})_{kn}$ vanishes.   The same remarks apply to the probability for spontaneous emission, since the integral in (36.11) is the same as that in (35.19) when the substitution (36.20) is made for $\mathbf{J}$.

The conditions on u_k and u_n for which the dipole matrix element is different from zero constitute the *selection rules*.   They are easily formulated if the potential V that appears in the unperturbed Hamiltonian of (35.13) is spherically symmetric.   It is shown in Sec. 14 that the energy eigenfunctions can then be written as products of functions of the radial distance r and spherical harmonics $Y_{lm}(\theta,\phi)$ defined in Eq. (14.16).   The matrix element $(\mathbf{r})_{kn}$ is the vector whose cartesian components are the corresponding matrix elements of x, y, and z.   The matrix element of z is $\int \bar{u}_k r \cos \theta u_n d\tau$, which can be written as a product of an integral over r and the angular integral

$$\int_0^\pi \int_0^{2\pi} \overline{Y}_{lm}(\theta,\phi) \cos \theta \, Y_{l'm'}(\theta,\phi) \sin \theta d\theta d\phi \qquad (37.1)$$

where the primed and unprimed subscripts are the angular-momentum quantum numbers for the lower state u_n and the upper state u_k, respectively.

The ϕ integration in (37.1) is $\int_0^{2\pi} e^{i(m'-m)\phi} d\phi$, which is zero unless $m' = m$.   The integration can then be written, apart from numerical factors,

$$\int_{-1}^1 w P_l^m(w) P_{l'}^m(w) dw, \qquad w = \cos \theta \qquad (37.2)$$

Now it can be shown with the help of the generating function (14.13) for the associated Legendre functions that

$$w P_l^m(w) = \frac{l + |m|}{2l + 1} P_{l-1}^m(w) + \frac{l - |m| + 1}{2l + 1} P_{l+1}^m(w)$$

Substitution of this into (37.2) shows, with the help of the orthogonality integral (14.15), that the matrix element of z vanishes unless $m' = m$ and $l' = l \pm 1$.   A similar treatment shows that the matrix element of $x + iy$ vanishes unless $m' = m - 1$ and $l' = l \pm 1$, and the matrix element of $x - iy$ vanishes unless $m' = m + 1$ and $l' = l \pm 1$.   These selection rules determine the possible allowed (electric-dipole) transitions of a single charged particle that moves in a central force field.

Polarization of Emitted Radiation. The discussion following Eq. (36.12) shows that the polarization of the emitted radiation is determined by the total current vector $\mathbf{J}_0$, and hence (because of 36.21) by the dipole matrix element. When the initial and final states have l values that differ by unity and the same magnetic quantum number m with respect to the z axis, only the matrix element of z fails to vanish. The radiation is then linearly polarized along the z axis if viewed in the xy plane, and there is no radiation along the z axis. When the magnetic quantum numbers of the initial and final states differ by unity, the x and y components of the dipole matrix element are 90° out of phase, and the z component vanishes; the radiation is then circularly polarized if viewed along the z axis, and linearly polarized perpendicular to the z axis if viewed in the xy plane. These results are of interest in connection with the polarization of the radiation from atoms placed in a magnetic field (see the discussion of the Zeeman effect in Sec. 39).

Conservation of Angular Momentum. The discussion of Eqs. (36.18) and (36.19) shows that the angular momentum that is carried away by an emitted quantum has its maximum value $\hbar$, and is directed along the z axis, when $J_{0y} = iJ_{0x}$. From (36.21) we see that this is the case in which $\overline{(y)_{kn}} = i\overline{(x)_{kn}}$, or $(y)_{kn} = -i(x)_{kn}$. Now $x = r\,\sin\,\theta\,\cos\,\phi = \frac{1}{2}r\,\sin\,\theta$ $\cdot\,(e^{i\phi} + e^{-i\phi})$, and $y = r\,\sin\,\theta\,\sin\,\phi = -\frac{1}{2}ir\,\sin\,\theta(e^{i\phi} - e^{-i\phi})$. Then it is apparent from the ϕ integration in (37.1) that in order for the matrix element of y to equal $-i$ times the matrix of x, the magnetic quantum number of the initial state u_k must be greater than the magnetic quantum number of the final state u_n by unity. Application of Eq. (14.23) shows that the z component of angular momentum of the particle has decreased by $\hbar$ during the transition. Thus angular momentum is conserved between the radiating particle and the emitted quantum.

The foregoing result is based on the connection between the classical and quantum current densities assumed in (36.20). The successful derivation of the Planck distribution law in Sec. 36 shows that (36.20) is correct so far as magnitude is concerned. The above demonstration of the conservation of angular momentum shows in addition that the phases of the initial and final states are inserted properly in (36.20); if, for example, $\mathbf{J}$ had been assumed proportional to $\bar{u}_k$ **grad** u_n, an inconsistent result would have been obtained in the last paragraph.

If the magnetic quantum number does not change in a transition, only the matrix element of z fails to vanish, and the discussion of (36.18) shows that the quantum carries off no angular momentum. This might seem at first to be in contradiction with the change by one unit of the orbital-angular-momentum quantum number l.   The x and y components of the angular momentum of the particle do not commute with the z component (which in this case is known to be $m\hbar$ and does not change), so that they cannot be precisely specified.   Their expectation or average values for states that are described by quantum numbers l and m are zero, since the diagonal elements of the matrices for the x and y components of the angular momentum are all zero [see Eqs. (24.15)].   Thus there is no observable change in any of the components of the particle's angular momentum, and so the expectation value of the angular momentum carried off by the quantum should be zero.   The x and y angular-momentum components for a particle in a stationary state can be thought of as fluctuating about zero in such a way that their average values are zero, although their average squares are not.   The change in l corresponds to changes in these average squares.

Selection Rules for Many-particle Systems.   When a quantum-mechanical system consists of several particles that do not interact with each other, the total Hamiltonian is simply a sum of terms like $H_0 + H'$ that appear in (35.13).   The unperturbed energy eigenfunctions are products of single-particle eigenfunctions such as are discussed in Sec. 32 (they can be unsymmetrized if the particles are not identical).   It is clear that the matrix element that appears in the first-order perturbation theory of Sec. 35 (absorption and induced emission) involves a multiple integral of the form

$$\int \cdots \int \bar{u}_{a'}(1)\bar{u}_{b'}(2)$$
$$\cdots [H'(1) + H'(2) + \cdots]u_a(1)u_b(2) \cdots d\tau_1 d\tau_2 \cdots$$

Because of the orthogonality of different u's for the same particle, this integral vanishes unless all the single-particle functions $u_{a'}, \ldots$ are equal to the corresponding functions $u_a, \ldots$, except for one.   Thus only one of the particles can change its state in a transition, and the selection rules for a central force field are precisely those given above. Since the spontaneous transition probability can be related to the same integral through the Planck distribution formula, these selection rules hold for spontaneous emission as well as for absorption and induced emission.

If the system consists of several charged particles whose mutual interactions cannot be neglected, we must base the selection rules on general conservation laws for total angular momentum and parity.   It is not difficult to generalize the work of Secs. 35 and 36 to show that the dominant term, when the wave length of the radiation is large in comparison with the dimensions of the system, is the matrix element of the total electric-dipole moment $e_1\mathbf{r}_1 + e_2\mathbf{r}_2 + \cdots$.   The angular momentum radiated by an oscillating dipole cannot, according to the discussion of (36.19), exceed $\hbar$ per quantum; this classical argument is based on an arbitrary current distribution, so that it is not invalidated if several particles contribute to the dipole.   The interpretation of the conservation of angular momentum between the emitted quantum and the radiating system is complicated by the semiclassical nature of the entire treatment.   A consistent treatment based on quantum electrodynamics shows that the correct selection rule based on this conservation law is that the total-angular-momentum quantum number of the system can remain unchanged, or increase or decrease by unity.   An exceptional case is that in which this quantum number is zero for both initial and final states. The initial and final wave functions are then spherically symmetric, and an extension of the argument given at the end of Sec. 35 shows that a radiative transition between these states is not only forbidden (no allowed dipole transition), but strictly forbidden (no first-order transition whatever).

The discussion of parity in connection with Eq. (23.26) shows that the parity of each energy eigenfunction can be well defined (even or odd) if the total Hamiltonian is unchanged by reflection of the coordinates of all particles through the origin.   All known Hamiltonians are of this type. Now the electric-dipole-moment operator given above is evidently odd with respect to reflection of all coordinates; thus its matrix elements vanish unless the initial and final states have opposite parities.   This selection rule is known as the *Laporte rule*.

Cerenkov Effect.   It is not difficult to show that a charged particle that moves freely in empty space does not radiate energy.   Electromagnetic radiation has the greatest momentum for a given amount of energy when it is all flowing in one direction, in which case the ratio of momentum to energy is $1/c$.   The relativistic relation between the total energy E (including rest energy) and the magnitude p of the momentum of a freely moving particle is $E^2 = p^2c^2 + m^2c^4$, where m is the rest mass.[1] Differentiation of this relation gives $2EdE = 2pc^2dp$, so that the ratio of momentum loss to energy loss of the particle if it radiates is

$$\frac{dp}{dE} = \frac{E}{pc^2} = \frac{1}{c}\left[1 + \left(\frac{mc}{p}\right)^2\right]^{\frac{1}{2}}$$

which is always greater than $1/c$.   Thus it is impossible for a freely moving particle to radiate, since if energy were conserved between the particle and the electromagnetic field, momentum would not be.

---

[1] See, for example, P. G. Bergmann, "Introduction to the Theory of Relativity," Chap. VI (Prentice-Hall, New York, 1942).

The situation is altered if other matter is present to take up the excess momentum. An electron bound in an atom or an electron that passes near an atomic nucleus can radiate; the latter case is usually described in terms of the deflection of the electron by the nucleus and the emission of radiation by the accelerated electron. An interesting example in which the presence of matter makes it possible for the conservation laws to be satisfied is provided by the uniform motion of a charged particle through a medium of refractive index n, when the speed v of the particle is greater than the speed of light in the medium:

$$v > \frac{c}{n} \tag{37.3}$$

The radiation from fast electrons that satisfy (37.3) has been observed by Cerenkov.[1] The theory of the *Cerenkov effect*[2] is developed on the basis of classical radiation theory in the remainder of this section. This treatment is satisfactory in so far as the structure of the medium can be represented by a refractive index.

Expression for the Current Density. We assume that the moving charge has dimensions that are small in comparison with emitted wave lengths of interest. Then if the particle has charge e, moves in the z direction with the speed v, and is at the origin at $t = 0$, the current density can be written

$$\begin{aligned}
J_x(\mathbf{r},t) &= J_y(\mathbf{r},t) = 0 \\
J_z(\mathbf{r},t) &= ev\delta(x)\delta(y)\delta(z - vt)
\end{aligned} \tag{37.4}$$

The Dirac δ function is that introduced in Sec. 11. Since the radiation theory developed in Sec. 36 is based on a current density that depends harmonically on the time, J_z must be expressed in terms of a Fourier integral

$$J_z(\mathbf{r},t) = \int_0^\infty [J_{z\omega}(\mathbf{r})e^{-i\omega t} + \text{c.c.}]d\omega \tag{37.5}$$

The Fourier amplitude of angular frequency ω is given by

$$J_{z\omega}(\mathbf{r}) = \frac{e}{2\pi}\,\delta(x)\delta(y)e^{\frac{i\omega z}{v}} \tag{37.6}$$

This can be verified by substituting (37.6) into (37.5) to obtain

$$\begin{aligned}
J_z(\mathbf{r},t) &= \frac{e}{2\pi}\,\delta(x)\delta(y)\int_0^\infty [e^{i\omega\left(\frac{z}{v}-t\right)} + e^{-i\omega\left(\frac{z}{v}-t\right)}]d\omega \\
&= \frac{e}{2\pi}\,\delta(x)\delta(y)\int_{-\infty}^\infty e^{i\omega\left(\frac{z}{v}-t\right)}d\omega
\end{aligned}$$

---

[1] P. A. Cerenkov, *Phys. Rev.*, **52**, 378 (1937).

[2] I. Frank and I. Tamm, *Comptes Rendus de l'Acad. Sci. U.R.S.S.*, **14**, 109 (1937); I. Tamm, *J. Phys. U.S.S.R.*, **1**, 439 (1939).

which with the help of (11.10) and the fifth of Eqs. (11.13) is seen to agree with (37.4).

Fourier Analysis of the Radiation Field. The electromagnetic fields can be expressed in analogy with (37.5):

$$\mathbf{E}(\mathbf{r},t) = \int_0^\infty [\mathbf{E}_\omega(\mathbf{r})e^{-i\omega t} + \text{c.c.}]d\omega$$

$$\mathbf{H}(\mathbf{r},t) = \int_0^\infty [\mathbf{H}_\omega(\mathbf{r})e^{-i\omega t} + \text{c.c.}]d\omega \qquad (37.7)$$

Because of the linear dependence of $\mathbf{E}$ and $\mathbf{H}$ on $\mathbf{J}$ through Maxwell's equations, each of the Fourier components $\mathbf{E}_\omega$ and $\mathbf{H}_\omega$ can be obtained entirely from the corresponding component $J_{z\omega}$ of the current density. The Poynting vector obtained from (37.7) is

$$\frac{c}{4\pi}\mathbf{E}(\mathbf{r},t) \times \mathbf{H}(\mathbf{r},t) = \frac{c}{4\pi}\int_0^\infty \int_0^\infty [\mathbf{E}_\omega(\mathbf{r}) \times \mathbf{H}_{\omega'}(\mathbf{r})e^{-i(\omega+\omega')t}$$
$$+ \overline{\mathbf{E}_\omega(\mathbf{r})} \times \overline{\mathbf{H}_{\omega'}(\mathbf{r})}e^{i(\omega+\omega')t} + \mathbf{E}_\omega(\mathbf{r}) \times \overline{\mathbf{H}_{\omega'}(\mathbf{r})}e^{-i(\omega-\omega')t}$$
$$+ \overline{\mathbf{E}_\omega(\mathbf{r})} \times \mathbf{H}_{\omega'}(\mathbf{r})e^{i(\omega-\omega')t}]d\omega d\omega' \quad (37.8)$$

Equation (37.8) can be used to find the spectral energy distribution of the radiation. The distribution of the radiated energy in frequency is usually of more interest than the distribution in time, if the emission process occupies a time that is short by laboratory standards. We therefore integrate (37.8) over t from $-\infty$ to $+\infty$ to obtain the total flow of energy per unit area. Since t appears only in the exponentials, we can use Eq. (11.10) to obtain δ functions in the frequencies. Then when the integration over ω' is carried through, the first two terms in the integrand of (37.8) contribute nothing, and the last two terms yield

$$\frac{c}{4\pi}\int_{-\infty}^\infty \mathbf{E}(\mathbf{r},t) \times \mathbf{H}(\mathbf{r},t)dt$$

$$= \tfrac{1}{2}c\int_0^\infty [\mathbf{E}_\omega(\mathbf{r}) \times \overline{\mathbf{H}_\omega(\mathbf{r})} + \overline{\mathbf{E}_\omega(\mathbf{r})} \times \mathbf{H}_\omega(\mathbf{r})]d\omega \quad (37.9)$$

The integrand of (37.9) is just twice the real part of $\mathbf{E}_\omega(\mathbf{r}) \times \overline{\mathbf{H}_\omega(\mathbf{r})}$, and in accordance with (36.8) can be called $(4\pi/c)\mathbf{P}_\omega(\mathbf{r})$. Since (37.9) has the form of an integral over frequency, we see that $2\pi\mathbf{P}_\omega(\mathbf{r})d\omega$ is the flow per unit area of energy that lies in the angular-frequency range ω to $\omega + d\omega$.

We assume that the medium with which we are concerned is a homogeneous isotropic dielectric that is characterized by a dielectric constant or specific inductive capacity ϵ. This means that c is to be replaced by $c/\epsilon^{\frac{1}{2}} = c/n$ in Secs. 35 and 36, where the refractive index n of the medium is equal to $\epsilon^{\frac{1}{2}}$; also, $\mathbf{k}$ is replaced by $n\mathbf{k}$.[1] Thus (36.11) becomes, in our present notation,

$$P_{k\omega}(\mathbf{r}) = \frac{nk^2}{2\pi r^2 c} \left| \int J_{\perp \mathbf{k},\omega}(\mathbf{r}') \exp\left(-in\mathbf{k} \cdot \mathbf{r}'\right) d\tau' \right|^2 \tag{37.10}$$

Here $P_{k\omega}$ is the component of $\mathbf{P}_\omega$ in the direction of observation (parallel to $\mathbf{k}$ or $\mathbf{r}$), and the magnitude of $\mathbf{k}$ has the earlier value ω/c.

Radiated Energy. The direction of observation is taken to have polar angles θ, ϕ with respect to the z axis. Then $\mathbf{k} \cdot \mathbf{r}'$ in (37.10) is equal to $k(x' \sin\theta \cos\phi + y' \sin\theta \sin\phi + z' \cos\theta)$, and $J_{\perp \mathbf{k},\omega} = J_{z\omega} \sin\theta$. Substitution of (37.6) into (37.10) then gives for the energy flow per unit area and angular frequency

$$2\pi P_{k\omega}(\mathbf{r}) = 2\pi \frac{nk^2}{2\pi r^2 c} \frac{e^2}{4\pi^2} \sin^2\theta \left| \int \int \int \delta(x')\delta(y') e^{\frac{i\omega z'}{v}} \right.$$

$$\left. \cdot\, e^{-ink(x' \sin\theta \cos\phi + y' \sin\theta \sin\phi + z' \cos\theta)} dx' dy' dz' \right|^2$$

$$= \frac{ne^2 \omega^2 \sin^2\theta}{4\pi^2 c^3 r^2} \left| \int \exp\left[i\omega z' \left(\frac{1}{v} - \frac{n\cos\theta}{c}\right) \right] dz' \right|^2 \tag{37.11}$$

In order that (37.11) be definite, the particle can be considered as radiating only over a finite length L of its path, so that the integral over z' extends, say, from $-\frac{1}{2}L$ to $\frac{1}{2}L$.

The squared integral in (37.11) is easily evaluated to give

$$\frac{4 \sin^2\left[\frac{1}{2}\omega L \left(\frac{1}{v} - \frac{n\cos\theta}{c}\right) \right]}{\omega^2 \left(\frac{1}{v} - \frac{n\cos\theta}{c}\right)^2} \tag{37.12}$$

For large L, this has a sharp maximum when the denominator is zero, at

$$\cos\theta_0 = \frac{c}{nv} \tag{37.13}$$

Thus the radiation appears at a cone in the forward direction whose half angle decreases as nv/c decreases. Since θ_0 becomes imaginary if $v < c/n$, there is no radiation if the condition (37.3) is violated; in particular, there is no radiation if $n = 1$ (empty space), since v is always less than c. The fact that (37.12) does not quite vanish for $\cos\theta$ less than unity even if $v < c/n$ is due to the choice of a finite path length L; the starting and stopping of the charge at the ends of its path mean that the particle is accelerated, and this makes some radiation possible.

[1] It can be shown that n must be such that c/n is the phase velocity, not the group velocity, of light in the medium. See Tamm, *op. cit.*, Sec. 5, or H. Motz and L. I. Schiff, *Am. J. Phys.*, **21**, 258 (1953).

The total energy radiated involves an integral of (37.11) over the surface of a sphere of radius r. This can be evaluated like the integral in (29.11), by making use of the sharpness of the maximum to extend the limits on $\cos \theta$ to $\pm \infty$ and to replace $\sin^2 \theta$ by $\sin^2 \theta_0$ obtained from (37.13). The integral of (37.12) is $4\pi^2 c L r^2 / n\omega$. Substitution into (37.11) gives for the total energy radiated by the particle per unit angular-frequency range in the distance L

$$\frac{\omega e^2 L \sin^2 \theta_0}{c^2} = \frac{\omega e^2 L}{c^2} \left(1 - \frac{c^2}{n^2 v^2} \right)$$

The number of quanta with angular frequency between ω and $\omega + d\omega$ emitted per unit distance by a particle of charge e moving with a speed v through a dielectric of refractive index n is then

$$\frac{e^2}{\hbar c^2} \left(1 - \frac{c^2}{n^2 v^2} \right) d\omega = \tfrac{1}{137} \left(1 - \frac{c^2}{n^2 v^2} \right) \frac{d\omega}{c} \qquad (37.14)$$

if e is the electronic charge. Thus the number of quanta emitted per unit frequency range depends on ω only through n. For a very fast electron ($v \cong c$) passing through water ($n \cong 1.33$), Eq. (37.14) shows that there are about 230 quanta emitted per centimeter of path in the visible region (wave lengths from 4,000 to 7,500 A).

Photoelectric Effect. When a bound system that contains charged particles is irradiated by sufficiently high energy quanta, there is a finite probability that the system will be broken up. This process is usually called the *photoelectric effect* in the case of atoms and *photodisintegration* in the case of nuclei. As an example, we consider the ejection of an electron from an atom by a photon of energy $\hbar\omega > \epsilon$, where $-\epsilon$ is the ground-state energy of the electron. The initial wave function of the electron is $u_0(\mathbf{r})$, and in its final state it has the kinetic energy

$$\frac{\hbar^2 k^2}{2m} = \hbar\omega - \epsilon \qquad (37.15)$$

We suppose the radiation to be incident along the positive z axis and to be polarized with its electric vector along the x axis. Then the matrix element for the transition is given by the second of Eqs. (35.14)

$$H'^0_{k0} = \frac{ie\hbar}{mc} \int \bar{u}_k \exp \left(\frac{i\omega z}{c} \right) A_0 \left(\frac{\partial u_0}{\partial x} \right) d\tau \qquad (37.16)$$

We assume that the final state can be represented to sufficient accuracy by the plane wave $u_k(\mathbf{r}) = L^{-\frac{3}{2}} \exp{(i\mathbf{k} \cdot \mathbf{r})}$. This is equivalent to the assumption that the Born approximation is valid for the scattering of the electron by the remaining ion.

With the help of a partial integration, Eq. (37.16) becomes

$$H'^0_{k0} = - \frac{e\hbar A_0 k_x}{mcL^3} \int u_0 \exp i \left(\frac{\omega z}{c} - \mathbf{k} \cdot \mathbf{r} \right) d\tau$$

From Eqs. (29.12) and (29.14), the transition probability per unit time from the bound to the ionized state is

$$w = \frac{mkL^3}{4\pi^2 \hbar^3} |H'^0_{k0}|^2 \sin \theta d\theta d\phi$$

It is convenient for what follows to introduce the momentum $\hbar \mathbf{K}$ that is transferred to the atom:

$$\mathbf{K} = \left(\frac{\omega}{c} \right) \mathbf{1}_z - \mathbf{k} \tag{37.17}$$

where $\mathbf{1}_z$ is a unit vector in the z direction. The differential cross section for the photoelectric effect is equal to w divided by the incident flux of photons. This flux is obtained by dividing the incident intensity (35.12) by $\hbar \omega$, so that

$$\sigma(\theta,\phi) \sin \theta d\theta d\phi = \frac{e^2 k k_x^2}{2\pi mc\omega} \left| \int u_0 \exp (i\mathbf{K} \cdot \mathbf{r}) d\tau \right|^2 \sin \theta d\theta d\phi \tag{37.18}$$

Angular Distribution. There are two factors in Eq. (37.18) that determine the angular distribution of the ejected photoelectrons. One of these is the factor k_x^2, which shows that the electrons tend to have a cosine-squared distribution with respect to the polarization vector of the incident radiation. If the radiation is unpolarized, k_x^2 must be replaced by $\frac{1}{2}(k_x^2 + k_y^2)$, so that there is a sine-squared distribution with respect to the direction of incidence. In either case, the electrons are ejected preferentially at right angles to the incident beam of photons.

The appearance of the momentum transfer vector $\mathbf{K}$ in the integrand of (37.18) also affects the angular distribution. The discussion of Sec. 26 shows that integrals of the kind that appear in Eq. (37.18) generally decrease as K increases (see, for example, Fig. 23). Now K is smallest when $\mathbf{k}$ is in the z direction, so that the K dependence of (37.18) tends to shift the maximum in the differential cross section toward the forward direction. However, this effect is only appreciable when k and ω/c are comparable in magnitude. Assuming for the moment that ϵ can be neglected in Eq. (37.15), the quantity $\omega/ck \cong \hbar k/2mc = v/2c$, where v is the speed of the ejected electron. Thus the forward shift of the cross-section maximum occurs for high-energy photons and ejected electrons, in which case ϵ can in fact be neglected as assumed above.[1]

Cross Section for the Atomic Photoelectric Effect. We now specialize to the situation in which the photoelectron is ejected from the lowest state (K or $1s$ shell) of an atom. The initial wave function $u_0(\mathbf{r})$ is then the wave function $u_{100}(r,\theta,\phi)$ of Eq. (16.24), and is given by

$$u_0(r) = (\pi a^3)^{-\frac{1}{2}} \exp\left(-\frac{r}{a}\right), \qquad a = \frac{a_0}{Z}, \qquad a_0 = \frac{\hbar^2}{me^2} \quad (37.19)$$

So long as u_0 is spherically symmetric, the angle integration in (37.18) is easily performed, and gives

$$\sigma(\theta,\phi) = \frac{8\pi e^2 k k_x^2}{mc\omega K^2}\left|\int_0^\infty u_0(r) \sin Kr \; rdr\right|^2 \quad (37.20)$$

Substitution of (37.19) into (37.20) yields

$$\sigma(\theta,\phi) = \frac{32 e^2 a^3 k k_x^2}{mc\omega(1 + K^2 a^2)^4} \quad (37.21)$$

The discussion at the end of Sec. 26 shows that the Born approximation is most nearly valid for high energy and for $Ze^2/\hbar v \ll 1$. Now $\epsilon = Z^2 e^2/2a_0$, so that $\hbar^2 k^2/2m\epsilon = (\hbar v/Ze^2)^2$. Thus ϵ can be neglected in Eq. (37.15). Since, as was shown above, $\omega/ck \cong v/2c$ in this case, the magnitude of K given by Eq. (37.17) is approximately $k(1 - v\cos\theta/2c)$. Further, $ka = \hbar v/Ze^2 \gg 1$. Thus the factor $1 + K^2 a^2$ in the denominator of Eq. (37.21) can be replaced approximately by $k^2 a^2 (1 - v\cos\theta/c)$. We then obtain for the high-energy photoelectric differential cross section

$$\sigma(\theta,\phi) \cong \frac{32 e^2}{mc\omega(ka)^5} \sin^2\theta \cos^2\phi \left(1 + \frac{4v}{c}\cos\theta\right) \quad (37.22)$$

Since the electron has been treated nonrelativistically, v/c must be fairly small in comparison with unity, and therefore terms of order v^2/c^2 have been neglected in Eq. (37.22). Integration over the angles yields the total cross section

$$\sigma \cong \frac{128\pi}{3}\frac{e^2}{mc\omega(ka)^5} \quad (37.23)$$

---

[1] The quantities k and ω/c can also be comparable very close to the photoelectric threshold, when $\hbar\omega$ is only slightly greater than ϵ. However, the Born approximation is not valid in this case.

It follows from (37.15) and (37.19) that σ is proportional to $Z^5/(\hbar\omega)^{\frac{7}{2}}$. In using Eq. (37.23), it must be remembered that σ is the total cross section for each of the K electrons, and hence must be doubled to obtain the total atomic cross section for the K-shell photoelectric effect.

It is interesting to note that the leading term of Eq. (37.22), in which v/c is neglected in comparison with unity, and all of Eq. (37.23) result from the electric-dipole approximation discussed in Sec. 35. In this approximation, exp $(i\omega z/c)$ is replaced by unity in Eq. (37.16).

Improvement on the Born Approximation. There are two respects in which the foregoing calculation is based on first-order perturbation theory. First, the matrix element (37.16) is regarded as small, so that the interaction between the electron and the electromagnetic field is treated to first order. Second, the electron wave function is taken to be a plane wave in the final state, so that the effect of the ionic potential on this state is neglected. It is very difficult to improve on the calculation from the first point of view, and hardly worthwhile because of the smallness of the electron-radiation interaction. On the other hand, an improvement with regard to the second point is feasible, and some trouble in this regard is justified since the results would then be applicable to low energies and to large values of Z; that is, $Ze^2/\hbar v$ would not then have to be small in comparison with unity.

In the case of the photoelectric effect in hydrogen, a Coulomb wave function of the general type discussed in Sec. 20 can be used for the final state, and this is also a good approximation for the K-shell photoelectric effect in heavier elements. One might expect at first that Eq. (20.2), which has the asymptotic form (20.9) of a plane plus an outgoing scattered wave, is the correct function to use.[1] Actually, it turns out that the final-state wave function must have the asymptotic form of a plane plus an *ingoing* spherical wave.

The reason for this can be seen qualitatively in the following way:[2] Such a calculation is intended to yield the probability amplitude for a transition in which the electron is ejected in the direction of propagation of the plane wave. However, if the final state is a plane plus outgoing spherical wave, one can expect that part of this amplitude is associated with electrons going in directions other than that of the plane wave, since

---

[1] The phase of the plane wave is actually distorted at infinity, so that it is not exactly a plane wave in the Coulomb case.

[2] A. Sommerfeld, "Wellenmechanik" (Ungar, New York) or "Atombau und Spektrallinien," vol. 2 (Friedrich Vieweg und Sohn, Braunschweig, 1939), p. 457. For further discussion and references to more recent work, see G. Breit and H. A. Bethe, *Phys. Rev.*, **93**, 888 (1954).

all directions are included in the outgoing spherical wave.   Conversely, part of the probability amplitude for ejection in the desired direction will be included in the calculations for other plane wave directions, since their outgoing waves contribute to the direction under consideration.   The only way to avoid this situation is to choose the final-state wave function in such a way that it contains no outgoing spherical wave; this is only possible if the wave function is asymptotically a plane plus an ingoing spherical wave.

Problems

1. Show that if div $J = \rho = 0$, the most general solution of Maxwell's equations can be expressed in terms of potentials such that div $A = \phi = 0$.

2. Show that the probability density associated with Eq. (35.1) is given by (7.1), and find the form of the probability current density that replaces (7.3).

3. Show that, if the gauge transformation (35.5) is accompanied by the transformation $\psi' = \psi \exp (ie\chi/\hbar c)$, the form of the wave equation (35.1) is unaffected.

4. Estimate the order of magnitude of eA/cp, when e is the electronic charge, A is the magnitude of the vector potential for the visible part of the spectrum that corresponds to the radiation in a cavity at several thousand degrees centigrade, and p is the momentum of an electron in the first excited state of hydrogen.

5. Verify Eq. (35.20) by means of the wave equation, without recourse to matrix methods.

6. Show that the transition probability for spontaneous emission is equal to the transition probability for induced emission that would result from an isotropic field of such intensity that there is one quantum per state of the field in the neighborhood of the transition frequency.

7. A hydrogen atom in its first excited $(2P)$ state is placed in a cavity.   At what temperature of the cavity are the transition probabilities for spontaneous and induced emission equal?

8. What is the spontaneous transition probability per unit time, expressed in sec^{-1}, of a hydrogen atom in its first excited state?

9. What is the selection rule for allowed transitions of a linear harmonic oscillator?   What is the spontaneous transition probability per unit time, expressed in sec^{-1}, of an oscillator in its first excited state, when e, m, and ω are the same as in Prob. 6?

10. Show that a logarithmic factor like that in Eq. (30.11) always appears in the cross section for excitation of a one-electron atom by electron impact, if the corresponding radiative transition is allowed.   Derive the simplest relation that you can between the differential cross section for excitation by electron impact and the corresponding transition probability for spontaneous emission, assuming the transition is allowed.

11. Make use of the dipole expression (36.12) for the radiated intensity to find the angular distribution of the radiation when $J_{0y} = iJ_{0x}$, $J_{0z} = 0$.   Show also that the total power radiated is still given by Eq. (36.13).

12. Starting from Eq. (37.5), derive a general expression for $J_{z\omega}(\mathbf{r})$ in terms of $J_z(\mathbf{r},t)$, assuming that the latter is real.   Use this to verify Eq. (37.6) when $J_z(\mathbf{r},t)$ is given by (37.4).

13. What is the polarization of the Cerenkov radiation?   Is any angular momentum carried off by the radiation field in this case?

14. Assume that the interaction between the neutron and the proton that make up a deuteron can be represented by a square well potential for which $a = 0$ (zero range or δ function interaction), and that the only bound energy level of the system has $l = 0$ and $\epsilon = 2.23$ Mev (million electron-volts).   Show that no error is involved in the calculation of the photodisintegration cross section if the final-state wave function is taken to be a plane wave.   Find the differential and total cross sections for unpolarized photons.

CHAPTER XI

ATOMS, MOLECULES, AND ATOMIC NUCLEI

This chapter is not intended to be a complete survey of the properties of atomic systems. It is primarily a presentation of a relatively few problems that arise in connection with the structure of matter, selected because they supply interesting and instructive applications of quantum mechanics. These problems are grouped according to subject; enough explanatory material is included so that the treatment is coherent, although severely limited in scope.

38. APPROXIMATIONS IN ATOMIC STRUCTURE[1]

The ground states of the two lightest atoms, hydrogen and helium, were considered in Secs. 16 and 27, respectively. Variation calculations similar to those described for helium have been carried through for others of the light atoms. This section describes some of the approximations that have been used for the heavier atoms. The alkali atoms are discussed separately in Sec. 39.

Central-field Approximation. The starting point of calculations on all except the lightest atoms is the *central-field approximation*. This assumes that each of the atomic electrons moves in a spherically symmetric potential energy $V(r)$ that is produced by the nucleus and all the other electrons. The approximation is a good one if the deviation from the $V(r)$ for one electron produced by close passage of other electrons is relatively small. This is actually the case, since the constant nuclear potential is of the order of Z times as large as the fluctuating potential due to each nearby electron, and the latter varies quite slowly (inversely) with the separation distance. The two principal problems are then the calculation of the central field, and the correction of the approximate results obtained from it. Before considering these problems, we discuss some general properties of the central field.

The potential energy $V(r)$ for a neutral atom has the Coulomb form $-e^2/r$ at a great distance r from the nucleus, since the removal of the electron whose potential is being measured leaves a singly charged positive

---

[1] For a more detailed discussion of the material of this section and the next, see E. U. Condon and G. H. Shortley, "The Theory of Atomic Spectra" (Cambridge, London, and Macmillan, New York, 1935).

ion. The electron in the hydrogen atom, for which the potential energy is $-e^2/r$ at all r, was shown in Sec. 16 to have an infinite number of bound energy levels characterized by the quantum numbers n, l, and m. An infinite number of energy levels is also expected for $V(r)$, since for large n, the electron wave function is small near the nucleus, and only the form of $V(r)$ for large r is significant. An important difference between the two situations is that the degeneracy between states of the same n and different l that occurs in hydrogen is removed in a non-Coulomb central field. This is because the electrons that have smaller angular momentum penetrate closer to the nucleus, and $V(r)$ is stronger (more negative) than $-e^2/r$ there, since the nucleus is less completely screened by the other electrons. Thus for given n, the states of lowest l have the lowest energy. The degeneracy with respect to m is not affected, since this occurs whenever the potential is spherically symmetric.

Because of the spin, four quantum numbers n, l, m_l, and m_s are required to specify the state of an electron in a central field. The orbital quantum numbers l and m_l are the same as l and m in the hydrogen atom, $m_s = \pm\frac{1}{2}$ specifies the spin orientation, and n is a natural generalization of the total quantum number that appears in hydrogen. Equation (16.14) shows that $n - l - 1$ is the number of nodes of the radial part of the hydrogen wave function; this definition of n is carried over to the general central field, so that l does not exceed $n - 1$.

Periodic System of the Elements. According to the Pauli exclusion principle (see the discussion of antisymmetric wave functions in Sec. 32), not more than one electron in an atom can have a particular set of values of the four quantum numbers given above. As Z increases, electrons fill the one-electron states of lowest energy in succession; the ground state of an atom in the central-field approximation is that in which there are no unfilled electron states that have lower energy than any that are occupied. Because of the degeneracy with respect to m_l and m_s, there can be as many as $2(2l + 1)$ electrons with the same energy in a *shell* that is specified by n and l. It is apparent then that the ground-state *configuration* of the electrons in an atom can be described by specifying the number of electrons in each shell. In the central-field approximation, all shells that contain any electrons are full except perhaps that which has the highest energy.

The chemical properties of atoms are determined for the most part by the least tightly bound, or *valence*, electrons, which are in the shell of highest energy. The most important factors are the number of occupied and unoccupied electron states in this shell, and the energy interval between this and the next higher (empty) shell. For example, an atom tends to be chemically inert if its highest shell is full and there is an appreciable energy gap to the next higher shell, since then electrons are not readily shared with other atoms to form a molecule. The quasi-periodic recurrence of similar highest shell structures as Z increases is responsible for the *periodic system* of the chemical elements.

In the usual spectroscopic notation, the n value of a shell is given as a number, the l value as a letter, and the number of electrons in the shell as a numerical superscript. The letter code for l, and the maximum number $2(2l + 1)$ of electrons in a shell, are as follows:

$$l = 0,\ 1,\ \ 2,\ \ 3,\ \ 4,\ \ 5,\ \ \ldots$$
$$s,\ p,\ \ d,\ \ f,\ \ g,\ \ h,\ \ \ldots$$
$$2(2l + 1) = 2,\ 6,\ 10,\ 14,\ 18,\ 22,\ \ldots$$

For example, the ground-state configurations of sodium ($Z = 11$) and of mercury ($Z = 80$) are

$$\text{Na: } 1s^2 2s^2 2p^6 3s$$
$$\text{Hg: } 1s^2 2s^2 2p^6 3s^2 3p^6 4s^2 3d^{10} 4p^6 5s^2 4d^{10} 5p^6 6s^2 4f^{14} 5d^{10}$$

The ground-state configurations of many of the elements can be written down simply from a knowledge of the order in which the energies of the shells increase. This order can be inferred from spectroscopic evidence, and is as follows:

$$1s, 2s, 2p, 3s, 3p, [4s, 3d], 4p, [5s, 4d], 5p, [6s, 4f, 5d], 6p, [7s, 5f, 6d]$$

The brackets enclose shells that have so nearly the same energy that they are not always filled in sequence. These shell energies are close together because the increase in n and the decrease in l tend to compensate each other; thus the $4s$ state, which has a higher energy than the $3d$ state in hydrogen, is depressed by the penetration caused by its low angular momentum. The s shell in each bracket is always filled first, although it can lose one or both of its electrons as the other shells in the bracket fill up. Apart from the brackets, there are no deviations from the indicated order of filling.

Table 2 gives the ground-state configurations of each of the elements.[1] An atom contains all the full shells that occur above and to the left of its position in the table. Since the number of s electrons varies as each d shell fills, the d columns are subdivided to show the number of s electrons.

[1] This table is taken from Condon and Shortley, *op. cit.*, p. 333. Recent data and estimates on the rare earths (lanthanide elements) are reviewed by W. F. Meggers, *Science*, **105**, 514 (1947). The assignments of the heaviest natural elements and the artificial transuranic elements (actinide elements) are as given by G. T. Seaborg in L. N. Ridenour, ed., "Modern Physics for the Engineer," Chap. 8, p. 213 (McGraw-Hill, New York, 1954). The following elements have acquired new names in recent years: niobium (Nb, 41), technetium (Tc, 43), promethium (Pm, 61), astatine (At, 85), francium (Fa, 87), neptunium (Np, 93), plutonium (Pu, 94), americium (Am, 95), curium (Cm, 96), berkelium (Bk, 97), and californium (Cf, 98). Elements 99 and 100 have been identified but not yet named.

TABLE 2.   GROUND-STATE ELECTRON CONFIGURATIONS OF THE ELEMENTS

	s	s^2	p	p^2	p^3	p^4	p^5	p^6		d	d^2	d^3	d^4	d^5	d^6	d^7	d^8	d^9	d^{10}
$1s$	H 1	He 2																	
$2s$	Li 3	Be 4																	
$2p$			B 5	C 6	N 7	O 8	F 9	Ne 10											
$3s$	Na 11	Mg 12																	
$3p$			Al 13	Si 14	P 15	S 16	Cl 17	A 18											
$4s, 3d$	K 19	Ca 20							$4s^0$										
									$4s$					Cr 24					Cu 29
									$4s^2$	Sc 21	Ti 22	V 23		Mn 25	Fe 26	Co 27	Ni 28		Zn 30
$4p$			Ga 31	Ge 32	As 33	Se 34	Br 35	Kr 36											
$5s, 4d$	Rb 37	Sr 38							$5s^0$										Pd 46
									$5s$				Nb 41	Mo 42	Tc 43	Ru 44	Rh 45		Ag 47
									$5s^2$	Y 39	Zr 40								Cd 48
$5p$			In 49	Sn 50	Sb 51	Te 52	I 53	Xe 54											
$6s, 4f, 5d$	Cs 55	Ba 56							$6s^0$									Ir 77	
									$6s$									Pt 78	Au 79
									$6s^2$	La* 57	Hf 72	Ta 73	W 74	Re 75	Os 76				Hg 80
$6p$			Tl 81	Pb 82	Bi 83	Po 84	At 85	Rn 86											
$7s, 5f, 6d$	Fa 87	Ra 88							$7s^0$										
									$7s$										
									$7s^2$	Ac 89	Th† 90								

*$4f$:

		f	f^2	f^3	f^4	f^5	f^6	f^7	f^8	f^9	f^{10}	f^{11}	f^{12}	f^{13}	f^{14}
$5d^0$		Ce (58)	Pr (59)	Nd 60	Pm (61)	Sm 62	Eu 63		Tb (65)	Dy (66)	Ho (67)	Er (68)	Tm 69	Yb 70	
$5d$								Gd 64							Lu 71

†$5f$:

		f	f^2	f^3	f^4	f^5	f^6	f^7	f^8	f^9	f^{10}	f^{11}	f^{12}	f^{13}	f^{14}
$6d^0$					Np 93	Pu 94	Am 95		Bk 97	Cf 98					
$6d$			Pa 91	U 92				Cm 96							

The two groups of atoms that appear to have a partially full f shell in their ground-state configurations fit in at * (rare earths) and at † (heaviest elements). The first group has the $6s$ shell full and the second has the $7s$ shell full; the distribution of electrons in d and f shells for each group is shown below the main table. According to Meggers, the entries in the f groups that are enclosed in parentheses are extrapolations or predictions based on the analyses of neighboring spectra.

A few of the periodicities are worth explicit mention. The first electron to go into each s shell beyond $1s$ gives an alkali, and the elements just before each of these (full $1s$ shell or a full p shell) are rare gases. The elements with the same number of electrons in a p shell have similar chemical properties; this is especially striking in the case of the halogens (one electron short of a full p shell). The elements with full $2s$ and $3s$ shells (Be and Mg) that are followed by p shells have somewhat different properties from the alkaline earths, which have full s shells followed by d or f shells. The filling of the $4s,3d$ shells gives elements somewhat similar to those arising from the filling of the $5s,4d$ shells. The elements that correspond to full bracketed shells (Zn, Cd, and Hg) are quite similar, as are the noble metals (Cu, Ag, and Au) in which an s electron is missing from the full bracketed shells.

Thomas-Fermi Statistical Model. We now turn to the first of the problems associated with the central-field approximation. There are two methods that have been used for the determination of the potential energy $V(r)$. The first of these, due to Thomas[1] and Fermi,[2] is discussed here, and the second, due to Hartree, is taken up later. The *Thomas-Fermi statistical model* assumes that $V(r)$ varies slowly enough in an electron wave length so that many electrons can be localized within a volume over which the potential changes by a small fraction of itself. The electrons can then be treated by statistical mechanics, and obey the Fermi-Dirac statistics mentioned in Sec. 32. At normal temperatures, the thermal energy κT is very small in comparison with $V(r)$ everywhere except at the edge of the atom, where the chance of finding an electron is small. In this case, the Fermi-Dirac statistics requires that the electron states fill in order of increasing energy, as assumed above. The difference between the present treatment and the more general discussion given earlier in this section lies in the additional assumption that $V(r)$ is sensibly constant over a region in which many electrons can be localized.

The number of electron states in a cube of edge length L at the walls of which the wave functions obey periodic boundary conditions was computed in Sec. 11 to be $(L/2\pi)^3 dk_x dk_y dk_z$. This must be multiplied by

[1] L. H. Thomas, *Proc. Camb. Phil. Soc.*, **23**, 542 (1927).
[2] E. Fermi, *Zeits. f. Physik*, **48**, 73 (1928).

2 to take account of the two possible spin states; then the number of states for which the magnitude of the momentum $\mathbf{p} = \hbar\mathbf{k}$ is less than or equal to p_0 is

$$2 \left(\frac{L}{2\pi}\right)^3 \int_0^{\frac{p_0}{\hbar}} \int_0^{\pi} \int_0^{2\pi} k^2 dk \sin\theta d\theta d\phi = \frac{p_0^3 L^3}{3\pi^2 \hbar^3}$$

If all these states are occupied, the number of electrons per unit volume whose kinetic energy does not exceed $p_0^2/2m$ is $p_0^3/3\pi^2\hbar^3$. Now the maximum kinetic energy at any distance r from the nucleus is $-V(r)$, since otherwise electrons would escape from the atom. We thus obtain a relation between the volume density of electrons, $n(r)$, and the potential energy

$$n(r) = \frac{[-2mV(r)]^{\frac{3}{2}}}{3\pi^2\hbar^3} \tag{38.1}$$

The electrostatic potential $V(r)/e$ is also determined by Poisson's equation in terms of the charge density $en(r)$

$$\frac{1}{e}\nabla^2 V = \frac{1}{er^2}\frac{d}{dr}\left(r^2\frac{dV}{dr}\right) = -4\pi en(r) \tag{38.2}$$

Equations (38.1) and (38.2) are two simultaneous equations for n and V. The boundary conditions on the solutions can be expressed in terms of V alone for a neutral atom of atomic number Z. As $r \to 0$, the leading term in the potential energy must be due to the nucleus, so that $V(r) \to -Ze^2/r$. As $r \to \infty$, there must be no net charge inside the sphere of radius r, so that V falls off more rapidly than $1/r$, and $rV(r) \to 0$. The boundary condition at infinity is different from that assumed earlier in this section, where V was taken to have the asymptotic form $-e^2/r$. The V discussed earlier is the potential experienced by one of the atomic electrons, while the Thomas-Fermi potential is that experienced by an infinitesimal test charge. The difference between the two potentials emphasizes the statistical nature of the approximation made by Thomas and Fermi. The solution for V is exact in the limit in which m becomes infinite and e becomes zero in such a way that m^3e^4 remains constant; then the electron wave length becomes zero, and the density of particles becomes infinite. In this limit the potential is constant over many wave lengths, and enough particles are present so that statistical mechanics can be applied.

Evaluation of the Potential. Elimination of $n(r)$ from Eqs. (38.1) and (38.2) leads to an equation for $-V(r)$

$$\frac{1}{r^2}\frac{d}{dr}\left[r^2\frac{d(-V)}{dr}\right] = \frac{4e^2[-2mV(r)]^{\frac{3}{2}}}{3\pi\hbar^3} \tag{38.3}$$

Equation (38.3) and the boundary conditions given above are conveniently expressed in a dimensionless form in which Z, E, m, and $\hbar$ appear only in scale factors.   We put

$$V(r) = -\frac{Ze^2}{r}\chi, \qquad r = bx$$

$$b = \frac{1}{2}\left(\frac{3\pi}{4}\right)^{\frac{2}{3}}\frac{\hbar^2}{me^2Z^{\frac{1}{3}}} = \frac{0.885a_0}{Z^{\frac{1}{3}}} \qquad (38.4)$$

where $a_0 = \hbar^2/me^2$.   With these substitutions, (38.3) becomes

$$x^{\frac{1}{2}}\frac{d^2\chi}{dx^2} = \chi^{\frac{3}{2}} \qquad (38.5)$$

$$\chi = 1 \text{ at } x = 0, \qquad \chi = 0 \text{ at } x = \infty$$

The most accurate solution of Eq. (38.5) was computed by Bush and Caldwell[1] with the help of the differential analyzer, and is expressed in the form of a numerical table.

Equations (38.4) show that the "radius" of an atom is inversely proportional to the cube root of the atomic number, if this radius is interpreted to be that of a sphere that encloses a fixed fraction of all the electrons (see Prob. 1).   These equations can also be used to show that the Thomas-Fermi approximation improves with increasing Z.   The potential at the atomic radius is proportional to $Z^{\frac{4}{3}}$, so that a typical electron wave length is proportional to $Z^{-\frac{2}{3}}$.   The distance over which the potential changes by a definite fraction of itself is proportional to the atomic radius, or $Z^{-\frac{1}{3}}$.   Thus the fractional change of the potential in an electron wave length is proportional to $Z^{-\frac{1}{3}}$, and decreases with increasing Z. Moreover, since the number of electrons is equal to Z, the use of the statistical method is better justified as Z increases.

Hartree's Self-consistent Fields.   The second method for obtaining a central field is due to Hartree.[2]   This model assumes that each electron moves in a central field that can be calculated from the nuclear potential and the wave functions of all the other electrons, by assuming that the charge density associated with an electron is e times its position probability density.   The Schrödinger equation is solved for each electron in its own central field, and the resulting wave functions made consistent with the fields from which they are calculated.   Thus the kth electron is described by a normalized wave function $u_k(\mathbf{r}_k)$ that is a solution of the equation

[1] V. Bush and S. H. Caldwell, *Phys. Rev.*, **38**, 1898 (1931).
[2] D. R. Hartree, *Proc. Camb. Phil. Soc.*, **24**, 111 (1928).

$$\left[-\frac{\hbar^2}{2m}\nabla_k^2 - \frac{Ze^2}{r_k} + \sum_{j\neq k} \int |u_j(\mathbf{r}_j)|^2 \frac{e^2}{r_{jk}}\,d\tau_j \right] u_k(\mathbf{r}_k) = \epsilon_k u_k(\mathbf{r}_k) \quad (38.6)$$

where $r_{jk} = |\mathbf{r}_j - \mathbf{r}_k|$. If there are Z electrons in the atom, (38.6) constitutes a set of Z simultaneous nonlinear integrodifferential equations for the Z functions $u_k(\mathbf{r}_k)$. It is therefore not feasible to solve these equations directly, and Hartree used a method of successive approximations.

A potential energy that approximately represents the second and third terms in (38.6) is assumed, electron wave functions computed, and new potentials for each electron found from these wave functions. This process is continued until the potentials are self-consistent to a high order of accuracy. The principal approximation made is the averaging of the potential energy given as the third term in (38.6) over the angles of $\mathbf{r}_k$ to make it spherically symmetric. The solutions of (38.6) can then be expressed as products of radial functions and spherical harmonics. A further simplification is made so that the $2(2l + 1)$ or fewer electrons in a shell all move in the same potential and have the same radial wave function.

It is apparent that the Hartree approximation neglects correlations between the positions of the electrons, since the entire wave function for all the electrons is assumed to be a simple product of one-electron functions

$$\psi(\mathbf{r}_1,\mathbf{r}_2, \ldots ,\mathbf{r}_Z) = u_1(\mathbf{r}_1)u_2(\mathbf{r}_2) \cdots u_Z(\mathbf{r}_Z) \quad (38.7)$$

It is also clear from (38.7) that antisymmetrized wave functions are not employed. The antisymmetry is considered only in so far as the quantum numbers of the one-electron states u_k are chosen in agreement with the exclusion principle.

Connection with the Variation Method. We now show that the Hartree approximation results from an optimum variation calculation with the trial function (38.7).[1] The wave equation with inclusion of interelectronic interactions but neglect of spin-orbit terms (see below) is

$$H\psi = E\psi$$
$$H = \sum_k \left(-\frac{\hbar^2}{2m}\nabla_k^2 - \frac{Ze^2}{r_k} \right) + \sum_{j>k}\sum \frac{e^2}{r_{jk}} \quad (38.8)$$

where $j > k$ implies a double summation, over all different pairs of indices j and k. We wish to minimize the expectation value of H.

---

[1] J. C. Slater, *Phys. Rev.*, **35**, 210 (1930); V. Fock, *Zeits. f. Physik.*, **61**, 126 (1930).

From (38.7) and (38.8) we obtain

$$\int \cdots \int \bar\psi H \psi d\tau_1 \cdots d\tau_Z$$

$$= \sum_k \int \bar u_k(\mathbf{r}_k) \left(-\frac{\hbar^2}{2m} \nabla_k^2 - \frac{Ze^2}{r_k} \right) u_k(\mathbf{r}_k) d\tau_k$$

$$+ \sum_{j>k} \sum \int \int \bar u_j(\mathbf{r}_j) \bar u_k(\mathbf{r}_k) \frac{e^2}{r_{jk}} u_j(\mathbf{r}_j) u_k(\mathbf{r}_k) d\tau_j d\tau_k \quad (38.9)$$

since the u_k are normalized. The optimum ψ is obtained by varying each of the u_k separately to minimize (38.9). The only dependence of (38.9) on a particular one-electron function u_k is through the terms

$$\int \bar u_k(\mathbf{r}_k) \left(-\frac{\hbar^2}{2m} \nabla_k^2 - \frac{Ze^2}{r_k} \right) u_k(\mathbf{r}_k) d\tau_k$$

$$+ \sum_{j \neq k} \int \int \bar u_j(\mathbf{r}_j) \bar u_k(\mathbf{r}_k) \frac{e^2}{r_{jk}} u_j(\mathbf{r}_j) u_k(\mathbf{r}_k) d\tau_j d\tau_k$$

$$= \int \bar u_k(\mathbf{r}_k) H_k u_k(\mathbf{r}_k) d\tau_k \quad (38.10)$$

$$H_k \equiv -\frac{\hbar^2}{2m} \nabla_k^2 - \frac{Ze^2}{r_k} + \sum_{j \neq k} \int |u_j(\mathbf{r}_j)|^2 \frac{e^2}{r_{jk}} d\tau_j$$

The integral in (38.10) is the expectation value of the operator H_k for the function u_k. From the discussion of Sec. 27, it follows that this is a minimum when u_k is an eigenfunction of H_k that corresponds to its lowest eigenvalue ϵ_k.

$$H_k u_k = \epsilon_k u_k \quad (38.11)$$

Since Eqs. (38.11) and (38.6) are identical, we see that the Hartree wave functions are the best from the point of view of the variation method that can be written in the form (38.7).

The energy associated with this wave function is just the integral (38.9), which can be written with the help of (38.6)

$$\int \cdots \int \bar\psi H \psi d\tau_1 \cdots d\tau_Z = \sum_k \epsilon_k$$

$$- \sum_{j>k} \sum \int \int |u_j(\mathbf{r}_j)|^2 |u_k(\mathbf{r}_k)|^2 \frac{e^2}{r_{jk}} d\tau_j d\tau_k \quad (38.12)$$

The electrostatic interaction terms between electrons are counted twice in the summation over ϵ_k, and so have to be subtracted out to give (38.12).

Thus the energy of the atom is not just the sum of the ϵ_k, although each ϵ_k is roughly the energy of removal of the kth electron. This last is not strictly true, since the removal of an electron alters the self-consistent fields, and hence the wave functions and ϵ's for the remaining electrons. However, ϵ_k is found to be an especially good approximation to the energy of removal in the case of an inner electron (X-ray level).

Corrections to the Central-field Approximation. We now turn to the second problem mentioned at the beginning of this section, the correction of the approximate results obtained from the central field. Two terms are omitted in the central-field approximation: the difference between the actual electrostatic interaction between electrons and the average interaction that is included in the central field, and the spin-orbit energy. The latter is an interaction energy between the spin and the orbital motion of each electron, and has the form

$$\sum_k \xi(r_k) \mathbf{L}_k \cdot \mathbf{S}_k \tag{38.13}$$

Here, $\mathbf{L}_k$ is the orbital-angular-momentum operator $\mathbf{r}_k \times \mathbf{p}_k$ of the kth electron, and has the properties of the $\mathbf{M}$ operator introduced in Sec. 24; the eigenvalues of $\mathbf{L}_k^2$ and L_{kz} are given in terms of the quantum numbers l and m_l for the kth electron as $l(l+1)\hbar^2$ and $m_l\hbar$, respectively. $\mathbf{S}_k$ is the spin angular momentum $\frac{1}{2}\hbar\mathbf{d}_k$ of the kth electron that was introduced in Sec. 33. The function $\xi(r)$ is given by[1]

$$\xi(r) = \frac{1}{2m^2c^2} \frac{1}{r} \frac{dV}{dr} \tag{38.14}$$

in terms of the central-field potential energy $V(r)$.

In considering the effects of these terms, we shall assume that the perturbed eigenfunctions, which are linear combinations of various configuration wave functions, have only negligibly small amounts of all but one configuration mixed in them. From Eq. (25.9), it is apparent that this is the case if the interconfiguration matrix elements of the perturbation are small in comparison with the energy intervals between unperturbed configuration energies.

It can be shown that the part of the summation in (38.13) that includes electrons in full shells is zero, since the function ξ is the same for all electrons in a shell and the contributions from electrons with opposite m_l and m_s cancel. Thus the electrons in full shells can be ignored and the

---

[1] L. H. Thomas, *Nature*, **117**, 514 (1926). This energy is a consequence of relativity, and is derived as such in Chap. XII. It was first obtained from the precession of the spin axis of the electron, part of which is of electromagnetic origin (Larmor precession) and part of which comes from relativistic kinematics (Thomas precession).

summation extended only over the remaining electrons. The case in which there is just one electron outside full shells is of interest in connection with the ground state and low excited states of the alkali atoms, and will be discussed in some detail in the next section. For the present, we consider very briefly the more general situation, always assuming that each atomic state is based on just one configuration of the electrons.

LS **Coupling Scheme.** There are, in general, a number of states that belong to the same configuration, and that are degenerate in the central-field approximation. These states differ in the assignment of m_l and m_s quantum numbers to the individual electrons. The theory of complex spectra consists in determining the linear combinations of such suitably antisymmetrized wave functions that diagonalize the perturbation to first order (see Sec. 25), along with the corresponding perturbed energy levels.

The most usual situation is that in which the hitherto-neglected electrostatic terms are larger than the spin-orbit energy; this is called the *Russell-Saunders case*.[1] States of the same configuration can be classified as eigenfunctions of any dynamical variables that commute with the Hamiltonian and hence are constants of the motion (see Sec. 23). When all perturbations are included, the only true constants of the motion are the total parity and the total angular momentum **J** of the electrons

$$\mathbf{J} = \mathbf{L} + \mathbf{S} = \sum_k (\mathbf{L}_k + \mathbf{S}_k) \tag{38.15}$$

J is a constant because the angles that specify the orientation of the atom as a whole, and that are the canonically conjugate variables to the components of **J**, do not appear in the Hamiltonian of an isolated atom. When the electrostatic perturbation is included but the spin-orbit energy neglected, the same argument can be applied to show that the total orbital angular momentum **L** and the total spin angular momentum **S** are separately constants of the motion. The individual $\mathbf{S}_k$ need not be constants, even though no spin-dependent forces act in this approximation, since the use of antisymmetric wave functions couples the spins to the electrostatic energy (see the discussion of the excited states of helium in Sec. 33).

A state can be specified by the quantum numbers J, L, S, M, M_L, and M_S, which are connected with eigenvalues of angular-momentum operators through

$$\mathbf{J}^2 = J(J+1)\hbar^2, \qquad J_z = M\hbar$$
$$\mathbf{L}^2 = L(L+1)\hbar^2, \qquad L_z = M_L\hbar \tag{38.16}$$
$$\mathbf{S}^2 = S(S+1)\hbar^2, \qquad S_z = M_S\hbar$$

[1] H. N. Russell and F. A. Saunders, *Astrophys. Jour.*, **61**, 38 (1925).

When the spin-orbit energy is neglected, the electrostatic energy separates states of different L; in some cases, only particular S values are permitted because of the exclusion principle. Only two of the other four quantum numbers are independent, so we can use either LSM_LM_S or $LSJM$ to specify a state. Because of the spherical symmetry of the Hamiltonian with respect to its space and spin parts separately, the energy is independent of the directional quantum numbers M_L and M_S, and there are $(2L + 1)(2S + 1)$ degenerate states. For given L and S, the states specified by J and M are linear combinations of those specified by M_L and M_S, so that the same amount of degeneracy appears in the $LSJM$ representation. This is called the *LS coupling scheme*, since the individual L_k are coupled together to form the total L, and the individual S_k to form the total S.

If now the spin-orbit energy is included, L and S are no longer constants of the motion, although J and M still are. However, we assume that states of different L and S are sufficiently well separated by the electrostatic energy so that their mixing due to spin-orbit energy can be neglected. This is analogous to the earlier assumption that different configurations are sufficiently well separated by the central field so that their mixing due to the electrostatic energy can be neglected. States of different J in the $LSJM$ representation are now split apart by the spin-orbit energy; the energy is still independent of M, so that there are $2J + 1$ degenerate states. A Russell-Saunders state is usually written in the form $^4D_{\frac{1}{2}}$, where the superscript is the *multiplicity* $2S + 1$, the letter (now capitalized) is the L value according to the code given earlier in this section, and the subscript is the J value; in this case $S = \frac{3}{2}$, $L = 2$, and $J = \frac{1}{2}$. Since $\mathbf{J} = \mathbf{L} + \mathbf{S}$, the argument at the end of Sec. 24 shows that J can only be one of the numbers $L + S$, $L + S - 1$, . . . , $|L - S|$.

Selection Rules. The selection rules in the Russell-Saunders case can be obtained from the discussion of Sec. 37. Only one electron is involved in a transition, so that the configuration changes through a change in one of the l's by one unit; this also changes the parity. Since the electric-dipole moment does not involve the spins, and the spin functions for different S are orthogonal (see Prob. 4), S does not change in an allowed transition. The conservation of angular momentum between atom and radiation field further requires that J and L each change by 1 or 0. Transitions between states both of which have $J = 0$ are strictly forbidden.

Intersystem lines that join states of different multiplicity (change in S) sometimes occur, and indicate a partial breakdown of LS coupling. The very intense mercury resonance line at 2,537 Å is an intersystem line: $^3P_1 \rightarrow {}^1S_0$. This transition is allowed so far as the changes in J, L, configuration and parity are concerned, but not as regards the change in S. The $^3P_1$ state is partially mixed by the spin-orbit energy with a higher singlet ($S = 0$) state of the same J and parity, and this makes an electric-dipole transition possible.

jj **Coupling Scheme.** The opposite approximation to that involved in LS coupling assumes that the spin-orbit energy is large in comparison with the electrostatic energy. If the latter is neglected, each electron can be characterized by the quantum numbers $nljm$ rather than nlm_lm_s, where $(\mathbf{L}_k + \mathbf{S}_k)^2 = j(j + 1)\hbar^2$ and $L_{kz} + S_{kz} = m\hbar$. The electrostatic energy then splits apart states of different J.

This is called the *jj coupling scheme*, since the orbital and spin angular momenta of the individual electrons are coupled together to form j's, from which the states are built up. It is mainly of interest in heavy atoms, where the large $V(r)$ makes the spin-orbit energy (38.13) the dominant perturbation.

39. THE ALKALI ATOMS

The ground-state configuration of an alkali atom consists of a series of full shells followed by a single s electron, and so is $^2S_{\frac{1}{2}}$. The inner rare-gas configuration is so stable that all but quite high excited states of the atom involve only the valence electron. Thus the alkalis can be treated to quite good approximation in terms of a model in which a single electron moves in a spherically symmetric non-Coulomb potential energy $V(r)$. In this section we calculate the energy levels and the intensities of allowed transitions in the absence and presence of an external magnetic field.

Doublet Separation. The configuration of an alkali atom can be specified by a single pair of quantum numbers nl. Since there is only one electron, the perturbing electrostatic term mentioned in the last section does not appear. In the absence of external fields the Hamiltonian, including the spin-orbit energy (38.13), is

$$H = -\frac{\hbar^2}{2m}\nabla^2 + V(r) + \xi(r)\mathbf{L}\cdot\mathbf{S} \tag{39.1}$$

where $\xi(r)$ is given by (38.14). As in Sec. 38, we neglect the mixing of different configurations produced by the spin-orbit energy, and regard this term as a perturbation that removes the m_lm_s degeneracy within each configuration. The total angular momentum $\mathbf{J} = \mathbf{L} + \mathbf{S}$ of the valence electron is a constant of the motion (see Prob. 5), so that states can be designated by jm instead of m_lm_s, where $\mathbf{J}^2 = j(j + 1)\hbar^2$ and $J_z = m\hbar$. The states of different j have different energies, but there is still a $(2j + 1)$-fold degeneracy due to m. The removal of the m degeneracy by a magnetic field is discussed later in this section.

The difference in energy between states of different j is due to the $\mathbf{L} \cdot \mathbf{S}$ term in (39.1), and can be found from its expectation value or diagonal matrix element [see Eq. (25.8)]. We have the operator relation

$$\mathbf{J}^2 = (\mathbf{L} + \mathbf{S})^2 = \mathbf{L}^2 + \mathbf{S}^2 + 2 \, \mathbf{L} \cdot \mathbf{S} \tag{39.2}$$

Since l, j, and s are all good quantum numbers ($s = \frac{1}{2}$ for one electron), Eq. (39.2) can be solved for the diagonal matrix element of $\mathbf{L} \cdot \mathbf{S}$

$$(\mathbf{L} \cdot \mathbf{S})_{lj,lj} = \tfrac{1}{2}[j(j + 1) - l(l + 1) - \tfrac{3}{4}]\hbar^2 \tag{39.3}$$

Now if l is different from 0, j can be either $l + \frac{1}{2}$ or $l - \frac{1}{2}$. Thus the first-order perturbation arising from $\xi(r)\mathbf{L} \cdot \mathbf{S}$ is

$$
\begin{array}{ll}
\tfrac{1}{2}l\zeta_{nl} & \text{if } j = l + \frac{1}{2} \\
-\tfrac{1}{2}(l + 1)\zeta_{nl} & \text{if } j = l - \frac{1}{2}
\end{array} \tag{39.4}
$$

$$\zeta_{nl} \equiv \hbar^2 \int_0^\infty |R_{nl}(r)|^2 \xi(r) r^2 dr, \qquad l > 0$$

where $R_{nl}(r)$ is the normalized radial part of the unperturbed eigenfunction associated with the nl configuration. Since $V(r)$ represents an attractive potential energy, $\xi(r)$ given by (38.14) is positive and ζ_{nl} is positive. Thus (39.4) shows that the state with higher j has the higher energy. The pair of states is called a *doublet;* the doublet structure characterizes all the moderately excited levels of the alkali atoms except those for which $l = 0$, in which case j can only be $\frac{1}{2}$.

The doublet separations can be calculated from (39.4) if the radial function is known. We can get a rough estimate of their dependence on n by using the hydrogenic wave functions given in Eq. (16.24), and assuming that $V(r)$ has the Coulomb form $-Ze^2/r$. Substitution into (38.14) and (39.4) gives, with the help of the generating function (16.21) for the associated Laguerre polynomials,

$$
\begin{aligned}
\zeta_{nl} &= \frac{\hbar^2 Z e^2}{2m^2 c^2} \int_0^\infty \frac{1}{r} R_{nl}^2(r) dr \\
&= \frac{e^2 \hbar^2 Z^4}{2m^2 c^2 a_0{}^3 n^3 l (l + \frac{1}{2})(l + 1)}
\end{aligned} \tag{39.5}
$$

This is valid only for $l > 0$; the singularity in $\xi(r)$ at $r = 0$ makes the integral for ζ_{n0} diverge there, so that the perturbation approximation is not valid. It follows from (39.4) and (39.5) that the doublet separation is proportional to n^{-3}, and this is in fair agreement with observation. The absolute value of the doublet separation and its dependence on l are not given at all by this simple theory, since the effective Z is difficult to estimate and depends markedly on l because of penetration.[1]

---

[1] The effect of the spin-orbit interaction on the energy levels of hydrogen is found in the next chapter as part of an exact relativistic calculation.

Doublet Intensity. We now calculate the relative intensities of the two lines of the allowed doublet $^2P_{\frac{3}{2}} \rightarrow {}^2S_{\frac{1}{2}}$ and $^2P_{\frac{1}{2}} \rightarrow {}^2S_{\frac{1}{2}}$, under the assumption that the radial wave functions are the same for the two excited ^2P states. Transitions of this type give rise to the principal series in the alkali spectra. From Eq. (36.22), the spontaneous transition probabilities, and hence the observed intensities if the two P states are equally likely to be occupied, are proportional to the squares of the dipole matrix elements.[1]

The dependence of the two excited ^2P states and the ground ^2S state on the angular and spin coordinates of the electron is obtained by finding linear combinations of products of the four spherical harmonics $Y_{1,1}(\theta,\phi)$, $Y_{1,0}(\theta,\phi)$, $Y_{1,-1}(\theta,\phi)$ and $Y_{0,0}(\theta,\phi)$, and the two spin wave functions $(+)$ and $(-)$, that are eigenfunctions of $\mathbf{J}^2$ and J_z (see Secs. 14 and 33 for discussion of the angle and spin functions). These combinations can be obtained from the spin functions for three electrons given at the end of Sec. 33. We replace $\mathbf{S}_1$ by $\mathbf{S}$, $\mathbf{S}_2 + \mathbf{S}_3$ by $\mathbf{L}$, and the spin functions (33.6) for the second and third electrons by the spherical harmonics $Y_{1,1}$, $Y_{1,0}$, $Y_{1,-1}$, and $Y_{0,0}$, respectively (see Prob. 3, Chap. IX). This gives at once

$$
\begin{cases}
{}^2P_{\frac{3}{2}} \begin{cases} m = & \tfrac{3}{2} & (+)Y_{1,1} \\ & \tfrac{1}{2} & 3^{-\frac{1}{2}}[2^{\frac{1}{2}}(+)Y_{1,0} + (-)Y_{1,1}] \\ & -\tfrac{1}{2} & 3^{-\frac{1}{2}}[2^{\frac{1}{2}}(-)Y_{1,0} + (+)Y_{1,-1}] \\ & -\tfrac{3}{2} & (-)Y_{1,-1} \end{cases} \\[2em]
{}^2P_{\frac{1}{2}} \begin{cases} m = & \tfrac{1}{2} & 3^{-\frac{1}{2}}[(+)Y_{1,0} - 2^{\frac{1}{2}}(-)Y_{1,1}] \\ & -\tfrac{1}{2} & 3^{-\frac{1}{2}}[(-)Y_{1,0} - 2^{\frac{1}{2}}(+)Y_{1,-1}] \end{cases} \\[1em]
{}^2S_{\frac{1}{2}} \begin{cases} m = & \tfrac{1}{2} & (+)Y_{0,0} \\ & -\tfrac{1}{2} & (-)Y_{0,0} \end{cases}
\end{cases}
\tag{39.6}
$$

The wave functions (39.6) can be used to calculate the matrix elements of $x = r \sin\theta \cos\phi$, $y = r \sin\theta \sin\phi$, and $z = r \cos\theta$. We assume that the radial functions associated with (39.6) are all the same, so that the radial part of the matrix-element integral is a common factor throughout. The angle parts of the integrals are easily evaluated by making use of the explicit expressions for the Y's in terms of θ and ϕ given in (14.16).[2] The products of spin functions follow the simple rules $(+)^*(+) = 1$, $(-)^*(+) = 0$, etc. In this way we obtain the following values for the squares of the magnitudes of the indicated matrix elements, expressed in units of $\frac{1}{18}$ of the common radial factor:

[1] The energy difference between the two upper states is so small that the ω^3 factor in (36.22) does not affect the intensity ratio appreciably.

[2] In the general case in which Y_{lm}'s with $l > 1$ are involved, it is often easier to use a formula for the integral of the product of three spherical harmonics given by J. A. Gaunt; see Condon and Shortley, *op. cit.*, p. 176.

$$^2P_{\frac{3}{2}} \rightarrow {}^2S_{\frac{1}{2}} \begin{cases} m = \tfrac{3}{2} \text{ to } m = \quad \tfrac{1}{2} & |x|^2 = |y|^2 = 3, & |z|^2 = 0 \\ \tfrac{3}{2} \text{ to } \qquad -\tfrac{1}{2} & |x|^2 = |y|^2 = |z|^2 = 0 \\ \tfrac{1}{2} \text{ to } \qquad \tfrac{1}{2} & |x|^2 = |y|^2 = 0, & |z|^2 = 4 \\ \tfrac{1}{2} \text{ to } \qquad -\tfrac{1}{2} & |x|^2 = |y|^2 = 1, & |z|^2 = 0 \end{cases}$$

(39.7)

$$^2P_{\frac{1}{2}} \rightarrow {}^2S_{\frac{1}{2}} \begin{cases} m = \tfrac{1}{2} \text{ to } m = \quad \tfrac{1}{2} & |x|^2 = |y|^2 = 0, & |z|^2 = 2 \\ \tfrac{1}{2} \text{ to } \qquad -\tfrac{1}{2} & |x|^2 = |y|^2 = 2, & |z|^2 = 0 \end{cases}$$

Similar results are obtained for the transitions that start from $m = -\tfrac{1}{2}$ and $-\tfrac{3}{2}$; altogether, they confirm the m selection rules of Sec. 37.

It follows from (39.7) that the sum of the intensities of all the lines that originate on each of the four $^2P_{\frac{3}{2}}$ states is equal to 6, in the above units. It is to be expected that these sums are equal since the four values of m differ only in the orientation of the angular momentum, and this should not affect the intensity. However, the total intensity from each of the two $^2P_{\frac{1}{2}}$ states is also equal to 6. The equality of total intensities from each state formed from a given L and S is a general property of LS coupling; this makes the observed intensity, which is that from all the states that are degenerate with respect to m, proportional to $2J + 1$.[1] In the example considered here, the two lines of the doublet have intensities in the ratio 2:1. This is observed for the lowest doublets of the alkalis, although for the higher doublets, the intensity ratio exceeds 2. This is because the spin-orbit energy actually mixes different configurations (^2P states with the same j but different n); the amount of mixing is different for the two j values, so that the two radial functions are not the same. A small admixture of the low-intensity upper states in the high-intensity lowest ^2P states has little effect, whereas in the opposite case, there is a large effect on the doublet intensity ratio.[2]

Effect of a Magnetic Field.[3] We now consider the effect of a magnetic field on the energy levels and transition intensities of an alkali atom. A *constant* magnetic field $\mathbf{H}$ can be represented by the vector potential

$$\mathbf{A} = (\tfrac{1}{2}\mathbf{H} \times \mathbf{r}) \tag{39.8}$$

since $\mathbf{H} = \text{curl } \mathbf{A}$. The divergence of (39.8) is zero, so that the terms involving $\mathbf{A}$ that appear in the Hamiltonian (23.24) are

$$\frac{ie\hbar}{mc} \mathbf{A} \cdot \text{grad} + \frac{e^2}{2mc^2} \mathbf{A}^2$$

$$= -\frac{e}{2mc} (\mathbf{H} \times \mathbf{r}) \cdot \mathbf{p} + \frac{e^2}{8mc^2} (\mathbf{H} \times \mathbf{r}) \cdot (\mathbf{H} \times \mathbf{r})$$

$$= -\frac{e}{2mc} \mathbf{H} \cdot \mathbf{L} + \frac{e^2}{8mc^2} \mathsf{H}^2 r^2 \sin^2 \theta \tag{39.9}$$

[1] Condon and Shortley, *op. cit.*, p. 238.
[2] E. Fermi, *Zeits. f. Physik*, **59**, 680 (1929).
[3] W. Heisenberg and P. Jordan, *Zeits. f. Physik.*, **37**, 263 (1926).

where $\mathbf{L} = \mathbf{r} \times \mathbf{p}$ and θ is the angle between $\mathbf{r}$ and $\mathbf{H}$; e is the electronic charge, and hence is a negative number.

The electron also has an intrinsic magnetic moment in the direction of its spin axis. The magnitude of this moment can be determined from comparison between experiment and the theory of the Zeeman effect presented below, and is in agreement with the value deduced from Dirac's relativistic theory of the electron (see Chap. XII); it is $e\hbar/2mc$, or e/mc times the spin angular momentum of the electron. This is twice the ratio of magnetic moment to angular momentum of a classical charge distribution for which the ratio of charge to mass density is constant. The magnetic moment is $(e/mc)\mathbf{S}$, and the extra energy in a magnetic field is

$$- \frac{e}{mc} \mathbf{H} \cdot \mathbf{S} \qquad (39.10)$$

The ratio of (39.9) to the kinetic energy is quite small for magnetic field strengths commonly attainable in the laboratory (see Prob. 7). It is therefore permissible to use perturbation theory to find the effect of the H terms on the wave functions and energy levels. In most cases, only the linear terms need be considered. However, for very strong fields and large orbits, the quadratic terms can become of interest (see the discussion of the quadratic Zeeman effect below). Also, the diamagnetic susceptibility can be obtained from the terms in the energy that are proportional to H^2.

Weak-field Case. For the present, we consider only the first-order effects of H. The Hamiltonian (39.1) then becomes, with (39.9) and (39.10),

$$H = - \frac{\hbar^2}{2m} \nabla^2 + V(r) + \xi(r)\mathbf{L} \cdot \mathbf{S} + \epsilon(L_z + 2S_z), \epsilon \equiv - \frac{e\mathsf{H}}{2mc} \quad (39.11)$$

where the field is along the z axis. The magnetic field can now be classified as weak or strong according as the last term in (39.11) is small or large in comparison with the spin-orbit energy. The *Zeeman effect* usually refers to the weak-field case, and the *Paschen-Back* effect to the strong-field case, although the term Zeeman effect is sometimes used to include all magnetic effects.

In the weak-field case, we can make use of the wave functions (39.6), which are eigenfunctions of $\mathbf{J}^2$ and J_z. It is easily verified that the magnetic energy $\epsilon(L_z + 2S_z) = \epsilon(J_z + S_z)$ has matrix elements between states of different j, but not between states of the same j and different m. We neglect the former, because of the relatively large energy separation between states of different j. Thus the magnetic energy is diagonal with respect to m for each j, and shifts the energy of each of the states (39.6) by its expectation value for that state. In each case, J_z is diagonal, so its expectation value is $m\hbar$. The expectation value of S_z for the $^2P_{\frac{3}{2}}$ state with $m = \frac{1}{2}$, for example, is

$$\iint 3^{-\frac{1}{2}}[2^{\frac{1}{2}}(+)^*\bar{Y}_{1,0} + (-)^*\bar{Y}_{1,1}]\tfrac{1}{2}\hbar\sigma_z 3^{-\frac{1}{2}}[2^{\frac{1}{2}}(+)\,Y_{1,0} + (-)Y_{1,1}]\sin\theta d\theta d\phi$$

$$= \frac{\hbar}{6}\int\int [2^{\frac{1}{2}}(+)^*\bar{Y}_{1,0} + (-)^*\bar{Y}_{1,1}][2^{\frac{1}{2}}(+)Y_{1,0} - (-)Y_{1,1}]\sin\theta d\theta d\phi$$

$$= \frac{\hbar}{6}(2-1) = \frac{\hbar}{6}$$

with the help of (33.5) and the orthonormality of the spin functions and the Y's. Thus the magnetic energy of this state is $\epsilon\hbar(\frac{1}{2} + \frac{1}{6}) = \frac{2}{3}\epsilon\hbar$. This and the similar results for the other states (39.6) can be expressed in terms of the *Landé g factor;* the magnetic energy is

$$\epsilon\hbar m g$$

$$g = \tfrac{4}{3} \text{ for } {}^2P_{\frac{3}{2}}, \qquad g = \tfrac{2}{3} \text{ for } {}^2P_{\frac{1}{2}}, \qquad g = 2 \text{ for } {}^2S_{\frac{1}{2}} \qquad (39.12)$$

The weak-field transition intensities are given directly by (39.7). According to the discussion of Sec. 37, the radiation from the transitions in which m changes by unity is circularly polarized when viewed along the field and linearly polarized perpendicular to the field when viewed in the xy plane; these are called the σ components (from the German *senkrecht*). When m does not change in a transition, the radiation does not appear along the field, and is polarized parallel to the field (π components) when viewed in the xy plane. For observation in the xy plane, the π intensity is proportional to $|z|^2$ in (39.7) and the σ intensity is proportional to either $|x|^2$ or $|y|^2$ (but not to their sum).

Strong-field Case. If the magnetic energy is large in comparison with the spin-orbit energy in (39.11), the field is said to be strong. In this case the states within a given nl configuration are better specified by m_l and m_s than by j and m as in (39.6). The magnetic energy is then diagonal and has the value

$$\epsilon\hbar(m_l + 2m_s) \qquad (39.13)$$

If the spin-orbit energy is neglected for the moment, the eight wave functions that correspond to (39.6), and their energy shifts (39.13), are

$$
{}^2P\begin{cases}
(+)Y_{1,1} & 2\epsilon\hbar \\
(+)Y_{1,0} & \epsilon\hbar \\
(+)Y_{1,-1} & 0 \\
(-)Y_{1,1} & 0 \\
(-)Y_{1,0} & -\epsilon\hbar \\
(-)Y_{1,-1} & -2\epsilon\hbar
\end{cases}
$$

$$
{}^2S\begin{cases}
(+)Y_{0,0} & \epsilon\hbar \\
(-)Y_{0,0} & -\epsilon\hbar
\end{cases}
\qquad (39.14)
$$

In the event that the magnetic field is very strong, the spin-orbit energy is most simply treated as a perturbation on the wave functions (39.14).   We consider instead the general case, which includes all relative magnitudes of the magnetic and spin-orbit energies.   This is done by working with the matrix of the last two terms in (39.11) in either of the representations (39.6) or (39.14).   The eigenvalues of the matrix are the energy levels, and the transformation that diagonalizes the matrix gives the wave functions in accordance with the discussion of Sec. 22. We start from (39.14), and notice at once that the two ^2S wave functions are the same as the $^2S_{\frac{1}{2}}$ functions of (39.6).   We ignore the effect of the spin-orbit energy on these two states, since it does not shift them with respect to each other; the energy shifts due to the magnetic field are $\pm\,\epsilon\hbar$.   Similarly, the first and last of the six ^2P wave functions are the same as the $^2P_{\frac{3}{2}}$ functions of (39.6) with $m = \pm\frac{3}{2}$; their energies are $\frac{1}{2}\zeta \pm 2\epsilon\hbar$, where ζ is given by (39.4).

The four remaining ^2P wave functions combine in pairs, according to whether $m = m_l + m_s$ is equal to $\frac{1}{2}$ or $-\frac{1}{2}$.   It is enough to consider just one of these pairs, say that for which $m = \frac{1}{2}$: $(+)Y_{1,0}$ and $(-)Y_{1,1}$. The matrix of the magnetic and spin-orbit energies in the representation specified by these two states can be found with the help of the angular-momentum matrices (24.15).

$$\begin{pmatrix} \epsilon\hbar & 2^{-\frac{1}{2}}\zeta \\ 2^{-\frac{1}{2}}\zeta & -\frac{1}{2}\zeta \end{pmatrix} \tag{39.15}$$

In accordance with the discussion of Eq. (21.19), the eigenvalues of the matrix (39.15) are found by solving the secular equation

$$\begin{vmatrix} \epsilon\hbar - \lambda & 2^{-\frac{1}{2}}\zeta \\ 2^{-\frac{1}{2}}\zeta & -\frac{1}{2}\zeta - \lambda \end{vmatrix} = \lambda^2 + (\tfrac{1}{2}\zeta - \epsilon\hbar)\lambda - \tfrac{1}{2}\zeta(\epsilon\hbar + \zeta) = 0$$

In this way we obtain for the energy shifts of these two states

$$\lambda_{\pm} = \tfrac{1}{2}[\epsilon\hbar - \tfrac{1}{2}\zeta \pm (\epsilon^2\hbar^2 + \epsilon\hbar\zeta + \tfrac{9}{4}\zeta^2)^{\frac{1}{2}}] \tag{39.16}$$

In the weak- and strong-field limits, the upper and lower signs in (39.16) lead to

$$\lambda_+ \to \tfrac{1}{2}\zeta + \tfrac{2}{3}\epsilon\hbar \quad \text{and} \quad \lambda_- \to -\zeta + \tfrac{1}{3}\epsilon\hbar \qquad \text{for } \frac{\epsilon\hbar}{\zeta} \to 0$$

$$\lambda_+ \to \epsilon\hbar \quad \text{and} \quad \lambda_- \to -\tfrac{1}{2}\zeta \qquad \text{for } \frac{\zeta}{\epsilon\hbar} \to 0$$

$$(39.17)$$

Equations (39.17) show that the state that corresponds to the upper sign in (39.16) is the weak-field state $j = \frac{3}{2}$, $m = \frac{1}{2}$ and the strong-field state $m_l = 0$, $m_s = \frac{1}{2}$.   Similarly, the lower sign in (39.16) corresponds to the weak-field state $j = \frac{1}{2}$, $m = \frac{1}{2}$ and to the strong field state $m_l = 1$, $m_s = -\frac{1}{2}$.

The transition intensities can be found in the general case by calculating the matrix elements of x, y, and z with the help of the eigenfunctions of $\xi(r)\mathbf{L} \cdot \mathbf{S} + \epsilon(L_z + 2S_z)$. These eigenfunctions are the first, sixth, seventh, and eighth of (39.14), and linear combinations of the other four functions that are obtained from the matrix that diagonalizes (39.15).

Quadratic Zeeman Effect. For very strong magnetic fields and large orbits or n values, effects of second order in H become appreciable. From (39.5), it is apparent that the effect of the spin-orbit energy becomes very small for large n, and a useful approximation is obtained by neglecting this part of the energy entirely. In this case the electron spin commutes with the Hamiltonian, so that m_s is a constant of the motion, and the spin can be ignored. The Hamiltonian (39.11) is then replaced by

$$ H = -\frac{\hbar^2}{2m} \nabla^2 + V(r) + \epsilon L_z + \tfrac{1}{2}m\epsilon^2 r^2 \sin^2 \theta \qquad (39.18) $$

Since $L_z = -i\hbar\partial/\partial\phi$ commutes with (39.18), m_l is a good quantum number, and the only effect of the term ϵL_z is to displace each energy level by the amount $\epsilon\hbar m_l$. Thus for large n, we need only be concerned with the effect of the last term $H' \equiv \tfrac{1}{2}m\epsilon^2 r^2 \sin^2 \theta$ in (39.18), for particular values of m_l and m_s.[1]

It follows from the work of Sec. 16 that the effective radius of a hydrogen atom is roughly proportional to n^2. For alkali-atom states of large n, $V(r)$ has practically the Coulomb form, and the wave functions are very nearly hydrogenic functions. Thus H' increases about as n^4. This means that n is no longer a good quantum number for sufficiently large n. For smaller n, l may not be a good quantum number since H' has off-diagonal matrix elements between states of different l, and the unperturbed energies of these states lie close together (they fail to be degenerate only because the wave functions for the smallest values of l penetrate the inner full shells). In this region, the perturbed energy levels can be found by diagonalizing the matrix of H' for given values of n, m_l, and m_s, when the $n - |m_l|$ rows and columns are labeled by l. The structure of the H' matrix can be inferred from Gaunt's formula (footnote 2, page 281); since $\sin^2 \theta$ can be expressed in terms of spherical harmonics of order 0 and 2, the only nonvanishing matrix elements $H'_{ll'}$ are for $l - l' = 0, \pm 2$. Thus the H' matrix has the form (if for example, $m_l = 0$)

$$
\begin{pmatrix}
H'_{00} & 0 & H'_{02} & 0 & 0 & \cdots \\
0 & H'_{11} & 0 & H'_{13} & 0 & \cdots \\
H'_{20} & 0 & H'_{22} & 0 & H'_{24} & \cdots \\
0 & H'_{31} & 0 & H'_{33} & 0 & \cdots \\
0 & 0 & H'_{42} & 0 & H'_{44} & \cdots \\
\cdots & \cdots & \cdots & \cdots & \cdots & \cdots
\end{pmatrix}
\qquad (39.19)
$$

[1] L. I. Schiff and H. Snyder, *Phys. Rev.*, **55**, 59 (1939).

The matrix (39.19) is equivalent to two independent matrices, one for even and the other for odd l, each with about $\frac{1}{2}n$ rows and columns. Direct diagonalization of these would be quite arduous for large n. However, the resulting energy levels are so close together that they cannot be resolved spectroscopically, so there is little reason to determine the individual levels. What can be observed is the aggregate of transitions between the ^2S ground state ($l = 0$) and the group of states that are obtained by diagonalization of (39.19); these appear to be a single broadened "line." Allowed transitions occur only by virtue of the state with $l = 1$ that is mixed into each of the eigenfunctions of (39.19), so that m_l can be only 0 or ± 1. This makes it possible to find the center of gravity of this line and its mean-square breadth without diagonalizing H', as we now show.

The unperturbed wave functions can be chosen so that H' is a real matrix. Then the unitary matrix S that diagonalizes H' can be real, so that Eq. (21.20) or Eq. (22.6) can be written

$$SH'S^* = E \tag{39.20}$$

where E is diagonal. In terms of matrix elements, this equation is

$$\sum_{k,l} S_{ik}H'_{kl}S_{jl} = E_i\delta_{ij}$$

The new eigenfunctions u_i that correspond to the energy eigenvalues E_i are given in terms of the unperturbed wave functions v_l by (22.3)

$$u_i = \sum_l S_{il}v_l$$

If now we neglect the dependence of the radiative transition probability on energy over the small range of energies involved in this group of states, the transition probability is proportional to the square of the amount of v_1 in each u_i, or to S_{i1}^2. Thus the energy levels E_i should be weighted in proportion to S_{i1}^2. The center of gravity of the group of perturbed energy levels is given by

$$E_{\text{avg.}} = \sum_i E_i S_{i1}^2 = H'_{11}$$

since (39.20) can be inverted to give $H' = S^*ES$. In similar fashion, the mean-square breadth of the line is

$$\sum_i (E_i - E_{\text{avg.}})^2 S_{i1}^2 = \sum_i E_i^2 S_{i1}^2 - E_{\text{avg.}}^2$$

$$= \sum_l H'^2_{1l} - E^2_{\text{avg.}} = H'^2_{12}$$

Thus only two of the matrix elements of H' need be calculated. It is apparent that both the displacement (apart from the factor $e\hbar/m_l$) and the breadth of the line are proportional to H^2.

40. MOLECULES

Molecules are considerably more complex in structure than atoms, and correspondingly less has been accomplished in the quantitative application of quantum mechanics to molecular problems. In this section, a general account of the nature of molecular energy levels is followed by a simple explicit calculation for the hydrogen molecule and a somewhat more general treatment of diatomic molecules.[1]

Classification of Energy Levels. The simplifying feature that is the basis of all molecular approximations is the large ratio of nuclear mass to electron mass. As we shall see shortly, this implies that the energy associated with the motion of the nuclei is much smaller than that associated with the motion of the electrons about the nuclei. Since the period of a motion is of the order of $\hbar$ divided by its energy, the nuclear periods are correspondingly longer than the electronic periods. It is then a good approximation to regard the nuclei as fixed in calculating the electronic motion. Moreover, the nuclear motion can be calculated under the assumption that the electrons have their steady motion for each instantaneous arrangement of the nuclei (adiabatic approximation).

The nuclei are expected to have a stable equilibrium arrangement somewhere between a completely collapsed structure (which is unstable, since the nuclei are positively charged and repel each other at short distances) and a completely dispersed structure (which is not the most stable structure if a molecule exists). The nuclear motions can then be classified into translations and rotations of the quasi-rigid equilibrium arrangement, and internal vibrations of the nuclei about equilibrium. As with atoms, the translational motion is the same as that of a free particle [see the discussion of Eqs. (16.5)], and gives rise to no nonclassical features.

We thus arrive at a classification of molecular energy levels into *electronic, vibrational,* and *rotational* types, and proceed to estimate their relative orders of magnitude. Suppose that the molecule has linear dimensions of order a. Then the energy E_e associated with the motion of a valence electron (one that occupies roughly the whole of the molecular volume, rather than one that is bound in an inner shell close to a nucleus)

[1] For more detailed discussions, see G. Herzberg, "Molecular Spectra and Molecular Structure," 2d ed. (Van Nostrand, New York, 1950); L. Pauling and E. B. Wilson, Jr., "Introduction to Quantum Mechanics," Chaps. X, XII, and XIII (McGraw-Hill, New York, 1935).

is of order $\hbar^2/ma^2$, where m is the electronic mass. This can be inferred by an argument like that given near the beginning of Sec. 9, by noting that the momentum uncertainty of the electron is at least of order $\hbar/a$, so that its minimum kinetic energy is $\hbar^2/ma^2$. We thus obtain

$$E_e \sim \frac{\hbar^2}{ma^2} \qquad (40.1)$$

For values of a of the order of a few angstrom units, this corresponds to transition frequencies in the visible and ultraviolet regions of the spectrum.

To estimate the vibrational energy, we regard each of the normal modes as a harmonic oscillator with which is associated a mass M and a stiffness constant K_0. M will be of the order of a typical nuclear mass. K_0 can be estimated by noting that a displacement along a normal mode by the order of the molecular size a must produce an energy change of the order of the electronic energy E_e, since such a large displacement would produce a substantial distortion of the electronic wave function; we thus put $K_0 \sim E_e/a^2$. Then the energy E_v associated with a fairly low mode of vibration is, from (13.8),

$$E_v \sim \hbar \left(\frac{K_0}{M}\right)^{\frac{1}{2}} \sim \frac{\hbar^2}{(mM)^{\frac{1}{2}}a^2} \sim \left(\frac{m}{M}\right)^{\frac{1}{2}} E_e \qquad (40.2)$$

where use has been made of (40.1). E_v is roughly a hundred times smaller than E_e, and corresponds to transitions in the near infrared.

The rotational energy E_r can be estimated from the moment of inertia of the molecule, which is of order Ma^2. As would be expected, the angular momentum of a fairly low mode of rotation turns out to be of order $\hbar$, so that

$$E_r \sim \frac{\hbar^2}{Ma^2} \sim \frac{m}{M} E_e \qquad (40.3)$$

This is about a hundred times smaller than E_v, and corresponds to transitions in the far infrared.

It might be expected from Eqs. (40.2) and (40.3) that the electronic, vibrational, and rotational energy levels can be obtained as successively higher orders in an approximation that is based in some way on the small ratio m/M (which is usually in the range 10^{-3} to 10^{-4}). This was shown to be the case by Born and Oppenheimer.[1] They used as expansion parameter the ratio of a typical nuclear vibrational displacement to the internuclear distance (which is of order a). An oscillator of energy

---

[1] M. Born and J. R. Oppenheimer, *Ann. d. Physik*, **84**, 457 (1927).

E_v and stiffness constant K_0 has a displacement of order

$$\left(\frac{E_v}{K_0}\right)^{\frac{1}{2}} \sim a\left(\frac{E_v}{E_e}\right)^{\frac{1}{2}},$$

so that the expansion parameter is

$$\left(\frac{E_v}{E_e}\right)^{\frac{1}{2}} \sim \left(\frac{m}{M}\right)^{\frac{1}{4}} \tag{40.4}$$

In terms of this, the electronic energy is of zero order, the vibrational energy of second order, and the rotational energy of fourth order; the first- and third-order energies vanish.

Wave Equation. The time-independent Schrödinger equation for a molecule is readily written down

$$\left(-\frac{\hbar^2}{2m}\sum_{i=1}^{n}\nabla_i^2 - \sum_{j=1}^{N}\frac{\hbar^2}{2M_j}\nabla_j^2 + V\right)\psi = E\psi \tag{40.5}$$

There are n electrons and N nuclei, and V is the sum of the electrostatic interactions between all pairs of them. It is apparent that the nuclear kinetic-energy terms are of fourth order in the expansion parameter (40.4). If they are neglected, the wave function ψ involves the nuclear coordinates R_j only parametrically, and (40.5) is a wave equation in the r_i for the motion of the electrons with respect to nuclei that are fixed in space. In this case, ψ is approximately $u_{R_j}(r_i)$ and corresponds to the energy eigenvalue $U(R_j)$. The nuclear motion can then be found by regarding $U(R_j)$ as a potential function and using it to obtain a nuclear wave function $w(R_j)$.

We therefore write ψ in the form

$$\psi(r_i, R_j) = u_{R_j}(r_i)w(R_j) \tag{40.6}$$

where u satisfies the equation

$$\left(-\frac{\hbar^2}{2m}\sum_{i=1}^{n}\nabla_i^2 + V\right)u_{R_j}(r_i) = U(R_j)u_{R_j}(r_i) \tag{40.7}$$

For each arrangement of the nuclei, $U(R_j)$ is obtained as an eigenvalue of Eq. (40.7). There will, in general, be several solutions that correspond to different electronic states of the molecule; care must be taken to ensure that u and U change continuously with R_j, especially if the system is degenerate. Substitution of (40.6) into (40.5) gives, with the help of

(40.7),

$$\left[-\sum_{j=1}^{N} \frac{\hbar^2}{2M_j} \nabla_j^2 + U(\mathbf{R}_j) \right] \psi = E\psi$$

which can be rewritten

$$u_{\mathbf{R}_j}(\mathbf{r}_i) \left[-\sum_{j=1}^{N} \frac{\hbar^2}{2M_j} \nabla_j^2 + U(\mathbf{R}_j) - E \right] w(\mathbf{R}_j)$$

$$= \sum_{j=1}^{N} \frac{\hbar^2}{2M_j} [w(\mathbf{R}_j)\nabla_j^2 u_{\mathbf{R}_j}(\mathbf{r}_i) + 2 \text{ grad}_j \, w(\mathbf{R}_j) \cdot \text{grad}_j \, u_{\mathbf{R}_j}(\mathbf{r}_i)] \quad (40.8)$$

If now the dependence of u on $\mathbf{R}_j$ is neglected, the right side of (40.8) drops out, and an approximate wave equation for the nuclear motion is obtained:

$$\left[-\sum_{j=1}^{N} \frac{\hbar^2}{2M_j} \nabla_j^2 + U(\mathbf{R}_j) \right] w(\mathbf{R}_j) = Ew(\mathbf{R}_j) \quad (40.9)$$

The neglect of the $\text{grad}_j \, u$ terms derives physically from the smallness of the amplitudes of the nuclear motion in comparison with the equilibrium internuclear distances [smallness of the expansion parameter (40.4)]; this implies that the electronic part u of the wave function does not change much as the nuclei move. Born and Oppenheimer have shown formally that this approximation is justified so long as not too high vibrational and rotational modes are excited.

The Hydrogen Molecule. It is clear from the foregoing discussion that two distinct problems arise in connection with molecular structure. The first is the solution of Eq. (40.7) to obtain electronic wave functions and a potential energy function $U(\mathbf{R}_j)$ of the nuclear coordinates. The second is the solution of (40.9) for the nuclear motion. The first problem can be solved only in the simplest cases. As an example, we now consider in outline an approximate solution for the hydrogen molecule due to Heitler and London.[1] Following this, we discuss the solution of Eq. (40.9) for a general diatomic molecule, making simple assumptions concerning the potential energy U.

The only nuclear coordinate $\mathbf{R}_j$ that appears in (40.7) in the case of the hydrogen molecule is the magnitude R of the distance between the two hydrogen nuclei. The Hamiltonian is that given in Eq. (27.11)

---

[1] W. Heitler and F. London, *Zeits. f. Physik,* **44,** 455 (1927).

(see Fig. 24); however, R is no longer large in comparison with

$$a_0 = \frac{\hbar^2}{me^2}$$

so that the approximations implied in (27.11) and (27.12) are no longer useful. Nevertheless, an approximate wave function based on a simple product of two ground-state hydrogen-atom functions gives remarkably good results. The reason for this is that exchange degeneracy (see Sec. 32) is taken into account: the degenerate wave functions for which electron 1 is on nucleus A and electron 2 on nucleus B, and for which electron 1 is on nucleus B and electron 2 on nucleus A, are both used at once. The new feature of the work of Heitler and London was the recognition that an appropriate linear combination of unperturbed degenerate wave functions gives a significantly lower energy than the separate wave functions; it is the basis of the present-day theory of *homopolar binding* in molecules. This property of degeneracy is sometimes referred to as *resonance*. An analogous situation is that in which an interaction between two classical oscillators that are in resonance (same unperturbed frequency) gives rise to a normal mode that has a lower frequency (and also one that has a higher frequency). In a similar way, an interaction between two resonant (degenerate) states in quantum mechanics gives rise to a lower energy eigenvalue (as well as to a higher one).[1] There may of course be more than two degenerate unperturbed states, and the degeneracy need not be of the exchange type.

Potential-energy Function. Equation (40.7) for the hydrogen molecule is

$$[H - U(R)]u_R(\mathbf{r}_1,\mathbf{r}_2) = 0$$

$$H = -\frac{\hbar^2}{2m}(\nabla_1^2 + \nabla_2^2) + e^2\left(\frac{1}{R} + \frac{1}{r_{12}} - \frac{1}{r_{1A}} - \frac{1}{r_{2B}} - \frac{1}{r_{1B}} - \frac{1}{r_{2A}}\right)$$

(40.10)

We wish to base our approximate calculation of $U(R)$ on the approximate wave functions

$$u_1(\mathbf{r}_1,\mathbf{r}_2) = u_A(\mathbf{r}_1)u_B(\mathbf{r}_2)$$
$$u_2(\mathbf{r}_1,\mathbf{r}_2) = u_A(\mathbf{r}_2)u_B(\mathbf{r}_1)$$

(40.11)

where u_A and u_B are ground-state hydrogen wave functions [u_{100} in the notation of (16.24)] based on nuclei A and B, respectively. It must first be noticed that the u_1 and u_2 of (40.11) are eigenfunctions of different unperturbed Hamiltonians, so that the degenerate perturbation theory of Sec. 25 is not applicable. This is unlike the situation with the helium

---

[1] This use of the word resonance is only remotely related to that which appeared in Sec. 19 in connection with scattering.

atom [see the discussion of (33.7)], where the two exchange-degenerate wave functions are solutions of the same unperturbed Hamiltonian.

We can, however, use the variation method of Sec. 27, in which case it is natural to adopt as the trial function an arbitrary linear combination of u_1 and u_2

$$\psi(\mathbf{r}_1,\mathbf{r}_2) = u_1(\mathbf{r}_1,\mathbf{r}_2) + Au_2(\mathbf{r}_1,\mathbf{r}_2) \tag{40.12}$$

where A is the variation parameter. Substitution of (40.12) into (27.5) gives

$$U(R) \leqq \frac{(1 + A^2)H_{11} + 2AH_{12}}{1 + A^2 + 2A\gamma}, \qquad \gamma \equiv \iint u_1 u_2 d\tau_1 d\tau_2 \tag{40.13}$$

$$H_{11} = H_{22} \equiv \iint u_1 H u_1 d\tau_1 d\tau_2, \qquad H_{12} = H_{21} \equiv \iint u_1 H u_2 d\tau_1 d\tau_2$$

These equalities between matrix elements are easily established with the help of Eq. (22.10) when it is remembered that the u's are real, and that H is Hermitian and symmetrical in the two electrons.

The matrix elements and γ depend on R. For any particular value of R, the derivative of the right side of (40.13) with respect to A is

$$\frac{2(1 - A^2)(H_{12} - \gamma H_{11})}{(1 + A^2 + 2A\gamma)^2}$$

which is zero for $A = \pm 1$. Since the right side of (40.13) is equal to H_{11} when A is $-\infty$, 0, and $+\infty$, one of the points $A = \pm 1$ must be a minimum and the other a maximum. The integrals in (40.13) can be expressed in terms of tabulated functions, and the minimum expectation value of H is obtained with $A = +1$:

$$\psi = u_1 + u_2$$
$$U(R) \leqq \frac{H_{11} + H_{12}}{1 + \gamma} \tag{40.14}$$

The upper limit on $U(R)$ given in (40.14) has the general appearance that is characteristic of the internuclear potential energy of a diatomic molecule (see Fig. 30) and is in good agreement with experiment.[1] Since ψ in (40.14) is symmetric in an interchange of the space coordinates of the two electrons, it must be multiplied by the antisymmetric singlet spin function given as the last of Eqs. (33.6).

It is interesting to compare the symmetry characters of the ground state of the hydrogen molecule and the excited states of the helium atom considered in Sec. 33, from a physical point of view. Because of the exclusion principle, electrons must be in different space states if they have parallel spins, and hence tend to keep away from each other. In the

[1] Pauling and Wilson, *op. cit.*, Sec. 43a.

excited $1s2s$ state of helium, for example, this reduces the electrostatic repulsion of the electrons and lowers the energy. Thus the triplet states of helium tend to lie lower than the singlet state of the same configuration. (The situation is different for the ground state, since only the singlet state can exist for the $1s^2$ configuration.) In the ground state of the hydrogen molecule, on the other hand, the lowest energy (strongest binding) is obtained when the electrons tend to concentrate between the two nuclei, since then the repulsion between the electrons is more than compensated by the attraction of both nuclei for each electron. This occurs when the electrons can occupy the same space state and hence when they have antiparallel spins. Thus it is the singlet state that leads to a stable molecule.

The Morse Potential. We now turn to diatomic molecules in general, and consider the nature of the solutions of Eq. (40.9) for the nuclear motion. If the nuclei have masses M_1 and M_2 and their relative position vector **R** has polar coordinates R, θ, ϕ, the equation for the relative motion becomes [see Eqs. (16.5)]

$$\left[-\frac{\hbar^2}{2M} \nabla^2 + U(R) \right] w(R, \theta, \phi) = Ew(R, \theta, \phi) \qquad (40.15)$$

where $M = M_1 M_2 / (M_1 + M_2)$ is the reduced mass.

It has been found by experience that the potential-energy function for the lowest electronic states of actual diatomic molecules can be represented quite accurately by a simple analytic function that contains three adjustable parameters

$$U(R) = U_0 \left[e^{-\frac{2(R - R_0)}{a}} - 2e^{-\frac{(R - R_0)}{a}} \right] \qquad (40.16)$$

Equation (40.16) represents the *Morse potential*,[1] and is drawn in Fig. 30. U approaches zero exponentially for large R, has the minimum value $-U_0$ at $R = R_0$, and becomes large and positive as R approaches zero if the "breadth" a of the attractive region is somewhat smaller than the equilibrium distance R_0.

Figure 30 has the general appearance that would be expected for a diatomic molecule. The zero of energy is arbitrarily chosen to occur when the neutral atoms are far apart; then U becomes negative at first as R decreases, because of the van der Waals attraction.[2] For smaller R this is replaced by the much stronger Heitler-London resonance attrac-

---

[1] P. M. Morse, *Phys. Rev.*, **34**, 57 (1929).

[2] One of the inaccuracies of the Morse potential is its replacement of the $1/R^6$ van der Waals term (see the middle of Sec. 27), by an exponential; however, the behavior of U at such large R has little influence on molecular energy levels.

tion.   As R continues to decrease, the close approach of the nuclei (or ionic cores) gives rise to a repulsion that causes U to increase and eventually become large and positive.[1]

Rotation and Vibration of Diatomic Molecules.   Equation (40.15) can be separated in spherical coordinates, as was Eq. (14.1), to give

$$w(R,\theta,\phi) = \frac{\chi(R)}{R}\, Y_{KM_K}(\theta,\phi)$$

K and M_K are the angular-momentum quantum numbers that are analogous to l and m, respectively, for a single particle in a central field.

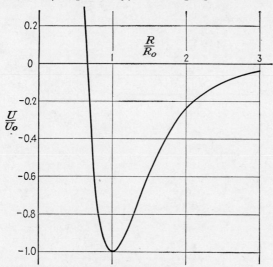

FIG. 30.   The Morse potential (40.16), with $a = \frac{1}{2}R_0$.

The radial equation is

$$-\frac{\hbar^2}{2M}\frac{d^2\chi}{dR^2} + W(R)\chi = E\chi \tag{40.17}$$

$$W(R) = U(R) + \frac{\hbar^2 K(K+1)}{2MR^2}, \quad K = 0,1,2,\ldots$$

Equation (40.17) is the wave equation for the one-dimensional motion of a particle of mass M in a potential $W(R)$, with the boundary condition that χ vanish at $R = 0$.   If K is not too large, the general shape of W resembles that of U shown in Fig. 30.   In this case, we are primarily interested in vibrations of small amplitude about the minimum.   We can then expand W about its minimum at R_1, which is only the same as R_0 if $K = 0$, to give

$$W(R) = W_0 + \tfrac{1}{2}K_0(R - R_1)^2 + b(R - R_1)^3 + c(R - R_1)^4 \tag{40.18}$$

[1] Unlike the true interaction, the Morse potential is finite at $R = 0$.

where higher order terms are neglected. If the b and c terms are also neglected and the domain of R is extended to $-\infty$, the eigenvalues of (40.17) are those of a linear harmonic oscillator with an additive term W_0. This is a good approximation for moderate values of the *rotational quantum number* K and the *vibrational quantum number* v. A somewhat better approximation can be obtained by regarding the b and c terms in (40.18) as perturbations on the oscillator. Since the b term produces only a second-order effect (see Prob. 2, Chap. VII), whereas the c term appears in first order (its expectation value can be computed by matrix methods as in Prob. 5, Chap. VI), both make contributions to E that have the same order of magnitude.

Energy Levels. The eigenvalues of (40.17) to lowest order in b and c are then

$$E = W_0 + \hbar \left(\frac{K_0}{M}\right)^{\frac{1}{2}} (v + \tfrac{1}{2}) - \frac{\hbar^2 b^2}{M K_0^2} [\tfrac{15}{4}(v + \tfrac{1}{2})^2 + \tfrac{7}{16}]$$

$$+ \frac{3\hbar^2 c}{2M K_0} [(v + \tfrac{1}{2})^2 + \tfrac{1}{4}], \qquad v = 0,1,2, \ldots \qquad (40.19)$$

W_0, K_0, b, and c can all be expanded in powers of $K(K + 1)$, where the coefficients depend on the parameters of the function $U(R)$. If U has the form (40.16), the following expressions can be obtained:

$$R_1 = R_0 + \frac{\hbar^2 K(K + 1)a^2}{2M R_0^3 U_0}$$

$$W_0 = - U_0 + \frac{\hbar^2 K(K + 1)}{2M R_0^2} - \frac{\hbar^4 K^2(K + 1)^2 a^2}{4M^2 R_0^6 U_0}$$

$$K_0 = \frac{2U_0}{a^2} - \frac{3\hbar^2 K(K + 1)}{M R_0^2 a^2} \frac{a}{R_0} \left(1 - \frac{a}{R_0}\right) \qquad (40.20)$$

$$b = - \frac{U_0}{a^3}, \qquad c = \frac{7U_0}{12a^4}$$

Only enough terms have been retained to give E correctly to second order in $(v + \tfrac{1}{2})$ and $K(K + 1)$.

The first of Eqs. (40.20) shows that the molecule stretches owing to rotation. The second equation is the equilibrium energy $-U_0$, plus the rotational energy to second order. The first-order rotational energy is $\hbar^2 K(K + 1)/2I_0$, where $I_0 = M R_0^2$ is the moment of inertia of the molecule about an axis perpendicular to the line joining the nuclei; this energy is the same as for a rigid rotator (see Prob. 12). The third equation includes the change in the stiffness due to stretching. The corrections for stretching in the anharmonic terms b and c can be neglected to this order. The second term on the right side of (40.19) can be expanded with the help of the expression for K_0 to give

$$\hbar \left(\frac{2U_0}{Ma^2}\right)^{\frac{1}{2}} (v + \tfrac{1}{2}) \left[1 - \frac{3\hbar^2 K(K+1)}{4MR_0^2 U_0} \cdot \frac{a}{R_0} \left(1 - \frac{a}{R_0}\right)\right]$$

The last two terms in (40.19) give the second-order vibrational energy

$$(- \tfrac{15}{16} + \tfrac{7}{16}) \frac{\hbar^2}{Ma^2} (v + \tfrac{1}{2})^2 = - \frac{\hbar^2}{2Ma^2} (v + \tfrac{1}{2})^2 \qquad (40.21)$$

since the constant factors cancel.

It is apparent that the rotational and vibrational energy levels agree in order of magnitude with the estimates made at the beginning of this section. As either v or K increases, the spacing between levels becomes smaller than that predicted from the simple rigid rotator and harmonic oscillator.

Effect of Nuclear Identity. In the event that the two nuclei of a diatomic molecule are identical, the wave function must be symmetric with respect to an interchange of their space and spin coordinates if the nuclei have zero or integer spin, or antisymmetric if they have half-odd-integer spin (see Sec. 33). The discussion of Sec. 14 shows that the parity of the nuclear wave function is determined by the angular function $Y_{KM_K}(\theta,\phi)$, and is even or odd according as K is even or odd. An interchange of the space coordinates of the two nuclei is equivalent to a change in sign of their relative position vector **R,** so that the parity determines the space symmetry of the wave function. We thus see that for nuclei of zero or integer spin, the spin function must be symmetric for even K and antisymmetric for odd K; for nuclei of half-odd-integer spin, the spin function must be antisymmetric for even K and symmetric for odd K.

The discussion of Sec. 33 shows that for two nuclei of spin $I\hbar$ each, the total of $(2I + 1)^2$ spin states can be divided into $(I + 1)(2I + 1)$ symmetric states and $I(2I + 1)$ antisymmetric states. Thus in a gas that is in statistical equilibrium, the ratio of the number of molecules with even K to the number with odd K will be $(I + 1)/I$ if I is zero or an integer, and $I/(I + 1)$ if I is half an odd integer.[1] This effect gives rise to alternating intensities in the band (rotational) spectrum of homonuclear diatomic molecules. Both the spin and the statistics of appropriate nuclei can be determined in this way, and the results are in agreement with the general statement in Sec. 33.

41. ATOMIC NUCLEI

The application of quantum mechanics to the investigation of the structure of atomic nuclei entails great mathematical complexities in all

---

[1] This ratio is, of course, modified by the Boltzmann factor if the spacing between rotational levels is not small in comparison with the thermal energy κT.

but the simplest cases. In this section we mention very briefly some general properties of nuclei and then consider the nuclear two-body problem.[1]

General Properties of Nuclei. Atomic nuclei consist of protons and neutrons, both of which are called *nucleons*. Other particles (mesons, electrons), which have a transient existence within nuclei, are usually ignored in structure theories. Protons are nuclei of hydrogen atoms, and neutrons are particles that have about the same mass, no electric charge, and the same spin and statistics as protons (spin $\frac{1}{2}\hbar$, Fermi-Dirac statistics). A nucleus can be characterized by its charge Ze, where Z is an integer and e is the positive proton charge, and its mass M, which is measured in units of $\frac{1}{16}$ of the mass of O^{16} (oxygen isotope of mass number 16). M is always found to be close to an integer A, called the *mass number*. The number of neutrons in a nucleus is equal to $A - Z$; thus the deuteron (heavy-hydrogen nucleus) H^2 consists of one proton and one neutron, the alpha particle (helium nucleus) He^4 of two protons and two neutrons, and the gold nucleus Au^{197} of 79 protons and 118 neutrons.

According to the theory of relativity, the difference between the sum of the masses of the Z protons and $A - Z$ neutrons in a nucleus and the mass M of that nucleus, multiplied by the square of the speed of light, is the energy evolved when the separate nucleons are brought together to form the nucleus. This energy is called the *binding energy* of the nucleus, and is conveniently measured in units of a million electron-volts (Mev). The *nuclear radius R* is a reasonably well-defined quantity. It can be measured in several ways, for example, from the scattering of high-energy neutrons, protons, and electrons. It is found experimentally that both the binding energy per nucleon and the volume per nucleon are roughly constant over most of the periodic system. The former is about 8 Mev, and the latter is usually expressed in the form $R = r_0 A^{\frac{1}{3}}$, where $r_0 \cong 1.2$ to 1.4×10^{-13} cm. The approximate constancy of the binding energy and volume per nucleon is referred to as the *saturation* property of nuclei.

Two-nucleon Interaction. The most fundamental problem to be solved in connection with nuclei is the determination of the parameters of the interaction energy between pairs of nucleons. It is possible that once these are known the problem of the structure of nuclei heavier than

---

[1] For further discussion, see H. A. Bethe, "Elementary Nuclear Theory" (Wiley, New York, 1947); L. Rosenfeld, "Nuclear Forces" (Interscience, New York, 1948); G. Gamow and C. L. Critchfield, "Theory of Atomic Nucleus and Nuclear Energy-sources" (Oxford, New York, 1949); E. Fermi, "Nuclear Physics" (University of Chicago Press, Chicago, 1950); J. M. Blatt and V. F. Weisskopf, "Theoretical Nuclear Physics" (Wiley, New York, 1952); R. G. Sachs, "Nuclear Theory" (Addison-Wesley, Cambridge, Mass., 1953); A. Bohr and B. R. Mottelson, *Kgl. Danske Vid. Sels. Mat.-fys. Medd.*, **27**, 16 (1953).

the deuteron would become merely an exceedingly complicated exercise in the application of quantum mechanics. This situation would be analogous to that which obtains in atomic and molecular structure, where the main interaction is known to be given by Coulomb's law. On the other hand, it is possible that knowledge of the two-body interactions is not enough to determine the structure of heavier nuclei, even in principle. This would be the case if there were additional interactions which occur only when three, four, or more nucleons are close together, so that their existence and character could not be inferred from a study of the two-nucleon system. The question of whether or not appreciable many-body interactions exist has not yet been settled, and we shall not discuss it further here.

We devote the remainder of this chapter to the two-nucleon system and assume that the main interaction is of short range. It is reasonable to expect this range to be substantially less than the radii of heavy nuclei, and calculations of the type described below show that it is of the order of 2×10^{-13} cm. We put aside for the present any possible dependence of the interaction potential energy $V(r)$ on quantities other than the magnitude of the separation distance r between the two nucleons. Our first problem then is to solve the Schrödinger equation for the relative motion of two particles of reduced mass μ in the potential $V(r)$. Since neutrons and protons have about the same mass, μ is very nearly equal to half the mass of either of them.

Neutron-Proton System. A simple assumption for the shape of $V(r)$ is the square well form (see Fig. 13, page 76): $V(r) = -V_0$ for $r < a$, $V(r) = 0$ for $r > a$. It was shown in Sec. 15 that there is no bound state of a particle of mass μ in this potential unless $V_0 a^2 > \pi^2 \hbar^2 / 8\mu$, which is equal to 1.01×10^{-24} Mev-cm^2 for the neutron-proton system. If we assume that $a = 2.00 \times 10^{-13}$ cm, V_0 must exceed 25.2 Mev in order for the deuteron to exist. Since the deuteron has only one bound state, it is reasonable to suppose that it corresponds to $l = 0$. Then the solution of Prob. 7, Chap. IV, shows that the measured binding energy of 2.23 Mev is obtained with $V_0 = 36.1$ Mev.

The scattering cross section for neutrons of very low energy on protons can then be obtained from Eq. (19.28). If we neglect E in comparison with V_0, we find that $\sigma = 3.5 \times 10^{-24}$ cm^2. The measured cross section for neutrons of a few electron-volts energy in hydrogen is about 20.4×10^{-24} cm^2; this energy is small enough so that it can be neglected in comparison with V_0 and large enough so that the binding of the proton in the hydrogen molecule does not affect the result. An explanation of this discrepancy in terms of the dependence of the neutron-proton interaction on the spin state was suggested in 1935 by E. Wigner (unpublished).   The deuteron is known to have spin $\hbar$, and so is in a triplet spin state.   However, as discussed in Sec. 34 in connection with exchange collisions of electrons with hydrogen atoms, the colliding neutron and proton will be in a triplet state in three-fourths of the collisions and in a singlet spin state in one-fourth of the collisions.   Thus the discrepancy is removed if the singlet cross section is taken to be 70.8×10^{-24} cm^2.

If we assume that a is also equal to 2.00×10^{-13} cm for the singlet interaction, Eq. (19.28) shows that this cross section is obtained for a potential depth of either 23.6 or 27.0 Mev.   It is apparent that this is the resonance scattering case discussed in Sec. 19 and that these two potentials correspond to virtual and bound singlet states, respectively. The decision as to which is correct cannot be made on the basis of the dependence of the scattering cross section on incident neutron energy; it is shown in Sec. 19 that with $l = 0$, σ is a monotonic decreasing function of E in both cases, and there is not enough difference in the behavior of the two functions.   It is found from other considerations[1] that the singlet state is virtual, so that the depth corresponding to this range is 23.6 Mev.

Arbitrary Shape of Potential.   The interaction potential energy between a pair of nucleons is characterized by a short range a and a large magnitude V_0.   Here, a and V_0 do not apply only to the square well shape but rather refer to the distance within which $V(r)$ is appreciably different from zero and to the approximate magnitude of $V(r)$ in this region, respectively.   For collisions of moderate energy, up to a few Mev, ka is fairly small compared to unity, where $k = (2\mu E)^{\frac{1}{2}}/\hbar$ and E is the kinetic energy in the center-of-mass coordinate system.   For example, with $a = 2 \times 10^{-13}$ cm, ka is equal to unity when the energy of the incident nucleon in the laboratory system is about 20 Mev.   Thus for moderate energies, only the $l = 0$ partial wave need be considered.   Also, both E and ϵ, the binding energy of the deuteron, are fairly small in comparison with V_0.   It follows that the form of the $l = 0$ radial wave function depends only slightly on the energy within the potential range and has its simple asymptotic form outside this range.   This suggests that the binding and the low-energy scattering produced by such a potential should depend primarily on the "strength" of the potential, measured roughly by $V_0 a^2$, and on the distance at which the wave function attains its asymptotic form, measured roughly by a.

It turns out that any strong, short-range, predominantly attractive potential can actually be represented by two parameters, which may be chosen to be a strength and a range, and which between them specify the

---

[1] Most reliably from the scattering of very slow neutrons in ortho- and para-hydrogen; the possibility of such a determination was first pointed out by J. Schwinger and E. Teller, *Phys. Rev.*, **52**, 286 (1937).

bound state energy $-\epsilon$ and the dependence of the scattering phase shift on energy for moderate values of E.[1] Thus low-energy experiments can be expected to determine only these two parameters and not the shape of the potential $V(r)$; this expectation is confirmed by the experimental results.

Relations for the Phase Shift. We work entirely with the $l = 0$ partial wave, and let $u(r)$ be the product of r and the radial wave function. The normalization of u is so chosen that its asymptotic form is

$$u(r) \rightarrow \psi(r) \tag{41.1}$$

outside the range of the potential, where

$$\psi(r) \equiv \frac{\sin\ (kr + \delta)}{\sin \delta} \tag{41.2}$$

for all r. The phase shift δ agrees with the definition given in Eq. (19.8), and the total cross section is

$$\sigma = \frac{4\pi}{k^2}\sin^2 \delta \tag{41.3}$$

as in Eq. (19.13).

The wave equations for particular energies E_1 and E_2 are

$$\frac{d^2u_1}{dr^2} + k_1^2u_1 - Uu_1 = 0$$
$$\frac{d^2u_2}{dr^2} + k_2^2u_2 - Uu_2 = 0 \tag{41.4}$$

where $U(r) = 2\mu V(r)/\hbar^2$. We multiply the first of Eqs. (41.4) by u_2, the second by u_1, and integrate the difference between them over r from $r = 0$ to a distance R that is somewhat larger than the range of the potential:

$$\left(u_2\frac{du_1}{dr} - u_1\frac{du_2}{dr} \right)\Bigg|_0^R = (k_2^2 - k_1^2)\int_0^R u_1u_2dr \tag{41.5}$$

The ψ's satisfy the same Eqs. (41.4) as the u's, except that the U terms are absent. Therefore Eq. (41.5) holds for the ψ's as well:

$$\left(\psi_2\frac{d\psi_1}{dr} - \psi_1\frac{d\psi_2}{dr} \right)\Bigg|_0^R = (k_2^2 - k_1^2)\int_0^R \psi_1\psi_2dr \tag{41.6}$$

If now Eq. (41.5) is subtracted from Eq. (41.6), the contributions to the

---

[1] Although suspected earlier, this result was first established by J. Schwinger in unpublished lectures (1947), using a variational method; the present treatment follows that of H. A. Bethe, *Phys. Rev.*, **76**, 38 (1949).

left side from the upper limit R cancel, since $u(R) = \psi(R)$. Then the limit $R \rightarrow \infty$ can be taken, to yield

$$\left(\psi_1 \frac{d\psi_2}{dr} - \psi_2 \frac{d\psi_1}{dr}\right)_{r=0} - \left(u_1 \frac{du_2}{dr} - u_2 \frac{du_1}{dr}\right)_{r=0}$$
$$= (k_2^2 - k_1^2) \int_0^\infty (\psi_1\psi_2 - u_1u_2)dr \quad (41.7)$$

From Eq. (41.2), the first parenthesis on the left side is equal to $k_2 \cot \delta_2 - k_1 \cot \delta_1$. Also, since $u(0) = 0$, the second parenthesis on the left side is zero. Thus Eq. (41.7) can be written

$$k_2 \cot \delta_2 - k_1 \cot \delta_1 = \tfrac{1}{2}(k_2^2 - k_1^2)\rho(E_1,E_2)$$
$$\rho(E_1,E_2) \equiv 2 \int_0^\infty (\psi_1\psi_2 - u_1u_2)dr \quad (41.8)$$

A modification of Eqs. (41.8) that is of interest is obtained by replacing E_1 by $-\epsilon$, $\psi_1(r)$ by $\psi_g(r) \equiv \exp(-\beta r)$, where $\beta^2 = 2\mu\epsilon/\hbar^2$, and $u_1(r)$ by the ground-state wave function $u_g(r)$ normalized in analogy with (41.1). The result is

$$k_2 \cot \delta_2 + \beta = \tfrac{1}{2}(k_2^2 + \beta^2)\rho(-\epsilon,E_2)$$
$$\rho(-\epsilon,E_2) \equiv 2 \int_0^\infty (\psi_g\psi_2 - u_gu_2)dr \quad (41.9)$$

Another modification consists in allowing E_1 to become zero:

$$k_2 \cot \delta_2 + \frac{1}{a_t} = \frac{1}{2} k_2^2\rho(0,E_2)$$
$$\rho(0,E_2) \equiv 2 \int_0^\infty (\psi_0\psi_2 - u_0u_2)dr \quad (41.10)$$
$$\psi_0 \equiv 1 - \frac{r}{a_t}, \qquad \frac{1}{a_t} = -\lim_{E\to 0} (k \cot \delta)$$

where the subscripts on u_0 and ψ_0 denote zero energy. The quantity a_t is called the *scattering length;* from Eq. (41.3) the scattering cross section at zero energy is equal to $4\pi a_t^2$. The subscript on a_t implies that it refers to the triplet, not the singlet interaction.

Effective Range. Equations (41.8), (41.9), and (41.10) are exact. We now make an approximation with regard to ρ that is suggested by the general form of the potential. It is apparent that Eq. (41.1) makes the integrand of ρ vanish outside the potential. Inside the potential, all the ψ's are very nearly equal to unity since kr and βr are small in comparison with unity; also, the u's are very nearly equal to each other since

U is much larger than k^2 or β^2. Thus ρ depends only slightly on its arguments, and can be calculated for any convenient energies. Our approximation, then, is to replace ρ in the above equations by

$$r_0 \equiv \rho(0,0) = 2 \int_0^\infty (\psi_0^2 - u_0^2)dr \qquad (41.11)$$

which is called the *effective range*. Alternatively, the effective range could be defined, for example, as

$$\rho(-\epsilon, -\epsilon) = 2 \int_0^\infty (\psi_g^2 - u_g^2)dr \qquad (41.12)$$

It is shown in Prob. 17 that the effective ranges computed from Eqs. (41.11) and (41.12) in a typical case agree with each other within a few per cent.

With this approximation, the scattering phase shift is given by Eq. (41.9) as (dropping the subscript 2)

$$k \cot \delta + \beta \cong \tfrac{1}{2}r_0(k^2 + \beta^2) \qquad (41.13)$$

and by Eq. (41.10) as

$$k \cot \delta + \frac{1}{a_t} \cong \frac{1}{2} r_0 k^2 \qquad (41.14)$$

Comparison of Eqs. (41.13) and (41.14) gives the following relation between a_t, β, and the triplet effective range r_0:

$$\frac{1}{a_t} \cong \beta - \frac{1}{2} r_0 \beta^2 \qquad (41.15)$$

With $1/\beta = 4.28 \times 10^{-13}$ cm, which corresponds to $\epsilon = 2.23$ Mev, and $a_t = 5.34 \times 10^{-13}$ cm, Eq. (41.15) gives $r_0 \cong 1.70 \times 10^{-13}$ cm.

Either of the quantities β or a_t may be thought of as a strength parameter for the potential and r_0 as a range parameter; however, β and a_t differ enough so that specification of any two of the three quantities fixes the third. Thus according to this shape-independent effective range theory, all the binding and moderate-energy scattering properties of the potential are determined by just two parameters. The experimental results show that this is actually the case and so confirm the assumption of a strong, short-range interaction on which the theory is based.

Exchange Operators. The spin dependence of the neutron-proton interaction noted above can be expressed in terms of the *spin-exchange operator* $\tfrac{1}{2}(1 + \boldsymbol{\sigma}_N \cdot \boldsymbol{\sigma}_P)$, where $\boldsymbol{\sigma}_N$ and $\boldsymbol{\sigma}_P$ are the Pauli spin matrices for the neutron and proton, respectively, defined as in Eqs. (33.3). As shown in Prob. 18, such an operator multiplies a triplet (symmetric) spin function by $+1$ and a singlet (antisymmetric) spin function by -1. It follows from the foregoing discussion that the coefficient of the spin-exchange part of the neutron-proton interaction is about one-fifth of the coefficient of the non-spin-exchange part.

A *space-exchange operator*[1] multiplies wave functions of even l by $+1$ and wave functions of odd l by -1; it has no effect on the results obtained thus far, which are all for $l = 0$. For higher energy scattering, the discussion of Sec. 19 shows that the partial wave with $l = 1$ can be significant. If the phase shift δ_1 for $l = 1$ is small in magnitude and the higher phase shifts can be neglected, Eq. (19.32) can be approximated as

$$\sigma(\theta) \cong \frac{1}{k^2} \left(\sin^2 \delta_0 + 3\delta_1 \sin 2\delta_0 \cos \theta \right)$$

For energies high enough so that δ_1 is appreciable, the $l = 0$ phase shift δ_0 is likely to be between 0 and 90°, so that the sign of the angular asymmetry is determined by the sign of δ_1.

If now the interaction were predominantly of the non-space-exchange type, the potential would be negative (attractive) for $l = 1$, and δ_1 would be positive. Then neutrons incident on protons would be preferentially scattered forward in both the center-of-mass and laboratory coordinate systems. If, on the other hand, the space-exchange operator were to dominate the interaction, the potential energy would be repulsive for $l = 1$, and δ_1 would be negative. Then the neutrons would be preferentially scattered backward in the center-of-mass system or at right angles in the laboratory system, and the protons would tend to recoil in the forward direction in both systems. This effect can be regarded physically as a non-space-exchange type scattering accompanied by an exchange of identity between the neutron and the proton.

High-energy scattering experiments show that the differential cross section is nearly symmetric about 90° in the center-of-mass system. If it were exactly symmetric, the simplest and most likely situation would be either that all the even l phase shifts are zero or that all the odd l phase shifts are zero (see Prob. 19). The first case is impossible, since it is known that $\delta_0 \neq 0$. We are thus led to the *Serber interaction* as an approximation to the space-exchange character of the neutron-proton potential: the coefficients of the space-exchange and non-space-exchange parts of the neutron-proton potential are equal and of the same sign, so that there is no interaction in odd l states.

Proton-Proton Scattering. The scattering of fast protons in hydrogen can be treated by the methods outlined in Sec. 20, with suitable allow-

---

[1] This was introduced by E. Majorana, *Zeits. f. Physik*, **82**, 137 (1933), as a modification of the original suggestion of W. Heisenberg, *Zeits. f. Physik*, **77**, 1 (1932).

ance for the identity and spin of the two colliding protons (see Sec. 33). When the interaction is a pure Coulomb field, combination of Eqs. (20.10) and (33.2) yields the *Mott scattering formula*[1]

$$\sigma(\theta) = \left(\frac{e^2}{2\mu v^2}\right)^2 \left\{ \operatorname{cosec}^4 \tfrac{1}{2}\theta + \sec^4 \tfrac{1}{2}\theta \right.$$
$$\left. - \operatorname{cosec}^2 \tfrac{1}{2}\theta \sec^2 \tfrac{1}{2}\theta \cos \left[\frac{e^2}{\hbar v} \ln \left(\tan^2 \tfrac{1}{2}\theta \right) \right] \right\} \quad (41.16)$$

which is expressed in the center-of-mass coordinate system. This formula represents only the experiments for protons of less than about 0.2 Mev bombarding energy, since for higher energies the protons approach closely enough so that the specifically nuclear interaction becomes appreciable. Up to several Mev energy, only the δ_0 term in (20.24) need be included. It must be remembered that because of the exclusion principle, the partial wave with $l = 0$ is associated with a singlet spin state. Thus experiments with fast protons are required if information concerning the triplet proton-proton interaction is to be obtained. An effective range theory can be made for the singlet proton-proton interaction,[2] and leads to about the same parameters as for the singlet neutron-proton interaction.

Problems

1. Find an expression for the electron density $n(r)$ in the Thomas-Fermi model in terms of the dimensionless function χ, and show that the radius of a sphere that encloses a fixed fraction of all the electrons is proportional to $Z^{-\frac{1}{3}}$.

2. Use Lagrange's method of undetermined multipliers to show that the condition that the integral in (38.9) is stationary, when the u's are varied but kept normalized, is given by (38.11).

3. Two p electrons ($l = 1$) can have $L = 0, 1,$ or 2 and $S = 0$ or 1, in the Russell-Saunders case. Are all combinations of L and S permitted if the n values of the two electrons are different? Are they all permitted if the n values are the same?

4. Show that spin wave functions in the Russell-Saunders case that are eigenfunctions of $\mathbf{S}^2$ with different values of the total-spin quantum number S are orthogonal. Use a method like that which was employed in Sec. 10 to show that energy eigenfunctions corresponding to different eigenvalues are orthogonal.

5. Show by direct computation that $\mathbf{J} = \mathbf{L} + \mathbf{S}$ commutes with $\mathbf{L \cdot S}$, and hence with the Hamiltonian (39.1).

6. Use the $\mathbf{M}$ matrices given in Eqs. (24.15) to show that the wave functions (39.6) have the indicated eigenvalues of $\mathbf{J}^2$ and J_z.

7. Estimate the ratio of the term in (39.9) that is linear in $\mathbf{H}$ to the kinetic-energy term, for a hydrogen atom in a magnetic field of 10^5 gauss.

---

[1] N. F. Mott, *Proc. Roy. Soc.*, **A126**, 259 (1930). μ is half the proton mass, and v is the relative speed.

[2] Bethe, *op. cit.*

8. Estimate the magnitude of the magnetic field strength for which the two perturbation terms in (39.11) are equal for an alkali atom.

9. Construct a diagram that shows the relative displacements and intensities of the π and σ Zeeman components of the $^2P \to {}^2S$ transitions in an alkali atom when the magnetic field is weak. Construct a similar diagram when the field is strong.

10. Show that the ratio of the distance traveled by the nuclei of a molecule during a period of the electronic motion, to the dimensions of the molecule, is of order $(m/M)^{\frac{1}{4}}$ in the case of vibrational motion, and (m/M) in the case of rotational motion. Do these results justify an adiabatic type of approximation?

11. Does the internuclear potential (40.14) obtained for the hydrogen molecule approach the $-1/R^6$ form obtained in Sec. 27 for large R? If not, why doesn't it?

12. Set up and solve the wave equation for a rigid rotator: an object that has no kinetic energy of rotation about a particular axis, and equal moments of inertia about the two perpendicular axes.

13. Derive the selection rules for transitions between rotational levels of a diatomic molecule.

14. Discuss the selection rules for vibrational transitions when the two nuclei of a diatomic molecule are the same and when they are different.

15. Calculate the contributions to the vibrational energy of a diatomic molecule of the neglected fifth- and sixth-power terms in the expansion (40.18), and show that their neglect is justified in arriving at the $(v + \frac{1}{2})^2$ energy given in (40.21). Use matrix methods to get the needed matrix elements of x^5 and x^6 for a harmonic oscillator.

16. Suppose that the interaction between a neutron and a proton is the same in the singlet as in the triplet state, and is represented by a square well. Is there any value of a that will fit both the deuteron binding energy ($l = 0$) and the slow-neutron scattering cross section? If so, what is it?

17. Use the value of the binding energy of the deuteron to calculate the triplet effective range of a square well potential from Eq. (41.11) and from Eq. (41.12), assuming that $a = 2.00 \times 10^{-13}$ cm. Compare these with each other and with the value for r_0 given in the text.

18. Show that the spin-exchange operator $\frac{1}{2}(1 + \mathbf{d}_N \cdot \mathbf{d}_P)$ has the properties ascribed to it in the text.

19. Assume that the neutron-proton differential scattering cross section is symmetric about 90° in the center-of-mass system, and neglect the difference between triplet and singlet interactions. Show that this is equivalent to the requirement that

$$\sum_l \sum_{l'} (2l + 1)(2l' + 1) \sin \delta_l \sin \delta_{l'} \cos (\delta_l - \delta_{l'}) P_l(\cos \theta) P_{l'}(\cos \theta) = 0$$

for all θ, where all l are even and all l' are odd. Show that a sufficient condition that this relation is satisfied is that all δ_l are either 0 (mod π) or η (mod π) and that all $\delta_{l'}$ are either 0 (mod π) or $\eta + \frac{1}{2}\pi$ (mod π), where η is arbitrary.[1] Show also that, if only one of the $\delta_{l'}$ is different from 0 (mod π), a necessary and sufficient condition that the above relation is satisfied is that all δ_l are either 0 (mod π) or $\delta_{l'} + \frac{1}{2}\pi$ (mod π).

20. Make use of the work of Sec. 20 to obtain an expression for the ratio of the proton-proton scattering with a phase shift δ_0 (and no others), to the Mott scattering given by Eq. (41.16).

---

[1] The term mod π signifies that an integer multiple of π may be added to or subtracted from the preceding quantity without invalidating the stated relationship.

21. The ground-state wave function ψ_0 of an atom or nucleus, if nondegenerate, has a definite value J_0 for its total-angular-momentum quantum number. Since the diagonal matrix element of an operator Ω for a state ψ vanishes unless $\bar{\psi}\Omega\psi$ is spherically symmetric, show that the expectation value of Ω for the state ψ_0 is zero unless the function $\Omega\psi_0$, when expanded as a series of eigenfunctions of the operator $\mathbf{J}^2$, contains a term with quantum number J_0. If Ω is the operator for a 2^l electric or magnetic multipole moment, show also that its expectation value is zero unless $J_0 \geq \frac{1}{2}l$ (compare with the discussion at the end of Sec. 25).

CHAPTER XII

RELATIVISTIC WAVE EQUATIONS

In this chapter we extend the nonrelativistic Schrödinger wave equation to the description of the motion of a particle that has a speed approaching that of light. This extension can be made in many ways, each of which is consistent with the Lorentz transformation equations of the special theory of relativity.[1] A characteristic feature of relativistic wave equations is that the spin of the particle is built into the theory from the beginning, and cannot be added afterward as Pauli added the electron spin to Schrödinger's nonrelativistic equation. This feature provides a useful gauge of the applicability of a particular equation to the description of a particular kind of particle. Two relativistic equations are considered here: the spin 0 equation due to Schrödinger that has since been found to describe a π meson, and the spin $\frac{1}{2}$ equation due to Dirac that describes an electron. In discussing these equations, we devote our attention mainly to the deductions that can be made from them and do not attempt to establish their Lorentz invariance. We shall, therefore, continue to use three-dimensional vector notation rather than the more elegant four-dimensional notation of special relativity theory. The invariance of an equation can usually be inferred quite convincingly from its symmetry between the space coordinates and the time.

42. SCHRÖDINGER'S RELATIVISTIC EQUATION

At the time when Schrödinger developed his nonrelativisitic wave equation, he also proposed an extension of it that meets the requirements of special relativity.[2] This equation follows quite naturally from the transition in classical dynamics from the nonrelativistic relation

$$E = \frac{\mathbf{p}^2}{2m} \tag{42.1}$$

between the energy and momentum of a free particle, to the corresponding relativistic relation

$$E^2 = c^2\mathbf{p}^2 + m^2c^4 \tag{42.2}$$

---

[1] For a review of special relativity, see, for example, P. G. Bergmann, "Introduction to the Theory of Relativity," Part I (Prentice-Hall, New York, 1946), or R. C. Tolman, "Relativity, Thermodynamics and Cosmology," Chaps. II, III, and IV (Oxford, New York, 1934).

[2] E. Schrödinger, *Ann. d. Physik*, **81**, 109 (1926), Sec. 6.

where now E includes the rest-mass energy mc^2. We proceed by adopting the substitutions (6.13) for E and $\mathbf{p}$

$$E \to i\hbar \frac{\partial}{\partial t}, \qquad \mathbf{p} \to -i\hbar\,\mathbf{grad} \qquad (42.3)$$

Free Particle. A relativistic wave equation for a free particle can be obtained by substituting (42.3) into (42.2) and operating on a wave function $\psi(\mathbf{r},t)$, just as the substitution of (42.3) into (42.1) yields Eq. (6.11). The result is

$$-\hbar^2 \frac{\partial^2 \psi}{\partial t^2} = -\hbar^2 c^2 \nabla^2 \psi + m^2 c^4 \psi \qquad (42.4)$$

Equation (42.4) has plane wave solutions of the form

$$\exp i(\mathbf{k} \cdot \mathbf{r} - \omega t) \qquad (42.5)$$

which are eigenfunctions of the operators E and $\mathbf{p}$ in (42.3) with eigenvalues $\hbar\omega$ and $\hbar\mathbf{k}$, respectively. It is apparent that (42.5) satisfies Eq. (42.4) if

$$\hbar\omega = \pm (\hbar^2 c^2 \mathbf{k}^2 + m^2 c^4)^{\frac{1}{2}} \qquad (42.6)$$

The positive and negative square roots in (42.6) correspond to an ambiguity in the sign of the energy that also results from the classical expression (42.2). We take only the positive square root for the present, and return to the negative-energy solutions at the end of Sec. 44.

Expressions for the charge and current densities can be found in analogy with those obtained in Sec. 7. The conservation equation

$$\frac{\partial}{\partial t} P(\mathbf{r},t) + \operatorname{div} \mathbf{S}(\mathbf{r},t) = 0 \qquad (42.7)$$

turns out to be invariant with respect to Lorentz transformations. We multiply (42.4) on the left by $\bar{\psi}$, the complex conjugate equation on the left by ψ, and subtract one from the other. Then (42.7) results, if we define real quantities

$$P(\mathbf{r},t) = \frac{i\hbar}{2mc^2} \left(\bar{\psi} \frac{\partial \psi}{\partial t} - \psi \frac{\partial \bar{\psi}}{\partial t} \right)$$
$$\mathbf{S}(\mathbf{r},t) = \frac{\hbar}{2im} (\bar{\psi}\,\mathbf{grad}\,\psi - \psi\,\mathbf{grad}\,\bar{\psi}) \qquad (42.8)$$

This expression for $\mathbf{S}$ is identical with the nonrelativistic form (7.3), and the expression for P can be shown to reduce to (7.1) in the nonrelativistic limit (see Prob. 2). It should be noted that P given by (42.8) is not necessarily positive, and hence cannot be interpreted as a position probability density. It can, however, be multiplied by e and interpreted as an electric charge density, since charge density can have either sign so long as it is real.

Electromagnetic Potentials. We can include the electromagnetic potentials $\mathbf{A}(\mathbf{r},t)$, $\phi(\mathbf{r},t)$ in the wave equation by making use of the fact that ϕ and $(1/c)\mathbf{A}$ have the same Lorentz-transformation properties as E and $\mathbf{p}$. In analogy with the nonrelativistic expression (23.14), we replace (42.2) by

$$(E - e\phi)^2 = (c\mathbf{p} - e\mathbf{A})^2 + m^2c^4 \tag{42.9}$$

for a particle of charge e. The substitutions (42.3) then give

$$\left(-\hbar^2 \frac{\partial^2}{\partial t^2} - 2ie\hbar\phi \frac{\partial}{\partial t} - ie\hbar \frac{\partial \phi}{\partial t} + e^2\phi^2\right)\psi$$
$$= [-\hbar^2c^2\nabla^2 + 2ie\hbar c\mathbf{A} \cdot \mathrm{grad} + ie\hbar c(\mathrm{div}\ \mathbf{A}) + e^2\mathbf{A}^2 + m^2c^4]\psi \tag{42.10}$$

We can now find the connection between Eq. (42.10) and the similar Eq. (23.24) in the nonrelativistic limit. We make the substitution

$$\psi(\mathbf{r},t) = \psi'(\mathbf{r},t)e^{-\frac{imc^2t}{\hbar}} \tag{42.11}$$

in (42.10), and assume that operation with $i\hbar(\partial/\partial t)$ on ψ' gives a result that is of the same order as $e\phi\psi'$ and small in comparison with $mc^2\psi'$. This is equivalent to subtracting out the rest energy and assuming that the remaining energies are small in comparison with it. Differentiation of (42.11) gives

$$\frac{\partial \psi}{\partial t} = \left(\frac{\partial \psi'}{\partial t} - \frac{imc^2}{\hbar}\psi'\right)e^{-\frac{imc^2t}{\hbar}}$$
$$\frac{\partial^2 \psi}{\partial t^2} = \left(\frac{\partial^2 \psi'}{\partial t^2} - \frac{2imc^2}{\hbar}\frac{\partial \psi'}{\partial t} - \frac{m^2c^4}{\hbar^2}\psi'\right)e^{-\frac{imc^2t}{\hbar}}$$

The first term in each of these derivatives can be neglected, as can the last two terms on the left side of (42.10), which then becomes

$$\left(2i\hbar mc^2 \frac{\partial \psi'}{\partial t} + m^2c^4\psi' - 2emc^2\phi\psi'\right)e^{-\frac{imc^2t}{\hbar}}$$

With these approximations, Eq. (42.10) becomes the same as (23.24) if ψ' is replaced by ψ.

There is no way in which the Pauli spin matrices (33.3) can be included in Eq. (42.10) without destroying the invariance of the theory. This is not surprising, since the spin matrices transform like the components of a three-dimensional, rather than a four-dimensional, vector, and since ψ has one component rather than two components like the spin functions (33.4). Thus the Schrödinger relativistic equation represents a particle that has no spin.

The structure of Eq. (42.9) shows that a "potential-energy" term cannot be added arbitrarily to (42.10), as the term $V\psi$ was added to (23.24) to give Eq. (35.1). The Lorentz-transformation properties of any such term must be investigated first. If it transforms like part of a four-dimensional vector, the rest of this vector must be included in some such manner as ϕ and $(1/c)\mathbf{A}$ were included in (42.9). If it is an invariant with respect to Lorentz transformations, it can be included as part of the rest energy mc^2.

Separation of the Equation. The wave equation (42.10) can be separated with respect to $\mathbf{r}$ and t if the potentials $\mathbf{A},\phi$ are independent of the time. We then put

$$\psi(\mathbf{r},t) = u(\mathbf{r})e^{-\frac{iEt}{\hbar}}$$

and substitute into (42.10) to obtain

$$(E - e\phi)^2 u$$
$$= [-\hbar^2 c^2 \nabla^2 + 2ie\hbar c\mathbf{A} \cdot \mathbf{grad} + ie\hbar c(\mathrm{div}\ \mathbf{A}) + e^2\mathbf{A}^2 + m^2 c^4]u \quad (42.12)$$

We now specialize to the case in which $\mathbf{A} = 0$ and $\phi(\mathbf{r})$ is spherically symmetric. Equation (42.12) then becomes

$$(-\hbar^2 c^2 \nabla^2 + m^2 c^4)u(\mathbf{r}) = [E - e\phi(r)]^2 u(\mathbf{r}) \quad (42.13)$$

which can be separated in spherical coordinates (see Sec. 14) to give

$$u(r,\theta,\phi) = R(r)Y_{lm}(\theta,\phi)$$
$$\left[-\frac{1}{r^2}\frac{d}{dr}\left(r^2\frac{d}{dr}\right) + \frac{l(l+1)}{r^2}\right]R = \left[\frac{(E - e\phi)^2 - m^2 c^4}{\hbar^2 c^2}\right]R, \quad (42.14)$$
$$l = 0,1,2, \ldots$$

This reduces to the nonrelativistic radial equation if we put $E = mc^2 + E'$, and assume that E' and $e\phi$ can be neglected in comparison with mc^2. Then the bracket on the right side of (42.14) becomes $(2m/\hbar^2)\ (E' - e\phi)$, as it should.

Energy Levels in a Coulomb Field. An exact solution of (42.14) can easily be obtained if we put $e\phi = -Ze^2/r$, by making use of the results of Sec. 16. This situation would represent a hydrogen atom were it not for the fact that the particle described by (42.10) has no spin, and so cannot be an electron.

If we put $\rho = \alpha r$, Eq. (42.14) can be written as

$$\frac{1}{\rho^2}\frac{d}{d\rho}\left(\rho^2\frac{dR}{d\rho}\right) + \left(\frac{\lambda}{\rho} - \frac{1}{4} - \frac{l(l+1) - \gamma^2}{\rho^2}\right)R = 0$$
$$\gamma \equiv \frac{Ze^2}{\hbar c}, \qquad \alpha^2 \equiv \frac{4(m^2 c^4 - E^2)}{\hbar^2 c^2}, \qquad \lambda \equiv \frac{2E\gamma}{\hbar c\alpha} \quad (42.15)$$

This has precisely the form of Eq. (16.7) except that $l(l + 1)$ has been replaced by $l(l + 1) - \gamma^2$. The parameter λ is determined by the boundary condition on R when $\rho = \infty$, and E is expressed in terms of λ by eliminating α from the last two of Eqs. (42.15):

$$E = mc^2 \left(1 + \frac{\gamma^2}{\lambda^2}\right)^{-\frac{1}{2}} \qquad (42.16)$$

A study of the way in which Eq. (16.7) was solved shows that solutions of (42.15) that are finite at $\rho = 0$ and ∞ exist only if

$$\lambda = n' + s + 1 \qquad (42.17)$$

where n' is zero or a positive integer and s is the nonnegative solution of the equation

$$s(s + 1) = l(l + 1) - \gamma^2 \qquad (42.18)$$

Equation (42.18) has the two solutions

$$s = -\tfrac{1}{2} \pm \tfrac{1}{2}[(2l + 1)^2 - 4\gamma^2]^{\frac{1}{2}} \qquad (42.19)$$

of which one is positive and the other negative for $l > 0$. For $l = 0$, both the s values given by (42.19) are negative; however, γ is quite small (very nearly equal to $Z/137$ if e is the electronic charge), so that use of the upper sign in (42.19) gives a value of s that is close to zero for physically interesting values of Z. Moreover, even though $R(r)$ behaves like r^s near $r = 0$, and so is singular at the origin, the integral of $P(\mathbf{r})$ given by (42.8) converges there so that the total electric charge is finite. We thus use the upper sign in (42.19) for all l, and obtain from (42.17)

$$\lambda = n' + \tfrac{1}{2} + [(l + \tfrac{1}{2})^2 - \gamma^2]^{\frac{1}{2}} \qquad (42.20)$$

Equations (42.16) and (42.20) give a fine structure to the nonrelativistic energy levels (16.15). This can be seen by expanding the expression for the energy levels in powers of γ^2. The result to terms of order γ^4 is

$$E = mc^2 \left[1 - \frac{\gamma^2}{2n^2} - \frac{\gamma^4}{2n^4}\left(\frac{n}{l + \frac{1}{2}} - \frac{3}{4}\right)\right] \qquad (42.21)$$

where $n = n' + l + 1$ is the total quantum number of Eq. (16.14), and can take on positive integer values. The first term on the right side of (42.21) is the rest energy. The second term is

$$-\frac{mc^2\gamma^2}{2n^2} = -\frac{mZ^2e^4}{2\hbar^2n^2},$$

and agrees with (16.15). The third term is the fine-structure energy, which removes the degeneracy between states of the same n and different *l.* The total spread of the fine-structure levels for a given n is easily seen from (42.21) to be

$$\frac{mc^2\gamma^4}{n^3} \frac{n-1}{n-\frac{1}{2}} \tag{42.22}$$

This is much larger than is observed experimentally in the spectrum of hydrogen.

43. DIRAC'S RELATIVISTIC EQUATION

Dirac[1] approached the problem of finding a relativistic wave equation by starting from the Hamiltonian form (23.1)

$$i\hbar \frac{\partial}{\partial t} \psi(\mathbf{r},t) = H\psi(\mathbf{r},t) \tag{43.1}$$

The classical relativistic Hamiltonian for a free particle is the positive square root of the right side of Eq. (42.2). However, if this is substituted into (43.1) and $\mathbf{p}$ is replaced by $-i\hbar\,\mathbf{grad}$, the resulting wave equation is unsymmetrical with respect to space and time derivatives, and hence not relativistic. Dirac therefore modified the Hamiltonian in such a way as to make it linear in the space derivatives.

Free-particle Equation. The simplest Hamiltonian that is linear in the momentum and mass terms is

$$H = -c\boldsymbol{\alpha} \cdot \mathbf{p} - \beta mc^2 \tag{43.2}$$

Substitution into (43.1) leads to the wave equation

$$(E + c\boldsymbol{\alpha} \cdot \mathbf{p} + \beta mc^2)\psi = 0$$

or

$$\left(i\hbar \frac{\partial}{\partial t} - i\hbar c\,\boldsymbol{\alpha} \cdot \mathbf{grad} + \beta mc^2\right)\psi = 0 \tag{43.3}$$

We now consider the four quantities α_x, α_y, α_z, and β. If (43.3) is to describe a free particle, there can be no terms in the Hamiltonian that depend on the space coordinates or the time, since such terms would have the properties of space-time-dependent energies and give rise to forces. Also, the space and time derivatives are to appear only in $\mathbf{p}$ and E, and not in $\boldsymbol{\alpha}$ and β, since (43.3) is to be linear in all these derivatives. We thus conclude that $\boldsymbol{\alpha}$ and β are independent of $\mathbf{r}$, t, $\mathbf{p}$, and E, and hence commute with all of them. This does not necessarily mean that $\boldsymbol{\alpha}$ and β are numbers, since they need not commute with each other.

---

[1] P. A. M. Dirac, *Proc. Roy. Soc.*, **A117**, 610 (1928); "The Principles of Quantum Mechanics," 3d ed., Chap. XI (Oxford, New York, 1947).

We can learn more about $\boldsymbol{\alpha}$ and β by requiring that any solution ψ of (43.3) also be a solution of Schrödinger's relativistic equation (42.4) (the converse need not be true). This is a reasonable requirement since in the absence of external fields, the wave-packet solutions of (43.3) whose motions resemble those of classical particles must have the classical relation (42.2) between energy, momentum, and mass (see Prob. 1). We therefore multiply Eq. (43.3) on the left by $(E - c\boldsymbol{\alpha} \cdot \mathbf{p} - \beta mc^2)$ to obtain

$$\{E^2 - c^2[\alpha_x^2 p_x^2 + \alpha_y^2 p_y^2 + \alpha_z^2 p_z^2 + (\alpha_x\alpha_y + \alpha_y\alpha_x)p_xp_y$$
$$+ (\alpha_y\alpha_z + \alpha_z\alpha_y)p_yp_z + (\alpha_z\alpha_x + \alpha_x\alpha_z)p_zp_x] - m^2c^4\beta^2$$
$$-mc^3[(\alpha_x\beta + \beta\alpha_x)p_x + (\alpha_y\beta + \beta\alpha_y)p_y + (\alpha_z\beta + \beta\alpha_z)p_z]\}\psi = 0 \quad (43.4)$$

where the substitutions (42.3) for E and $\mathbf{p}$ in terms of differential operators are implied. Equation (43.4) agrees with (42.4) if $\boldsymbol{\alpha},\beta$ satisfy the relations

$$\alpha_x^2 = \alpha_y^2 = \alpha_z^2 = \beta^2 = 1$$
$$\alpha_x\alpha_y + \alpha_y\alpha_x = \alpha_y\alpha_z + \alpha_z\alpha_y = \alpha_z\alpha_x + \alpha_x\alpha_z = 0 \quad (43.5)$$
$$\alpha_x\beta + \beta\alpha_x = \alpha_y\beta + \beta\alpha_y = \alpha_z\beta + \beta\alpha_z = 0$$

The four quantities are said to *anticommute* in pairs, and their squares are unity.

Since $\boldsymbol{\alpha}, \beta$ anticommute rather than commute with each other, they cannot be numbers. We have seen in Chap. VI that quantities of this type can be expressed in terms of matrices, and it is convenient for calculation to have a matrix representation of them. We note first that since the H given by (43.2) is Hermitian, each of the four matrices $\boldsymbol{\alpha},\beta$ must be Hermitian, and hence square. Our problem is to find an explicit representation in which, say, one of these matrices is diagonal (then the others cannot be diagonal since they do not commute with this one). In the interests of simplicity, we shall require the representation to have as low a rank as possible.

Matrices for $\boldsymbol{\alpha}$ and β. The squares of all four matrices are unity, so that their eigenvalues are $+1$ and -1. We arbitrarily choose β as the matrix that is to be diagonal, and rearrange its rows and columns so that all the $+1$ eigenvalues are grouped together in a matrix of rank n, and all the -1 eigenvalues are grouped in a matrix of rank m. Since β anticommutes with $\boldsymbol{\alpha}$, it cannot be a constant matrix, and so both n and m must be greater than zero. The β matrix can be represented schematically as

$$\beta = \begin{pmatrix} 1 & 0 \\ 0 & -1 \end{pmatrix} \quad (43.6)$$

which is an abbreviation for

$$
\begin{pmatrix}
1 & 0 & \cdot & \cdot & 0 & 0 & \cdot & \cdot \\
0 & 1 & \cdot & \cdot & 0 & 0 & \cdot & \cdot \\
\cdot & \cdot & \cdot & \cdot & \cdot & \cdot & \cdot & \cdot \\
\cdot & \cdot & \cdot & \cdot & \cdot & \cdot & \cdot & \cdot \\
0 & 0 & \cdot & \cdot & -1 & 0 & \cdot & \cdot \\
0 & 0 & \cdot & \cdot & 0 & -1 & \cdot & \cdot \\
\cdot & \cdot & \cdot & \cdot & \cdot & \cdot & \cdot & \cdot \\
\cdot & \cdot & \cdot & \cdot & \cdot & \cdot & \cdot & \cdot
\end{pmatrix}
\tag{43.7}
$$

The dashed lines in (43.7) separate the submatrices 1, 0, 0, and -1 that appear in (43.6).[1] We now consider the matrix equation $\alpha_x \beta + \beta \alpha_x = 0$, the jl element of which is

$$(\alpha_x)_{jl}(\beta_j + \beta_l) = 0$$

Here β_j and β_l are two of the eigenvalues of β, which are arranged in accordance with (43.6) or (43.7). If $\beta_j = \beta_l$, then $(\alpha_x)_{jl} = 0$, whereas if β_j and β_l have opposite signs, $(\alpha_x)_{jl}$ need not be zero. Thus the matrix for α_x can be written in the form

$$
\alpha_x = \begin{pmatrix} 0 & \alpha_{x1} \\ \alpha_{x2} & 0 \end{pmatrix}
\tag{43.8}
$$

where α_{x1} has n rows and m columns, and α_{x2} has m rows and n columns. Since the square of (43.8) is a unit matrix, we see also that

$$\alpha_{x1}\alpha_{x2} = 1, \qquad \alpha_{x2}\alpha_{x1} = 1 \tag{43.9}$$

The unit matrix that appears on the right side of the first of Eqs. (43.9) has n rows and columns, and the unit matrix in the second equation has m rows and columns. It is not difficult to show that no matrices can be found that satisfy (43.9) if n,m equal 1,2 or 2,1. We therefore consider the two possibilities $n = m = 1$ and $n = m = 2$, as giving matrices of minimum rank.[2] It is apparent that α_y and α_z can be written in forms similar to (43.8).

We have already obtained three anticommuting matrices of the form (43.6) or (43.8) with $n = m = 1$. These are the Pauli spin matrices (33.3)

$$
\sigma_x = \begin{pmatrix} 0 & 1 \\ 1 & 0 \end{pmatrix}, \qquad
\sigma_y = \begin{pmatrix} 0 & -i \\ i & 0 \end{pmatrix}, \qquad
\sigma_z = \begin{pmatrix} 1 & 0 \\ 0 & -1 \end{pmatrix}
\tag{43.10}
$$

which satisfy the equations

$$\sigma_x\sigma_y = -\sigma_y\sigma_x = i\sigma_z \tag{43.11}$$

---

[1] The matrices 1, 0 are the same as the unit and null matrices **1**, **O** defined in Sec. 21.

[2] Higher rank matrices correspond to particles with spin greater than $\frac{1}{2}$.

together with the two similar relations obtained by permuting x, y, z. Any matrix with two rows and columns has four elements, and so can be expressed as a linear combination of the four linearly independent matrices $\sigma_x, \sigma_y, \sigma_z$, and 1. Then it is not difficult to show that a fourth matrix that anticommutes with all three of those in (43.10) cannot be found.

We therefore try $n = m = 2$, and for simplicity take $\alpha_{x1} = \alpha_{x2}$, etc. Then Eqs. (43.9) become $\alpha_{x1}^2 = 1$, and the equation $\alpha_x\alpha_y + \alpha_y\alpha_x = 0$ becomes $\alpha_{x1}\alpha_{y1} + \alpha_{y1}\alpha_{x1} = 0$. From these and the similar relations obtained by permuting x,y,z, we see at once that we can identify α_{x1} with σ_x, etc. We thus arrive at an explicit matrix representation for β, α :

$$\beta = \begin{pmatrix} 1 & 0 & 0 & 0 \\ 0 & 1 & 0 & 0 \\ 0 & 0 & -1 & 0 \\ 0 & 0 & 0 & -1 \end{pmatrix}, \quad \alpha_x = \begin{pmatrix} 0 & 0 & 0 & 1 \\ 0 & 0 & 1 & 0 \\ 0 & 1 & 0 & 0 \\ 1 & 0 & 0 & 0 \end{pmatrix}$$

$$\alpha_y = \begin{pmatrix} 0 & 0 & 0 & -i \\ 0 & 0 & i & 0 \\ 0 & -i & 0 & 0 \\ i & 0 & 0 & 0 \end{pmatrix}, \quad \alpha_z = \begin{pmatrix} 0 & 0 & 1 & 0 \\ 0 & 0 & 0 & -1 \\ 1 & 0 & 0 & 0 \\ 0 & -1 & 0 & 0 \end{pmatrix}$$

(43.12)

These matrices are evidently Hermitian; we abbreviate them as

$$\beta = \begin{pmatrix} 1 & 0 \\ 0 & -1 \end{pmatrix}, \quad \alpha = \begin{pmatrix} 0 & \sigma \\ \sigma & 0 \end{pmatrix} \quad (43.13)$$

where each "element" is a matrix with two rows and columns.[1]

Free-particle Solutions. Now that α and β are represented by matrices, Eq. (43.3) has no meaning unless the wave function ψ is itself a matrix with four rows and one column:

$$\psi(\mathbf{r},t) = \begin{pmatrix} \psi_1(\mathbf{r},t) \\ \psi_2(\mathbf{r},t) \\ \psi_3(\mathbf{r},t) \\ \psi_4(\mathbf{r},t) \end{pmatrix} \quad (43.14)$$

Then (43.3) is equivalent to four simultaneous first-order partial differential equations that are linear and homogeneous in the four ψ's.

Plane wave solutions of the form

$$\psi_j(\mathbf{r},t) = u_j \exp i(\mathbf{k} \cdot \mathbf{r} - \omega t), \quad j = 1,2,3,4 \quad (43.15)$$

[1] The relativistic character of the Dirac equation can be made more apparent if (43.3) is multiplied through on the left by β; this enhances the symmetry between space and time derivatives, since the four matrices β, $\beta\alpha$ have similar properties to the four matrices β, α.

can now be found, where the u_j are numbers. These are eigenfunctions of the energy and momentum operators (42.3) with eigenvalues $\hbar\omega$ and $\hbar\mathbf{k}$, respectively. Substitution of (43.15) and (43.12) into (43.3) gives a set of algebraic equations for the u_j, where $E = \hbar\omega$ and $\mathbf{p} = \hbar\mathbf{k}$ are now numbers,

$$
\begin{aligned}
(E + mc^2)u_1 + cp_z u_3 + c(p_x - ip_y)u_4 &= 0 \\
(E + mc^2)u_2 + c(p_x + ip_y)u_3 - cp_z u_4 &= 0 \\
(E - mc^2)u_3 + cp_z u_1 + c(p_x - ip_y)u_2 &= 0 \\
(E - mc^2)u_4 + c(p_x + ip_y)u_1 - cp_z u_2 &= 0
\end{aligned}
\tag{43.16}
$$

These equations are homogeneous in the u_j, and have solutions only if the determinant of the coefficients is zero. This determinant is

$$
(E^2 - m^2c^4 - c^2\mathbf{p}^2)^2,
$$

so that the relation between E and $\mathbf{p}$ is in agreement with (42.2).

Explicit solutions can be obtained for any momentum $\mathbf{p}$ by choosing a sign for the energy, say $E_+ = +(c^2\mathbf{p}^2 + m^2c^4)^{\frac{1}{2}}$. Then there are two linearly independent solutions, which are conveniently written as

$$
u_1 = -\frac{cp_z}{E_+ + mc^2}, \qquad u_2 = -\frac{c(p_x + ip_y)}{E_+ + mc^2}, \qquad u_3 = 1, \qquad u_4 = 0
$$

$$
\tag{43.17}
$$

$$
u_1 = -\frac{c(p_x - ip_y)}{E_+ + mc^2}, \qquad u_2 = \frac{cp_z}{E_+ + mc^2}, \qquad u_3 = 0, \qquad u_4 = 1
$$

Similarly, if we choose the negative square root $E_- = -(c^2\mathbf{p}^2 + m^2c^4)^{\frac{1}{2}}$, we obtain two new solutions, which are conveniently written as

$$
u_1 = 1, \qquad u_2 = 0, \qquad u_3 = \frac{cp_z}{-E_- + mc^2}, \qquad u_4 = \frac{c(p_x + ip_y)}{-E_- + mc^2}
$$

$$
\tag{43.18}
$$

$$
u_1 = 0, \qquad u_2 = 1, \qquad u_3 = \frac{c(p_x - ip_y)}{-E_- + mc^2}, \qquad u_4 = -\frac{cp_z}{-E_- + mc^2}
$$

Each of these four solutions can be normalized, in the sense that $\psi^*\psi = 1$, by multiplying it by the factor $\{1 + [c^2\mathbf{p}^2/(E_+ + mc^2)^2]\}^{-\frac{1}{2}}$; ψ^* is the Hermitian adjoint of ψ, and is a matrix with one row and four columns.

It is apparent that the solutions (43.17) correspond to positive energy, and the solutions (43.18) to negative energy. In the nonrelativistic limit, in which $E_+ = -E_-$ is close to mc^2 and large in comparison with $c|\mathbf{p}|$, u_1 and u_2 are of order v/c times u_3 or u_4 for the positive-energy solutions (v is the speed of the particle); the opposite is true for the negative-energy solutions. The physical distinction between the two solutions for each sign of the energy can be seen by defining three new spin matrices

σ'_x, σ'_y, σ'_z that have four rows and columns

$$\mathbf{\delta}' = \begin{pmatrix} \mathbf{\delta} & 0 \\ 0 & \mathbf{\delta} \end{pmatrix} \qquad (43.19)$$

We shall see at the beginning of Sec. 44 that $\frac{1}{2}\hbar\mathbf{\delta}'$ can be interpreted as the operator that represents spin angular momentum. When the small components of the wave function can be neglected, it is easy to see that ψ is an eigenfunction of σ'_z with eigenvalue $+1$ for the first of each pair of solutions (43.17) and (43.18), and eigenvalue -1 for the second solution of each pair.

Charge and Current Densities. We can obtain a conservation equation by multiplying the second of Eqs. (43.3) on the left by ψ^*, the Hermitian adjoint equation

$$-i\hbar \frac{\partial \psi^*}{\partial t} + i\hbar c(\mathbf{grad}\ \psi^*) \cdot \mathbf{\alpha} + \psi^* \beta mc^2 = 0$$

on the right by ψ, and taking the difference of the two results. We then get Eq. (42.7) if we define the real quantities

$$\begin{aligned} P(\mathbf{r},t) &= \psi^*\psi \\ \mathbf{S}(\mathbf{r},t) &= -c\psi^*\mathbf{\alpha}\psi \end{aligned} \qquad (43.20)$$

The expression for P has the nonrelativistic form (7.1); since it is never negative, it can be interpreted as a position probability density. It can be shown that the expression (43.20) for $\mathbf{S}$ reduces to (7.3) in the nonrelativistic limit (see Prob. 6).

The operator $-c\mathbf{\alpha}$ can be interpreted more directly as a particle velocity by calculating the time derivative of the position vector $\mathbf{r}$ from Eq. (23.2). With the Hamiltonian (43.2) and the commutation relations (23.16), we obtain

$$\frac{dx}{dt} = \frac{1}{i\hbar}(xH - Hx) = -c\alpha_x \qquad (43.21)$$

Thus the eigenvalues of a velocity component are $\pm c$. This result can be made plausible from a physical point of view with the help of the uncertainty relation (3.1). A very precise measurement of instantaneous velocity [which according to (43.21) is not the same as momentum in a relativistic theory] requires the accurate measurement of the position of the particle at two slightly different times. Such accurate position measurements imply that the momentum of the particle is completely unknown, so that all momentum values are about equally probable. Then very large momenta are much more likely to result than small momenta, and these correspond to velocity components close to the speed of light.

Electromagnetic Potentials.   Terms that involve the electromagnetic potentials can be added to Eq. (43.3) in a relativistic way by making the usual replacements $c\mathbf{p} \to c\mathbf{p} - e\mathbf{A}$ and $E \to E - e\phi$, where the particle described by the equation has electric charge e.   We thus obtain

$$[E - e\phi + \boldsymbol{\alpha} \cdot (c\mathbf{p} - e\mathbf{A}) + \beta mc^2]\psi = 0 \qquad (43.22)$$

Here E and $\mathbf{p}$ stand for the operators (42.3).   This equation can be reduced to a form that is similar to (42.10) by multiplying it on the left with $[E - e\phi - \boldsymbol{\alpha} \cdot (c\mathbf{p} - e\mathbf{A}) - \beta mc^2]$.   The result is

$$\{(E - e\phi)^2 - [\boldsymbol{\alpha} \cdot (c\mathbf{p} - e\mathbf{A})]^2 - m^2c^4$$
$$+ (E - e\phi)\boldsymbol{\alpha} \cdot (c\mathbf{p} - e\mathbf{A}) - \boldsymbol{\alpha} \cdot (c\mathbf{p} - e\mathbf{A})(E - e\phi)\}\psi = 0 \quad (43.23)$$

The second operator in (43.23) can be reduced by making use of the following relation:

$$(\boldsymbol{\alpha} \cdot \mathbf{B})(\boldsymbol{\alpha} \cdot \mathbf{C}) = \mathbf{B} \cdot \mathbf{C} + i\boldsymbol{\sigma}' \cdot (\mathbf{B} \times \mathbf{C}) \qquad (43.24)$$

where $\mathbf{B}$ and $\mathbf{C}$ commute with $\boldsymbol{\alpha}$ but not necessarily with each other (see Prob. 7).   We identify both $\mathbf{B}$ and $\mathbf{C}$ with $(c\mathbf{p} - e\mathbf{A})$; we also require the relation

$$(c\mathbf{p} - e\mathbf{A}) \times (c\mathbf{p} - e\mathbf{A}) = -ce(\mathbf{A} \times \mathbf{p} + \mathbf{p} \times \mathbf{A}) = ie\hbar c\,\text{curl } \mathbf{A} = ie\hbar c\mathbf{H}$$

where use has been made of (23.15).   With this substitution, Eq. (43.24) becomes

$$[\boldsymbol{\alpha} \cdot (c\mathbf{p} - e\mathbf{A})]^2 = (c\mathbf{p} - e\mathbf{A})^2 - e\hbar c\boldsymbol{\sigma}' \cdot \mathbf{H}$$

The last two operators in (43.23) can be rewritten as

$$-e\boldsymbol{\alpha} \cdot (E\mathbf{A} - \mathbf{A}E) - ce\boldsymbol{\alpha} \cdot (\phi\mathbf{p} - \mathbf{p}\phi)$$
$$= -ie\hbar\boldsymbol{\alpha} \cdot \frac{\partial A}{\partial t} - ie\hbar c\boldsymbol{\alpha} \cdot \text{grad } \phi = ie\hbar c\boldsymbol{\alpha} \cdot \mathbf{E}$$

where use has again been made of (23.15).   Equation (43.23) then becomes

$$[(E - e\phi)^2 - (c\mathbf{p} - e\mathbf{A})^2 - m^2c^4 + e\hbar c\boldsymbol{\sigma}' \cdot \mathbf{H} + ie\hbar c\boldsymbol{\alpha} \cdot \mathbf{E}]\psi = 0 \quad (43.25)$$

The first three terms are precisely the same as (42.10).   The physical significance of the last two terms will now be shown from consideration of the nonrelativistic limit of the entire equation.

We could proceed just as we did in obtaining the nonrelativistic limit of Eq. (42.10).   A slightly different approach consists in putting

$$E = E' + mc^2 \qquad (43.26)$$

and assuming that E' and $e\phi$ are small in comparison with mc^2; this is equivalent to the substitution (42.11) and the subsequent approximations. We can then make the replacement

$$(E - e\phi)^2 - m^2 c^4 \cong 2mc^2(E' - e\phi)$$

in (43.25) to obtain

$$E'\psi = \left[\frac{1}{2m} \left(\mathbf{p} - \frac{e}{c} \mathbf{A} \right)^2 + e\phi - \frac{e\hbar}{2mc} \mathbf{\sigma}' \cdot \mathbf{H} - \frac{ie\hbar}{2mc} \mathbf{\alpha} \cdot \mathbf{E} \right] \psi \quad (43.27)$$

Now E' is equivalent to the time derivative operator $i\hbar(\partial/\partial t)$ if a factor $e^{-\frac{imc^2 t}{\hbar}}$ is taken out of ψ. Thus (43.27) is the nonrelativistic Schrödinger equation (23.24), with two additional terms that involve $\mathbf{H}$ and $\mathbf{E}$ directly.

The $\mathbf{H}$ term has the form associated with the energy of a magnetic dipole of moment $(e\hbar/2mc)\mathbf{\sigma}'$. Now it was shown in (43.18), for a free particle, that the third and fourth components of the wave function are large in comparison with the first and second components for the positive-energy solutions in the nonrelativistic limit. This can also be shown without difficulty, when the particle is not free, from the structure of the general equation (43.22). Equation (43.19) shows that $\mathbf{\sigma}'$ operating on the four-component wave function is the same as $\mathbf{\sigma}$ operating on the large components alone. Thus the two large components of (43.27) with the $\mathbf{H}$ term give just the nonrelativistic equation with the Pauli spin matrices and the correct coefficient for the magnetic moment of an electron [see Eq. (39.10)].

We now show that in practical cases, the $\mathbf{E}$ term in (43.27) is of order $(v/c)^2$ times the $e\phi$ term, and so is to be neglected in the nonrelativistic limit.[1] We note first that the expectation value of $\mathbf{\alpha}$ is of order $(v/c)\int \psi^* \psi d\tau$, since (43.13) shows that $\mathbf{\alpha}$ mixes the large and small components (we also saw earlier that $-c\mathbf{\alpha}$ is the velocity operator). For an electron that is part of a system of linear dimensions a, $e\phi$ is of order eEa, and $\hbar/a \sim p \sim mv$. Thus the ratio of the $\mathbf{E}$ to the $e\phi$ terms in (43.27) is of order

$$\frac{e\hbar v E}{mc^2} \frac{1}{eEa} \sim \frac{v^2}{c^2}$$

In contrast with this, we have already seen in Eqs. (39.9) and (39.10) that the $\mathbf{H}$ term in (43.27) is of the same order as the other magnetic terms that are linear in $\mathbf{A}$. While the $\mathbf{E}$ term must be omitted from (43.27) for a consistent nonrelativistic approximation, it cannot be dropped from the relativistic equation (43.25), where it is required to preserve Lorentz invariance.

[1] For a spherically symmetric electrostatic potential it leads to the spin-orbit energy, which is actually of order $(v/c)^2 e\phi$; see Eq. (44.8).

44. DIRAC'S EQUATION FOR A CENTRAL FIELD

In the last section, the existence of the magnetic moment of an electron was demonstrated explicitly by showing that the expected extra magnetic energy appears in the nonrelativistic approximation. The electron spin carries no energy in itself, and so can be observed only through its coupling with the orbital motion of the electron. In the first part of this section, we make this coupling apparent in two ways: through conservation of total angular momentum, and through the spin-orbit energy that was introduced in Sec. 38. In both cases we work with such potentials $\mathbf{A}, \phi$ that there is no transfer of angular momentum to the electron; this implies that we have a central field ($\mathbf{A} = 0$ and ϕ spherically symmetric). In the latter part of this section, we separate the Dirac equation for a general central field, and find the energy levels of the hydrogen atom.

Spin Angular Momentum. With $\mathbf{A}(\mathbf{r},t) = 0$ and $\phi(\mathbf{r},t) = \phi(r)$, Eq. (43.22) can be written as

$$i\hbar \frac{\partial \psi}{\partial t} = H\psi$$
$$H = -c\boldsymbol{\alpha} \cdot \mathbf{p} - \beta mc^2 + V \tag{44.1}$$

where $V = e\phi$. We might expect that the orbital angular momentum $\mathbf{L} = \mathbf{r} \times \mathbf{p}$ is a constant of the motion in such a central field. In order to investigate this point, we calculate the time rate of change of $\mathbf{L}$ with the help of Eqs. (23.2) and (23.16):

$$\begin{aligned} i\hbar \frac{dL_x}{dt} &= L_x H - H L_x \\ &= -c\boldsymbol{\alpha} \cdot [(yp_z - zp_y)\mathbf{p} - \mathbf{p}(yp_z - zp_y)] \\ &= i\hbar c(\alpha_z p_y - \alpha_y p_z) \end{aligned} \tag{44.2}$$

since $\mathbf{L}$ commutes with any spherically symmetric function such as $V(r)$. It is apparent that $\mathbf{L}$ does not commute with H, and hence is not a constant of the motion. However, we expect on physical grounds that it is possible to define a total angular momentum that is constant in a central field of force. This means that we must find another operator such that the commutator of its x component with H is the negative of the right side of 44.2); the sum of this operator and $\mathbf{L}$ is then a constant of the motion and can be interpreted as the total angular momentum.

It is not difficult to see that the desired operator is a multiple of the $\boldsymbol{\sigma}'$ defined in (43.19). From (43.11) and (43.13), we find that σ'_x commutes with α_x and β, although not with the other components of $\boldsymbol{\alpha}$:

$$\sigma'_x \alpha_y - \alpha_y \sigma'_x = \begin{pmatrix} \sigma_x & 0 \\ 0 & \sigma_x \end{pmatrix} \begin{pmatrix} 0 & \sigma_y \\ \sigma_y & 0 \end{pmatrix} - \begin{pmatrix} 0 & \sigma_y \\ \sigma_y & 0 \end{pmatrix} \begin{pmatrix} \sigma_x & 0 \\ 0 & \sigma_x \end{pmatrix}$$

$$= \begin{pmatrix} 0 & i\sigma_z \\ i\sigma_z & 0 \end{pmatrix} - \begin{pmatrix} 0 & -i\sigma_z \\ -i\sigma_z & 0 \end{pmatrix} = 2i\alpha_z$$

The time rate of change of σ' can now be obtained:

$$i\hbar \frac{d\sigma'_x}{dt} = \sigma'_x H - H\sigma'_x = -2ic(\alpha_z p_y - \alpha_y p_z) \tag{44.3}$$

It is apparent from (44.2) and (44.3) that the quantity $L + \frac{1}{2}\hbar\sigma'$ commutes with H and can therefore be taken to be the total angular momentum. We refer to the operator

$$\mathbf{S} = \tfrac{1}{2}\hbar\sigma' \tag{44.4}$$

as the spin angular momentum of the electron.

Approximate Reduction; Spin-orbit Energy. We now wish to show that the spin-orbit energy (38.13) is a consequence of the Dirac equation. This term can be shown to be of order $(v/c)^2$ times the potential energy:

$$\frac{1}{V} \frac{1}{2m^2c^2} \frac{1}{r} \frac{dV}{dr} \, (\mathbf{L} \cdot \mathbf{S}) \sim \frac{1}{V} \frac{1}{m^2c^2} \frac{V}{a^2} \, pa\hbar \sim \frac{v^2}{c^2}$$

where a represents the linear dimensions of the system, and

$$\frac{\hbar}{a} \sim p \sim mv.$$

Thus the approximations that led to (43.27) are not adequate for the present purpose.

In order to obtain a consistent approximation that is expressed in terms of the more familiar two-component wave functions, we replace ψ in (44.1) by ψ_1 and ψ_2, which now represent respectively the first two and the last two components of ψ. We assume that ψ_1, ψ_2 together constitute a nonrelativistic energy eigenfunction, which means that

$$E = E' + mc^2$$

is regarded as a number rather than an operator; E' and V are assumed to be small in comparison with mc^2. The wave equation then becomes

$$(E' + 2mc^2 - V)\psi_1 + c\sigma \cdot \mathbf{p}\psi_2 = 0$$
$$(E' - V)\psi_2 + c\sigma \cdot \mathbf{p}\psi_1 = 0 \tag{44.5}$$

where $\mathbf{p}$ is still an operator. It is apparent from the first of these equations that ψ_1 is of order v/c times ψ_2, so we eliminate it to obtain an equation in terms of ψ_2 alone. The substitution

$$\psi_1 = -(E' + 2mc^2 - V)^{-1}c\sigma \cdot \mathbf{p}\psi_2$$

in the second of Eqs. (44.5) gives

$$E'\psi_2 = \frac{1}{2m}\,(\mathbf{\sigma} \cdot \mathbf{p})\left(1 + \frac{E' - V}{2mc^2}\right)^{-1}(\mathbf{\sigma} \cdot \mathbf{p})\psi_2 + V\psi_2 \qquad (44.6)$$

Thus far, no approximations have been made.

The desired approximation is obtained by keeping the lowest terms in an expansion in powers of $(E' - V)/2mc^2$. The following relations are easily established:

$$\left(1 + \frac{E' - V}{2mc^2}\right)^{-1} \cong 1 - \frac{E' - V}{2mc^2}$$
$$\mathbf{p}V = V\mathbf{p} - i\hbar\,\text{grad}\,V$$
$$(\mathbf{\sigma} \cdot \text{grad}\,V)(\mathbf{\sigma} \cdot \mathbf{p}) = (\text{grad}\,V) \cdot \mathbf{p} + i\mathbf{\sigma} \cdot [(\text{grad}\,V) \times \mathbf{p}]$$

With the help of these, (44.6) becomes

$$E'\psi_2 = \left[\left(1 - \frac{E' - V}{2mc^2}\right)\frac{\mathbf{p}^2}{2m} + V\right]\psi_2$$
$$- \frac{\hbar^2}{4m^2c^2}(\text{grad}\,V) \cdot (\text{grad}\,\psi_2) + \frac{\hbar^2}{4m^2c^2}\,\mathbf{\sigma} \cdot [(\text{grad}\,V) \times \mathbf{p}\psi_2] \qquad (44.7)$$

Further simplifications can be made if V is spherically symmetric. We use the relations

$$(\text{grad}\,V) \cdot \text{grad} = \frac{dV}{dr}\frac{\partial}{\partial r}$$
$$\text{grad}\,V = \frac{1}{r}\frac{dV}{dr}\,\mathbf{r}$$

and note that $E' - V$ is approximately equal to $\mathbf{p}^2/2m$, the accuracy being sufficient to replace the second-order term $(E' - V)\mathbf{p}^2$ in (44.7) by $\mathbf{p}^4/2m$. We can then rewrite (44.7) as

$$E'\psi_2 = \left[\frac{\mathbf{p}^2}{2m} - \frac{\mathbf{p}^4}{8m^3c^2} + V - \frac{\hbar^2}{4m^2c^2}\frac{dV}{dr}\frac{\partial}{\partial r} + \frac{1}{2m^2c^2}\frac{1}{r}\frac{dV}{dr}\mathbf{S} \cdot \mathbf{L}\right]\psi_2 \qquad (44.8)$$

where now $\mathbf{S} = \frac{1}{2}\hbar\mathbf{\sigma}$ and $\mathbf{L} = \mathbf{r} \times \mathbf{p}$.

The first and third terms on the right side of (44.8) give the nonrelativistic Schrödinger equation. The second term has the form of the classical relativistic mass correction, which can be obtained by expanding the square root of (42.2):

$$E' = E - mc^2 = (c^2\mathbf{p}^2 + m^2c^4)^{\frac{1}{2}} - mc^2 \cong \frac{\mathbf{p}^2}{2m} - \frac{\mathbf{p}^4}{8m^3c^2}$$

The last term is the spin-orbit energy (38.14), which is now seen to appear as an automatic consequence of the Dirac equation. The fourth term is a similar relativistic correction to the potential energy, which does not have a classical analogue. Since it does not involve the angular momenta, it is much more difficult to demonstrate experimentally than the spin-orbit energy.[1]

Separation of the Equation. The Dirac equation for a central field can be separated without approximation in spherical coordinates. The procedure is more complicated than for either of the Schrödinger equations because of the interdependence of orbital and spin angular momenta. We start by defining radial momentum and velocity operators

$$p_r = r^{-1}(\mathbf{r} \cdot \mathbf{p} - i\hbar), \qquad \alpha_r = r^{-1}(\boldsymbol{\alpha} \cdot \mathbf{r}) \tag{44.9}$$

both of which can be shown to be Hermitian. We also define an operator k that will shortly be seen to be related to the total angular momentum:

$$\hbar k = \beta(\boldsymbol{\sigma}' \cdot \mathbf{L} + \hbar) \tag{44.10}$$

where $\mathbf{L} = \mathbf{r} \times \mathbf{p}$. It can be shown by direct substitution, with the help of (43.24), that

$$\alpha_r p_r + i\hbar r^{-1}\alpha_r \beta k = \boldsymbol{\alpha} \cdot \mathbf{p}$$

The Hamiltonian (44.1) then becomes

$$H = -c\alpha_r p_r - \frac{i\hbar c}{r} \alpha_r \beta k - \beta mc^2 + V \tag{44.11}$$

The following relations can be established with the help of the definitions (44.9) and (44.10) and the relations of Sec. 43:

$$\alpha_r k - k\alpha_r = 0, \qquad \beta k - k\beta = 0, \qquad p_r k - kp_r = 0$$

These show that k commutes with the Hamiltonian (44.11), and so is a constant of the motion. The eigenvalues of k can be inferred by squaring (44.10).

$$\hbar^2 k^2 = (\boldsymbol{\sigma}' \cdot \mathbf{L})^2 + 2\hbar(\boldsymbol{\sigma}' \cdot \mathbf{L}) + \hbar^2 = (\mathbf{L} + \tfrac{1}{2}\hbar\boldsymbol{\sigma}')^2 + \tfrac{1}{4}\hbar^2 \tag{44.12}$$

The quantity $(\mathbf{L} + \tfrac{1}{2}\hbar\boldsymbol{\sigma}')^2$ is the square of the total angular momentum, and has eigenvalues $j(j + 1)\hbar^2$, where j is half a positive odd integer. Thus k^2 has eigenvalues $(j + \tfrac{1}{2})^2$, so that k can be $\pm 1, \pm 2, \ldots$.

We now choose a representation in which H and k are diagonal and represented by the numbers E and k, respectively. α_r and β can then be represented by any Hermitian matrices that satisfy the relations

$$\alpha_r^2 = \beta^2 = 1, \qquad \alpha_r \beta + \beta \alpha_r = 0$$

---

[1] For further discussion of this term, see E. U. Condon and G. H. Shortley, "The Theory of Atomic Spectra," p. 130 (Cambridge, London, 1935).

which are not difficult to verify.   Such matrices can have two rows and columns; for example, we can put

$$\beta = \begin{pmatrix} 1 & 0 \\ 0 & -1 \end{pmatrix}, \qquad \alpha_r = \begin{pmatrix} 0 & -i \\ i & 0 \end{pmatrix} \tag{44.13}$$

Now the angular and spin parts of the wave function are fixed by the requirement that ψ be an eigenfunction of the k operator (44.10).   For such purposes as the computation of energy levels, we need be concerned only with the radial part; because of the structure of (44.13), this has two components, which we write

$$\begin{pmatrix} r^{-1}F(r) \\ r^{-1}G(r) \end{pmatrix} \tag{44.14}$$

Substitution of (44.13) and (44.14) into the wave equation with the Hamiltonian (44.11) gives us the radial equations for an electron moving in a central field.   We make use of the relation

$$p_r = -i\hbar \left(\frac{\partial}{\partial r} + \frac{1}{r} \right)$$

to obtain

$$(E + mc^2 - V)F - \hbar c \frac{dG}{dr} - \frac{\hbar ck}{r} G = 0$$
$$(E - mc^2 - V)G + \hbar c \frac{dF}{dr} - \frac{\hbar ck}{r} F = 0 \tag{44.15}$$

It is convenient to make the numerical substitutions

$$\alpha_1 = \frac{mc^2 + E}{\hbar c}, \qquad \alpha_2 = \frac{mc^2 - E}{\hbar c}, \qquad \rho = \alpha r$$
$$\alpha = +(\alpha_1 \alpha_2)^{\frac{1}{2}} = \frac{(m^2 c^4 - E^2)^{\frac{1}{2}}}{\hbar c} \tag{44.16}$$

in terms of which Eqs. (44.15) become

$$\left(\frac{d}{d\rho} + \frac{k}{\rho} \right) G - \left(\frac{\alpha_1}{\alpha} - \frac{V}{\hbar c\alpha} \right) F = 0$$
$$\left(\frac{d}{d\rho} - \frac{k}{\rho} \right) F - \left(\frac{\alpha_2}{\alpha} + \frac{V}{\hbar c\alpha} \right) G = 0 \tag{44.17}$$

The Hydrogen Atom.   We now find the energy eigenvalues of (44.17) when $V(r) = -Ze^2/r$; with $\gamma \equiv Ze^2/\hbar c$, the quantity $V/\hbar c\alpha$ becomes $-\gamma/\rho$.   We follow a procedure that is analogous to that of Sec. 16, and put

$$F(\rho) = f(\rho)e^{-\rho}, \qquad G(\rho) = g(\rho)e^{-\rho} \tag{44.18}$$

The equations for f and g are

$$g' - g + \frac{kg}{\rho} - \left(\frac{\alpha_1}{\alpha} + \frac{\gamma}{\rho}\right)f = 0$$

$$f' - f - \frac{kf}{\rho} - \left(\frac{\alpha_2}{\alpha} - \frac{\gamma}{\rho}\right)g = 0$$

(44.19)

We look for solutions of (44.19) in the form of power series

$$f = \rho^s(a_0 + a_1\rho + \cdots), \qquad a_0 \neq 0$$

$$g = \rho^s(b_0 + b_1\rho + \cdots), \qquad b_0 \neq 0$$

(44.20)

Since (44.14) is supposed to be finite at $r = 0$, we expect that s is greater than or equal to one. However, in analogy with the solution of the Schrödinger relativistic equation (42.15) for the Coulomb field, we shall admit a value of s slightly less than one, since the volume integral of $\psi^*\psi$ will still be finite.

We substitute (44.20) into (44.19), and equate the coefficients of $\rho^{s+\nu-1}$ to zero:

$$(s + \nu + k)b_\nu - b_{\nu-1} - \gamma a_\nu - \frac{\alpha_1}{\alpha} a_{\nu-1} = 0$$

$$(s + \nu - k)a_\nu - a_{\nu-1} + \gamma b_\nu - \frac{\alpha_2}{\alpha} b_{\nu-1} = 0$$

(44.21)

for $\nu > 0$. When $\nu = 0$, the equations analogous to (44.21) are

$$(s + k)b_0 - \gamma a_0 = 0$$

$$(s - k)a_0 + \gamma b_0 = 0$$

(44.22)

Equations (44.22) have the required nonvanishing solution for a_0 and b_0 only if the determinant of their coefficients vanishes; this gives

$$s = \pm (k^2 - \gamma^2)^{\frac{1}{2}}$$

(44.23)

Because of the boundary condition at the origin, we take the upper sign for s in (44.23).

A relation between a_ν and b_ν can be obtained by multiplying the first of Eqs. (44.21) by α, the second by α_1, and subtracting.

$$b_\nu[\alpha(s + \nu + k) - \alpha_1\gamma] = a_\nu[\alpha_1(s + \nu - k) + \alpha\gamma]$$

(44.24)

where use has been made of (44.16). We can now examine the behavior of the solution at large r. Unless both the series (44.20) terminate, this behavior is determined by their high terms, so we can neglect constant factors in comparison with ν. We then obtain from (44.21) and (44.24)

$$a_\nu \cong \frac{2}{\nu} a_{\nu-1}, \qquad b_\nu \cong \frac{2}{\nu} b_{\nu-1}$$

This means that both series have the asymptotic form $e^{2\rho}$, and regular solutions are obtained only if they terminate. Suppose that this occurs at $\nu = n'$, so that $a_{n'+1} = b_{n'+1} = 0$. Then both Eqs. (44.21) give the relation

$$\alpha_1 a_{n'} = -\alpha b_{n'}, \qquad n' = 0,1,2, \ldots \quad (44.25)$$

We obtain energy levels by setting $\nu = n'$ in (44.24), and making use of (44.25). With the help of (44.16), we find that

$$2\alpha(s + n') = \gamma(\alpha_1 - \alpha_2) = \frac{2E\gamma}{\hbar c}$$

The square of this is

$$(m^2c^4 - E^2)(s + n')^2 = E^2\gamma^2$$

which is easily solved to give

$$E = mc^2\left[1 + \frac{\gamma^2}{(s + n')^2}\right]^{-\frac{1}{2}} \qquad (44.26)$$

Equations (44.23) and (44.26) are equivalent to the formula first derived by Sommerfeld[1] on the basis of the old quantum theory. This formula accounts quite well for the spectrum of hydrogen.[2] The fine structure is made evident by expanding (44.26) in powers of γ^2. The result to terms of order γ^4 resembles (42.21) but is not quite the same:

$$E = mc^2\left[1 - \frac{\gamma^2}{2n^2} - \frac{\gamma^4}{2n^4}\left(\frac{n}{|k|} - \frac{3}{4}\right)\right] \qquad (44.27)$$

where $n = n' + |k|$ is the total quantum number of Eq. (16.14), and $|k|$ can take on positive integer values. The total spread in energy of the fine-structure levels for a given n is easily seen from (44.27) to be

$$\frac{mc^2\gamma^4}{n^3}\frac{n - 1}{2n}$$

This is substantially less than the value (42.22) obtained from the Schrödinger relativistic equation, and is in agreement with experiment.

Classification of Energy Levels. For $n' > 0$, all positive and negative integer values of k are permissible [we saw from (44.12) that k cannot be zero]. For $n' = 0$, however, a contradiction can arise between (44.22) and (44.25); these give

$$\frac{b_0}{a_0} = \frac{\gamma}{s + k} \qquad \text{and} \qquad \frac{b_0}{a_0} = -\frac{\alpha_1}{\alpha} \qquad (44.28)$$

---

[1] A. Sommerfeld, *Ann. d. Physik*, **51**, 1 (1916).

[2] There are, however, small but important deviations from this formula; see W. E. Lamb, *Reports on Progress in Physics*, **14**, 19 (1951).

respectively. Since $s < |k|$, the first of these expressions is positive or negative according as k is positive or negative, whereas the second is always negative. Thus for $n' = 0$, k can assume only negative integer values.

Thus far we have only shown that the j value of a level is equal to $|k| - \frac{1}{2}$. In order to connect l with the level, we must make the non-relativistic approximation that the orbital angular momentum is well defined. Since in this case G in (44.14) is much larger than F, we can replace β by -1 and $\mathbf{\sigma}'$ by $\mathbf{\sigma}$ in (44.10). Now in this approximation, $(\mathbf{L} + \frac{1}{2}\hbar\mathbf{\sigma})^2 = [l(l+1) + \frac{3}{4}]\hbar^2 + \hbar\mathbf{\sigma} \cdot \mathbf{L}$, and is also equal to $j(j+1)\hbar^2$. We obtain in this way

$$k = l(l+1) - j(j+1) - \tfrac{1}{4} = \begin{cases} -l-1, & j = l + \tfrac{1}{2} \\ l, & j = l - \tfrac{1}{2} \end{cases}$$

As an example of the energy levels in hydrogen, we consider the case $n = 3$. The radial quantum number n' can be 0, 1, or 2, and k can be $\pm(3 - n')$ except that k can be only -3 when $n' = 0$. The levels with their nonrelativistic classifications are

n'	k	l	j	
0	-3	2	$\frac{5}{2}$	$^2D_{\frac{5}{2}}$
1	2	2	$\frac{3}{2}$	$^2D_{\frac{3}{2}}$
1	-2	1	$\frac{3}{2}$	$^2P_{\frac{3}{2}}$
2	1	1	$\frac{1}{2}$	$^2P_{\frac{1}{2}}$
2	-1	0	$\frac{1}{2}$	$^2S_{\frac{1}{2}}$

According to (44.23) and (44.26), states with the same $|k|$ or j have the same energy; Eq. (44.27) shows that the energy increases with increasing $|k|$.

Negative Energy States. We have seen that both the Schrödinger and Dirac relativistic equations admit of solutions for which a particle has negative kinetic energy and negative rest mass. These solutions correspond to the negative square root of the classical energy equation (42.2). The negative-energy solutions cannot be ignored in the quantum theory, as they are in the classical theory, since there is nothing to prevent a charged particle from making a radiative transition from a state of positive energy to a state of negative energy.

Dirac proposed that we regard the negative energy states of Eq. (43.22) as being full, in which case the exclusion principle prevents transitions into such occupied states. The normal state of the vacuum then consists of an infinite density of negative-energy electrons. It is assumed that there are no electromagnetic or gravitational effects of these electrons, but that deviations from the norm produced by emptying one or more of the negative energy states can be observed. The absence of a negatively charged electron that has negative mass and kinetic energy would then be expected to manifest itself as a positively charged particle that has an equal positive mass and kinetic energy. In this way, a "hole" theory of *positrons* can be formulated.

With so many electrons present, however, the theory is no longer the one-particle theory contemplated when the wave equation was set up. A many-particle theory can be based on the Dirac equation in accordance with the formalism of quantized fields discussed in the next chapter, and a theory of positrons can be developed.

It might at first be thought that a similar technique cannot be applied to the Schrödinger relativistic equation, since it describes a particle of zero spin, which we expect to obey Einstein-Bose statistics rather than the exclusion principle. However, Pauli and Weisskopf[1] have shown that the quantized field energy is always positive in this case, even though the parameter E in the wave equation can be either positive or negative. Moreover, the charge in the quantized field can have either sign, corresponding to the ambiguity of the sign of P noted after Eq. (42.8). Thus both the theories discussed in this chapter predict the existence of particles that have positive energies and both signs of electric charge. The appearance of spin angular momentum as a consequence of the Dirac equation shows that this is the theory that describes electrons.

Problems

1. Show that the expectation values of E^2 and $\mathbf{p}^2$ for a general wave-packet solution of Eq. (42.4) satisfy the equation $\langle E^2 \rangle = c^2 \langle p^2 \rangle + m^2 c^4$. Discuss the connection between this result and the classical equation (42.2).

2. Use the nonrelativistic approximation implied in (42.11) and in the immediately following discussion to show that the expression (42.8) for P reduces to (7.1) in the proper limit.

3. Solve the Schrödinger relativistic equation for an attractive square well potential of depth V_0 and radius a, after determining the continuity conditions at $r = a$. Obtain an explicit expression for the minimum V_0 with given a that just binds a particle of mass m.

4. Show explicitly that the wave functions (43.17) and (43.18) are not eigenfunctions of any component of the spin angular momentum $\frac{1}{2}\hbar\boldsymbol{\sigma}'$.

5. Show that any matrix with two rows and columns can be expressed as a linear combination of σ_x, σ_y, σ_z, and 1. Use this result to show that there is no matrix that anticommutes with each of the first three of these.

6. Show that the current density given by (43.20) for a free-particle wave function agrees with the corresponding nonrelativistic expression in the proper limit.

7. Make use of Eqs. (43.11), (43.13), and (43.19) to verify Eq. (43.24).

8. Prove that the operators α_r and k defined by Eqs. (44.9) and (44.10) commute with each other, and that $\hbar^2 k^2$ is given by the right side of (44.12).

9. Discuss the connection between the $\boldsymbol{\alpha} \cdot \mathbf{E}$ term in Eq. (43.27) and the spin-orbit energy.

[1] W. Pauli and V. Weisskopf, *Helv. Phys. Acta*, **7**, 709 (1934).

10. Show that the negative square roots that could appear in arriving at Eqs. (42.16) and (44.26) actually do not correspond to bound states.

11. Show explicitly that elimination of b_0/a_0 between the two Eqs. (44.28) gives the correct energy levels for $n' = 0$ if $k < 0$, but not if $k > 0$.

12. Use the selection rules $\Delta l = \pm 1$, $\Delta j = 0, \pm 1$ to list the frequencies of the allowed transitions between the states with $n = 2$ and $n = 3$ for the Coulomb field, in both the Schrödinger and Dirac relativistic theories. In particular, show that the latter theory gives seven lines, of which five are distinct, whereas the former gives three lines that are much more spread apart.

13. Solve the Dirac equation for an attractive square well potential of depth V_0 and radius a, after determining the continuity conditions at $r = a$. Obtain an explicit expression for the minimum V_0 with given a that just binds a particle of mass m, and compare with the answer to Prob. 3.

CHAPTER XIII

THE QUANTIZATION OF WAVE FIELDS

The theory of quantum mechanics presented thus far in this book has dealt with systems that, in the classical limit, consist of material particles. We wish now to extend the theory so that it can be applied to the electromagnetic field, and thus provide a consistent basis for the quantum theory of radiation. The quantization of a wave field imparts to it some particle properties; in the case of the electromagnetic field, a theory of light quanta (photons) results. The field quantization technique can also be applied to a ψ field, such as that described by the nonrelativistic Schrödinger equation (6.16) or by one of the relativistic equations (42.4) or (43.3). As we shall see (Sec. 46), it then converts a one-particle theory into a many-particle theory; in the nonrelativistic case, this is equivalent to the transition from Eq. (6.16) to (16.1) or (32.1). Because of this equivalence, it might seem that the quantization of ψ fields merely provides another formal approach to the many-particle problem. However, the new formalism can also deal as well with processes that involve the creation or destruction of material particles (radioactive beta decay, meson-nucleon interaction).

This chapter and the next are intended to serve as an introduction to quantum field theory.[1] We start in Sec. 45 with a discussion of the classical and quantum equations of motion for a wave field, without specifying the detailed nature of the field. The application to Eq. (6.16) is used as a first example in Sec. 46, since the analysis is relatively simple and uncomplicated by considerations of relativity. The quantization of the Dirac equation (43.3) is carried through in Sec. 47. Several other particle wave equations (including the relativistic Schrödinger equation) have also been quantized; they are mainly of interest in connection with meson theory, and are not discussed here. The electromagnetic field is considered in the next chapter.

[1] For further discussion, see G. Wentzel, "Einführung in die Quantentheorie der Wellenfelder," (Franz Deuticke, Vienna, 1943; reprinted by Edwards Bros, Inc., Ann Arbor, 1946; English translation published by Interscience, New York, 1949); W. Heisenberg, "The Physical Principles of the Quantum Theory," Appendix, Secs. 9–12 (University of Chicago Press, Chicago, 1930); P. A. M. Dirac, "The Principles of Quantum Mechanics," 3d ed., Chaps. X, XII (Oxford, New York, 1947). See also H. Goldstein, "Classical Mechanics," Chap. 11 (Addison-Wesley, Cambridge, Mass., 1950); H. C. Corben and P. Stehle, "Classical Mechanics," pp. 210–212 (Wiley, New York, 1950).

45. CLASSICAL AND QUANTUM FIELD EQUATIONS

A general procedure for the quantization of the equations of motion of a classical system was obtained in Sec. 23. We start with the Lagrangian function for the system, and verify that it gives the correct classical equations. The momenta canonically conjugate to the coordinates of the system are found from the Lagrangian, and a Hamiltonian function is set up. The classical Hamiltonian equations of motion are then converted into quantum equations by the substitution of commutator brackets for Poisson brackets. We now show how this procedure can be applied in its entirety to a wave field $\psi(\mathbf{r},t)$, which we assume for the moment to be real.[1]

Coordinates of the Field. A wave field is specified by its amplitudes at all points of space and the dependence of these amplitudes on the time, in much the same way as a system of particles is specified by the positional coordinates q_i and their dependence on the time. The field evidently has an infinite number of degrees of freedom, and is analogous to a system that consists of an infinite number of particles. It is natural, then, to use the amplitudes $\psi(\mathbf{r},t)$ at all points $\mathbf{r}$ as coordinates in analogy with the particle coordinates $q_i(t)$ of Sec. 23.

It is not necessary, however, to proceed in this way. As an alternative, we can expand ψ in some complete orthonormal set of functions u_k:

$$\psi(\mathbf{r},t) = \mathsf{S}a_k(t)u_k(\mathbf{r}) \tag{45.1}$$

The expansion coefficients a_k in (45.1) can be regarded as the field coordinates, and the field equations can be expressed in terms of either ψ or the a_k. We shall use the wave amplitudes at all points as the field coordinates in this section. It will be convenient for some of the later work to make use of the coefficients a_k.

Lagrangian Equation. The Lagrangian $L(q_i,\dot{q}_i,t)$ used in Sec. 23 is a function of the time and a functional of the possible paths $q_i(t)$ of the system. The actual paths are derived from the variational principle (23.3):

$$\delta \int_{t_1}^{t_2} Ldt = 0, \qquad \delta q_i(t_1) = \delta q_i(t_2) = 0$$

By analogy, we expect the field Lagrangian to be a functional of the field amplitude $\psi(\mathbf{r},t)$. It can usually be expressed as the integral over all space of a *Lagrangian density L:*

$$L = \int L(\psi, \operatorname{grad} \psi, \dot{\psi}, t)d\tau \tag{45.2}$$

[1] W. Heisenberg and W. Pauli, *Zeits. f. Physik,* **56**, 1 (1929); **59**, 168 (1930).

where $\dot{\psi} = \partial\psi/\partial t$. The appearance of **grad** ψ as an argument of L is a consequence of the continuous dependence of ψ on **r** (continuously infinite number of degrees of freedom); higher derivatives of ψ could also be present, but do not seem to arise in problems of physical interest. The variational principle that corresponds to (23.3) is

$$\delta \int_{t_1}^{t_2} L dt = \delta \int_{t_1}^{t_2} \int L dt d\tau = \int_{t_1}^{t_2} \int (\delta L) dt d\tau = 0 \qquad (45.3)$$

where the infinitesimal variation $\delta\psi$ of ψ is subject to the restrictions

$$\delta\psi(\mathbf{r},t_1) = \delta\psi(\mathbf{r},t_2) = 0 \qquad (45.4)$$

If L has the form indicated in (45.2), its variation can be written

$$\delta L = \frac{\partial L}{\partial \psi} \delta\psi + \sum_{xyz} \frac{\partial L}{\partial(\partial\psi/\partial x)} \delta\left(\frac{\partial\psi}{\partial x}\right) + \frac{\partial L}{\partial \dot{\psi}} \delta\dot{\psi} \qquad (45.5)$$

where the summation over x, y, z implies the sum of three terms with y and z substituted for x. Now $\delta\dot{\psi}$ is the difference between the original and varied $\dot{\psi}$, and hence is the time derivative of the variation of ψ. This and the similar expression for $\delta(\partial\psi/\partial x)$ can be written

$$\delta\dot{\psi} = \frac{\partial}{\partial t}(\delta\psi), \qquad \delta\left(\frac{\partial\psi}{\partial x}\right) = \frac{\partial}{\partial x}(\delta\psi)$$

Equation (45.3) then becomes

$$\int_{t_1}^{t_2} \int \left[\frac{\partial L}{\partial \psi} \delta\psi + \sum_{xyz} \frac{\partial L}{\partial(\partial\psi/\partial x)} \frac{\partial}{\partial x}(\delta\psi) + \frac{\partial L}{\partial \dot{\psi}} \frac{\partial}{\partial t}(\delta\psi)\right] dt d\tau = 0 \quad (45.6)$$

The summation terms in (45.6) can be integrated by parts with respect to the space coordinates; the surface terms vanish, either because ψ falls off rapidly enough at infinite distance, or because ψ obeys periodic boundary conditions at the walls of a large but finite box. The last term of (45.6) can be integrated by parts with respect to the time, and the boundary terms vanish because of (45.4). Equation (45.6) can therefore be written

$$\int_{t_1}^{t_2} \int \left\{\frac{\partial L}{\partial \psi} - \sum_{xyz} \frac{\partial}{\partial x}\left[\frac{\partial L}{\partial(\partial\psi/\partial x)}\right] - \frac{\partial}{\partial t}\left(\frac{\partial L}{\partial \dot{\psi}}\right)\right\} \delta\psi \, dt d\tau = 0 \quad (45.7)$$

Since (45.3) is valid for an arbitrary variation $\delta\psi$ at each point in space, Eq. (45.7) is equivalent to the differential equation

$$\frac{\partial L}{\partial \psi} - \sum_{xyz} \frac{\partial}{\partial x}\left[\frac{\partial L}{\partial(\partial\psi/\partial x)}\right] - \frac{\partial}{\partial t}\left(\frac{\partial L}{\partial \dot{\psi}}\right) = 0 \qquad (45.8)$$

Equation (45.8) is the classical field equation derived from the Lagrangian density $L(\psi, \text{grad } \psi, \dot{\psi}, t)$.

Functional Derivative.   In order to pursue further the analogy with particle mechanics, it is desirable to rewrite Eq. (45.8) in terms of L rather than $\mathbf{L}$.   Since the aggregate of values of ψ and $\dot{\psi}$ at all points is analogous to the q_i and $\dot{q}_i$ of particle theory, we require derivatives of L with respect to ψ and $\dot{\psi}$ at particular points.   These are called *functional derivatives*, and are denoted by $\partial L/\partial\psi$ and $\partial L/\partial\dot{\psi}$.[1]   Expressions for them can be obtained by dividing up all space into small cells and replacing volume integrals by summations over these cells.   The average values of quantities such as ψ, **grad** ψ, and $\dot{\psi}$ in the ith cell are denoted by subscripts i, and the volume of that cell by $\delta\tau_i$.   Then

$$\sum_i L[\psi_i, (\text{grad } \psi)_i, \dot{\psi}_i, t]\delta\tau_i$$

approaches L in the limit in which all the $\delta\tau_i$ approach zero.

In similar fashion, the t integrand in Eq. (45.6) or (45.7) can be replaced by

$$\sum_i \left\{\frac{\partial L}{\partial\psi} - \sum_{xyz}\frac{\partial}{\partial x}\left[\frac{\partial L}{\partial(\partial\psi/\partial x)}\right]\right\}_i \delta\psi_i\delta\tau_i + \sum_i \left(\frac{\partial L}{\partial\dot{\psi}}\right)_i \delta\dot{\psi}_i\delta\tau_i$$

where the variation in L is now produced by independent variations in the ψ_i and the $\dot{\psi}_i$.   Suppose now that all the $\delta\psi_i$ and $\delta\dot{\psi}_i$ are zero except for a particular $\delta\psi_j$.   It is natural to relate the functional derivative of L with respect to ψ for a point in the jth cell to the ratio of δL to $\delta\psi_j$; we therefore define

$$\frac{\partial L}{\partial\psi} = \lim_{\delta\tau_j\to 0}\frac{\delta L}{\delta\psi_j\delta\tau_j} = \frac{\partial L}{\partial\psi} - \sum_{xyz}\frac{\partial}{\partial x}\left[\frac{\partial L}{\partial(\partial\psi/\partial x)}\right] \qquad (45.9)$$

Similarly, the functional derivative of L with respect to $\dot{\psi}$ is defined by setting all the $\delta\psi_i$ and $\delta\dot{\psi}_i$ equal to zero except for a particular $\delta\dot{\psi}_j$:

$$\frac{\partial L}{\partial\dot{\psi}} = \lim_{\delta\tau_j\to 0}\frac{\delta L}{\delta\dot{\psi}_j\delta\tau_j} = \frac{\partial L}{\partial\dot{\psi}} \qquad (45.10)$$

Here again the point **r** at which the functional derivative is evaluated is in the jth cell.   Substitution of (45.9) and (45.10) into (45.8) gives

$$\frac{\partial}{\partial t}\frac{\partial L}{\partial\dot{\psi}} - \frac{\partial L}{\partial\psi} = 0 \qquad (45.11)$$

which closely resembles the Lagrangian equations (23.4) for a system of particles.

[1] For an alternative treatment, see the paragraph following Eq. (27.26).

Hamiltonian Equations. The momentum canonically conjugate to ψ_j can be defined as in particle mechanics to be the ratio of δL to the infinitesimal change $\delta\dot\psi_j$ when all the other $\delta\dot\psi_i$ and all the $\delta\psi_i$ are zero. We thus obtain

$$P_j = \frac{\delta L}{\delta\dot\psi_j} = \delta\tau_j\left(\frac{\partial L}{\partial\dot\psi}\right)_j \tag{45.12}$$

It follows from (45.11) and (45.12) that

$$\dot P_j = \delta\tau_j\left(\frac{\partial L}{\partial\psi}\right)_j \tag{45.13}$$

The analogy with Eq. (23.5) then gives for the Hamiltonian

$$H = \sum_i P_i\dot\psi_i - L = \sum_i \left(\frac{\partial L}{\partial\dot\psi}\right)_i \dot\psi_i\delta\tau_i - L \tag{45.14}$$

We write H as the volume integral of a *Hamiltonian density* **H**, and assume that the cells are small enough so that the difference between a volume integral and the corresponding cell summation can be ignored; we then have

$$H = \int H d\tau, \qquad H = \pi\dot\psi - L, \qquad \pi \equiv \frac{\partial L}{\partial\dot\psi} = \frac{\partial L}{\partial\dot\psi} \tag{45.15}$$

The approximate Hamiltonian (45.14), with the relations (45.12) and (45.13), can be manipulated in precisely the same way as the Hamiltonian for a system of particles. Instead of showing this explicitly, we now work with the true field Hamiltonian H given in (45.15), which is a functional of ψ and π from which $\dot\psi$ has been eliminated. The classical Hamiltonian equations of motion will be derived without further recourse to the cell approximation. The variation of L produced by variations of ψ and $\dot\psi$ can be written, with the help of (45.11) and (45.15),

$$\delta L = \int \left(\frac{\partial L}{\partial\psi}\delta\psi + \frac{\partial L}{\partial\dot\psi}\delta\dot\psi\right) d\tau = \int (\dot\pi\delta\psi + \pi\delta\dot\psi)d\tau$$
$$= \int[\delta(\pi\dot\psi) + \dot\pi\delta\psi - \dot\psi\delta\pi]d\tau$$
$$= \delta H + \delta L + \int(\dot\pi\delta\psi - \dot\psi\delta\pi)d\tau \tag{45.16}$$

The variation of H produced by the corresponding variations of ψ and π can be written

$$\delta H = \int \left(\frac{\partial H}{\partial\psi}\delta\psi + \frac{\partial H}{\partial\pi}\delta\pi\right) d\tau \tag{45.17}$$

It follows from the earlier discussion of functional derivatives that

$$\frac{\partial H}{\partial \psi} = \frac{\partial H}{\partial \psi} - \sum_{xyz} \frac{\partial}{\partial x} \frac{\partial H}{\partial(\partial \psi/\partial x)}$$

$$\frac{\partial H}{\partial \pi} = \frac{\partial H}{\partial \pi} - \sum_{xyz} \frac{\partial}{\partial x} \frac{\partial H}{\partial(\partial \pi/\partial x)}$$

(45.18)

Comparison of Eqs. (45.16) and (45.17) for arbitrary variations $\delta\psi$ and $\delta\pi$ then gives the classical field equations in Hamiltonian form

$$\dot{\psi} = \frac{\partial H}{\partial \pi}, \qquad \dot{\pi} = -\frac{\partial H}{\partial \psi}$$

(45.19)

The Hamiltonian equation for the time rate of change of a functional F of ψ and π can now be found. We express F as the volume integral of the corresponding functional density $F(\psi,\pi)$, which for simplicity is assumed not to depend explicitly on the time or on the gradients of ψ or π. The foregoing analysis can be used to show that

$$\dot{F} = \int \left(\frac{\partial F}{\partial \psi} \dot{\psi} + \frac{\partial F}{\partial \pi} \dot{\pi} \right) d\tau$$

$$= \int \left(\frac{\partial F}{\partial \psi} \frac{\partial H}{\partial \pi} - \frac{\partial F}{\partial \pi} \frac{\partial H}{\partial \psi} \right) d\tau$$

$$\equiv \{F,H\}$$

(45.20)

This equation also serves to define the Poisson-bracket expression for two functionals of the field variables. The right side of Eq. (45.20) is not changed if F also depends on **grad** ψ or **grad** π (see Prob. 2). It is apparent from (45.20) that H is a constant of the motion if it does not depend explicitly on the time; in this case, H is the total energy of the field.

Quantum Equations for the Field. The analogy between particle coordinates and momenta q_i,p_i and the cell averages ψ_i,P_i suggests that we choose as quantum conditions for the field

$$[\psi_i,\psi_j] = [P_i,P_j] = 0, \qquad [\psi_i,P_j] = i\hbar\delta_{ij}$$

(45.21)

where the commutator brackets are defined by Eq. (23.9). This means that we have converted the wave field from a numerical function to an operator that can be represented by a matrix as in Sec. 23.

We now assume that the cell volumes are very small. Then Eqs. (45.21) can be rewritten with the help of (45.12) and (45.15) in terms of ψ and π:

$$[\psi(\mathbf{r},t),\psi(\mathbf{r}',t)] = [\pi(\mathbf{r},t),\pi(\mathbf{r}',t)] = 0$$
$$[\psi(\mathbf{r},t),\pi(\mathbf{r}',t)] = i\hbar\delta(\mathbf{r},\mathbf{r}')$$

where $\delta(\mathbf{r},\mathbf{r}') = 1/\delta\tau_i$ if $\mathbf{r}$ and $\mathbf{r}'$ are in the same cell and zero otherwise. The function $\delta(\mathbf{r},\mathbf{r}')$ has the property that $\int f(\mathbf{r})\delta(\mathbf{r},\mathbf{r}')d\tau$ is equal to the average value of f for the cell in which $\mathbf{r}'$ is situated. Thus in the limit in which the cell volumes approach zero, $\delta(\mathbf{r},\mathbf{r}')$ can be replaced by the three-dimensional Dirac δ function $\delta(\mathbf{r} - \mathbf{r}')$, defined in Eq. (11.14). The quantum conditions for the canonical field variables then become

$$[\psi(\mathbf{r},t),\psi(\mathbf{r}',t)] = [\pi(\mathbf{r},t),\pi(\mathbf{r}',t)] = 0$$
$$[\psi(\mathbf{r},t),\pi(\mathbf{r}',t)] = i\hbar\delta(\mathbf{r} - \mathbf{r}') \tag{45.22}$$

The equation of motion for any quantum dynamical variable F is obtained as in Sec. 23 if the Poisson bracket in Eq. (45.20) is replaced by the commutator bracket divided by $i\hbar$.

$$i\hbar\dot{F} = [F,H] \tag{45.23}$$

The commutator bracket can be evaluated with the help of (45.22) when explicit expressions for F and H in terms of ψ and π are given. Thus Eqs. (45.22) and (45.23) completely describe the behavior of the quantized field that is specified by the Hamiltonian H.

Fields with More than One Component. Thus far in this section we have dealt with fields that can be described by a single real amplitude. If the field has more than one component $\psi_1, \psi_2, \ldots$, the Lagrangian density has the form $L(\psi_1, \text{grad } \psi_1, \dot{\psi}_1, \psi_2, \text{grad } \psi_2, \dot{\psi}_2, \ldots, t)$. Then if each of the field components is varied independently, the variational equation (45.3) leads to an equation of the form (45.8) or (45.11) for each of $\psi_1, \psi_2, \ldots$. A momentum canonically conjugate to each ψ_s can be defined as in Eq. (45.15) to be $\pi_s = \partial L/\partial\dot{\psi}_s$. The Hamiltonian density has the form

$$H = \sum_s \pi_s\dot{\psi}_s - L \tag{45.24}$$

and the Hamiltonian equations consist of a pair like (45.19) for each s. Equation (45.23) is unchanged, and the commutation relations (45.22) are replaced by

$$[\psi_s(\mathbf{r},t),\psi_{s'}(\mathbf{r}',t)] = [\pi_s(\mathbf{r},t),\pi_{s'}(\mathbf{r}',t)] = 0$$
$$[\psi_s(\mathbf{r},t),\pi_{s'}(\mathbf{r}',t)] = i\hbar\delta_{ss'}\delta(\mathbf{r} - \mathbf{r}') \tag{45.25}$$

A case of immediate interest is a single complex field ψ, for which we can write

$$\psi = 2^{-\frac{1}{2}}(\psi_1 + i\psi_2), \qquad \bar{\psi} = 2^{-\frac{1}{2}}(\psi_1 - i\psi_2) \tag{45.26}$$

where ψ_1 and ψ_2 are real. We show first that the equations of the form (45.8) obtained by independent variation of ψ and of $\bar{\psi}$ are equivalent to those obtained by variation of ψ_1 and ψ_2. It follows from (45.26) that

$$\frac{\partial}{\partial \psi} = 2^{-\frac{1}{2}}\left(\frac{\partial}{\partial \psi_1} - i\frac{\partial}{\partial \psi_2}\right), \qquad \frac{\partial}{\partial \bar\psi} = 2^{-\frac{1}{2}}\left(\frac{\partial}{\partial \psi_1} + i\frac{\partial}{\partial \psi_2}\right)$$

Thus the sum and difference of the ψ_1 equation and i times the ψ_2 equation give the Lagrangian equations that result from independent variation of $\bar\psi$ and ψ, respectively, in (45.3). In similar fashion, the momenta canonically conjugate to ψ and $\bar\psi$ are seen to be

$$\pi = 2^{-\frac{1}{2}}(\pi_1 - i\pi_2) \qquad \text{and} \qquad \bar\pi = 2^{-\frac{1}{2}}(\pi_1 + i\pi_2) \qquad (45.27)$$

respectively.[1] Then $\pi_1\dot\psi_1 + \pi_2\dot\psi_2 = \pi\dot\psi + \bar\pi\dot{\bar\psi}$, and the Hamiltonian is unchanged. The commutation relations for ψ, $\bar\psi$, π, and $\bar\pi$ can be obtained from Eqs. (45.25) (with $s = 1$ and 2), together with (45.26) and (45.27). All pairs of variables except the following commute:

$$\begin{aligned}[\psi(\mathbf{r},t),\pi(\mathbf{r}',t)] &= i\hbar\delta(\mathbf{r} - \mathbf{r}') \\ [\bar\psi(\mathbf{r},t),\bar\pi(\mathbf{r}',t)] &= i\hbar\delta(\mathbf{r} - \mathbf{r}')\end{aligned} \qquad (45.28)$$

46. QUANTIZATION OF THE NONRELATIVISTIC SCHRÖDINGER EQUATION

As a first example of the application of the field quantization technique developed in the preceding section, we consider here the quantization of the nonrelativistic Schrödinger equation (6.16). This application implies that we are treating Eq. (6.16) as though it were a classical equation that describes the motion of some kind of material fluid. As we shall see, the resulting quantized field theory is equivalent to a many-particle Schrödinger equation, like (16.1) or (32.1). For this reason, field quantization is often called *second quantization;* this term implies that the transition from classical particle mechanics to equation (6.16) constitutes the first quantization.

Lagrangian and Hamiltonian Equations. The Lagrangian density may be taken to be

$$L = i\hbar\bar\psi\dot\psi - \frac{\hbar^2}{2m}\operatorname{grad}\bar\psi \cdot \operatorname{grad}\psi - V(\mathbf{r},t)\bar\psi\psi \qquad (46.1)$$

As shown at the end of the last section, ψ and $\bar\psi$ can be varied separately to obtain the Lagrangian equations of motion. The equation of the form (45.8) that results from variation of ψ is

$$-i\hbar\dot{\bar\psi} = -\frac{\hbar^2}{2m}\nabla^2\bar\psi + V(\mathbf{r},t)\bar\psi$$

which is the complex conjugate of Eq. (6.16). Variation of $\bar\psi$ gives Eq. (6.16):

[1] See footnote 1, page 349.

$$i\hbar\dot{\psi} = -\frac{\hbar^2}{2m}\nabla^2\psi + V(\mathbf{r},t)\psi \qquad (46.2)$$

The momentum canonically conjugate to ψ is

$$\pi = \frac{\partial L}{\partial\dot{\psi}} = i\hbar\bar{\psi} \qquad (46.3)$$

However $\dot{\bar{\psi}}$ does not appear in the Lagrangian density, so that $\bar{\pi}$ is identically zero.[1]   It is therefore impossible to satisfy the second of the commutation relations (45.28) (or the corresponding classical Poisson-bracket relation), so that $\bar{\psi},\bar{\pi}$ cannot be regarded as a pair of canonically conjugate variables.   They can easily be eliminated from the Hamiltonian since $\bar{\pi}$ never appears and Eq. (46.3) gives $\bar{\psi}$ in terms of π.[2]

The Hamiltonian density is

$$H = \pi\dot{\psi} - L = -\frac{i\hbar}{2m}\operatorname{grad}\pi\cdot\operatorname{grad}\psi - \frac{i}{\hbar}V\pi\psi \qquad (46.4)$$

The Hamiltonian equations of motion obtained from (45.19), with the help of (45.18), are

$$\dot{\psi} = -\frac{i}{\hbar}V\psi + \frac{i\hbar}{2m}\nabla^2\psi$$

$$\dot{\pi} = \frac{i}{\hbar}V\pi - \frac{i\hbar}{2m}\nabla^2\pi$$

The first of these equations is the same as (46.2), and the second equation, together with (46.3), is the complex conjugate of (46.2).   We have thus shown, from the point of view of classical field theory, that the Lagrangian density (46.1), and the canonical variables and Hamiltonian derived from it, are in agreement with the wave equation (6.16) or (46.2).

Quantum Equations. The quantum equations are obtained by adopting the volume integral of (46.4) as the Hamiltonian, (45.23) as the equation of motion, and the first of Eqs. (45.28) as the quantum condition on the wave field.   Since ψ is now an operator rather than a nu-

---

[1] The notation of Eqs. (45.27) does not necessarily imply that $\bar{\pi}$ is the complex conjugate of π, since these quantities were defined as canonical momenta.   It is not difficult to see that π and $\bar{\pi}$ are actually complex conjugates of each other if L is real; in this case the π_1 and π_2 that appear in (45.27) are also real.

[2] The conclusion that π can be identified with $\bar{\psi}$ is related to the appearance of only the first-order time derivative in the wave equation (46.2), since in this case ψ can be expressed in terms of ψ and its space derivatives through the wave equation.   If the wave equation is of second order in the time derivative, ψ and $\dot{\psi}$ are independent; then π is related to $\dot{\bar{\psi}}$ rather than to $\bar{\psi}$, and both ψ,π and $\bar{\psi},\bar{\pi}$ are pairs of canonical variables. The nonrelativistic Schrödinger equation and the Dirac equation are of the former type, while the relativistic Schrödinger equation is of the latter type.

merical function, $\tilde{\psi}$ is to be interpreted as the Hermitian adjoint of ψ rather than as its complex conjugate. We therefore follow the notation of Sec. 21 and denote it by ψ^*. It is convenient to make use of Eq. (46.3) to replace π by $i\hbar\psi^*$, in which case the Hamiltonian becomes

$$H = \int \left(\frac{\hbar^2}{2m} \operatorname{grad} \psi^* \cdot \operatorname{grad} \psi + V\psi^*\psi \right) d\tau \qquad (46.5)$$

Application of Eqs. (21.14) and (21.15) then shows that H is Hermitian. The quantized Hamiltonian given in (46.5) is the operator that represents the total energy of the field; it is not to be confused with the operator given in (22.2), which is the energy operator for a single particle that is described by the wave equation (6.16) or (23.1). We have as yet given no explicit representations for the new operators ψ and H, and therefore cannot say on what they operate. The choice of a particular representation is not necessary so far as the equations of motion are concerned, but is desirable in the physical interpretation of the formalism that we give later in this section.

The commutation relations are

$$[\psi(\mathbf{r}), \psi(\mathbf{r}')] = [\psi^*(\mathbf{r}), \psi^*(\mathbf{r}')] = 0$$
$$[\psi(\mathbf{r}), \psi^*(\mathbf{r}')] = \delta(\mathbf{r} - \mathbf{r}') \qquad (46.6)$$

The omission of t from the argument of the field variables implies that both fields in a commutator bracket refer to the same time.[1]

Substitution of ψ for F in Eq. (45.23) gives

$$i\hbar\dot{\psi} = [\psi, H]$$
$$= \left[\psi, \int \frac{\hbar^2}{2m} \operatorname{grad}' \psi^{*\prime} \cdot \operatorname{grad}' \psi' d\tau' \right] + \left[\psi, \int V'\psi^{*\prime}\psi' d\tau' \right] \qquad (46.7)$$

where primes indicate that an integration variable $\mathbf{r}'$ has been substituted for $\mathbf{r}$. The second term on the right side is easily evaluated with the help of (46.6) to give

$$\int V'(\psi\psi^{*\prime}\psi' - \psi^{*\prime}\psi'\psi) d\tau' = \int V'(\psi\psi^{*\prime} - \psi^{*\prime}\psi)\psi' d\tau'$$
$$= \int V'\psi'\delta(\mathbf{r} - \mathbf{r}') d\tau' = V\psi \qquad (46.8)$$

ψ commutes with V, which is a numerical function. Evaluation of the first term on the right side of (46.7) is simplified by performing a partial integration on $\int \operatorname{grad}' \psi^{*\prime} \cdot \operatorname{grad}' \psi' d\tau'$ to obtain $-\int \psi^{*\prime}\nabla'^2\psi' d\tau'$; the surface terms vanish because ψ either vanishes at infinity or obeys periodic bound-

---

[1] Commutation relations between quantities that refer to different times are of interest in connection with relativistic theories (see Sec. 47).

ary conditions.   We thus obtain

$$[\psi, \int \mathbf{grad}'\ \psi^{*\prime} \cdot \mathbf{grad}'\ \psi' d\tau'] = -[\psi, \int \psi^{*\prime} \nabla'^2 \psi' d\tau']$$
$$= -\int [\psi, \psi^{*\prime}] \nabla'^2 \psi' d\tau'$$
$$= -\int (\nabla'^2 \psi') \delta(\mathbf{r} - \mathbf{r}') d\tau' = -\nabla^2 \psi \quad (46.9)$$

Substitution of (46.8) and (46.9) into (46.7) yields Eq. (46.2), so that the equations obtained from classical and quantum field theory agree.   A similar calculation shows that the equation $i\hbar\dot{\psi}^* = [\psi^*, H]$ yields the Hermitian adjoint of Eq. (46.2); it can also be seen directly that this equation is the Hermitian adjoint of the equation $i\hbar\dot{\psi} = [\psi, H]$ so long as H is Hermitian.

If V is independent of t, H has no explicit dependence on the time, and Eq. (45.23) shows that H is a constant of the motion.   Thus the energy in the field is constant.   Another interesting operator is

$$N = \int \psi^* \psi d\tau$$

which we assume represents the number of particles in the field.   We note first that N is Hermitian.   Its time derivative is given by

$$i\hbar\dot{N} = [N, H]$$
$$= \left[\int \psi^* \psi d\tau, \int \left(\frac{\hbar^2}{2m} \mathbf{grad}'\ \psi^{*\prime} \cdot \mathbf{grad}'\ \psi' + V'\psi^{*\prime}\psi' \right) d\tau' \right] \quad (46.10)$$

The commutator of N with the V part of H can be written as

$$\int\int V' (\psi^* \psi \psi^{*\prime} \psi' - \psi^{*\prime}\psi'\psi^*\psi) d\tau d\tau';$$

with the help of (46.6) the parenthesis in the integrand is

$$\psi^*\psi\psi^{*\prime}\psi' - \psi^{*\prime}\psi'\psi^*\psi = \psi^*[\psi^{*\prime}\psi + \delta(\mathbf{r} - \mathbf{r}')]\psi' - \psi^{*\prime}\psi'\psi^*\psi$$
$$= \psi^*\psi^{*\prime}\psi'\psi + \psi^*\psi'\delta(\mathbf{r} - \mathbf{r}') - \psi^{*\prime}\psi'\psi^*\psi$$
$$= \psi^{*\prime}[\psi'\psi^* - \delta(\mathbf{r} - \mathbf{r}')]\psi + \psi^*\psi'\delta(\mathbf{r} - \mathbf{r}')$$
$$\qquad\qquad - \psi^{*\prime}\psi'\psi^*\psi$$
$$= 0$$

since the δ function vanishes unless $\mathbf{r} = \mathbf{r}'$.   A similar but slightly more complicated calculation shows that

$$[\psi^*\psi,\ \mathbf{grad}'\ \psi^{*\prime} \cdot \mathbf{grad}'\ \psi'] = [\psi^* \mathbf{grad}'\ \psi' - (\mathbf{grad}'\ \psi^{*\prime})\psi] \cdot \mathbf{grad}'\ \delta(\mathbf{r} - \mathbf{r}')$$

The double integral of this over $\mathbf{r}$ and $\mathbf{r}'$ is zero.   Thus Eq. (46.10) shows that N is a constant of the motion.

It can also be shown that the commutator brackets in (46.6) are constants of the motion, so that they are always true if they are true at a particular time.

The N Representation. We now specialize to a representation in which the operator N is diagonal. Since N is Hermitian, its eigenvalues are real. A convenient and general way of specifying this representation is by means of an expansion like (45.1) in terms of a complete orthonormal set of functions $u_k(\mathbf{r})$, which we assume for definiteness to be discrete. We put

$$\psi(\mathbf{r},t) = \sum_k a_k(t)u_k(\mathbf{r}), \qquad \psi^*(\mathbf{r},t) = \sum_k a_k^*(t)\bar{u}_k(\mathbf{r}) \qquad (46.11)$$

where the u_k are numerical functions of the space coordinates and the a_k are operators that depend on the time. Equations (46.11) can be solved for the a_k:

$$a_k(t) = \int \bar{u}_k(\mathbf{r})\psi(\mathbf{r},t)d\tau, \qquad a_k^* = \int u_k(\mathbf{r})\psi^*(\mathbf{r},t)d\tau$$

Thus if we multiply the last of the commutation relations (46.6) by $\bar{u}_k(\mathbf{r})u_l(\mathbf{r}')$ on both sides and integrate over $\mathbf{r}$ and $\mathbf{r}'$, we obtain

$$[a_k(t), a_l^*(t)] = \int\int \bar{u}_k(\mathbf{r})u_l(\mathbf{r}')\delta(\mathbf{r}-\mathbf{r}')d\tau d\tau' = \delta_{kl} \qquad (46.12)$$

because of the orthonormality of the u_k. In similar fashion, it is apparent that a_k and a_l commute, and that a_k^* and a_l^* commute, for all k and l. Substitution of (46.11) into the expression for N shows that

$$N = \sum_k N_k \quad \text{where } N_k = a_k^* a_k \qquad (46.13)$$

It is easily seen that each N_k commutes with all others, so that they can be diagonalized simultaneously.

In order to find a representation in which N and all the N_k are diagonal, we write each of the a_k in the form

$$a_k = 2^{-\frac{1}{2}}(q_k + ip_k), \qquad a_k^* = 2^{-\frac{1}{2}}(q_k - ip_k) \qquad (46.14)$$

where q_k and p_k are Hermitian. This is always possible since Eqs. (46.14) can be solved to give

$$q_k = 2^{-\frac{1}{2}}(a_k + a_k^*), \qquad p_k = -i2^{-\frac{1}{2}}(a_k - a_k^*)$$

and these operators are evidently Hermitian. It follows from (46.12) that

$$[q_k,q_l] = [p_k,p_l] = 0, \qquad [q_k,p_l] = i\delta_{kl} \qquad (46.15)$$

and that

$$N_k = \tfrac{1}{2}(p_k^2 + q_k^2) - \tfrac{1}{2} \qquad (46.16)$$

Equations (46.15) and (46.16) have the advantage over the equivalent earlier equations (46.12) and (46.13) that their solution has already been obtained in connection with the theory of the linear harmonic oscillator. We now show that some of the results of Sec. 13 provide explicit matrices for the p_k and q_k that make the N_k diagonal.

Connection with the Harmonic Oscillator.   The quantum motion of a particle of mass m acted on by a force $-Kx$, where x is the displacement from equilibrium, was discussed in Sec. 13 from the point of view of the Schrödinger equation.   As shown in Sec. 22 and 23, the solution of this problem is equivalent to the diagonalization of the energy matrix

$$\frac{p^2}{2m} + \tfrac{1}{2}Kx^2$$

when the coordinate x and the canonically conjugate momentum p satisfy a commutation relation like (23.13):

$$[x,p] = i\hbar$$

The energy eigenvalues were found to be given by Eq. (13.8):

$$(n + \tfrac{1}{2})\hbar\left(\frac{K}{m}\right)^{\frac{1}{2}}, \qquad n = 0,1,2, \cdots$$

The matrix for x in the representation in which the energy is diagonal is given by Eqs. (13.18).[1]

If now we identify x with q_k, p with p_k, and set $\hbar$, m, and K equal to unity, we see at once that $N_k + \tfrac{1}{2}$ can be identified with the energy of the oscillator and has the eigenvalues $n_k + \tfrac{1}{2}$, where n_k is a positive integer or zero.   Equations (13.18) then show that the matrix for q_k has the form

$$(q_k)_{n_k, n_k+1} = (q_k)_{n_k+1, n_k} = \left(\frac{n_k + 1}{2}\right)^{\frac{1}{2}} \tag{46.17}$$

with other matrix elements vanishing.   A calculation similar to that which resulted in (13.18) can be used to show that the matrix for p_k has the form

$$(p_k)_{n_k, n_k+1} = -(p_k)_{n_k+1, n_k} = -i\left(\frac{n_k + 1}{2}\right)^{\frac{1}{2}} \tag{46.18}$$

with other matrix elements vanishing.   The matrices for a_k and a_k^* can then be obtained from (46.14):

$$(a_k)_{n_k, n_k+1} = (a_k^*)_{n_k+1, n_k} = (n_k + 1)^{\frac{1}{2}} \tag{46.19}$$

All other matrix elements vanish.   Equations (46.17), (46.18), and (46.19) imply that the nonvanishing matrix elements refer to pairs of states for

---

[1] These results can also be obtained by purely matrix methods, without explicit solution of the Schrödinger equation; see Dirac, *op. cit.*, Sec. 34.

which all the other n_l have the same values, since q_k, p_k, a_k, and a_k^* each commute with N_l for $l \neq k$.

The matrix for x in the harmonic-oscillator problem can be related to a set of wave functions $u_n(x)$ given by (13.13), such that

$$x_{nn'} = \int \bar{u}_n(x) x u_{n'}(x) dx.$$

We also expect that the matrices for q_k, p_k, a_k, and a_k^* can be related in a similar way to some kind of quantities that play the role of wave functions in the quantized field theory. We call these quantities *wave functionals* Ψ of the numbers n_k; they can be thought of as one-column matrices that have the properties

$$\Psi^*(n_1, \ldots, n_k, \ldots)\Psi(n_1', \ldots, n_k', \ldots)$$
$$= \delta_{n_1 n_1'} \cdots \delta_{n_k n_k'} \cdots$$
$$\Psi^*(n_1, \ldots, n_k, \ldots)a_k\Psi(n_1', \ldots, n_k', \ldots)$$
$$= (n_k + 1)^{\frac{1}{2}}\delta_{n_1 n_1'} \cdots \delta_{n_k+1, n_k'} \cdots \quad (46.20)$$
$$\Psi^*(n_1, \ldots, n_k, \ldots)a_k^*\Psi(n_1', \ldots, n_k', \ldots)$$
$$= n_k^{\frac{1}{2}}\delta_{n_1 n_1'} \cdots \delta_{n_k-1, n_k'} \cdots$$

in agreement with Eqs. (46.19). Equations (46.20) are equivalent to the statement that the Ψ's are orthonormal and satisfy the relations

$$a_k\Psi(n_1, \ldots, n_k, \ldots)$$
$$= n_k^{\frac{1}{2}}\Psi(n_1, \ldots, n_k - 1, \ldots)$$
$$a_k^*\Psi(n_1, \ldots, n_k, \ldots)$$
$$= (n_k + 1)^{\frac{1}{2}}\Psi(n_1, \ldots, n_k + 1, \ldots) \quad (46.21)$$

Physical Interpretation. Since we regard N as the operator for the total number of particles in the quantized field, it is reasonable to assume that N_k is the operator for the number of particles in a state of the field that is described by the space function $u_k(\mathbf{r})$. We thus have the result that a precise measurement of the number of particles in any state must be one of the positive integers or zero. Equation (46.13) then shows that this also applies to the total number of particles.

Although N is a constant of the motion, N_k need not be. Substitution of N_k for F in Eq. (45.23) gives

$$i\hbar \dot{N}_k = [a_k^* a_k, H]$$

H can be expressed in terms of the a_k by substituting (46.11) into (46.5).

$$H = \sum_{jl} a_j^* a_l \int \left(\frac{\hbar^2}{2m} \operatorname{grad} \bar{u}_j \cdot \operatorname{grad} u_l + V\bar{u}_j u_l\right) d\tau$$
$$= \sum_{jl} a_j^* a_l \int \bar{u}_j \left(-\frac{\hbar^2}{2m} \nabla^2 + V\right) u_l d\tau \quad (46.22)$$

It is not difficult to show from (46.12) that a particular N_k is constant if and only if all the volume integrals in (46.22) are zero for which either j or l is equal to k. These integrals are just the matrix elements of the one-particle Hamiltonian (22.2), so that the necessary and sufficient condition that N_k be a constant of the motion is that all such off-diagonal elements that involve the state u_k be zero.[1]

The case in which the u_k are eigenfunctions of (22.2) with eigenvalues E_k is of particular interest. The integrals in (46.22) are then $E_l \delta_{jl}$, and the field Hamiltonian becomes

$$H = \sum_k a_k^* a_k E_k = \sum_k N_k E_k \qquad (46.23)$$

This particular N representation is one in which H is also diagonal; the wave functional $\Psi(n_1, \dots, n_k, \dots)$ has the eigenvalue $\sum_k n_k E_k$ for the total-energy operator H. It is apparent that all the N_k are constant in this case.

The first of Eqs. (46.21) permits the interpretation of a_k as a *destruction operator* for particles in the state k, since it converts a wave functional into a multiple of one that has one less particle in that state. Similarly, a_k^* can be interpreted as a *creation operator*, since it increases the number of particles in the kth state by unity.

Connection with the Many-particle Schrödinger Equation. The quantized field theory is closely related to the many-particle Schrödinger equation discussed in Sec. 32. If the u_k are eigenfunctions of the one-particle Hamiltonian (22.2), the field theory shows that stationary solutions exist for which the number of particles n_k in the kth state is a constant positive integer or zero, and the energy is $\sum_k n_k E_k$. Each solution can be specified by a wave functional $\Psi(n_1, \dots, n_k, \dots)$; the Ψ's form a complete set, and there is just one solution for each set of numbers $n_1, \dots$. A stationary many-particle wave function like the ψ in Eq. (32.1) can be written as a product of one-particle wave functions $u_k(\mathbf{r}) e^{-\frac{iE_k t}{\hbar}}$ if there is no interaction between particles. The linear combination of such products that is symmetric with respect to interchange of any pair of particle coordinates can be specified uniquely by stating the number of particles in each state. Again, the number of particles in each state is a positive integer or zero, and the energy is the sum of all the particle energies.

---

[1] This result for the quantized field is closely related to the corresponding result, contained in Eq. (29.5), for the one-particle probability amplitude.

We see then that the quantized field theory developed thus far in this section is equivalent to the Schrödinger equation for several non-interacting particles, provided that only the symmetric solutions are retained in the latter case. We are thus led to a theory of particles that obey Einstein-Bose statistics. It can be shown that the two theories are completely equivalent even if interactions between particles are taken into account.[1]

It is natural to see if there is some way in which the quantized field formalism can be modified to yield a theory of particles that obey Fermi-Dirac statistics. As discussed in Sec. 32, a system of such particles can be described by a many-particle wave function that is antisymmetric with respect to interchange of any pair of particle coordinates. The required linear combination of products of one-particle wave functions can be specified uniquely by stating the number of particles in each state, provided that each of these numbers is either 0 or 1. The desired modification of the theory must, therefore, limit the eigenvalues of each operator N_k to 0 and 1.

Anticommutation Relations. A review of the foregoing theory shows that the conclusion that the eigenvalues of each N_k are the positive integers and zero stems from the commutation relations (46.12) for the a_k and a_k^*. Equations (46.12) in turn arise from the commutation relations (46.6) for ψ and ψ^*. Thus we must modify Eqs. (46.6) if we are to obtain a theory of particles that obey the exclusion principle. It is reasonable to require that this modification be made in such a way that the quantum equation of motion for ψ is the wave equation (46.2) when the Hamiltonian has the form (46.5).

It was found by Jordan and Wigner[2] that the desired modification consists in the replacement of the commutator brackets $[A,B] \equiv AB - BA$ in Eqs. (45.22) and (46.6) by *anticommutator brackets* $[A,B]_+ \equiv AB + BA$. This means that Eqs. (46.6) are replaced by

$$[\psi(\mathbf{r}),\psi(\mathbf{r}')]_+ = \psi(\mathbf{r})\psi(\mathbf{r}') + \psi(\mathbf{r}')\psi(\mathbf{r}) = 0$$
$$[\psi^*(\mathbf{r}),\psi^*(\mathbf{r}')]_+ = \psi^*(\mathbf{r})\psi^*(\mathbf{r}') + \psi^*(\mathbf{r}')\psi^*(\mathbf{r}) = 0 \qquad (46.24)$$
$$[\psi(\mathbf{r}),\psi^*(\mathbf{r}')]_+ = \psi(\mathbf{r})\psi^*(\mathbf{r}') + \psi^*(\mathbf{r}')\psi(\mathbf{r}) = \delta(\mathbf{r} - \mathbf{r}')$$

It then follows directly from Eqs. (46.11) and (46.24) that

$$[a_k,a_l]_+ = a_k a_l + a_l a_k = 0$$
$$[a_k^*,a_l^*]_+ = a_k^* a_l^* + a_l^* a_k^* = 0 \qquad (46.25)$$
$$[a_k,a_l^*]_+ = a_k a_l^* + a_l^* a_k = \delta_{kl}$$

[1] See Heisenberg, *op. cit.*, Appendix, Sec. 11.
[2] P. Jordan and E. Wigner, *Zeits. f. Physik*, **47**, 631 (1928).

We define $N_k = a_k^* a_k$ as before, and notice first that each N_k commutes with all the others, so that they can be diagonalized simultaneously. The eigenvalues of N_k can be obtained from the matrix equation

$$
\begin{aligned}
N_k^2 &= a_k^* a_k a_k^* a_k \\
&= a_k^*(1 - a_k^* a_k)a_k = a_k^* a_k = N_k
\end{aligned}
\tag{46.26}
$$

where use has been made of Eqs. (46.25). If N_k is in diagonal form and has the eigenvalues $n_k', n_k'', \ldots$, it is apparent that N_k^2 is also in diagonal form and has the eigenvalues $n_k'^2, n_k''^2, \ldots$. Thus the matrix equation (46.26) is equivalent to the algebraic equations

$$
n_k'^2 = n_k', \qquad n_k''^2 = n_k'', \ldots
$$

for the eigenvalues. These are quadratic equations that have two roots: 0 and 1. Thus the eigenvalues of each N_k are 0 and 1, and the particles obey the exclusion principle. The eigenvalues of $N = \sum_k N_k$ are the positive integers and zero, as before. The earlier expressions (46.22) and (46.23) for the Hamiltonian are unchanged, and the energy eigenvalues are $\sum_k n_k E_k$.

Equation of Motion. In order to find the quantum equation of motion for ψ when the Hamiltonian is given by (46.5), we must decide whether or not the general equation of motion (45.23) is to be retained. The latter equation was obtained by replacing the Poisson bracket by the commutator bracket in the classical equation (45.20). This replacement was justified by analogy with the particle theory of Sec. 23, by the identical algebraic properties of the two kinds of bracket expressions given in (23.12), and by the correspondence-theory argument of Prob. 10, Chap. VI. Thus abandonment of Eq. (45.23) means that the classical equation (45.20) is likewise abandoned; since many of the quantities with which we are concerned (number of particles, energy, etc.) have well-defined classical analogues, we shall retain (45.23) as the general quantum equation of motion.

The equation for ψ is then given by (46.7), where now the anticommutation relations (46.24) are to be used in evaluating the right side. This causes (46.8) to be replaced by

$$
\begin{aligned}
\int V'(\psi \psi^* \psi' - \psi^* \psi' \psi)d\tau' &= \int V'(\psi \psi^{*'} + \psi^{*'} \psi)\psi' d\tau' \\
&= \int V' \psi' \delta(\mathbf{r} - \mathbf{r}')d\tau' = V\psi
\end{aligned}
$$

The similar treatment of the first term on the right side of (46.7) gives no change in the right side of (46.9). Thus the wave equation (46.2) is unaffected by the substitution of anticommutation for commutation relations between the wave amplitudes. It can also be shown without difficulty that N and the anticommutator brackets in (46.24) are constants of the motion.

Physical Implications of Anticommutation. Since anticommutator brackets do not possess the algebraic properties of Poisson brackets, we can conclude that there is no classical analogue for the quantities ψ and a_k that satisfy the relations (46.24) and (46.25). This does not mean, however, that N and H do not possess classical limits, for they are constructed of bilinear combinations of ψ or a_k and commute with each other.

These conclusions can be confirmed on the basis of physical considerations. In order that a field amplitude be strong enough to be classically measurable, it must be possible to have a very large number of particles in the same state so that their fields are coherent. This implies that such particles obey Einstein-Bose statistics. We can, for example, conclude that light quanta or photons obey Einstein-Bose statistics, since it is known that strong electric and magnetic fields can be produced and are classically measurable. In the case of metallic electrons, which obey Fermi-Dirac statistics, quantities like energy, and charge and current density, are classically measurable since they can be expressed as bilinear combinations of the field amplitude, while the electron field amplitude itself is not.[1]

Representation of the Anticommuting a_k Operators. An explicit representation for the operators that appear in (46.25) is easily obtained in the hypothetical but instructive case in which the system has only one state. The matrix equations to be solved are

$$a^2 = a^{*2} = 0, \qquad aa^* + a^*a = 1, \qquad N = a^*a \qquad (46.27)$$

Equations (46.27) are just those solved in Prob. 2, Chap. VI. We have already seen in (46.26) that $N^2 = N$, so that N has the eigenvalues 0 and 1. If there is no degeneracy, N can be represented by the diagonal matrix

$$N = \begin{pmatrix} 0 & 0 \\ 0 & 1 \end{pmatrix} \qquad (46.28)$$

It is interesting to note that a cannot be diagonalized since N has a non-vanishing eigenvalue. If it could be, the first of Eqs. (46.27) would show

---

[1] The classical measurability of the field amplitude for any charged particle (Einstein-Bose or Fermi-Dirac statistics) implies that ψ appears linearly in H, since the energy must then depend on ψ itself as well as on bilinear combinations of ψ. This in turn implies that terms linear in a_k or a_k^* appear in the Hamiltonian, so that single charged particles can be destroyed or created. Thus ψ cannot be measured classically if the theory is such that electric charge is conserved.

that the square of each of its eigenvalues is zero; this would mean that a, and hence a^* and N, are identically zero, so that N could not have the form (46.28) in any representation.

Explicit matrices for a and a^* that agree with (46.27) and (46.28) are

$$a = \begin{pmatrix} 0 & 1 \\ 0 & 0 \end{pmatrix}, \qquad a^* = \begin{pmatrix} 0 & 0 \\ 1 & 0 \end{pmatrix} \tag{46.29}$$

The two wave functionals that represent the two possible states of this system can be expressed as

$$\Psi(0) = \begin{pmatrix} 1 \\ 0 \end{pmatrix}, \qquad \Psi(1) = \begin{pmatrix} 0 \\ 1 \end{pmatrix} \tag{46.30}$$

It is easily seen that the first of (46.30) has the eigenvalue 0 for the operator N given in (46.28), and the second wave functional has the eigenvalue 1. The following relations are easily obtained from Eqs. (46.29) and (46.30):

$$a\Psi(n) = n\Psi(1 - n), \qquad a^*\Psi(n) = (1 - n)\Psi(1 - n), \quad n = 0,1 \tag{46.31}$$

Thus a and a^* again play the roles of destruction and creation operators, respectively.

In the actual problem, the number of states of the system is infinite, and it is not convenient to write down explicit matrices like those in (46.28), (46.29), and (46.30). We can, however, find the effects of operation with a_k and a_k^* on a wave functional $\Psi(n_1, \ldots, n_k, \ldots)$ that has the eigenvalue n_k ($= 0$ or 1) for the operator N_k. The desired relations would have the form (46.31), were it not that a series of such equations (with subscripts added) would not agree with the first two of Eqs. (46.25).

We therefore proceed in the following way. We order the states k of the system in an arbitrary but definite way: $1, 2, \ldots, k, \ldots$. Then the effect of operating with each a_k or a_k^* on Ψ has the form (46.31), except that a multiplying plus sign or minus sign is introduced, according as the kth state is preceded in the assumed order by an even or an odd number of *occupied* states. We thus replace Eqs. (46.21) by

$$a_k\Psi(n_1, \ldots, n_k, \ldots)$$
$$= \theta_k n_k \Psi(n_1, \ldots, 1 - n_k, \ldots)$$
$$a_k^*\Psi(n_1, \ldots, n_k, \ldots)$$
$$= \theta_k(1 - n_k)\Psi(n_1, \ldots, 1 - n_k, \ldots) \tag{46.32}$$
$$\theta_k = (-1)^{\nu_k}, \qquad \nu_k = \sum_{j=1}^{k-1} n_j$$

As an example, we calculate the effect of operating with $a_k a_l$ and with $a_l a_k$ on a wave functional Ψ, where we assume for definiteness that the order is such that $l > k$. If each operation is not to give a zero result, both n_k and n_l in the original Ψ must equal unity. Operation with $a_k a_l$ empties first the lth and then the kth state, and introduces a factor $\theta_l \theta_k$. Operation with $a_l a_k$ empties the kth state first, so that θ_k is unchanged. But when the lth state is emptied in this case, there is one less particle in the states below the lth than there was in the previous case, since the kth state is now empty, whereas it was occupied before. Thus the sign of θ_l is changed. We find then that $a_k a_l \Psi = -a_l a_k \Psi$, in agreement with the first of Eqs. (46.25). In similar fashion, it can be shown that Eqs. (46.32) agree with the result of operating with the other two of Eqs. (46.25) on any Ψ. Since the aggregate of wave functionals represents all possible states of the many-particle system, the Ψ's constitute a complete set, and Eqs. (46.25) follow as operator equations from Eqs. (46.32).

47. QUANTIZATION OF THE DIRAC EQUATION

As our second example, we now consider the quantization of Dirac's relativistic equation (43.3) for a free electron. Our procedure again consists in treating the one-particle equation as though it were a classical field equation. The resulting quantized field theory represents the motion of a number of noninteracting free electrons.

Lagrangian and Hamiltonian Equations. The Dirac wave function ψ has four components that we denote by ψ_j ($j = 1, 2, 3, 4$). The Lagrangian density may be taken to be

$$L = \sum_j \bar{\psi}_j \left(i\hbar \dot{\psi}_j - i\hbar c \sum_l \alpha_{jl} \cdot \mathbf{grad}\ \psi + mc^2 \sum_l \beta_{jl} \psi_l \right) \qquad (47.1)$$

where the matrices α_{jl} and β_{jl} are given in Eqs. (43.12). We must now use the multicomponent extension of the field theory described at the end of Sec. 45. Variation of one of the components ψ_l of ψ leads to an equation of the type (45.8):

$$mc^2 \sum_j \bar{\psi}_j \beta_{jl} + i\hbar c \sum_j \mathbf{grad}\ \bar{\psi}_j \cdot \alpha_{jl} - i\hbar \dot{\bar{\psi}}_l = 0 \qquad (47.2)$$

The four equations like (47.2) may be written together as

$$-i\hbar \dot{\psi}^* + i\hbar c\ \mathbf{grad}\ \psi^* \cdot \alpha + mc^2 \psi^* \beta = 0$$

where ψ^* is the Hermitian adjoint of ψ and is a matrix with one row and four columns; this equation is the Hermitian adjoint of (43.3). In similar fashion, it is easily shown that separate variation of the four fields $\bar{\psi}_j$

results in four equations that can be written together as

$$i\hbar\dot\psi - i\hbar c\boldsymbol\alpha \cdot \text{grad } \psi + mc^2\beta\psi = 0 \qquad (47.3)$$

which is the same as the Dirac equation (43.3).

The momentum canonically conjugate to ψ_j is

$$\pi_j = \frac{\partial L}{\partial \dot\psi_j} = i\hbar\psi_j^* \qquad (47.4)$$

As with the nonrelativistic Schrödinger equation, the momentum $\bar\pi_j$ canonically conjugate to ψ_j^* is identically zero; we therefore eliminate ψ_j^* from the Hamiltonian with the help of (47.4).   Then the Hamiltonian density is

$$H = \sum_j \pi_j\dot\psi_j - L$$

$$= c \sum_{jl} \pi_j\alpha_{jl} \cdot \text{grad } \psi_l + \frac{imc^2}{\hbar} \sum_{jl} \pi_j\beta_{jl}\psi_l \qquad (47.5)$$

It is not difficult to show (see Prob. 12) that the first of the Hamiltonian equations (45.19) is the same as (47.3), and that the second Hamiltonian equation, together with (47.4), gives the Hermitian adjoint of (47.3). This completes our demonstration that (47.1), (47.4), and (47.5) are in agreement with the Dirac equation.

Quantum Equations.   As with the nonrelativistic Schrödinger equation, it is convenient to rewrite the Hamiltonian with the help of (47.4)

$$H = \int \left(i\hbar c \sum_{jl} \psi_j^*\alpha_{jl} \cdot \text{grad } \psi_l - mc^2 \sum_{jl} \psi_j^*\beta_{jl}\psi_l\right) d\tau$$

$$= \int(i\hbar c\psi^*\boldsymbol\alpha \cdot \text{grad } \psi - mc^2\psi^*\beta\psi)d\tau \qquad (47.6)$$

In spite of its appearance this expression is actually real, as can be seen by performing a partial integration on half of the first term to obtain

$$H = \int[\tfrac{1}{2}i\hbar c(\psi^*\boldsymbol\alpha \cdot \text{grad } \psi - \text{grad } \psi^* \cdot \boldsymbol\alpha\psi) - mc^2\psi^*\beta\psi]d\tau \qquad (47.7)$$

The surface terms vanish because ψ either vanishes at infinity or obeys periodic boundary conditions.

We have already seen (Sec. 32) that electrons obey the exclusion principle.   We therefore quantize the field by imposing anticommutation relations on the components of ψ.   With the help of (47.4) these become

$$\begin{aligned}
[\psi_j(\mathbf{r}),\psi_l(\mathbf{r}')]_+ &= [\psi_j^*(\mathbf{r}),\psi_l^*(\mathbf{r}')]_+ = 0 \\
[\psi_j(\mathbf{r}),\psi_l^*(\mathbf{r}')]_+ &= \delta_{jl}\delta(\mathbf{r} - \mathbf{r}')
\end{aligned} \qquad (47.8)$$

The substitution of ψ_j^* for $\bar{\psi}_j$ implies that each ψ_j is now a quantum-mechanical operator rather than a numerical function; we interpret ψ^* to mean the matrix that has one row and four columns, whose elements are the operators ψ_j^*.

The quantum equation for ψ is obtained by substituting ψ_j for F in Eq. (45.23), where H is given by (47.6) or (47.7).

$$i\hbar\dot\psi_j = \left[\psi_j, \int \left(i\hbar c \sum_{kl} \psi_k^{*\prime}\alpha_{kl}\cdot \mathbf{grad}' \,\psi_l' - mc^2 \sum_{kl} \psi_k^{*\prime}\beta_{kl}\psi_l'\right) d\tau'\right] \quad (47.9)$$

Primes indicate that an integration variable $\mathbf{r}'$ has been substituted for $\mathbf{r}$. The second term on the right side can be evaluated with the help of (47.8) as follows:

$$\left[\psi_j, \int -mc^2 \sum_{kl} \psi_k^{*\prime}\beta_{kl}\psi_l' d\tau'\right]$$

$$= -mc^2 \sum_{kl} \beta_{kl} \int [\psi_j, \psi_k^{*\prime}\psi_l']d\tau'$$

$$= -mc^2 \sum_{kl} \beta_{kl} \int (\psi_j\psi_k^{*\prime}\psi_l' - \psi_k^{*\prime}\psi_l'\psi_j)d\tau'$$

$$= -mc^2 \sum_{kl} \beta_{kl} \int (\psi_j\psi_k^{*\prime} + \psi_k^{*\prime}\psi_j)\psi_l' d\tau'$$

$$= -mc^2 \sum_{kl} \beta_{kl}\delta_{jk} \int \psi_l'\delta(\mathbf{r}-\mathbf{r}')d\tau' = -mc^2 \sum_l \beta_{jl}\psi_l$$

Evaluation of the first term on the right side of (47.9) is accomplished in the same way, since ψ_j anticommutes with $\mathbf{grad}'\,\psi_l'$ as well as with ψ_l':

$$\left[\psi_j, \int i\hbar c \sum_{kl} \psi_k^{*\prime}\alpha_{kl}\cdot \mathbf{grad}' \,\psi_l' d\tau'\right] = i\hbar c \sum_l \alpha_{jl}\cdot \mathbf{grad}\,\psi_l$$

Thus the four equations like (47.9) are equivalent to the Dirac equation (47.3). A similar calculation shows that the four equations of the form $i\hbar\dot\psi_j^* = [\psi_j^*,H]$ yield the Hermitian adjoint of (47.3).

The operator N for the total number of electrons in the field can be written

$$N = \int \psi^*\psi d\tau = \int \sum_j \psi_j^*\psi_j d\tau \quad (47.10)$$

It is apparent that N is Hermitian, and it can also be shown that

$$i\hbar\dot N = [N,H] = 0$$

so that N is a constant of the motion (see Prob. 13). As with the non-relativistic theory of Sec. 46, the anticommutator brackets in (47.8) can be shown to be constant in time.

The N Representation. A representation in which N is diagonal is conveniently found by expanding ψ in plane wave solutions of the Dirac equation for a single free electron. The entire procedure is exactly analogous to that followed in the last section, but is complicated by the multicomponent nature of the Dirac field. We shall continue to denote the four components of ψ and of the plane waves by a subscript j or l. The propagation vector of a plane wave (momentum divided by $\hbar$) will be denoted by $\mathbf{k}$, and it will be assumed that these waves obey periodic boundary conditions at the walls of a large cubical box of edge length L.

We saw in Sec. 43 that there are four solutions for each value of $\mathbf{k}$; these will be distinguished by the letter s ($= 1, 2, 3, 4$), so that both $\mathbf{k}$ and s must be given in order to specify a one-electron plane wave solution. The free electron solutions that form a complete orthonormal set of functions within the volume L^3 are then

$$v_j(\mathbf{k},s;\mathbf{r}) = u_j(\mathbf{k},s)L^{-\frac{3}{2}} \exp i\mathbf{k} \cdot \mathbf{r} \qquad (47.11)$$

The $u_j(\mathbf{k},s)$ are numbers obtained by multiplying the four sets of u_j given in Eqs. (43.17) and (43.18) through by the normalizing factor given there. The two solutions (43.17) will be denoted by $s = 1, 2$, and correspond to the two spin orientations for the positive energy:

$$E_{\mathbf{k}s} = +(\hbar^2 c^2 \mathbf{k}^2 + m^2 c^4)^{\frac{1}{2}}, \qquad s = 1,2 \qquad (47.12)$$

The two solutions (43.18) are for negative energy:

$$E_{\mathbf{k}s} = -(\hbar^2 c^2 \mathbf{k}^2 + m^2 c^4)^{\frac{1}{2}}, \qquad s = 3,4 \qquad (47.13)$$

The orthonormality relations for the v_j of Eq. (47.11) are easily seen to be

$$\int \sum_j \bar{v}_j(\mathbf{k},s;\mathbf{r})v_j(\mathbf{k}',s';\mathbf{r})d\tau = \delta_{\mathbf{k}\mathbf{k}'}\delta_{ss'} \qquad (47.14)$$

As in Eqs. (46.11), we expand ψ_j and ψ_j^* in terms of the v_j:

$$\begin{aligned}
\psi_j(\mathbf{r},t) &= \sum_{\mathbf{k}s} a(\mathbf{k},s;t)v_j(\mathbf{k},s;\mathbf{r}) \\
\psi_j^*(\mathbf{r},t) &= \sum_{\mathbf{k}s} a^*(\mathbf{k},s;t)\bar{v}_j(\mathbf{k},s;\mathbf{r})
\end{aligned} \qquad (47.15)$$

The coefficients a and a^* are quantum-mechanical operators that depend on the time. With the help of the orthonormality property (47.14) it is not difficult to show that the anticommutation relations (47.8) are equivalent to

$$\begin{aligned}
[a(\mathbf{k},s;t),a(\mathbf{k}',s';t)]_+ &= [a^*(\mathbf{k},s;t),a^*(\mathbf{k}',s';t)]_+ = 0 \\
[a(\mathbf{k},s;t),a^*(\mathbf{k}',s';t)]_+ &= \delta_{\mathbf{k}\mathbf{k}'}\delta_{ss'}
\end{aligned} \qquad (47.16)$$

Substitution of (47.15) into (47.10) shows that

$$N = \sum_{ks} N_{ks} \quad \text{where } N_{ks} = a^*(k,s;t)a(k,s;t) \quad (47.17)$$

The work of Sec. 46 shows that the eigenvalues of each N_{ks} are 0 and 1, so that there cannot be more than one electron in each state (which is specified by the spin orientation, the value of the momentum, and the sign of the energy). Explicit expressions for the a's, analogous to (46.32), can also be written down.

Substitution of (47.15) into the expression (47.6) for the field Hamiltonian gives

$$H = \sum_{jl} \int (i\hbar c \psi_j^* \alpha_{jl} \cdot \text{grad } \psi_l - mc^2 \psi_j^* \beta_{jl} \psi_l) d\tau$$

$$= \sum_{jl} \int \sum_{ks} \sum_{k's'} a^*(k,s;t)a(k',s';t)\bar{v}_j(k,s;r)$$

$$\cdot (i\hbar c \alpha_{jl} \cdot \text{grad } - mc^2 \beta_{jl})v_l(k',s';r)d\tau$$

The solution of Eqs. (43.16) shows that the v_j defined by (47.11) satisfy the equations

$$\sum_l (i\hbar c \alpha_{jl} \cdot \text{grad } - mc^2 \beta_{jl})v_l(k',s';r) = E_{k's'}v_j(k',s';r)$$

We then obtain, with the help of (47.14),

$$H = \sum_{ks} a^*(k,s;t)a(k,s;t)E_{ks} = \sum_{ks} N_{ks}E_{ks} \quad (47.18)$$

where the E_{ks} are given by (47.12) and (47.13). It follows at once that the N_{ks} are constants of the motion, since they commute with each other and hence with H.

Negative Energy States and Positrons. All the results obtained thus far in this section can be obtained from the assumption that the ψ's and a's commute, as well as from the assumption that they anticommute. This makes it seem that the Dirac theory can describe either particles of spin $\frac{1}{2}\hbar$ that obey Einstein-Bose statistics, or electrons that obey the exclusion principle. It is easily seen, however, that the field energy operator (47.18) has negative eigenvalues of arbitrarily large magnitude, which correspond to electrons in negative energy states ($s = 3,4$). The existence of such eigenvalues implies that there is no equilibrium condition of the field when electromagnetic interactions are taken into account, since an electron will make radiative transitions to states of lower and lower energy.   This difficulty cannot be avoided so long as the particles are assumed to obey Einstein-Bose statistics.

It was proposed by Dirac[1] that the undesirable transitions to negative energy states be eliminated from the theory by the assumption that the normal condition of empty space is that in which all positive energy states are empty and all negative energy states are full:

$$N_{k1} = N_{k2} = 0, \qquad N_{k3} = N_{k4} = 1 \quad \text{for all } \mathbf{k} \quad (47.19)$$

This is an equilibrium condition of the field, since the exclusion principle prevents transitions into the negative energy states.   It is also assumed that the infinite density of negative-energy electrons produces no observable electromagnetic or gravitational effects, but that departures from the vacuum values (47.19) are observable in the usual way.   We therefore subtract the vacuum values

$$\sum_{\mathbf{k}} \sum_{s=3,4} e \qquad \text{and} \qquad \sum_{\mathbf{k}} \sum_{s=3,4} E_{\mathbf{k}s}$$

for the total electric charge and total energy, from the total charge and energy operators eN and H, respectively; e is the (negative) charge of an electron.

The resulting expression for the total observable charge is

$$e \sum_{\mathbf{k}} \left(\sum_{s=1,2} N_{\mathbf{k}s} - \sum_{s=3,4} N_{\mathbf{k}s}' \right), \; N_{\mathbf{k}s}' \equiv 1 - N_{\mathbf{k}s} = a(\mathbf{k},s;t)a^*(\mathbf{k},s;t) \quad (47.20)$$

The new operator $N_{\mathbf{k}s}'$ has the eigenvalue 0 when the state $\mathbf{k}s$ is full and the eigenvalue 1 when that state is empty.   The similar expression for the total observable energy is

$$\sum_{\mathbf{k}} \left(\sum_{s=1,2} N_{\mathbf{k}s} E_{\mathbf{k}s} + \sum_{s=3,4} N_{\mathbf{k}s}' |E_{\mathbf{k}s}| \right) \qquad (47.21)$$

According to (47.20), each positive-energy particle acts like a negative electron, and each *missing* negative-energy particle like a positive electron; (47.21) then shows that the observable energy is positive, and equal to the sum of a positive term for each positive-energy particle and for each missing negative-energy particle.   It is therefore reasonable to interpret the "holes" in the otherwise occupied set of negative energy states as positive electrons or positrons.   Because of the relation (47.13) between energy and momentum, positrons have the same rest mass as electrons.   The existence of positrons was predicted by Dirac on the basis of this theory in advance of their discovery in cosmic radiation.[2]

---

[1] See also J. R. Oppenheimer, *Phys. Rev.*, **35**, 562 (1930).

[2] For further discussion of the formal aspects of positron theory, see Wentzel, *op. cit.*, Chap. V.

We have seen that the Dirac theory, which describes particles of spin $\frac{1}{2}\hbar$, can only be quantized in accordance with the exclusion principle. This is a special case of a general result, obtained by Pauli,[1] according to which particles of zero or integer spin obey Einstein-Bose statistics and particles of half-odd-integer spin obey Fermi-Dirac statistics. The connection between spin and statistics can be derived only for relativistic theories. For example, the negative energy states that prevent Einstein-Bose quantization of the Dirac equation appear only in a relativistic theory, and the nonrelativistic Schrödinger equation was successfully quantized in both ways in Sec. 46.

Anticommutation Relations at Different Times. All the commutation and anticommutation relations that have been used up to now have been between quantities that refer to the same time. In a relativistic theory, however, there is some reason for being interested in relations of this kind between quantities that refer to different times. Such relations can be used to investigate the causal connections between events that occur at different times and places, and hence the relativistic character of the field theory as a whole.

To see this, suppose that we have a physically observable quantity, such as particle or charge density, which can be represented by an operator that depends on $\mathbf{r}$ and t. It is interesting to inquire under what circumstances the values of this observable at different space-time points can be measured without interference of one measurement with the other. Measurements without interference can be made if the two operators that represent the observable at the two points commute with each other, since then their matrices can be diagonalized simultaneously and precise results (eigenvalues) can be obtained from both measurements. We expect that observables at the same time and different space points will always commute, since there is no way in which an effect can be propagated over a finite distance in zero time. In a nonrelativistic theory, observables at different time and space points need not commute, for there is no limit to the speed at which effects can be propagated. In a relativistic theory, however, we expect that observables at different space-time points always commute if the spatial separation of the two points is greater than c times the time interval. Thus commutation or anticommutation relations at different times can provide a direct physical check on a relativistic theory, but are of little interest in connection with a nonrelativistic theory.

The anticommutation relations (47.8) or (47.16) are conveniently extended to different times by finding the equations of motion for the a's. We have from Eqs. (45.23), (47.16), and (47.18) that

[1] W. Pauli, *Phys. Rev.*, **58,** 716 (1940).

$$i\hbar\dot{a}(\mathbf{k},s;\ t) = [a(\mathbf{k},s;\ t),H] = E_{\mathbf{k}s}a(\mathbf{k},s;\ t)$$
$$i\hbar\dot{a}^*(\mathbf{k},s;\ t) = [a^*(\mathbf{k},s;\ t),H] = -E_{\mathbf{k}s}a^*(\mathbf{k},s;\ t)$$

These are easily integrated to give

$$a(\mathbf{k},s;t) = a(\mathbf{k},s;0)\ \exp\left(-\frac{iE_{\mathbf{k}s}t}{\hbar}\right)$$

$$a^*(\mathbf{k},s;t) = a^*(\mathbf{k},s;0)\ \exp\frac{iE_{\mathbf{k}s}t}{\hbar} \tag{47.22}$$

Equations (47.16) apply when both the times that appear are the same; they can both be taken to be zero, in which case we can use (47.22) to obtain

$$[a(\mathbf{k},s;\ t),a(\mathbf{k}',s';\ t')]_+ = [a^*(\mathbf{k},s;\ t)a^*(\mathbf{k}',s';\ t')]_+ = 0$$

$$[a(\mathbf{k},s;\ t),a^*(\mathbf{k}',s';\ t')]_+ = \delta_{\mathbf{k}\mathbf{k}'}\delta_{ss'}\ \exp\frac{iE_{\mathbf{k}s}(t'-t)}{\hbar} \tag{47.23}$$

Substitution of (47.23) into (47.15) enables us to calculate the anticommutation relations for ψ's at different times. It is apparent that

$$[\psi_j(\mathbf{r},t),\psi_l(\mathbf{r}',t')]_+ = [\psi_j^*(\mathbf{r},t),\psi_l^*(\mathbf{r}',t')]_+ = 0 \tag{47.24}$$

The anticommutator bracket for ψ and ψ^* becomes

$$[\psi_j(\mathbf{r},t),\psi_l^*(\mathbf{r}',t')]_+ = \sum_{\mathbf{k}\mathbf{k}'ss'} [a(\mathbf{k},s;\ t),a^*(\mathbf{k}',s';\ t')]_+ v_j(\mathbf{k},s;\ \mathbf{r})\bar{v}_l(\mathbf{k}',s';\ \mathbf{r}')$$

$$= \sum_{\mathbf{k}s} v_j(\mathbf{k},s;\ \mathbf{r})\bar{v}_l(\mathbf{k},s;\ \mathbf{r})\ \exp\frac{iE_{\mathbf{k}s}(t'-t)}{\hbar} \tag{47.25}$$

The last sum could be simplified at once by making use of the closure property

$$\sum_s u_j(\mathbf{k},s)\bar{u}_l(\mathbf{k},s) = \delta_{jl} \tag{47.26}$$

which follows from (43.17) and (43.18), were it not for the fact that $E_{\mathbf{k}s}$ has different signs for different values of s.

As it is, we can still use (47.26) if we first rewrite the exponential in (47.25) so that it does not involve s explicitly. We put

$$\exp\left(-\frac{iE_{\mathbf{k}s}\tau}{\hbar}\right) = \cos\frac{E_{\mathbf{k}s}\tau}{\hbar} - i\ \sin\frac{E_{\mathbf{k}s}\tau}{\hbar}$$

$$= \cos\frac{|E_{\mathbf{k}s}|\tau}{\hbar} - \frac{iE_{\mathbf{k}s}}{\hbar}\frac{\sin\left(|E_{\mathbf{k}s}|\tau/\hbar\right)}{|E_{\mathbf{k}s}|/\hbar}$$

where $\tau = t - t'$, $|E_{\mathbf{k}s}|/\hbar = +c(k^2 + k_0^2)^{\frac{1}{2}}$ is independent of s, and $k_0 = mc/\hbar$. We can write this as

$$\exp\left(-\frac{iE_{\mathbf{k}s}\tau}{\hbar}\right) = \left(\frac{\partial}{\partial\tau} - \frac{iE_{\mathbf{k}s}}{\hbar}\right)\frac{\sin c\tau(k^2 + k_0^2)^{\frac{1}{2}}}{c(k^2 + k_0^2)^{\frac{1}{2}}}$$

The remaining factor E_{ks} can be replaced by an operator:

$$E_{ks}v_j(\mathbf{k},s;\mathbf{r}) = \sum_{l'} (i\hbar c\alpha_{jl'} \cdot \mathbf{grad} - mc^2\beta_{jl'})v_{l'}(\mathbf{k},s;\mathbf{r})$$

Substitution into (47.25) gives, with the help of (47.26),

$$[\psi_j(\mathbf{r},t),\psi_l^*(\mathbf{r}',t')]_+ = \sum_{\mathbf{k},s} \bar{v}_l(\mathbf{k},s;\mathbf{r}')$$

$$\cdot \sum_{l'} \left(\delta_{jl'}\frac{\partial}{\partial\tau} + c\alpha_{jl'} \cdot \mathbf{grad} + ick_0\beta_{jl'} \right) v_{l'}(\mathbf{k},s;\mathbf{r}) \frac{\sin c\tau(k^2 + k_0^2)^{\frac{1}{2}}}{c(k^2 + k_0^2)^{\frac{1}{2}}}$$

$$= \left(\delta_{jl}\frac{\partial}{\partial\tau} + c\alpha_{jl} \cdot \mathbf{grad} + ick_0\beta_{jl} \right)$$

$$\cdot \sum_{\mathbf{k}} L^{-3} [\exp i\mathbf{k} \cdot (\mathbf{r} - \mathbf{r}')] \frac{\sin c\tau(k^2 + k_0^2)^{\frac{1}{2}}}{c(k^2 + k_0^2)^{\frac{1}{2}}}$$

$$= \left(\delta_{jl}\frac{\partial}{\partial t} + c\alpha_{jl} \cdot \mathbf{grad} + ick_0\beta_{jl} \right)D(\mathbf{r} - \mathbf{r}',t - t') \quad (47.27)$$

where

$$D(\mathbf{r},t) \equiv \sum_{\mathbf{k}} L^{-3}(\exp i\mathbf{k} \cdot \mathbf{r}) \frac{\sin ct(k^2 + k_0^2)^{\frac{1}{2}}}{c(k^2 + k_0^2)^{\frac{1}{2}}} \quad (47.28)$$

It can be shown that (47.27) reduces to the third of Eqs. (47.8) when $t' = t$ (see Prob. 14).

Commutation Relation for the Charge Density. The charge density in the Dirac theory, without the modification (47.20) that results in positrons, is

$$\rho(\mathbf{r},t) = e\psi^*(\mathbf{r},t)\psi(\mathbf{r},t) = e\sum_j \psi_j^*(\mathbf{r},t)\psi_j(\mathbf{r},t)$$

In order to discuss the extent to which measurements of ρ at different space-time points interfere with each other, we must calculate the commutator bracket

$$[\rho(\mathbf{r},t),\rho(\mathbf{r}',t')] = e^2 \sum_{jl} [\psi_j^*(\mathbf{r},t)\psi_j(\mathbf{r},t)\psi_l^*(\mathbf{r}',t')\psi_l(\mathbf{r}',t')$$

$$-\psi_l^*(\mathbf{r}',t')\psi_l(\mathbf{r}',t')\psi_j^*(\mathbf{r},t)\psi_j(\mathbf{r},t)]$$

With the help of Eqs. (47.24) and (47.27), this can be reduced to

$$[\rho(\mathbf{r},t),\rho(\mathbf{r}',t')] = e^2 \sum_{jl} \psi_j^*(\mathbf{r},t)\psi_l(\mathbf{r}',t') \left(\delta_{jl}\frac{\partial}{\partial t} + c\alpha_{jl} \cdot \mathbf{grad} + ick_0\beta_{jl} \right)$$

$$\cdot D(\mathbf{r} - \mathbf{r}',t - t') - \text{H.A.}$$

where H.A. signifies the Hermitian adjoint of the preceding term. In general, $\rho(\mathbf{r},t)$ will commute with $\rho(\mathbf{r}',t')$ only when $D(\mathbf{r}-\mathbf{r}', t-t')$ is zero.

We therefore examine the structure of the D function by replacing the $\mathbf{k}$ sum in (47.28) by an integral, as in Eq. (11.14):[1]

$$D(\mathbf{r},t) \xrightarrow[L \to \infty]{} (2\pi)^{-3} \int (\exp i\mathbf{k} \cdot \mathbf{r}) \frac{\sin ct(k^2 + k_0^2)^{\frac{1}{2}}}{c(k^2 + k_0^2)^{\frac{1}{2}}} d\tau_k \qquad (47.29)$$

The integration over the polar angles of $\mathbf{k}$ is readily carried out; the result can be written

$$D(\mathbf{r},t) = (2\pi^2 rc)^{-1} \int_0^\infty k(k^2 + k_0^2)^{-\frac{1}{2}} \sin kr \, \sin ct(k^2 + k_0^2)^{\frac{1}{2}} dk$$

$$= -(4\pi^2 rc)^{-1} \frac{\partial}{\partial r} \int_{-\infty}^\infty (k^2 + k_0^2)^{-\frac{1}{2}} \cos kr \, \sin ct(k^2 + k_0^2)^{\frac{1}{2}} dk$$

The substitution $k = k_0 \sinh x$ transforms this into

$$D(\mathbf{r},t) = -(4\pi^2 rc)^{-1} \frac{\partial}{\partial r} \int_{-\infty}^\infty \cos (k_0 r \sinh x) \sin (k_0 ct \cosh x) dx \qquad (47.30)$$

The integrand in (47.30) can be rewritten as

$$\tfrac{1}{2} \sin (k_0 ct \cosh x + k_0 r \sinh x) + \tfrac{1}{2} \sin (k_0 ct \cosh x - k_0 r \sinh x) \qquad (47.31)$$

Further reduction depends on the relative magnitudes of ct and r. Suppose first that ct is positive and greater than r, which is always positive; we can then put

$$k_0 ct \cosh x \pm k_0 r \sinh x = k_0(c^2 t^2 - r^2)^{\frac{1}{2}} \cosh (x \pm \theta), \qquad \tanh \theta \equiv \frac{r}{ct}$$

The integral in (47.30) then becomes

$$\tfrac{1}{2} \int_{-\infty}^\infty \sin [z \cosh (x + \theta)] dx + \tfrac{1}{2} \int_{-\infty}^\infty \sin [z \cosh (x - \theta)] dx,$$
$$z \equiv k_0(c^2 t^2 - r^2)^{\frac{1}{2}} \qquad (47.32)$$

These have the form of one of the integral representations of a Bessel function:[2]

$$J_0(z) = \frac{1}{\pi} \int_{-\infty}^\infty \sin (z \cosh x) dx$$

---

[1] P. A. M. Dirac, *Proc. Camb. Phil. Soc.*, **30**, 150 (1934).

[2] E. T. Whittaker and G. N. Watson, "A Course of Modern Analysis," 4th ed., p. 382 (Cambridge, London, 1935).

The two integrals in (47.32) are equal, and their sum is then equal to $\pi J_0(z)$. It is apparent that for ct negative and less than $-r$, the integral in (47.30) is equal to $-\pi J_0(z)$.

To consider the case in which ct lies between r and $-r$, suppose first that ct is positive and less than r. We then use a different expression for the arguments of the sines in (47.31):

$$k_0ct \cosh x \pm k_0r \sinh x = \pm k_0(r^2 - c^2t^2)^{\frac{1}{2}} \sinh (x \pm \theta'), \quad \tanh \theta' \equiv \frac{ct}{r}$$

The integral in (47.30) then becomes

$$\frac{1}{2}\int_{-\infty}^{\infty} \sin [z' \sinh (x + \theta')]dx - \frac{1}{2}\int_{-\infty}^{\infty} \sin [z' \sinh (x - \theta')]dx,$$
$$z' \equiv k_0(r^2 - c^2t^2)^{\frac{1}{2}}$$

Each of these integrals vanishes, since the integrands are odd functions of $x + \theta'$ or $x - \theta'$. We see then that the integral in (47.30) is equal to

$$\begin{array}{ll}
\pi J_0[k_0(c^2t^2 - r^2)^{\frac{1}{2}}] & \text{for } ct > r \\
0 & \text{for } r > ct > -r \qquad (47.33) \\
-\pi J_0[k_0(c^2t^2 - r^2)^{\frac{1}{2}}] & \text{for } -r > ct
\end{array}$$

We have thus shown that there is no interference between measurements of charge density at two different space-time points if and only if the spatial distance between the points is greater than c times the time interval. In this case there is no physical mechanism whereby a disturbance can be communicated from either point to the other.

The hypersurfaces $ct = \pm r$ in four-dimensional space-time constitute the *light cone*, which is the locus of all light pulses that pass through the space point $\mathbf{r} = 0$ at the time $t = 0$. An explicit expression for $D(\mathbf{r},t)$ infinitesimally close to the light cone can be obtained by noting that (47.33) changes discontinuously from π to 0 as r increases in crossing the $ct = r$ half of the light cone, and changes discontinuously from $-\pi$ to 0 as r increases in crossing the $ct = -r$ half of the light cone. Now the derivative of an increasing step function is a positive δ function, so that we obtain from (47.30):

$$D(\mathbf{r},t) \cong (4\pi rc)^{-1}[\delta(r - ct) - \delta(r + ct)], \qquad ct \cong \pm r \qquad (47.34)$$

It is interesting to verify that the right side of (47.27), with the expression (47.34) for D near the light cone, reduces to $\delta_{jl}\delta(\mathbf{r})$ when $t = 0$; this shows that (47.27) agrees with the third of Eqs. (47.8) in the proper limit, as of course it must (see also Prob. 14). To see this, we note that the terms $(c\alpha_{jl} \cdot \mathbf{grad} + ick_0\beta_{jl})D(\mathbf{r},t)$ vanish when $t = 0$, since the two δ functions in (47.34) cancel. The term $(\partial/\partial t)D(\mathbf{r},t)$, however, becomes

$-(2\pi r)^{-1}\delta'(r)$ when $t = 0$. We now show that this quantity is equivalent to $\delta(\mathbf{r})$. Let $f(\mathbf{r})$ be an arbitrary continuous function that has a continuous gradient at $\mathbf{r} = 0$; then $\int f(\mathbf{r})\delta(\mathbf{r})d\tau = f(0)$. We also have that

$$-\int f(\mathbf{r})(2\pi r)^{-1}\delta'(r)d\tau = -\int_0^\infty f(r)(2\pi r)^{-1}\delta'(r)4\pi r^2 dr$$

$$= -\int_0^\infty f(r)2r\delta'(r)dr$$

$$= -\int_{-\infty}^\infty f(r)r\delta'(r)dr \qquad (47.35)$$

Since the fourth of Eqs. (11.13) states that $r\delta'(r)$ can be replaced by $-\delta(r)$, we see that (47.35) is equal to $f(0)$.

Problems

1. Make use of Eqs. (45.12), (45.13), and (45.14) to show that the classical Hamiltonian equations of motion for a field agree with the Lagrangian equations in the cell approximation.

2. Show that $\dot{F} = \{F,H\}$ even if the functional density F depends on $\mathbf{grad}\ \psi$ and $\mathbf{grad}\ \pi$ as well as on ψ and π.

3. The wave amplitude $\psi(\mathbf{r}_0,t)$ can be regarded as a functional to which corresponds the functional density $\psi(\mathbf{r},t)\delta(\mathbf{r} - \mathbf{r}_0)$, and similarly for π. Show that Eq. (45.20) gives the correct equations of motion for ψ and π when use is made of these functional densities. Also use them to calculate the Poisson-bracket expression for ψ and π at different points and the same time.

4. Show in detail that the commutator of N and the kinetic-energy term $\mathbf{grad}\ \psi^* \cdot \mathbf{grad}\ \psi$ in (46.10) is zero, and that the commutator brackets in (46.6) are constant in time.

5. Make use of Eqs. (46.14) and (46.15), and the answer to Prob. 1, Chap. VI, to show that the matrix for a_k defined by (46.11) cannot be diagonalized.

6. Extend (46.11) and the following equations to the situation in which the u_k constitute a continuous set of functions. Then make use of Prob. 2, Chap. III, to show that the measured number of particles in the infinitesimal neighborhood of any point is a positive integer or zero.

7. Show that Eqs. (46.21) are completely equivalent to Eqs. (46.20) if the Ψ's are orthonormal.

8. Show that the anticommutator bracket has different algebraic properties from the commutator bracket and the Poisson bracket.

9. It is shown in the text that an electron field amplitude is not classically measurable, since electrons obey the exclusion principle and have electric charge. Explain how it is that the diffraction pattern of electrons scattered by a crystal, which represents interference of electron amplitudes, can be measured classically.

10. Show that N is a constant of the motion for nonrelativistic Fermi-Dirac particles.

11. Consider a system of Fermi-Dirac particles for which there are two states. Obtain explicit matrices for the a's and Ψ's that are analogous to (46.29) and (46.30).

12. Show that the unquantized Hamiltonian equations for the Dirac theory agree with the corresponding Lagrangian equations.

13. Show that N given by (47.10) commutes with the Dirac field Hamiltonian (47.6).

14. Show that the anticommutation relation (47.27) for ψ and ψ^* at different space-time points reduces to the third of Eqs. (47.8) when the times are made the same.   Make use of the replacement of the **k** sum in (47.28) by the **k** integral in (47.29), and a representation of the δ function given in Sec. 11.

15. Show that $[\rho(\mathbf{r},t), \rho(\mathbf{r}',t)] = 0$ for both quantizations of the nonrelativistic Schrödinger equation, and for the quantized Dirac theory.

16. Show that if the wave functionals satisfy Schrödinger-type equations $i\hbar\dot\Psi = H\Psi$, $-i\hbar\dot\Psi^* = \Psi^*H$, then the calculation of the time derivative of a general matrix element of F results in Eq. (45.23) [compare with the transition from (23.1) to (23.2)].   Show also that if the set of Ψ's diagonalizes H as well as N, each Ψ oscillates in time with a frequency determined by the corresponding eigenvalue of H.

CHAPTER XIV

QUANTUM ELECTRODYNAMICS

The field quantization technique developed in the last chapter will now be applied to the electromagnetic field. In this case, the classical wave theory contains no suggestion of photons, while the quantized theory successfully explains the wave-photon duality discussed in Chap. I. It is convenient to consider first the electromagnetic field in empty space (Sec. 48), and then to take up the interaction between electrons and the field (Sec. 49). Some problems that illustrate the theory are solved in Sec. 50.[1] Since we are not concerned with establishing the Lorentz invariance of the theory, we use three-dimensional rather than four-dimensional notation throughout.

48. ELECTROMAGNETIC FIELD IN VACUUM

We shall follow the methods developed in Sec. 45. The equations of motion of the electromagnetic field are Maxwell's equations, and we start by finding a Lagrangian whose variation yields these equations. From this, canonical momenta can be defined, and a Hamiltonian can be set up. Quantization is effected by replacing the classical Poisson brackets by commutator brackets. We shall not consider the possible existence of anticommutation relations between the field variables, since experiment shows that strong electric and magnetic fields are classically measurable and that photons obey Einstein-Bose statistics.

Lagrangian Equations. Maxwell's equations in empty space are obtained by setting ρ and $\mathbf{J}$ equal to zero in Eqs. (35.2):

$$\operatorname{curl} \mathbf{E} + \frac{1}{c} \frac{\partial \mathbf{H}}{\partial t} = 0, \qquad \operatorname{curl} \mathbf{H} - \frac{1}{c} \frac{\partial \mathbf{E}}{\partial t} = 0 \tag{48.1}$$
$$\operatorname{div} \mathbf{E} = 0, \qquad \operatorname{div} \mathbf{H} = 0$$

The Lagrangian is most conveniently expressed in terms of the potentials $\mathbf{A}, \phi$ that are partially defined by

$$\mathbf{E} = -\frac{1}{c} \frac{\partial \mathbf{A}}{\partial t} - \operatorname{grad} \phi, \qquad \mathbf{H} = \operatorname{curl} \mathbf{A} \tag{48.2}$$

---

[1] For further discussion, see the first group of references cited in footnote 1, page 341, and also E. Fermi, *Rev. Mod. Phys.*, **4**, 87 (1932); L. Rosenfeld, *Ann. Inst. Henri Poincaré*, **1**, 25 (1931); W. Heitler, "The Quantum Theory of Radiation," 3d ed. (Oxford, New York, 1954); F. J. Dyson, "Advanced Quantum Mechanics," 2d ed. (multigraphed lecture notes, Cornell University, 1954).

As discussed in Sec. 35, this does not specify the potentials completely, since gauge transformations of the potentials can still be made without altering the electric and magnetic field strengths computed from (48.2).

The Lagrangian density can be taken to be

$$L = \frac{1}{8\pi}\left(\frac{1}{c}\frac{\partial \mathbf{A}}{\partial t} + \text{grad } \phi\right)^2 - \frac{1}{8\pi}(\text{curl } \mathbf{A})^2 \qquad (48.3)$$

The Lagrangian equations are obtained from (45.8) if we regard A_x, A_y, A_z, and ϕ as the field variables. Variation of the components of $\mathbf{A}$ gives three equations that can be written together as

$$-\frac{1}{4\pi}\text{ curl curl } \mathbf{A} - \frac{1}{4\pi c}\frac{\partial}{\partial t}\left(\frac{1}{c}\frac{\partial \mathbf{A}}{\partial t} + \text{grad } \phi\right) = 0$$

This is the same as tne second of Eqs. (48.1). Variation of ϕ gives

$$-\frac{1}{4\pi}\text{ div }\left(\frac{1}{c}\frac{\partial \mathbf{A}}{\partial t} + \text{grad } \phi\right) = 0$$

which is the same as the third of Eqs. (48.1). The definitions (48.2) for the potentials automatically satisfy the other two of Maxwell's equations.

Hamiltonian Equations. The momentum canonically conjugate to A_x is found from (45.15) and (48.3) to be

$$P_x = \frac{1}{4\pi c}\left(\frac{1}{c}\frac{\partial A_x}{\partial t} + \frac{\partial \phi}{\partial x}\right) \qquad (48.4)$$

with similar expressions for the other two momenta. The momentum canonically conjugate to ϕ vanishes identically, since ϕ does not appear in the Lagrangian density. A similar situation was encountered with ψ in the nonrelativistic Schrödinger equation (Sec. 46) and in the Dirac equation (Sec. 47); as before, it means that ϕ cannot be treated as a field variable and must be eliminated from the Hamiltonian.[1]

The Hamiltonian density is obtained from (45.24):

$$H = \mathbf{P} \cdot \frac{\partial \mathbf{A}}{\partial t} - L = 2\pi c^2 \mathbf{P}^2 + \frac{1}{8\pi}(\text{curl } \mathbf{A})^2 - c\mathbf{P} \cdot \text{grad } \phi \quad (48.5)$$

where use has been made of (48.4) to replace $\partial \mathbf{A}/\partial t$ by terms involving $\mathbf{P}$. The Hamiltonian equations of motion (45.19) are

$$\frac{\partial \mathbf{A}}{\partial t} = 4\pi c^2 \mathbf{P} - c\text{ grad } \phi, \qquad \frac{\partial \mathbf{P}}{\partial t} = -\frac{1}{4\pi}\text{ curl curl } \mathbf{A} \qquad (48.6)$$

---

[1] For an alternative approach, see P. A. M. Dirac, V. Fock, and B. Podolsky, *Phys. Zeits. Sowjetunion*, **2**, 468 (1932).

The first of these equations is the same as (48.4); it is necessary that (48.4) be obtained over again in this way, since the Hamiltonian formalism consists only of (48.5) and the canonical variables **A** and **P**. We can now make use of this equation to define a quantity **E** that is equal to $-4\pi c$**P**. Then the second of Eqs. (48.6) agrees with the second of Maxwell's equations (48.1), if we also define a quantity **H** to be equal to **curl A**. The first and fourth of Eqs. (48.1) are satisfied because of the way in which **E** and **H** are defined.

The third of Maxwell's equations cannot be obtained as a Hamiltonian equation based on (48.5). We can, however, say that we shall be concerned only with those solutions of the Hamiltonian equations for which div **E** $= 0$, or div **P** $= 0$, at some definite time. If then we can show that this restriction is maintained at all times, the solutions so chosen form a consistent and satisfactory set. The time derivative of div **P** is found from the second of Eqs. (48.6) to be

$$\frac{\partial}{\partial t} \text{div } \mathbf{P} = -\frac{1}{4\pi} \text{div } \mathbf{curl} \, \mathbf{curl} \, \mathbf{A} = 0$$

Since the field equations are of first order in the time derivatives, we have shown that the restriction that div **E** $= 0$ at one instant of time is equivalent to the validity of the third of Eqs. (48.1) at all times.

We now see that the last term in the Hamiltonian density (48.5) contributes nothing to the field Hamiltonian. Its volume integral can be transformed by means of a partial integration into $c \int \phi$ div **P**$d\tau$, which is equal to zero; the surface term vanishes because **P** either vanishes sufficiently rapidly at infinity or obeys periodic boundary conditions at the walls of a large box. The Hamiltonian is then

$$H = \int \left[2\pi c^2 \mathbf{P}^2 + \frac{1}{8\pi} (\mathbf{curl} \, \mathbf{A})^2 \right] d\tau \qquad (48.7)$$

and ϕ has disappeared. This is in agreement with the usual expression $(1/8\pi) \int (\mathbf{E}^2 + \mathbf{H}^2) d\tau$ for the total energy in the electromagnetic field.

Quantum Equations. The classical electromagnetic field is converted into a quantum field in the following way. We start with the Hamiltonian (48.7) and the canonical field variables **A,P**. Since ϕ no longer appears, it is convenient to choose the gauge so that $\phi = 0$. The general equation of motion is (45.23), and the commutation relations (45.25) between the field variables become

$$\begin{aligned} [A_s(\mathbf{r},t), A_{s'}(\mathbf{r}',t)] &= [P_s(\mathbf{r},t), P_{s'}(\mathbf{r}',t)] = 0 \\ [A_s(\mathbf{r},t), P_{s'}(\mathbf{r}',t)] &= i\hbar \delta_{ss'} \delta(\mathbf{r} - \mathbf{r}') \end{aligned} \qquad (48.8)$$

Each of the indices s,s' can be x, y, or z.

The equation of motion for a typical component of **A** is

$$i\hbar \dot{A}_x(\mathbf{r},t) = [A_x(\mathbf{r},t), H]$$

A_x commutes with the $(\mathbf{curl\ A})^2$ term in H, and also with that part of the $\mathbf{P}^2$ term that involves $P_y^2 + P_z^2$; thus we need calculate only the commutator of A_x and the P_x^2 term in H. This is $2\pi c^2$ times the integral over $\mathbf{r}'$ of $[A_x, P_x'^2]$, where the prime indicates that the argument is $\mathbf{r}'$ rather than $\mathbf{r}$.

$$\begin{aligned}
[A_x(\mathbf{r},t), P_x^2(\mathbf{r}',t)] &= A_x P_x'^2 - P_x'^2 A_x \\
&= [P_x' A_x + i\hbar\delta(\mathbf{r}-\mathbf{r}')]P_x' - P_x'^2 A_x \\
&= P_x'[P_x' A_x + i\hbar\delta(\mathbf{r}-\mathbf{r}')] + i\hbar\delta(\mathbf{r}-\mathbf{r}')P_x' - P_x'^2 A_x \\
&= 2i\hbar\delta(\mathbf{r}-\mathbf{r}')P_x(\mathbf{r}',t)
\end{aligned}$$

Integration over $\mathbf{r}'$ gives the relation

$$\begin{aligned}
i\hbar \dot{A}_x(\mathbf{r},t) &= 2\pi c^2 \int 2i\hbar\delta(\mathbf{r}-\mathbf{r}')P_x(\mathbf{r}',t)d\tau' \\
&= 4\pi c^2 i\hbar P_x(\mathbf{r},t)
\end{aligned} \tag{48.9}$$

This is the same as the corresponding classical equation, which is the first of Eqs. (48.6), when $\phi = 0$.

The equation of motion for a typical component of **P** is

$$i\hbar \dot{P}_x(\mathbf{r},t) = [P_x(\mathbf{r},t), H]$$

P_x commutes with all the integrand of H except for that part which contains the sum of the squares of the y and z components of **curl A**. The calculation of this commutator bracket is straightforward but tedious (see Prob. 1), and yields an expression for $\dot{\mathbf{P}}$ that is in agreement with the second of Eqs. (48.6). Thus if we define $\mathbf{E} = -4\pi c\mathbf{P}$ and $\mathbf{H} = \mathbf{curl\ A}$, the quantum equations of motion for **A** and **P** agree with the first, second, and fourth of Maxwell's equations (48.1).

The third of Maxwell's equations must be imposed as a *supplementary condition*, as in the classical case. If we set div **P** equal to zero at a particular time, it is always zero since its time derivative is zero. Equation (48.9) then shows that the time derivative of div **A** is always zero, or that div **A** is a constant in time. It is convenient to restrict the choice of gauge further so that div **A** is zero everywhere at a particular time, in which case we see that it is zero at all space-time points. It is apparent, however, that the introduction of the supplementary condition is inconsistent with the commutation relations (48.8). For example, the commutator bracket of A_x and div **P** should be zero, since div **P** is zero, but is computed from (48.8) to be

$$[A_x(\mathbf{r},t), \mathrm{div}'\ \mathbf{P}(\mathbf{r}',t)] = i\hbar \frac{\partial}{\partial x'}\delta(\mathbf{r}-\mathbf{r}')$$

It is not surprising that this inconsistency should arise, since Eqs. (48.8) imply that there are three independent pairs of canonical variables, whereas the restrictions div $\mathbf{P} = 0$ and div $\mathbf{A} = 0$ cause only two of these pairs to be linearly independent. We should therefore modify the commutation relations so that they are consistent with the supplementary condition.

The nature of this modification is established in Prob. 2. It turns out that the commutator brackets of $\mathbf{A}(\mathbf{r},t)$ and $\mathbf{P}(\mathbf{r}',t)$ do not vanish when $\mathbf{r} - \mathbf{r}'$ is finite. This would appear at first to contradict the physical principle that there can be no interference between measurements performed at different places and the same time (see the discussion of Sec. 47). However, the vector potential $\mathbf{A}$ is not in itself a physical quantity; only the electric and magnetic fields are directly measurable. We shall now show with the help of (48.8) that the commutation relations of $\mathbf{E}$ and $\mathbf{H}$ have the required infinitesimal character and are, moreover, consistent with the supplementary condition div $\mathbf{E} = 0$. It can also be shown (see Prob. 3) that the same results are obtained by starting with the modified canonical commutation relations of Prob. 2.

Commutation Relations for $\mathbf{E}$ and $\mathbf{H}$. The electric and magnetic fields are defined by the equations

$$\mathbf{E} = -4\pi c\mathbf{P}, \qquad \mathbf{H} = \text{curl } \mathbf{A} \qquad (48.10)$$

where the commutation relations for $\mathbf{A}$ and $\mathbf{P}$ are assumed to have the form (48.8). We see at once that

$$[\mathsf{E}_s(\mathbf{r},t),\, \mathsf{E}_{s'}(\mathbf{r}',t)] = [\mathsf{H}_s(\mathbf{r},t),\, \mathsf{H}_{s'}(\mathbf{r}',t)] = 0 \qquad (48.11)$$

where each of the indices s,s' can be x, y, or z. The commutator bracket for typical parallel components of $\mathbf{E}$ and $\mathbf{H}$ is

$$[\mathsf{E}_x(\mathbf{r},t),\, \mathsf{H}_x(\mathbf{r}',t)] = -4\pi c\left[P_x, \left(\frac{\partial A_z'}{\partial y'} - \frac{\partial A_y'}{\partial z'}\right)\right] = 0 \qquad (48.12)$$

For typical perpendicular components of $\mathbf{E}$ and $\mathbf{H}$, we obtain

$$[\mathsf{E}_x(\mathbf{r},t),\, \mathsf{H}_y(\mathbf{r}',t)] = -4\pi c\left[P_x, \left(\frac{\partial A_x'}{\partial z'} - \frac{\partial A_z'}{\partial x'}\right)\right]$$

$$= -4\pi c\,\frac{\partial}{\partial z'}\, [P_x, A_x']$$

$$= 4\pi ci\hbar\,\frac{\partial}{\partial z'}\, \delta(\mathbf{r} - \mathbf{r}') \qquad (48.13)$$

Other relations similar to (48.13) are obtained by cyclic permutation of x,y,z.

It follows at once from (48.11) that div **E** commutes with all components of **E**. The commutator bracket of div **E** and a typical component of **H** is, with the help of (48.13),

$$[\text{div } \mathbf{E}, H_x'] = \left[\frac{\partial E_y}{\partial y}, H_x'\right] + \left[\frac{\partial E_z}{\partial z}, H_x'\right]$$

$$= 4\pi ci\hbar\left[-\frac{\partial}{\partial y}\frac{\partial}{\partial z'}\delta(\mathbf{r}' - \mathbf{r}) + \frac{\partial}{\partial z}\frac{\partial}{\partial y'}\delta(\mathbf{r}' - \mathbf{r})\right] \quad (48.14)$$

Since $(\partial/\partial y')\delta(\mathbf{r}' - \mathbf{r}) = -(\partial/\partial y)\delta(\mathbf{r}' - \mathbf{r})$, we see that the right side of (48.14) is zero. Thus div **E** commutes with **E** and **H**, and hence also with the Hamiltonian, which from (48.7) can be written as

$$H = \frac{1}{8\pi}\int (\mathbf{E}^2 + \mathbf{H}^2)d\tau \quad (48.15)$$

This means that div **E** is a constant of the motion, and so is zero at all space-time points if it is made to vanish everywhere at a particular time.

As would be expected, the field commutation relations (48.11), (48.12), and (48.13), together with the Hamiltonian (48.15), can be used in place of the canonical formalism originally developed in terms of **A** and **P**. We have already seen that div **E** is a constant of the motion; a similar calculation shows that div **H** is constant, so that it can also be made to vanish at all space-time points. The first two of Maxwell's equations (48.1) then follow as special cases of the general equation of motion (45.23) (see Prob. 5):

$$i\hbar\dot{E}_x = [E_x, H] = \frac{1}{8\pi}\int [E_x, (H_y'^2 + H_z'^2)]d\tau'$$

$$= i\hbar c(\text{curl } \mathbf{H})_x$$

$$i\hbar\dot{H}_x = [H_x, H] = \frac{1}{8\pi}\int [H_x, (E_y'^2 + E_z'^2)]d\tau'$$

$$= -i\hbar c(\text{curl } \mathbf{E})_x$$

$$(48.16)$$

Plane Wave Representation. For many applications, a representation of the potentials and fields in a complete orthonormal set of plane waves is useful. These plane waves are taken to be vector functions of **r** that are polarized perpendicular to the propagation vector so that the conditions div **A** = div **P** = 0 are satisfied.

$$\mathbf{u}_{k\lambda}(\mathbf{r}) = L^{-\frac{3}{2}}\varepsilon_{k\lambda}\exp i\mathbf{k}\cdot\mathbf{r}, \qquad \lambda = 1,2$$

The vectors **k** are chosen as in (11.3), so that the $\mathbf{u}_{k\lambda}$ satisfy periodic boundary conditions at the walls of a large cubical box of volume L^3. The $\varepsilon_{k\lambda}$ are unit vectors, and ε_{k1}, ε_{k2}, and **k** form a right-handed set, so that $\mathbf{k}\cdot\varepsilon_{k\lambda} = 0$ and div $\mathbf{u}_{k\lambda} = 0$. It is easily verified that the orthonormality property assumes the form

$$\int \bar{u}_{k\lambda} \cdot u_{k'\lambda'} d\tau = \delta_{kk'}\delta_{\lambda\lambda'}$$

We expand $\mathbf{A}$ and $\mathbf{P}$ in terms of the $u_{k\lambda}$:

$$\mathbf{A}(\mathbf{r},t) = \sum_{k\lambda}{}' [q_{k\lambda}(t)u_{k\lambda}(\mathbf{r}) + q_{k\lambda}{}^*(t)\bar{u}_{k\lambda}(\mathbf{r})]$$

$$\mathbf{P}(\mathbf{r},t) = \sum_{k\lambda}{}' [p_{k\lambda}(t)u_{k\lambda}(\mathbf{r}) + p_{k\lambda}{}^*(t)\bar{u}_{k\lambda}(\mathbf{r})]$$

(48.17)

The operators $q_{k\lambda}{}^*$ and $p_{k\lambda}{}^*$ are the Hermitian adjoints of $q_{k\lambda}$ and $p_{k\lambda}$, respectively; thus $\mathbf{A}$ and $\mathbf{P}$ are Hermitian. The primes indicate that the summations extend over half the $\mathbf{k}$ space, so that the plane waves $\bar{u}_{k\lambda}$ do not duplicate $u_{-k\lambda}$.

We take for the commutation relations between the q's and p's

$$[q_{k\lambda}(t), p_{k'\lambda'}{}^*(t)] = [q_{k\lambda}{}^*(t), p_{k'\lambda'}(t)] = i\hbar\delta_{kk'}\delta_{\lambda'\lambda} \qquad (48.18)$$

with all other pairs commuting, and verify that they give the correct commutation relations between $\mathbf{A}$ and $\mathbf{P}$. It is apparent that

$$[A_s(\mathbf{r},t), A_{s'}(\mathbf{r}',t)] = [P_s(\mathbf{r},t), P_{s'}(\mathbf{r}',t)] = 0$$

We also obtain from (48.17) and (48.18)

$$[A_s(\mathbf{r},t), P_{s'}(\mathbf{r}',t)] = \sum_{k\lambda}{}' \sum_{k'\lambda'}{}' \{[q_{k\lambda}(t), p_{k'\lambda'}{}^*(t)]u_{k\lambda,s}(\mathbf{r})\bar{u}_{k'\lambda',s'}(\mathbf{r}')$$

$$+ [q_{k\lambda}{}^*(t), p_{k'\lambda'}(t)]\bar{u}_{k\lambda,s}(\mathbf{r})u_{k'\lambda',s'}(\mathbf{r}')\}$$

$$= i\hbar L^{-3} \sum_{k\lambda} \epsilon_{k\lambda,s}\epsilon_{k\lambda,s'}[\exp i\mathbf{k} \cdot (\mathbf{r} - \mathbf{r}')] \qquad (48.19)$$

The subscripts s,s' denote cartesian components of the vectors on which they appear; the prime has been removed from the last summation in (48.19) since the primed summation over terms with both $\mathbf{k}$ and $-\mathbf{k}$ is equivalent to a summation of $\mathbf{k}$ terms over the entire $\mathbf{k}$ space.

If there were three mutually perpendicular unit vectors $\epsilon_{k\lambda}$, then the three numbers $\epsilon_{k\lambda,s}$ would be the direction cosines of the cartesian direction s, and we would have that $\sum_\lambda \epsilon_{k\lambda,s}\epsilon_{k\lambda,s'} = \delta_{ss'}$. Since there are just two unit vectors $\epsilon_{k\lambda}$ that are perpendicular to each other and to $\mathbf{k}$, we can write

$$\sum_\lambda \epsilon_{k\lambda,s}\epsilon_{k\lambda,s'} = \delta_{ss'} - \frac{k_s k_{s'}}{k^2}$$

We also have that

$$k_s k_{s'}[\exp i\mathbf{k} \cdot (\mathbf{r} - \mathbf{r}')] = \frac{\partial}{\partial r_s} \frac{\partial}{\partial r'_{s'}} [\exp i\mathbf{k} \cdot (\mathbf{r} - \mathbf{r}')]$$

With these substitutions, and the replacement of $L^{-3} \sum_{\mathbf{k}}$ by $(2\pi)^{-3}\int d\tau_k$ when L is large, we can rewrite (48.19) as

$$[A_s(\mathbf{r},t), P_{s'}(\mathbf{r}',t)] = i\hbar\delta_{ss'}\{(2\pi)^{-3}\int[\exp i\mathbf{k} \cdot (\mathbf{r} - \mathbf{r}')]d\tau_k\}$$

$$- i\hbar \frac{\partial}{\partial r_s} \frac{\partial}{\partial r'_{s'}} \left\{(2\pi)^{-3} \int \frac{1}{k^2} [\exp i\mathbf{k} \cdot (\mathbf{r} - \mathbf{r}')]d\tau_k\right\} \quad (48.20)$$

The first brace expression in (48.20) is equal to $\delta(\mathbf{r} - \mathbf{r}')$. The second brace is the Green's function $G_0(\mathbf{r},\mathbf{r}')$ given in (26.12), which according to (26.15) is equal to $(4\pi|\mathbf{r} - \mathbf{r}'|)^{-1}$. The commutator bracket (48.20) then becomes

$$[A_s(\mathbf{r},t), P_{s'}(\mathbf{r}',t)] = i\hbar\delta_{ss'}\delta(\mathbf{r} - \mathbf{r}') - \frac{i\hbar}{4\pi} \frac{\partial}{\partial r_s} \frac{\partial}{\partial r'_{s'}} \left(\frac{1}{|\mathbf{r} - \mathbf{r}'|}\right) \quad (48.21)$$

which is that assumed in Prob. 2; the other commutator brackets vanish. This confirms the choice of the commutation relations (48.18).

Quantized Field Energy. Substitution of (48.17) into the field Hamiltonian (48.7) gives

$$H = \sum_{\mathbf{k}\lambda}' \left(4\pi c^2 p_{\mathbf{k}\lambda}p_{\mathbf{k}\lambda}{}^* + \frac{k^2}{4\pi} q_{\mathbf{k}\lambda}q_{\mathbf{k}\lambda}{}^*\right) \quad (48.22)$$

since $q_{\mathbf{k}\lambda}$ and $q_{\mathbf{k}\lambda}{}^*$, and $p_{\mathbf{k}\lambda}$ and $p_{\mathbf{k}\lambda}{}^*$ commute; here use has been made of the restriction on the summation to half the $\mathbf{k}$ space, which makes all integrals of the form $\int u_{\mathbf{k}\lambda} \cdot u_{\mathbf{k}'\lambda'}d\tau$ vanish.

We wish now to find the eigenvalues of H when the commutation relations are as given in (48.18). This can be done by choosing linear combinations of the plane wave amplitudes that make H formally equivalent to the sum of the energies of a number of harmonic oscillators (see Sec. 46). Now each index pair $\mathbf{k},\lambda$ corresponds to two linearly polarized plane waves that travel in opposite senses along the $\mathbf{k}$ direction. Thus we want our new linear combinations of $q_{\mathbf{k}\lambda}u_{\mathbf{k}\lambda}$ and $p_{\mathbf{k}\lambda}u_{\mathbf{k}\lambda}$ to have the general forms

$$a_{\mathbf{k}\lambda} \exp i(\mathbf{k} \cdot \mathbf{r} - kct), \qquad a'_{\mathbf{k}\lambda}{}^* \exp i(\mathbf{k} \cdot \mathbf{r} + kct) \quad (48.23)$$

where $a_{\mathbf{k}\lambda}$ and $a'_{\mathbf{k}\lambda}$ are operators that are independent of $\mathbf{r}$ and t. The first of these is a plane wave that travels in the positive $\mathbf{k}$ direction and has the positive angular frequency kc, and the second is the Hermitian adjoint of a plane wave that travels in the negative $\mathbf{k}$ direction and has the same frequency.

With the remarks of the last paragraph as a guide, we proceed to find the time dependence of $q_{k\lambda}$ and $p_{k\lambda}$. Their equations of motion are given by (45.23):

$$i\hbar\dot{q}_{k\lambda} = [q_{k\lambda}, H] = 4\pi i\hbar c^2 p_{k\lambda}$$
$$i\hbar\dot{p}_{k\lambda} = [p_{k\lambda}, H] = -\frac{i\hbar k^2}{4\pi} q_{k\lambda} \tag{48.24}$$

Elimination of $p_{k\lambda}$ gives a second-order equation for $q_{k\lambda}$

$$\ddot{q}_{k\lambda} = 4\pi c^2 \dot{p}_{k\lambda} = -k^2 c^2 q_{k\lambda}$$

This is easily integrated to give

$$q_{k\lambda}(t) = a_{k\lambda} e^{-ikct} + a'_{k\lambda}{}^* e^{ikct} \tag{48.25}$$

where we have followed the pattern indicated by (48.23). We then obtain from the first of Eqs. (48.24)

$$p_{k\lambda}(t) = -\frac{ik}{4\pi c} a_{k\lambda} e^{-ikct} + \frac{ik}{4\pi c} a'_{k\lambda}{}^* e^{ikct} \tag{48.26}$$

Equations (48.25) and (48.26) can be solved for the a's.

$$a_{k\lambda} = \tfrac{1}{2}\left(q_{k\lambda} + \frac{4\pi ic}{k} p_{k\lambda} \right) e^{ikct}$$
$$a'_{k\lambda}{}^* = \tfrac{1}{2}\left(q_{k\lambda} - \frac{4\pi ic}{k} p_{k\lambda} \right) e^{-ikct} \tag{48.27}$$

Similar relations hold for their Hermitian adjoints. The commutation relations for the a's can be obtained from (48.27) and (48.18):

$$[a_{k\lambda}, a^*_{k'\lambda'}] = [a'_{k\lambda}, a'{}^*_{k'\lambda'}] = \frac{2\pi\hbar c}{k} \delta_{kk'}\delta_{\lambda\lambda'} \tag{48.28}$$

with all other pairs commuting; these are independent of the time, as they should be.

Substitution of (48.25) and (48.26) into the Hamiltonian (48.22) gives

$$H = \sum_{k\lambda}{}' \frac{k^2}{2\pi} (a_{k\lambda} a_{k\lambda}{}^* + a'_{k\lambda}{}^* a'_{k\lambda}) \tag{48.29}$$

If we adopt the definitions

$$N_{k\lambda} = \frac{k}{2\pi\hbar c} a_{k\lambda}{}^* a_{k\lambda}, \qquad N'_{k\lambda} = \frac{k}{2\pi\hbar c} a'_{k\lambda}{}^* a'_{k\lambda} \tag{48.30}$$

we see from the work of Sec. 46 that $N_{k\lambda}$ and $N'_{k\lambda}$ each have the eigenvalues $0,1,2,\ldots$. In terms of the N's, the Hamiltonian (48.29) becomes

$$H = \sum_{k\lambda}' \hbar ck(N_{k\lambda} + N'_{k\lambda} + 1) \qquad (48.31)$$

Because of the structure of (48.23) and (48.25), we can identify $a'_{k\lambda}$ with $a_{-k\lambda}$, and $N'_{k\lambda}$ with $N_{-k\lambda}$. Then the restriction on the summation of (48.31) to half the **k** space can be removed to give

$$H = \sum_{k\lambda} \hbar ck(N_{k\lambda} + \tfrac{1}{2}) \qquad (48.32)$$

Equation (48.32) is equivalent to Planck's quantum hypothesis: the energy associated with each plane electromagnetic wave is an integer multiple of the fundamental quantum $h\nu = \hbar kc$. In addition to the Planck energy, however, there is the harmonic-oscillator zero-point energy of one-half quantum per state of the field, which is infinite since there are an infinite number of states. This infinite energy is not objectionable since it does not interact with charged matter.[1]

Quantized Field Momentum. The momentum density of an electromagnetic field is the Poynting vector $(c/4\pi)\mathbf{E}(\mathbf{r},t) \times \mathbf{H}(\mathbf{r},t)$ divided by c^2. The total momentum in the field can then be written in terms of the canonical variables, with the help of (48.10),

$$\mathbf{G} = \frac{1}{4\pi c} \int \mathbf{E} \times \mathbf{H} d\tau = -\int \mathbf{P} \times (\mathrm{curl}\, \mathbf{A}) d\tau$$

Substitution from (48.17), (48.25), (48.26), and (48.30) gives

$$
\begin{aligned}
\mathbf{G} &= i \sum_{k\lambda}' \mathbf{k}(p_{k\lambda}q_{k\lambda}{}^* - p_{k\lambda}{}^*q_{k\lambda}) \\
&= \frac{1}{4\pi c} \sum_{k\lambda}' \mathbf{k}k[(a_{k\lambda}a_{k\lambda}{}^* + a_{k\lambda}{}^*a_{k\lambda}) - (a'_{k\lambda}a'_{k\lambda}{}^* + a'_{k\lambda}{}^*a'_{k\lambda})] \\
&= \sum_{k\lambda}' \hbar\mathbf{k}[(N_{k\lambda} + \tfrac{1}{2}) - (N'_{k\lambda} + \tfrac{1}{2})] = \sum_{k\lambda} \hbar\mathbf{k}N_{k\lambda} \qquad (48.33)
\end{aligned}
$$

where the restriction on the summation is removed as in the transition from (48.31) to (48.32). In this case, the zero-point terms cancel for plane waves that travel in opposite directions.

Equations (48.32) and (48.33) show that the energy and momentum of each plane wave are quantized in units of $\hbar kc$ for the energy and $\hbar\mathbf{k}$ for the momentum. It will also be shown explicitly in Sec. 50 that the inter-

---

[1] See also the discussion following Eq. (50.17).

action between matter and radiation is such as to account both for the interference of light and for the discrete properties of light quanta.

$A(r,t)$ **in the Plane Wave Representation.** The vector potential appears in the interaction between electrons and the electromagnetic field discussed in the next two sections. We shall therefore require an expression for $A(r,t)$ in the plane wave representation that is specified by the eigenvalues $n_{k\lambda}$ of the operators $N_{k\lambda}$. A typical wave functional for this representation can be written as $\Psi(\cdots n_{k\lambda} \cdots)$, which describes a state of the electromagnetic field in which there are $n_{k\lambda}$ light quanta with momentum $\hbar k$ and polarization $\varepsilon_{k\lambda}$. We then see from Eq. (48.28) and the work of Sec. 46 that the operators $a_{k\lambda}$ and $a_{k\lambda}*$ have the properties

$$a_{k\lambda}\Psi(\cdots n_{k\lambda} \cdots) = \left(\frac{2\pi\hbar c n_{k\lambda}}{k}\right)^{\frac{1}{2}} \Psi(\cdots n_{k\lambda} - 1 \cdots)$$

$$a_{k\lambda}*\Psi(\cdots n_{k\lambda} \cdots) = \left(\frac{2\pi\hbar c(n_{k\lambda} + 1)}{k}\right)^{\frac{1}{2}} \Psi(\cdots n_{k\lambda} + 1 \cdots) \qquad (48.34)$$

We obtain from (48.17) and (48.25)

$$A(r,t) = L^{-\frac{3}{2}} \sum_{k\lambda}' \varepsilon_{k\lambda}[(a_{k\lambda}e^{-ikct} + a'_{k\lambda}*e^{ikct})(\exp i k \cdot r)$$

$$+ (a_{k\lambda}*e^{ikct} + a'_{k\lambda}e^{-ikct}) \exp(-i k \cdot r)]$$

$$= L^{-\frac{3}{2}} \sum_{k\lambda} \varepsilon_{k\lambda}\{a_{k\lambda}[\exp i(k \cdot r - kct)]$$

$$+ a_{k\lambda}* \exp[-i(k \cdot r - kct)]\} \qquad (48.35)$$

Here again the restriction has been removed from the summation by identifying $a'_{k\lambda}$ with $a_{-k\lambda}$. This expression for the vector potential is easily seen to be Hermitian, as it must be. It follows from the structure of (48.34) that $a_{k\lambda}$ and $a_{k\lambda}*$ are destruction and creation operators, respectively, for a light quantum in the state k,λ. Thus a term in the Hamiltonian linear in A would give rise to the emission and absorption of light quanta.

Commutation Relations at Different Times. It is interesting to generalize the commutation relations (48.11), (48.12), and (48.13) for the components of E and H, to the case in which the times are different.[1] As with the quantized Dirac equation (Sec. 47), the result shows under what circumstances measurements of the electromagnetic fields at different space-time points affect each other.

Expansions for E and H in terms of the $a_{k\lambda}$, that are analogous to (48.35), can be found without difficulty:

[1] These commutation relations are due to P. Jordan and W. Pauli, *Zeits. f. Physik,* **47**, 151 (1928).

$$\mathsf{E}(\mathbf{r},t) = L^{-\frac{3}{2}} \sum_{\mathbf{k}\lambda} ik\varepsilon_{\mathbf{k}\lambda}\{a_{\mathbf{k}\lambda}[\exp i(\mathbf{k}\cdot\mathbf{r} - kct)]$$
$$- a_{\mathbf{k}\lambda}{}^* \exp[-i(\mathbf{k}\cdot\mathbf{r} - kct)]\} \quad (48.36)$$
$$\mathsf{H}(\mathbf{r},t) = L^{-\frac{3}{2}} \sum_{\mathbf{k}\lambda} i(\mathbf{k}\times\varepsilon_{\mathbf{k}\lambda})\{a_{\mathbf{k}\lambda}[\exp i(\mathbf{k}\cdot\mathbf{r} - kct)]$$
$$- a_{\mathbf{k}\lambda}{}^* \exp[-i(\mathbf{k}\cdot\mathbf{r} - kct)]\}$$

The commutator bracket for two cartesian components of the electric field strength is

$$[E_s(\mathbf{r},t), E_{s'}(\mathbf{r}',t')] = L^{-3} \sum_{\mathbf{k}\lambda} 4\pi i\hbar ck\epsilon_{\mathbf{k}\lambda,s}\epsilon_{\mathbf{k}\lambda,s'} \sin(\mathbf{k}\cdot\boldsymbol{\varrho} - kc\tau) \quad (48.37)$$
$$\boldsymbol{\varrho} = \mathbf{r} - \mathbf{r}', \qquad \tau = t - t'$$

where use has been made of (48.28). The summation over the polarization index λ can be evaluated by the technique used on the similar summation in (48.19):

$$\sum_\lambda \epsilon_{\mathbf{k}\lambda,s}\epsilon_{\mathbf{k}\lambda,s'} \sin(\mathbf{k}\cdot\boldsymbol{\varrho} - kc\tau) = \frac{1}{k^2}(k^2\delta_{ss'} - k_s k_{s'}) \sin(\mathbf{k}\cdot\boldsymbol{\varrho} - kc\tau)$$

$$= \frac{1}{k^2}\left[\frac{\delta_{ss'}}{c^2}\frac{\partial}{\partial t}\frac{\partial}{\partial t'} - \frac{\partial}{\partial r_s}\frac{\partial}{\partial r'_{s'}}\right] \sin(\mathbf{k}\cdot\boldsymbol{\varrho} - kc\tau) \quad (48.38)$$

The summation over $\mathbf{k}$ can be evaluated by replacing it with an integral for large L:

$$L^{-3} \sum_{\mathbf{k}} k^{-1} \sin(\mathbf{k}\cdot\boldsymbol{\varrho} - kc\tau) \xrightarrow[L\to\infty]{} (2\pi)^{-3} \int k^{-1} \sin(\mathbf{k}\cdot\boldsymbol{\varrho} - kc\tau)d\tau_k$$

$$= (2\pi)^{-3}\int (2ik)^{-1}[\exp(i\mathbf{k}\cdot\boldsymbol{\varrho} - ikc\tau)$$
$$- \exp(-i\mathbf{k}\cdot\boldsymbol{\varrho} + ikc\tau)]d\tau_k$$
$$= (2\pi)^{-3}\int (2ik)^{-1}[\exp(i\mathbf{k}\cdot\boldsymbol{\varrho} - ikc\tau)$$
$$- \exp(i\mathbf{k}\cdot\boldsymbol{\varrho} + ikc\tau)]d\tau_k$$
$$= -(2\pi)^{-3}\int k^{-1}\exp(i\mathbf{k}\cdot\boldsymbol{\varrho})\sin kc\tau\, d\tau_k$$

We denote the last expression by $-cD_0(\boldsymbol{\varrho},\tau)$, where D_0 is the same as the D function of Eq. (47.29) except that k_0 is set equal to zero.

We can see from (47.30) and (47.33) that $D_0(\boldsymbol{\varrho},\tau)$ is obtained as the result of operating with $-(4\pi^2\rho c)^{-1}(\partial/\partial\rho)$ on a function that is equal to $+\pi$ for $c\tau > \rho$, 0 for $\rho > c\tau > -\rho$, and $-\pi$ for $-\rho > c\tau$. Thus D_0 has the form (47.34) for all ρ, not just for ρ in the infinitesimal neighborhood of $|c\tau|$:

$$D_0(\boldsymbol{\varrho},\tau) = (4\pi\rho c)^{-1}[\delta(\rho - c\tau) - \delta(\rho + c\tau)], \qquad \rho = |\mathbf{r} - \mathbf{r}'| \quad (48.39)$$

It then follows from (48.37) and (48.38) that

$$[E_s(\mathbf{r},t), E_{s'}(\mathbf{r}',t')]$$

$$= -4\pi i \hbar c^2 \left[\frac{\delta_{ss'}}{c^2} \frac{\partial}{\partial t} \frac{\partial}{\partial t'} - \frac{\partial}{\partial r_s} \frac{\partial}{\partial r_{s'}} \right] D_0(\mathbf{r} - \mathbf{r}', t - t') \quad (48.40)$$

The commutator bracket for two cartesian components of the magnetic field strength can be found in the same way, and is

$$[H_s(\mathbf{r},t), H_{s'}(\mathbf{r}',t')] = [E_s(\mathbf{r},t), E_{s'}(\mathbf{r}',t')] \quad (48.41)$$

An expression for the commutation relation between components of **E** and **H** can also be obtained from (48.36).

$$[E_s(\mathbf{r},t), H_{s'}(\mathbf{r}',t')]$$

$$= L^{-3} \sum_{\mathbf{k}} 4\pi i \hbar c k (\epsilon_{\mathbf{k}1,s}\epsilon_{\mathbf{k}2,s'} - \epsilon_{\mathbf{k}2,s}\epsilon_{\mathbf{k}1,s'}) \sin(\mathbf{k} \cdot \boldsymbol{\varrho} - kc\tau) \quad (48.42)$$

It is apparent that (48.42) vanishes if $s = s'$, so that parallel components of the electric and magnetic field strengths commute at all space-time points. If $s \neq s'$, we can put $s = x$, $s' = y$, where x,y,z form a right-handed set of axes, in which case we see that

$$\epsilon_{\mathbf{k}1,x}\epsilon_{\mathbf{k}2,y} - \epsilon_{\mathbf{k}2,x}\epsilon_{\mathbf{k}1,y} = (\boldsymbol{\epsilon}_{\mathbf{k}1} \times \boldsymbol{\epsilon}_{\mathbf{k}2})_z = \frac{k_z}{k}$$

An analysis similar to that which led from (48.37) to (48.40) then shows that

$$[E_x(\mathbf{r},t), H_y(\mathbf{r}',t')] = 4\pi i \hbar c \frac{\partial}{\partial z} \frac{\partial}{\partial t'} D_0(\mathbf{r} - \mathbf{r}', t - t') \quad (48.43)$$

The subscripts x,y,z can be permuted cyclically in (48.43).

Since all these commutation relations involve the D_0 function (48.39), we see that all components of the field strengths commute except in the infinitesimal neighborhood of the light cone $c(t - t') = \pm|\mathbf{r} - \mathbf{r}'|$. Thus the field strengths at space-time points so situated that a light signal cannot pass from either one to the other, commute with each other and can both be measured precisely. This shows that the quantized electromagnetic field is propagated with the classical speed of light c. A discussion of the connection between these commutation relations and the uncertainty principle has been given by Bohr and Rosenfeld.[1]

49. INTERACTION BETWEEN ELECTRONS AND THE ELECTROMAGNETIC FIELD

The quantization of Dirac's relativistic wave equation for free electrons was carried through in Sec. 47. We shall now combine this free-

[1] N. Bohr and L. Rosenfeld, *Det Kgl. Danske Vidensk. Selskab, Mat.-fys. Medd.*, **12**, 8 (1933).

electron theory with the quantum theory of the electromagnetic field in vacuum, given in Sec. 48. The resulting formalism is called *quantum electrodynamics;* it provides a description of the interaction between electrons and the electromagnetic field.

Lagrangian and Hamiltonian Equations. We wish first to obtain a Lagrangian whose variation yields the earlier equations of motion for the electron field and the electromagnetic field. Dirac's electron field equation is (43.22):

$$i\hbar \frac{\partial \psi}{\partial t} - e\phi\psi + \boldsymbol{\alpha} \cdot (-i\hbar c\ \mathbf{grad}\ \psi - e\mathbf{A}\psi) + mc^2\beta\psi = 0 \qquad (49.1)$$

where e is the charge on the electron, and hence is a negative number. Maxwell's equations for the electromagnetic field are given in (35.2):

$$\mathbf{curl}\ \mathbf{E} + \frac{1}{c}\frac{\partial \mathbf{H}}{\partial t} = 0, \qquad \mathbf{curl}\ \mathbf{H} - \frac{1}{c}\frac{\partial \mathbf{E}}{\partial t} = \frac{4\pi}{c}\mathbf{J}$$
$$\mathrm{div}\ \mathbf{E} = 4\pi\rho, \qquad \mathrm{div}\ \mathbf{H} = 0 \qquad (49.2)$$

The electric charge and current densities that go into (49.2) can be obtained from equations (43.20):

$$\rho = e\psi^*\psi, \qquad \mathbf{J} = -ec\psi^*\boldsymbol{\alpha}\psi \qquad (49.3)$$

We assume for the present that ρ and $\mathbf{J}$ are due entirely to electrons. We can verify the electric continuity or conservation equation (35.3) by multiplying (49.1) on the left by ψ^*, its Hermitian adjoint equation on the right by ψ, and taking the difference of the two results.

The desired Lagrangian is just the sum of the Lagrangians for the separate electron and electromagnetic fields, with the electron operators $i\hbar(\partial/\partial t)$ and $-i\hbar c\ \mathbf{grad}$ replaced by $i\hbar(\partial/\partial t) - e\phi$ and $-i\hbar c\ \mathbf{grad} - e\mathbf{A}$, respectively. We thus obtain from (47.1) and (48.3)

$$L = \int \psi^*\left[i\hbar \frac{\partial \psi}{\partial t} - e\phi\psi + \boldsymbol{\alpha} \cdot (-i\hbar c\ \mathbf{grad} - e\mathbf{A})\psi + mc^2\beta\psi\right] d\tau$$
$$+ \frac{1}{8\pi}\int\left[\left(\frac{1}{c}\frac{\partial \mathbf{A}}{\partial t} + \mathbf{grad}\ \phi\right)^2 - (\mathbf{curl}\ \mathbf{A})^2\right] d\tau \qquad (49.4)$$

It can be shown that variation of ψ^* in (49.4) leads to (49.1), variation of ψ leads to the Hermitian adjoint of (49.1), and variation of $\mathbf{A}$ leads to Eqs. (49.2) when use is made of (49.3) and (48.2) (see Prob. 9).

The Lagrangian (49.4) suffers from the defects noted earlier in connection with (47.1) and (48.3). Since ψ^* and ϕ do not appear in (49.4), their canonical momenta cannot be defined, and so ψ^* and ϕ must be eliminated as coordinate variables from the Hamiltonian theory. As before, the momentum canonically conjugate to a component ψ_j of ψ is

$i\hbar\psi_j$, and the momentum canonically conjugate to a component A_x of **A** is $P_x = (4\pi c)^{-1}[(1/c)(\partial A_x/\partial t) + (\partial\phi/\partial x)]$. The Hamiltonian then becomes

$$H = \int \left(i\hbar\psi^* \frac{\partial\psi}{\partial t} + \mathbf{P}\cdot\frac{\partial\mathbf{A}}{\partial t} \right) d\tau - L$$

$$= \int \psi^*[\boldsymbol{\alpha}\cdot(i\hbar c\,\mathbf{grad} + e\mathbf{A})\psi + e\phi\psi - mc^2\beta\psi]d\tau$$

$$+ \int \left[2\pi c^2\mathbf{P}^2 + \frac{1}{8\pi}(\mathbf{curl\ A})^2 - c\mathbf{P}\cdot\mathbf{grad}\ \phi \right] d\tau \quad (49.5)$$

and ψ^* appears as a canonical momentum variable.

It is not difficult to show that the Hamiltonian equations of motion for ψ and its canonical momentum $i\hbar\psi^*$ are (49.1) and its Hermitian adjoint, respectively. The Hamiltonian equations for **A** and **P** are

$$\frac{\partial\mathbf{A}}{\partial t} = 4\pi c^2\mathbf{P} - c\,\mathbf{grad}\ \phi$$

$$\frac{\partial\mathbf{P}}{\partial t} = -\frac{1}{4\pi}\,\mathbf{curl\ curl\ A} - e\psi^*\boldsymbol{\alpha}\psi \quad (49.6)$$

Thus if we define $\mathbf{E} = -4\pi c\mathbf{P}$ and $\mathbf{H} = \mathbf{curl\ A}$, as before, we obtain the first, second, and fourth of Maxwell's equations (49.2).

Elimination of ϕ. The third of Maxwell's equations (49.2) must be obtained as a supplementary condition, as the corresponding equation was in Sec. 48. We shall therefore be concerned only with those solutions of the Hamiltonian equations for which $\mathrm{div}\ \mathbf{E} - 4\pi e\psi^*\psi = 0$ at some definite time. If then the time derivative of this quantity is zero, the restriction is maintained at all times, and the solutions so chosen form a consistent and satisfactory set. With the help of the second of Eqs. (49.6) and the definition of **E**, we see that

$$\frac{\partial}{\partial t}(\mathrm{div}\ \mathbf{E} - 4\pi e\psi^*\psi) = 4\pi e\left[c\,\mathrm{div}(\psi^*\boldsymbol{\alpha}\psi) - \frac{\partial}{\partial t}(\psi^*\psi) \right]$$

This is zero because of (49.3) and the equation of continuity for the electric charge and current densities.

We can now see that the two terms on the right side of (49.5) that involve ϕ cancel each other. The second ϕ term can be integrated by parts to give

$$-c\int\mathbf{P}\cdot\mathbf{grad}\ \phi\ d\tau = c\int\phi\ \mathrm{div}\ \mathbf{P}\ d\tau = -\int\phi\rho d\tau$$

which is equal to and opposite in sign from the first ϕ term $e\int\phi\psi^*\psi d\tau$. Thus ϕ has disappeared from the Hamiltonian, and may be chosen in any convenient way.   The choice is made so that when $\mathbf{P}$ (or $\mathbf{E}$) is divided into *solenoidal* and *irrotational* parts, the latter is expressed entirely in terms of ϕ.   We put

$$\mathbf{P} = \mathbf{P}_1 + \mathbf{P}_2$$
$$\text{div } \mathbf{P}_1 = 0 \qquad\qquad (\mathbf{P}_1 \text{ is solenoidal}) \qquad (49.7)$$
$$\text{curl } \mathbf{P}_2 = 0 \qquad\qquad (\mathbf{P}_2 \text{ is irrotational})$$

If now we put $\mathbf{P}_2 = (4\pi c)^{-1} \text{ grad } \phi$, we see that the third of Eqs. (49.7) is satisfied, and that the first of Eqs. (49.6) becomes

$$\frac{\partial \mathbf{A}}{\partial t} = 4\pi c^2 \mathbf{P}_1 \qquad (49.8)$$

It is now possible to have div $\mathbf{A} = 0$ at all times if it is true at any one time, since (49.8) and the second of Eqs. (49.7) show that $(\partial/\partial t)$ div $\mathbf{A} = 0$.   We therefore choose the gauge so that div $\mathbf{A} = 0$.

The ϕ potential reappears in the Hamiltonian (49.5) through the $\mathbf{P}^2$ term.   The volume integral of $\mathbf{P}^2$ can be written, with the help of the expression for $\mathbf{P}_2$ and a partial integration,

$$\int \mathbf{P}^2 d\tau = \int \mathbf{P}_1^2 d\tau + \int (2\mathbf{P}_1 + \mathbf{P}_2) \cdot \mathbf{P}_2 d\tau$$
$$= \int \mathbf{P}_1^2 d\tau + \frac{1}{4\pi c} \int (2\mathbf{P}_1 + \mathbf{P}_2) \cdot \text{grad } \phi \, d\tau$$
$$= \int \mathbf{P}_1^2 d\tau - \frac{1}{4\pi c} \int \phi \text{ div } (2\mathbf{P}_1 + \mathbf{P}_2) d\tau$$

Now div $\mathbf{P}_1 = 0$, and the supplementary condition is that div $\mathbf{P}_2 = -\rho/c$; thus the $\mathbf{P}^2$ term in H becomes

$$2\pi c^2 \int \mathbf{P}^2 d\tau = 2\pi c^2 \int \mathbf{P}_1^2 d\tau + \tfrac{1}{2} \int \phi \rho d\tau \qquad (49.9)$$

The choice of ϕ tells us that

$$\nabla^2 \phi = 4\pi c \text{ div } \mathbf{P}_2 = -4\pi\rho$$

This equation can be integrated by making use of the Green's function (26.15) with $k = 0$; the result is

$$\phi(\mathbf{r},t) = \int \frac{\rho(\mathbf{r}',t)}{|\mathbf{r} - \mathbf{r}'|} \, d\tau' \qquad (49.10)$$

The Hamiltonian (49.5) can now be rewritten, with the help of (49.9) and (49.10),

$$H = \int \psi^*[\boldsymbol{\alpha} \cdot (i\hbar c \text{ grad} + e\mathbf{A})\psi - mc^2\beta\psi]d\tau$$
$$+ \int \left[2\pi c^2 \mathbf{P}_1^2 + \frac{1}{8\pi} (\text{curl } \mathbf{A})^2 \right] d\tau + \tfrac{1}{2} \int \int \frac{\rho(\mathbf{r},t)\rho(\mathbf{r}',t)}{|\mathbf{r} - \mathbf{r}'|} \, d\tau d\tau' \qquad (49.11)$$

Here, div $\mathbf{P}_1$ = div $\mathbf{A}$ = 0, and $\rho(\mathbf{r},t) = e\psi^*(\mathbf{r},t)\psi(\mathbf{r},t)$. The last term in (49.11) is the internal Coulomb energy of the electric charge distribution $\rho(\mathbf{r},t)$; it results from the elimination of ϕ and the irrotational part of $\mathbf{P}$, and does not have to be inserted into the theory as a separate assumption.

The solenoidal field vectors ($\mathbf{P}_1$ and $\mathbf{A}$) are usually referred to as the *transverse* part of the electromagnetic field, since the electric and magnetic field strengths in the corresponding plane wave solutions are transverse to the direction of propagation, as in Sec. 48. The irrotational Coulomb field vector ($\mathbf{P}_2$) is called the *longitudinal* part of the field, since Eq. (49.10) shows that the contribution to $\mathbf{P}_2$ at one point from an infinitesimal element of charge at another point is along the line joining the two points.

Quantization of the Fields. We can now obtain a quantum theory of the interacting electron and electromagnetic fields by adopting the equation of motion (45.23), the electron field anticommutation relations (47.8), and the electromagnetic field commutation relations (48.21) with $\mathbf{P}_1$ substituted for $\mathbf{P}$. It will also be assumed that all components of ψ and ψ^* commute with all components of $\mathbf{A}$ and $\mathbf{P}_1$.

The order of factors like ψ_j^* and ψ_l that are multiplied together in the Hamiltonian (49.11) is of course immaterial in the unquantized case. In the quantum theory, however, these factors do not commute with each other, and the result of a particular calculation will depend on the order in which they appear in the Hamiltonian. We shall see at the end of this section that a suitable Hamiltonian is obtained if all terms are left as they are, except for a change in the integrand of the Coulomb term. This integrand in (49.11) contains the term

$$\rho(\mathbf{r},t)\rho(\mathbf{r}',t) = \sum_{j=1}^{4} \sum_{l=1}^{4} \psi_j^*(\mathbf{r},t)\psi_j(\mathbf{r},t)\psi_l^*(\mathbf{r}',t)\psi_l(\mathbf{r}',t) \qquad (49.12)$$

which we replace by[1]

$$\sum_{j=1}^{4} \sum_{l=1}^{4} \psi_j^*(\mathbf{r},t)\psi_l^*(\mathbf{r}',t)\psi_l(\mathbf{r}',t)\psi_j(\mathbf{r},t) \qquad (49.13)$$

It can be shown with the help of the anticommutation relations (47.8) that (49.12) is equal to (49.13) plus

$$\sum_{j=1}^{4} \psi_j^*(\mathbf{r},t)\psi_j(\mathbf{r}',t)\delta(\mathbf{r}-\mathbf{r}')$$

[1] Note that both (49.12) and (49.13) are Hermitian.

Thus the change from (49.12) to (49.13) is equivalent to the subtraction from the Hamiltonian (49.11) of the quantity

$$\frac{e^2}{2} \int \int \frac{\psi^*(\mathbf{r},t)\psi(\mathbf{r}',t)\delta(\mathbf{r} - \mathbf{r}')}{|\mathbf{r} - \mathbf{r}'|} \, d\tau d\tau' \qquad (49.14)$$

This is evidently infinite unless $\psi^*(\mathbf{r},t)\psi(\mathbf{r}',t)$ is zero; it will be shown below that this can happen only if there are no electrons in the field.

The quantum equations of motion are obtained from (45.23), when the Hamiltonian (49.11) is modified by substitution of (49.13) for (49.12). The electromagnetic field equations agree with those obtained in Sec. 48, except that $\mathbf{P}_1$ replaces $\mathbf{P}$ and the electric-current term appears as in the second of Eqs. (49.6). The electron field equation is the same as (49.1), except that ϕ is replaced by

$$e \int \frac{\psi^*(\mathbf{r}',t)\psi(\mathbf{r}',t)}{|\mathbf{r} - \mathbf{r}'|} \, d\tau'$$

It can then be shown that the time derivatives of the bracket expressions in (47.8) and (48.21) are zero, so that these equations hold for all time if they are valid initially, as was assumed (see Prob. 11).

Inclusion of Static Fields. Thus far we have assumed that the electric charge and current densities arise entirely from the electrons that are described by the Dirac ψ field. The effect of a static charge distribution can easily be included, by the addition of a term $4\pi\rho_s$ to the right side of the third of Eqs. (49.2), and a term $-e\phi_s\psi$ to the left side of (49.1), where $\nabla^2\phi_s = -4\pi\rho_s$. It is not difficult to see that the only effect on the Hamiltonian (49.11) is to add a term $\int e\phi_s\psi^*\psi d\tau$.

The situation of greatest practical interest is that for which[1]

$$\phi_s = -Ze/r.$$

This corresponds to a fixed (infinitely massive) point nucleus of atomic number Z, placed at the origin. With this addition, and the modification (49.13), the Hamiltonian (49.11) becomes

$$H = \int \psi^* \left[\boldsymbol{\alpha} \cdot (i\hbar c \; \mathbf{grad} + e\mathbf{A})\psi - \frac{Ze^2}{r} \, \psi - mc^2\beta\psi \right] d\tau$$

$$+ \int \left[2\pi c^2 \mathbf{P}_1^2 + \frac{1}{8\pi} (\mathbf{curl} \; \mathbf{A})^2 \right] d\tau + \frac{e^2}{2} \int \int \sum_{jl} \frac{\psi_j^* \psi_l^{*\prime} \psi_l' \psi_j}{|\mathbf{r} - \mathbf{r}'|} \, d\tau d\tau' \quad (49.15)$$

where the primes indicate that the arguments are $\mathbf{r}'$ rather than $\mathbf{r}$.

Use of Perturbation Theory. It is natural to attempt to find the eigenvalues of the Hamiltonian (49.15), which would be the energy levels of the system of electrons, electromagnetic field, and nuclear Coulomb

[1] e is the electronic charge, and hence negative.

field. All such attempts have failed, and there is reason to believe that these eigenvalues do not exist: that it is impossible to diagonalize this Hamiltonian. This reason derives from a perturbation approach that is based on the smallness of e. If e is set equal to zero, (49.15) becomes simply the sum of the free-electron Hamiltonian (47.6) and the vacuum electromagnetic-field Hamiltonian (48.7). These Hamiltonians have already been diagonalized; the eigenvalues correspond to solutions in which there are definite numbers of free electrons and of light quanta, with no interaction between any of them.

For a finite value of e, neither the nuclear term of order Ze^2, nor the interelectron Coulomb interaction of order e^2, causes a fundamental difficulty. As we show below, the latter term would give an infinite *electrostatic* or *longitudinal self-energy* (just as in the classical theory of point charges), were it not for the somewhat arbitrary substitution of (49.13) for (49.12). A more serious trouble arises from the $e\boldsymbol{\alpha} \cdot \mathbf{A}$ term, which couples the electrons to the transverse electromagnetic field. This term is responsible for all interactions between electrons and light quanta, and will be used in the next section for the calculation of the emission and absorption of light by an atom. One of the effects that the $e\boldsymbol{\alpha} \cdot \mathbf{A}$ term produces is an infinite *transverse self-energy* of a free electron, due to the virtual emission and reabsorption of light quanta by it; we shall ignore this effect in what follows.[1]

We shall work mainly with the perturbation approach. In the remainder of this section we consider the matrix elements of the interelectron Coulomb interaction, and ignore the transverse electromagnetic field. This example is of interest since it shows how the infinite electrostatic self-energy is eliminated, and how the exchange interaction between electrons (which obey Fermi-Dirac statistics and are described by antisymmetric many-particle wave functions) comes out of the quantized field theory. The perturbation treatment of the $e\boldsymbol{\alpha} \cdot \mathbf{A}$ term will be taken up in Sec. 50.

Matrix Elements of the Coulomb Interaction. We now consider the Hamiltonian (49.15) with the transverse electromagnetic field omitted:

$$H = \int \psi^* \left(i\hbar c \, \boldsymbol{\alpha} \cdot \mathbf{grad} \, \psi - \frac{Ze^2}{r} \psi - mc^2\beta\psi \right) d\tau$$

$$+ \frac{e^2}{2} \int \int \sum_{jl} \frac{\psi_j^* \psi_l^{*\prime} \psi_l^\prime \psi_j}{|\mathbf{r} - \mathbf{r}^\prime|} \, d\tau d\tau^\prime \quad (49.16)$$

---

[1] A relativistically invariant way of subtracting out infinities of this type has been developed by S. Tomonaga, *Progress of Theor. Physics* (Kyoto), **1**, 27 (1946), *Phys. Rev.*, **74**, 224 (1948), and J. Schwinger, *Phys. Rev.*, **74**, 1439 (1948), **75**, 651 (1949). See also R. P. Feynman, *Phys. Rev.*, **76**, 749, 769 (1949); Dyson, *op. cit.* and *Phys. Rev.*, **75**, 486, 1736 (1949); Heitler, *op. cit.*, Chap. VI.

This turns out to be an adequate approximation when the speed of the electrons is small in comparison with the speed of light, since then light quanta are not likely to be emitted. In this case, it is possible to use the nonrelativistic Schrödinger equation (with spin included) to describe the electrons, although we shall continue to use the Dirac equation.

There is a complete orthonormal set of energy eigenfunctions for a single electron in a Coulomb field, that we denote by $w_j(n,\mathbf{r})$:[1]

$$\int \sum_j \bar{w}_j(n,\mathbf{r})w_j(n',\mathbf{r})d\tau = \delta_{nn'}$$

$$\sum_l \left(i\hbar c \boldsymbol{\alpha}_{jl} \cdot \mathbf{grad} - \frac{Ze^2}{r}\delta_{jl} - mc^2\beta_{jl} \right) w_l(n,\mathbf{r}) = E_n w_j(n,\mathbf{r})$$

(49.17)

These can become the free-electron solutions (47.11) when Z is set equal to zero. We expand ψ and ψ^* in terms of the w's as in (47.15):

$$\psi_j(\mathbf{r},t) = \sum_n b(n,t)w_j(n,\mathbf{r})$$

$$\psi_j^*(\mathbf{r},t) = \sum_n b^*(n,t)\bar{w}_j(n,\mathbf{r})$$

(49.18)

where the b's are operators that obey anticommutation relations like (47.16):

$$[b(n,t), b(n',t)]_+ = [b^*(n,t), b^*(n',t)]_+ = 0$$
$$[b(n,t), b^*(n',t)]_+ = \delta_{nn'}$$

(49.19)

Substitution of (49.18) into (47.10) gives, with the help of the orthonormality relation in (49.17),

$$N = \int \psi^*\psi d\tau = \sum_n b^*(n,t)b(n,t) = \sum_n N_n, \quad N_n \equiv b^*(n,t)b(n,t)$$

In similar fashion, the first term in the Hamiltonian (49.16) becomes

$$\sum_n b^*(n,t)b(n,t)E_n = \sum_n N_n E_n$$

(49.20)

In any calculation in which the second term in (49.16) is regarded as a perturbation on the first term, we are interested in finding the matrix elements of the second term in the representation (specified by the b's

---

[1] This set includes positive- and negative-energy continuum states as well as bound states; it is made discrete by adopting periodic boundary conditions. The index n includes specification of the spin.

and w's) that diagonalizes the first term.   Substitution of (49.18) into the Coulomb-interaction term gives

$$\frac{e^2}{2} \sum_{nn'n''n'''} b^*(n,t)b^*(n',t)b(n'',t)b(n''',t)$$

$$\cdot \sum_{jl} \int \int |\mathbf{r} - \mathbf{r}'|^{-1}\bar{w}_j(n,\mathbf{r})\bar{w}_l(n',\mathbf{r}')w_l(n'',\mathbf{r}')w_j(n''',\mathbf{r})d\tau d\tau' \quad (49.21)$$

We wish to find the matrix element of the operator (49.21) that corresponds to any pair of unperturbed wave functionals (see Sec. 46).   Since electrons obey the exclusion principle, these wave functionals can be specified by stating which of the single-electron states n are occupied. Now, the b's are destruction operators, and the b^*'s are creation operators. Since two of each appear in each term of (49.21), this operator has non-vanishing matrix elements only for wave functionals that correspond to the same total number of electrons, and for which not more than two electrons are assigned to different states in the two wave functionals. Moreover, since the two destruction operators appear to the right of the two creation operators in each term of (49.21), the only nonvanishing matrix elements are for wave functionals that correspond to the presence of two or more electrons.

We see then that (49.21) is a null operator so far as a single electron is concerned, so that the infinite longitudinal self-energy of single electrons has been eliminated.   We now show that this elimination was effected by the replacement of (49.12) by (49.13).   The difference energy (49.14) can be written

$$\frac{e^2}{2} \sum_{nn'} b^*(n,t)b(n',t) \sum_j \int \int |\mathbf{r} - \mathbf{r}'|^{-1}\bar{w}_j(n,\mathbf{r})w_j(n',\mathbf{r}')\delta(\mathbf{r} - \mathbf{r}')d\tau d\tau'$$

$$(49.22)$$

Since $b(n',t)$ destroys an electron in the state n', and $b^*(n,t)$ creates an electron in the state n, the diagonal matrix elements of (49.22) are those for which $n' = n$.   Then $b^*(n,t)b(n',t)$ can be replaced by $N_n\delta_{nn'}$, and there is a positively infinite contribution to the expectation value of (49.22) for each electron that is present.   Thus the substitution of (49.13) for (49.12) was equivalent to the subtraction of the infinite electrostatic self-energy of each electron from the Hamiltonian.

The expectation value or diagonal matrix element of (49.21) for a wave functional that corresponds to two or more electrons is a sum of terms, each of which involves a pair of occupied electron states.   The term that refers to the states 1 and 2, for example, contains the matrix elements of four combinations of b's multiplied by appropriate volume integrals; these four combinations are abbreviated as $b_2^* b_1^* b_2 b_1$, $b_1^* b_2^* b_2 b_1$, $b_2^* b_1^* b_1 b_2$, and $b_1^* b_2^* b_1 b_2$. The anticommutation relations (49.19) show that the second and third of these are equal to each other and opposite in sign to the first and fourth. We can also see from (49.19) that (compare with Prob. 12)

$$\Psi^*(1,1, \ldots) b_1^* b_2^* b_2 b_1 \Psi(1,1, \ldots)$$
$$= \Psi^*(1,1, \ldots) N_1 N_2 \Psi(1,1, \ldots) = +1 \quad (49.23)$$

Equation (49.23) then shows that the part of the expectation value of (49.21) that refers to the occupied states 1 and 2 is

$$e^2 \int \int |\mathbf{r} - \mathbf{r}'|^{-1} \sum_j |w_j(1,\mathbf{r})|^2 \sum_l |w_l(2,\mathbf{r}')|^2 d\tau d\tau'$$
$$- e^2 \int \int |\mathbf{r} - \mathbf{r}'|^{-1} \sum_j \bar{w}_j(1,\mathbf{r}) w_j(2,\mathbf{r}) \sum_l \bar{w}_l(2,\mathbf{r}') w_l(1,\mathbf{r}') d\tau d\tau' \quad (49.24)$$

The second integral in (49.24) is called the *exchange energy*, and also appears when the expectation value of the Coulomb interaction is calculated for an antisymmetric many-electron wave function like (32.7).

50. RADIATION THEORY

The quantum theory of radiation consists of the perturbation treatment of the $e\boldsymbol{\alpha} \cdot \mathbf{A}$ term, and usually also the Ze^2/r term, in the Hamiltonian (49.15). Calculations have been carried through for several processes of physical interest that are of various orders in the electronic charge e.[1] In most cases it is unnecessary to use the quantized Dirac field that is implied by (49.15), since only one electron at a time is involved and the theory of Sec. 43 is adequate.

In this section we consider only the simplest processes of emission and absorption of light by an atom, and continue to use the complete quantized field theory. We assume that the nuclear Coulomb energy and the interelectron interaction energy can be combined into an effective atomic potential energy $V(r)$ of the Hartree type for the electron under consideration (see Sec. 38). The resulting formulas agree with those obtained in Chap. X by means of a semiclassical treatment. At the end of this section, we show how quantum electrodynamics provides a quantitative explanation of the diffraction experiment discussed in Sec. 2. Both the wave-like properties of radiation (appearance of a diffraction pattern) and the particle-like properties (ionization of an atom by absorption of a light quantum) result from Eq. (49.15) or (50.2).

---

[1] Details of some of these calculations and references to the original papers are given by Heitler, *op. cit.*

Formulation in Terms of Transition Probabilities. The development of quantized field theory in the last two chapters has been entirely from the point of view of Heisenberg's form of the equations of motion of the field variables (see Sec. 23). This formulation centers attention on the dynamical variables rather than on the states of the system. Now, however, we wish to calculate transition probabilities between states of the system of electrons and electromagnetic field, and in this way obtain expressions for the rates of emission and absorption of light quanta by an atom. This suggests that we make use of the time-dependent perturbation theory of Sec. 29, which was in fact first developed by Dirac in connection with the present problem.[1]

The states are represented by wave functionals that can be taken to satisfy the Schrödinger-type equations

$$i\hbar\dot{\Psi} = H\Psi$$
$$-i\hbar\dot{\Psi}^* = \Psi^*H$$

(50.1)

where H is given by (49.15). It can then be shown that the dependence on time of the matrices that represent dynamical variables such as ψ and $\mathbf{A}$ arises from the change in time of the wave functionals Ψ that are used to calculate the matrix elements (see Prob. 16, Chap. XIII). Thus the time dependence is transferred from the dynamical variables to the wave functionals; the former will now be regarded as operators whose structures are independent of t.

Before proceeding further, we simplify the Hamiltonian by approximately replacing the effect of the nucleus and all the other electrons on a particular electron by a Hartree-type potential energy $V(r)$. With this change, Eq. (49.15) becomes

$$H = H_0 + H'$$
$$H_0 = \int \psi^*[i\hbar c\boldsymbol{\alpha} \cdot \mathbf{grad}\, \psi + V(r)\psi - mc^2\beta\psi]d\tau$$
$$+ \int \left[2\pi c^2 \mathbf{P}_1^2 + \frac{1}{8\pi} (\mathbf{curl}\, \mathbf{A})^2 \right] d\tau$$
$$H' = e\int\psi^*\boldsymbol{\alpha} \cdot \mathbf{A}\psi d\tau$$

(50.2)

The unperturbed Hamiltonian H_0 can be rewritten by expanding $\mathbf{A}$ in plane waves and ψ in eigenfunctions of Eq. (49.17), where the nuclear potential $-Ze^2/r$ is replaced by $V(r)$. We obtain from (49.20) and (48.32)

---

[1] P. A. M. Dirac, *Proc. Roy. Soc.*, **A112**, 661 (1926), Sec. 5; **A114**, 243 (1927).

$$H_0 = \sum_n N_n E_n + \sum_{k\lambda} \hbar ck(N_{k\lambda} + \tfrac{1}{2})$$

$$N_n = b_n^* b_n, \qquad N_{k\lambda} = \frac{k}{2\pi\hbar c}\, a_{k\lambda}{}^* a_{k\lambda} \tag{50.3}$$

The commutation relations are given by (49.19) and (48.28):

$$[b_n, b_{n'}]_+ = [b_n^*, b_{n'}{}^*]_+ = 0, \qquad [b_n, b_{n'}{}^*]_+ = \delta_{nn'}$$

$$[a_{k\lambda}, a_{k'\lambda'}] = [a^*{}_{k\lambda}, a^*{}_{k'\lambda'}] = 0, \qquad [a_{k\lambda}, a^*{}_{k'\lambda'}] = \frac{2\pi\hbar c}{k}\, \delta_{kk'}\delta_{\lambda\lambda'}$$

The a's and b's commute with each other.

The perturbing energy H' in (50.2) can also be rewritten by making use of the expansions (49.18) and (48.35). We can choose t to be an arbitrary constant (say $t = 0$) in these expressions, since the time dependence of the field variables now arises from the wave functionals. The result is

$$H' = eL^{-\frac{3}{2}} \sum_{nn'k\lambda} \int \sum_{jl} b_n^* \bar{w}_j(n,\mathbf{r}) \varepsilon_{k\lambda} \cdot \boldsymbol{\alpha}_{jl}$$

$$\cdot\, [a_{k\lambda} \exp (i\mathbf{k} \cdot \mathbf{r}) + a_{k\lambda}{}^* \exp (-i\mathbf{k} \cdot \mathbf{r})] b_{n'} w_l(n',\mathbf{r}) d\tau \tag{50.4}$$

We specify the unperturbed wave functionals by giving the quantum numbers n of the occupied electron states and the number of light quanta $n_{k\lambda}$ in each plane wave state of the electromagnetic field:

$$N_n \Psi = \begin{cases} \Psi & \text{if the state } n \text{ is occupied} \\ 0 & \text{if the state } n \text{ is empty} \end{cases} \tag{50.5}$$

$$N_{k\lambda} \Psi = n_{k\lambda} \Psi$$

It then follows from (50.1) (with H replaced by H_0) together with (50.3) and (50.5), that Ψ oscillates in time with a frequency that is determined by the sum of the energies of the electrons and light quanta present. If we omit the infinite zero-point energy of the electromagnetic field, we see that Ψ has the time dependence

$$\exp\left[-\frac{it}{\hbar}\left(\sum_n{}' E_n + \sum_{k\lambda} \hbar ck n_{k\lambda} \right) \right] \tag{50.6}$$

where the prime denotes a summation over only the occupied electron states n.

We are now in a position to apply the time-dependent perturbation theory of Sec. 29. The form of (50.6) shows that only transitions that conserve the total energy of electrons and light quanta take place. We require the matrix elements of H' in the representation in which H_0 is diagonal. These can be obtained by operating with (50.4) on the wave functionals Ψ in accordance with Eqs. (48.34) for the a's and equations like (46.32) for the b's, and making use of the orthonormality property expressed by the first of Eqs. (46.20).

Matrix Elements of the Perturbation. The perturbation H' given by (50.4) is a sum of terms, each of which contains one b, one b^*, and either an a or an a^*. Thus the effect of H' on a wave functional is to destroy an electron in one state, create an electron in the same or a different state, and either destroy or create a light quantum. This corresponds physically to the transition of an electron from one state in the potential $V(r)$ to another, accompanied by the absorption or emission of a light quantum.

We consider first a transition in which a light quantum is absorbed. The initial wave functional $\Psi_1 e^{-i\omega_1 t}$ represents a state of the entire system in which there are $n_{k\lambda}$ light quanta in the state k,λ, an electron in the state n', and perhaps other light quanta and electrons that do not take part in the transition. The final wave functional $\Psi_2 e^{-i\omega_2 t}$ represents a state in which there are $n_{k\lambda} - 1$ light quanta in the state k,λ, an electron in the state n instead of the state n', and whatever other light quanta and electrons that were present in the initial state. The transition frequency $\omega_{21} \equiv \omega_2 - \omega_1$ is given by

$$\hbar\omega_{21} = E_n - E_{n'} - \hbar c k \qquad (50.7)$$

The matrix element of H' for this transition is[1]

$$H'_{21} = eL^{-\frac{3}{2}}\left(\frac{2\pi\hbar c n_{k\lambda}}{k}\right)^{\frac{1}{2}} \int \sum_{jl} \bar{w}_j(n,\mathbf{r})(\exp i\mathbf{k}\cdot\mathbf{r})\varepsilon_{k\lambda}\cdot\alpha_{jl}w_l(n',\mathbf{r})d\tau \qquad (50.8)$$

We can approximate to (50.8) in the nonrelativistic limit by replacing the Dirac single-electron wave functions $w_j(n,\mathbf{r})$ by Schrödinger wave functions $w_n(\mathbf{r})$. We then see from Eq. (43.21) and Prob. 6, Chap. XII, that the velocity operator is $-c\alpha$, and that this can be replaced by $(-i\hbar/m)\mathbf{grad}$ in the nonrelativistic limit. The matrix element (50.8) then becomes

$$H'_{21} = \frac{ie\hbar}{mc}L^{-\frac{3}{2}}\left(\frac{2\pi\hbar c n_{k\lambda}}{k}\right)^{\frac{1}{2}} \int \bar{w}_n(\mathbf{r})(\exp i\mathbf{k}\cdot\mathbf{r})\varepsilon_{k\lambda}\cdot\mathbf{grad}\,w_{n'}(\mathbf{r})d\tau \qquad (50.9)$$

The factor $\exp i\mathbf{k}\cdot\mathbf{r}$ can be placed on either side of the gradient operator, since only the component of **grad** along $\varepsilon_{k\lambda}$ comes in, and this is perpendicular to **k**.

---

[1] The sign factor $\theta_n\theta_{n'}$, which arises from Eqs. (46.32), can be ignored in the remainder of this section.

Transition Probability for Absorption. We shall make use of the nonrelativistic approximation in the subsequent development, since the results obtained are then directly comparable with those of Chap. X. Equation (29.9) gives the amplitude of a particular wave functional at the time t. From this and Eq. (50.9) we obtain the total transition probability per unit time for absorption of a light quantum in any of the states $\mathbf{k},\lambda$:

$$\frac{1}{t} \sum_{\mathbf{k}\lambda} \frac{4|H'_{21}|^2}{\hbar^2} \frac{\sin^2 \frac{1}{2}\omega_{21}t}{\omega_{21}^2}$$

$$= \sum_{\mathbf{k}\lambda} \frac{8\pi e^2 \hbar n_{\mathbf{k}\lambda}}{m^2 \omega L^3} \left| \int \bar{w}_n (\exp i\mathbf{k} \cdot \mathbf{r}) \varepsilon_{\mathbf{k}\lambda} \cdot \mathbf{grad}\ w_{n'}\, d\tau \right|^2 \frac{\sin^2 \frac{1}{2}\omega_{21}t}{\omega_{21}^2 t} \quad (50.10)$$

where we have put $\omega \equiv kc$.

We now suppose, as in the work of Sec. 35, that the states n and n' are discrete, and that the incident radiation covers a range of angular frequencies ω in the neighborhood of $(E_n - E_{n'})/\hbar$. The radiation can then be described by an intensity $I(\omega)d\omega$ for the infinitesimal frequency range $d\omega$. It is convenient to replace the summation over states $\mathbf{k},\lambda$ of the radiation field by an integration over ω. Each quantum contributes an amount $\hbar\omega/L^3$ to the energy density, or an amount $\hbar c\omega/L^3$ to the intensity. We can therefore replace

$$\sum_{\mathbf{k}\lambda} \{\quad\} n_{\mathbf{k}\lambda} \quad \text{by} \quad \int \{\quad\} \frac{L^3 I(\omega)d\omega}{\hbar c\omega} \quad (50.11)$$

The time-dependent factor on the right side of (50.10) has a sharp maximum at $\omega_{21} = 0$, which because of (50.7) is the same as

$$\hbar\omega = E_n - E_{n'}.$$

The other factors are relatively slowly varying; after the substitution (50.11) is made, they can be taken outside of the ω integral, which can be written

$$\int_{-\infty}^{\infty} \frac{\sin^2 \frac{1}{2}\omega_{21}t}{\omega_{21}^2 t}\, d\omega_{21} = \frac{1}{2}\pi$$

Thus the absorption probability (50.10) becomes

$$\frac{4\pi^2 e^2 I(\omega)}{m^2 c\omega^2} \left| \int \bar{w}_n (\exp i\mathbf{k} \cdot \mathbf{r}) \varepsilon_{\mathbf{k}\lambda} \cdot \mathbf{grad}\ w_{n'}\, d\tau \right|^2 \quad (50.12)$$

which agrees with the corresponding expression (35.17) obtained in Chap X.

Transition Probability for Emission. The energy relation (50.7) implies that the electronic state n has a higher energy than the state n'. We can now find the transition probability per unit time for emission of a light quantum when the electron goes from state n to state n'. The $a_{k\lambda}*$ term in (50.4) is involved, and the matrix element analogous to (50.9) is

$$\frac{ieh}{mc} L^{-\frac{3}{2}} \left(\frac{2\pi\hbar c(n_{k\lambda} + 1)}{k} \right)^{\frac{1}{2}} \int \bar{w}_{n'}[\exp(-i\mathbf{k}\cdot\mathbf{r})]\boldsymbol{\varepsilon}_{k\lambda}\cdot\mathbf{grad}\, w_n\, d\tau, \quad (50.13)$$

where $n_{k\lambda}$ is the number of light quanta *initially* present in the electromagnetic field state $\mathbf{k},\lambda$. A calculation similar to that which led from (50.9) to (50.12) gives for the emission probability

$$\frac{4\pi e^2 I(\omega)}{m^2 c\omega^2}\left| \int \bar{w}_{n'}[\exp(-i\mathbf{k}\cdot\mathbf{r})]\boldsymbol{\varepsilon}_{k\lambda}\cdot\mathbf{grad}\, w_n\, d\tau \right|^2$$

$$+ \sum_{k\lambda} \frac{8\pi e^2 \hbar}{m^2 \omega L^3}\left| \int \bar{w}_{n'}[\exp(-i\mathbf{k}\cdot\mathbf{r})]\boldsymbol{\varepsilon}_{k\lambda}\cdot\mathbf{grad}\, w_n\, d\tau \right|^2 \frac{\sin^2 \frac{1}{2}\omega_{21}t}{\omega_{21}^2 t} \quad (50.14)$$

These two terms evidently arise from $n_{k\lambda}$ and from 1, respectively, in the factor $(n_{k\lambda} + 1)^{\frac{1}{2}}$ of (50.13). The first term is proportional to the intensity of the incident radiation, and agrees with the expression (35.19) for the induced emission probability. The second term is independent of the intensity of the radiation present initially; we now show that it agrees with the spontaneous emission probability obtained in Chap. X.

We can simplify the second term in (50.14) by replacing the summation over $\mathbf{k}$ with an integral over ω or ω_{21}. In order to do this, we require an expression for the number of states of the electromagnetic field that lie in the angular-frequency range ω to $\omega + d\omega$. It follows from the discussion of periodic boundary conditions in Sec. 11 [see Eqs. (11.3)] that there are $(L/2\pi)^3 dk_x dk_y dk_z$ plane waves with propagation vectors in the range $dk_x dk_y dk_z$. Thus if we specify the direction of the propagation vector $\mathbf{k}$ by the polar angles θ,ϕ with respect to some fixed set of axes, the number of plane waves with angular frequency in the range $d\omega$ that have directions of propagation in the angular range $d\theta d\phi$ is

$$\left(\frac{L^3 \omega^2}{8\pi^3 c^3} \right) \sin\theta d\theta d\phi d\omega.$$

The integration over ω in the second term of (50.14) can be carried out as before; the result is

$$\int_0^\pi \int_0^{2\pi} \sum_\lambda \frac{e^2 \hbar\omega}{2\pi m^2 c^3}\left| \int \bar{w}_{n'}[\exp(-i\mathbf{k}\cdot\mathbf{r})]\boldsymbol{\varepsilon}_{k\lambda}\cdot\mathbf{grad}\, w_n d\tau \right|^2 \sin\theta d\theta d\phi \quad (50.15)$$

The expression to the right of the summation in (50.15) is the probability per unit time for spontaneous emission of a light quantum with propagation vector **k** in the angular range $d\theta d\phi$, and polarization λ. Thus (50.15) is the total spontaneous emission probability associated with the transition $n \to n'$. In order to compare it with the corresponding expression in Sec. 36, we specialize to the dipole case by replacing exp $(-i\mathbf{k} \cdot \mathbf{r})$ by unity and **grad** by $-(m\omega/\hbar)\mathbf{r}$ in the integrand of the matrix element [see Eq. (35.20)]:

$$\int_0^\pi \int_0^{2\pi} \sum_\lambda \frac{e^2\omega^3}{2\pi\hbar c^3} \left| \boldsymbol{\varepsilon}_{\mathbf{k}\lambda} \cdot \int \bar{w}_{n'}\mathbf{r}w_n d\tau \right|^2 \sin\theta d\theta d\phi \qquad (50.16)$$

The two directions of polarization for each propagation vector can be chosen in any way so long as they are perpendicular to each other and to **k**. If we choose one in the plane of **k** and the matrix element $(\mathbf{r})_{n'n}$, and the other perpendicular to this plane, only the former is emitted; then a factor $\sin^2\theta$ appears in the integrand, where θ is the angle between **k** and $(\mathbf{r})_{n'n}$. Thus the polarization and angular distribution of the emitted radiation are in agreement with those found in Sec. 36. The total spontaneous dipole emission probability obtained from (50.16) is

$$\int_0^\pi \int_0^{2\pi} \frac{e^2\omega^3}{2\pi\hbar c^3} \sin^2\theta \left(\overline{\int \bar{w}_{n'}\mathbf{r}w_n d\tau} \cdot \int \bar{w}_{n'}\mathbf{r}w_n d\tau\right) \sin\theta d\theta d\phi$$
$$= \frac{4e^2\omega^3}{3\hbar c^3} |(\mathbf{r})_{n'n}|^2 \quad (50.17)$$

which agrees with (36.22).

Both the spontaneous and induced emission probabilities appear as the result of a single calculation in quantum electrodynamics, while these two effects were calculated in quite different ways in Chap. X. As was pointed out above, the spontaneous emission arises from the 1 in the factor $(n_{\mathbf{k}\lambda} + 1)^{\frac{1}{2}}$ that appears in the second of Eqs. (48.34). This in turn comes from the commutation relations (48.28), and hence is a purely quantum-mechanical effect. From a formal point of view, we can say that the spontaneous emission probability is equal to the probability of emission that would be induced by the presence of one quantum in each state of the electromagnetic field (see Prob. 4, Chap. X). Now we have already seen in Eq. (48.32) that the smallest possible energy of the field corresponds to the presence of one-half quantum per state. This suggests that we regard the spontaneous emission as being induced by the zero-point oscillations of the electromagnetic field; note, however, that these oscillations are twice as effective in producing emissive transitions as are actual quanta, and are incapable of producing absorptive transitions.

Analysis of a Diffraction Experiment. As our final example, we consider the diffraction experiment that was discussed in Sec. 2.[1] It is desirable to simplify the calculation as much as possible, and we start by reducing the arrangement of Fig. 1 to its essentials. These essentials consist of a source of light S, a diaphragm A with two slits cut in it, and a detector of light that can be placed at various points in the plane B. The source is taken to be a single atom that is in an excited state and can radiate a light quantum. The detector is taken to be a different kind of atom in its ground state, which becomes ionized if it absorbs the light quantum given off by the source atom (photoelectric effect). The diaphragm is assumed to be made of perfectly reflecting material; its atomic structure is ignored, and it simply imposes certain boundary conditions on the electromagnetic field.

The physical process in which we are interested is that in which the initially excited source atom emits a light quantum, and the detector atom absorbs the quantum and is ionized. Actually, however, the light quantum cannot be observed in transit unless an arrangement like that of Fig. 2 is used, and we are not interested in such an experiment. What we wish to calculate is the transition probability from a state in which the source atom is excited, the detector atom is in its ground state, and no quanta are present, to a state in which the source atom is in its ground state, the detector atom is ionized, and no quanta are present. This tells us how the probability of observing ionization depends on position in the plane B when a light source is placed at S. We shall see that this probability is proportional to the intensity calculated by classical electromagnetic theory when a light source is at S. In this way, quantum electrodynamics predicts both the diffraction pattern that is characteristic of light waves, and the ejected photoelectrons that are characteristic of light quanta.

The form of the Hamiltonian [Eqs. (50.2) and (50.3)] tells us that electrons on different atoms interact with each other only through the coupling between each electron and the electromagnetic field. Thus the process with which we are concerned occurs only in second order of the perturbation energy H' of (50.2).[2] Since no quanta are present initially or finally, the intermediate states are those for which a single quantum is present, and either both atoms are in their ground states or the source

---

[1] See also G. Racah, *Accad. Lincei Rend.*, **11**, 837, 1100 (1930); W. Heisenberg, *Ann. d. Physik*, **9**, 338 (1931); E. Fermi, *op. cit.*, Sec. 10.

[2] We assume that the spontaneous radiation probability of the source atom is small enough so that the remarks of footnote 1, page 198, are applicable. Then the over-all transition probability per unit time is constant for times that are long enough so that energy is conserved between initial and final states.

atom is excited and the detector atom is ionized. The first type of intermediate state corresponds to a double process in which the source atom makes a transition to its ground state and emits a light quantum, and the detector atom makes a transition to its ionized state and absorbs this quantum. Since the intermediate state need not conserve energy, the light-quantum energy does not have to equal the initial excitation energy of the source atom (see Sec. 29). The second type of intermediate state corresponds to a double process in which the detector atom makes a transition to its ionized state and emits a light quantum, and the source atom makes a transition to its ground state and absorbs this quantum. In this case, it is apparent that the intermediate state cannot conserve energy. The second-order matrix element for the over-all process is obtained by summing expressions like (29.20) over all possible intermediate light-quantum states of both types.

The structure of the calculation that follows does not depend on the particular experimental arrangement of Fig. 1. The actual diffraction pattern is not found explicitly; instead it is shown that the quantum and classical results agree for any arrangement of perfectly reflecting diaphragms, with or without slits. This conclusion is not surprising, since Maxwell's equations have the same form in classical and quantum electrodynamics. Nevertheless, it is interesting for us to see explicitly in what way agreement is obtained. It is shown below that the summation over intermediate light-quantum states gives an expression that is equivalent to the point-source solution (Green's function) of the electromagnetic wave equation.

Representation of the Electromagnetic Field. The expansion of the electromagnetic field in plane waves that was introduced in Sec. 48 and used earlier in this section is not suitable for the present problem, since plane waves do not satisfy the proper boundary conditions at the surface of the diaphragm. The functions that do satisfy these boundary conditions are quite complicated, and we do not attempt to find explicit expressions for them. We simply assume that they exist and form a complete set in terms of which the vector potential can be expanded. The assumption that the surface of the diaphragm is perfectly reflecting means in the general case that these functions have to be real. We make the set discrete by placing the entire system in a large but finite closed box that has perfectly reflecting walls. The cartesian components of the vector functions $u_k(\mathbf{r})$ satisfy the second-order wave equation

$$\nabla^2 u_{ks} + \frac{\omega_k^2}{c^2} u_{ks} = 0, \qquad s = x,y,z \qquad (50.18)$$

where div $\mathbf{u}_k = 0$. Since the tangential components of the electric field and the vector potential vanish at a perfectly reflecting surface, the boundary condition is

$$\mathbf{n} \times \mathbf{u}_k = 0 \qquad (50.19)$$

where $\mathbf{n}$ is the vector normal to the surface of the diaphragm or to the walls of the box.

We now show that two of these functions that correspond to different eigenvalues ω_k are orthogonal to each other. We multiply (50.18) by $u_{k's}(\mathbf{r})$, the corresponding equation for $u_{k's}(\mathbf{r})$ by $u_{ks}(\mathbf{r})$, take the difference of the two results and sum over $s = x,y,z$. The result can be written, with the help of Green's theorem,

$$\int \sum_{s=x,y,z} \left(u_{k's} \frac{\partial u_{ks}}{\partial n} - u_{ks} \frac{\partial u_{k's}}{\partial n} \right) dA = \frac{\omega_{k'}^2 - \omega_k^2}{c^2} \int \mathbf{u}_{k'} \cdot \mathbf{u}_k d\tau \qquad (50.20)$$

where $(\partial/\partial n)$ denotes the component of the gradient in the direction of the outward normal. The surface integral on the left extends over both the diaphragm and the walls of the box. According to (50.19), the tangential components of $\mathbf{u}_k$ vanish on the boundary surfaces; this implies that the tangential derivatives of these components are also zero. Then since div $\mathbf{u}_k = 0$, the normal derivative of the normal component of $\mathbf{u}_k$ vanishes. It follows that at the bounding surfaces, $\mathbf{u}_k$ is a vector perpendicular to the surface, and $\partial\mathbf{u}_k/\partial n$ is a vector parallel to the surface, so that their scalar product is zero. Thus the surface integral on the left side of (50.20) vanishes, and $\int \mathbf{u}_{k'} \cdot \mathbf{u}_k d\tau = 0$ if $\omega_{k'} \neq \omega_k$. Any degenerate solutions of (50.18) can be chosen orthogonal to each other, and all solutions can be normalized in the entire region, so we can put

$$\int \mathbf{u}_{k'} \cdot \mathbf{u}_k d\tau = \delta_{kk'} \qquad (50.21)$$

We now proceed as in Sec. 48 to expand $\mathbf{A}$ and $\mathbf{P}$ for the vacuum field in terms of the functions $\mathbf{u}_k$:

$$\mathbf{A}(\mathbf{r},t) = \sum_k q_k(t)\mathbf{u}_k(\mathbf{r}), \qquad \mathbf{P}(\mathbf{r},t) = \sum_k p_k(t)\mathbf{u}_k(\mathbf{r}) \qquad (50.22)$$

where q_k and p_k are Hermitian and satisfy the commutation relations

$$[q_k(t), p_{k'}(t)] = i\hbar\delta_{kk'}$$
$$[q_k(t), q_{k'}(t)] = [p_k(t), p_{k'}(t)] = 0 \qquad (50.23)$$

Substitution of (50.22) into the electromagnetic field Hamiltonian (48.7) gives, with the help of (50.21),

$$H_{em} = \sum_k 2\pi c^2 p_k^2 + \frac{1}{8\pi} \sum_{kl} q_k q_l \int (\mathbf{curl}\ \mathbf{u}_k) \cdot (\mathbf{curl}\ \mathbf{u}_l) d\tau$$

The integral on the right can be simplified by means of a partial integration:

$$\int(\mathbf{curl}\ \mathbf{u}_k) \cdot (\mathbf{curl}\ \mathbf{u}_l)d\tau = \int \mathbf{u}_k \cdot \mathbf{curl\ curl}\ \mathbf{u}_l\ d\tau$$

where the surface integral vanishes because of the boundary conditions. This integral can be simplified further if $\mathbf{u}_l$ is expressed in cartesian coordinates and use is made of Eqs. (50.18) and (50.21):

$$\int(\mathbf{curl}\ \mathbf{u}_k) \cdot (\mathbf{curl}\ \mathbf{u}_l)d\tau = -\int \mathbf{u}_k \cdot \nabla^2 \mathbf{u}_l d\tau$$

$$= \frac{\omega_l^2}{c^2}\int \mathbf{u}_k \cdot \mathbf{u}_l d\tau = \frac{\omega_l^2}{c^2}\ \delta_{kl}$$

The field Hamiltonian then becomes

$$H_{em} = \sum_k \left(2\pi c^2 p_k^2 + \frac{\omega_k^2}{8\pi c^2}\ q_k^2\right) \tag{50.24}$$

The quantum equations of motion for q_k and p_k are obtained from (45.23), (50.23), and (50.24):

$$\dot{q}_k = 4\pi c^2 p_k, \qquad \dot{p}_k = -\frac{\omega_k^2}{4\pi c^2}\ q_k$$

These are readily integrated to give

$$q_k = a_k e^{-i\omega_k t} + a_k^* e^{i\omega_k t}$$

$$p_k = -\frac{i\omega_k}{4\pi c^2}\ (a_k e^{-i\omega_k t} - a_k^* e^{i\omega_k t})$$

where a_k and a_k^* are operators that do not depend on the time. It is easily verified that the a's satisfy commutation relations like (48.28):

$$[a_k, a_{k'}^*] = \frac{2\pi\hbar c^2}{\omega_k}\ \delta_{kk'}$$

with all other pairs commuting. Thus we can identify a_k and a_k^* with destruction and creation operators, respectively, for quanta in the state k of the electromagnetic field. The Hamiltonian (50.24) becomes

$$H_{em} = \sum_k \hbar\omega_k(N_k + \tfrac{1}{2}), \qquad N_k = \frac{\omega_k}{2\pi\hbar c^2}\ a_k^* a_k$$

This is in agreement with (48.32) since ω_k corresponds to the quantity ck in Sec. 48.

Matrix Elements. The second-order matrix element (29.20) can be written as the sum of two terms that correspond to the two types of intermediate states discussed above.   The first term can be written

$$\sum_k \frac{(H'_B)_{i,0k}(H'_S)_{0k,1}}{E_{S1} - E_{S0} - \hbar\omega_k} \tag{50.25}$$

$(H'_S)_{0k,1}$ is the matrix element for the transition of the source atom from the excited state of energy E_{S1} to the ground state of energy E_{S0} with emission of a quantum in the state k:[1]

$$(H'_S)_{0k,1} = \frac{ie\hbar}{mc}\left(\frac{2\pi\hbar c^2}{\omega_k}\right)^{\frac{1}{2}}\int \bar{w}_{S0}(\mathbf{r}')\mathbf{u}_k(\mathbf{r}') \cdot \mathbf{grad}'\, w_{S1}(\mathbf{r}')d\tau'$$

$(H'_B)_{i,0k}$ is the matrix element for the transition of the detector atom from the ground state of energy E_{B0} to an ionized state of energy E_{Bi} with absorption of the quantum in the state k:

$$(H'_B)_{i,0k} = \frac{ie\hbar}{mc}\left(\frac{2\pi\hbar c^2}{\omega_k}\right)^{\frac{1}{2}}\int \bar{w}_{Bi}(\mathbf{r})\mathbf{u}_k(\mathbf{r}) \cdot \mathbf{grad}\, w_{B0}(\mathbf{r})d\tau$$

The second term can similarly be written

$$\sum_k \frac{(H'_S)_{0,1k}(H'_B)_{ik,0}}{E_{B0} - E_{Bi} - \hbar\omega_k} \tag{50.26}$$

It is readily verified from the earlier work that $(H'_S)_{0,1k} = (H'_S)_{0k,1}$ and $(H'_B)_{ik,0} = (H'_B)_{i,0k}$.

The time-dependent perturbation theory of Sec. 29 tells us that the transition probability per unit time is appreciable only if energy is conserved between initial and final states.   Thus we are interested in those ionized states for which

$$E_{Bi} - E_{B0} = E_{S1} - E_{S0}$$

If we call this energy difference $\hbar\omega$, the sum of (50.25) and (50.26) can be written

$$\frac{4\pi e^2\hbar^2}{m^2}\int\int \sum_{s,s'=x,y,z} \bar{w}'_{S0}\frac{\partial w'_{S1}}{\partial r'_{s'}}\bar{w}_{Bi}\frac{\partial w_{B0}}{\partial r_s}\left[\sum_k \frac{u_{ks'}(\mathbf{r}')u_{ks}(\mathbf{r})}{\omega_k^2 - \omega^2}\right]d\tau d\tau' \tag{50.27}$$

The electronic wave functions w that appear in (50.27) are well localized around either the source atom or the detector atom.   Since we are primarily interested in macroscopic observations, we neglect the

---

[1] As was done earlier in this section, we change to a representation in which the time dependence appears in the wave functionals rather than in the operators, since this lends itself more readily to application of the time-dependent perturbation theory.

spatial extent of these wave functions. The transition probability then depends on the positions $\mathbf{r}'$ of source and $\mathbf{r}$ of detector through the expression in square brackets. For a large containing box, the summation over k is to be replaced by an integration over ω_k, where the contour C is chosen in accordance with Eq. (29.24). We define a density of states $\rho(k)$, such that $\rho(k)d\omega_k$ is the number of states of the electromagnetic field in the angular-frequency range $d\omega_k$. We can then put

$$\begin{bmatrix} \quad \end{bmatrix} = \int_C \frac{u_{ks'}(\mathbf{r}')u_{ks}(\mathbf{r})}{\omega_k^2 - \omega^2} \, \rho(k)d\omega_k \equiv P + iR \qquad (50.28)$$

where P is the principal value of the integral and R is π times the residue of the integrand at the pole $\omega_k = \omega$. It is apparent that P and R are real. The transition probability is proportional to the square of the magnitude of (50.28), or to

$$P^2 + R^2 \qquad (50.29)$$

Classical Diffraction Pattern. We have now to compare this result with the classical expression for the intensity of light produced at $\mathbf{r}$ by a source at $\mathbf{r}'$. This can be found from a solution of the wave equation (35.9) for the vector potential $\mathbf{A}(\mathbf{r},t)$ that is produced by a current density $\mathbf{J}(\mathbf{r},t)$:

$$\nabla^2 \mathbf{A} - \frac{1}{c^2} \frac{\partial^2 \mathbf{A}}{\partial t^2} = -\frac{4\pi}{c} \mathbf{J} \qquad (50.30)$$

We are interested in a solution of Eq. (50.30) when the source current $\mathbf{J}$ is small in spatial dimensions and oscillates sinusoidally in the time. It will be apparent from what follows that an analytical difficulty is encountered if the time dependence of $\mathbf{J}$ is purely harmonic. We therefore make the physically plausible assumption that $\mathbf{J}$ represents a damped oscillator, and later take the limit in which the damping constant is negligibly small. We put

$$\mathbf{J}(\mathbf{r},t) = \mathbf{J}(\mathbf{r})e^{-\gamma t} \cos \omega t$$
$$= \tfrac{1}{2}\mathbf{J}(\mathbf{r})[e^{(-\gamma+i\omega)t} + e^{(-\gamma-i\omega)t}]$$

Since Eq. (50.30) is linear, its steady-state solutions have the form

$$\mathbf{A}(\mathbf{r},t) = \tfrac{1}{2}\mathbf{A}(\mathbf{r})e^{(-\gamma+i\omega)t} + \tfrac{1}{2}\overline{\mathbf{A}}(\mathbf{r})e^{(-\gamma-i\omega)t} \qquad (50.31)$$

where $\mathbf{A}(\mathbf{r})$ satisfies the equation

$$\nabla^2 \mathbf{A}(\mathbf{r}) + \frac{1}{c^2}(\omega + i\gamma)^2 \mathbf{A}(\mathbf{r}) = -\frac{4\pi}{c} \mathbf{J}(\mathbf{r}) \qquad (50.32)$$

Equation (50.32) can be solved in the same way as was the inhomogeneous wave equation (26.7). We expand $\mathbf{A}(\mathbf{r})$ in terms of the complete set $\mathbf{u}_k(\mathbf{r})$ of real vector functions that satisfy the boundary conditions stated earlier:

$$\mathbf{A}(\mathbf{r}) = \sum_k A_k \mathbf{u}_k(\mathbf{r}) \tag{50.33}$$

The constant expansion coefficients A_k may be complex since $\mathbf{A}(\mathbf{r})$ is not necessarily real [the vector potential $\mathbf{A}(\mathbf{r},t)$ is of course real]. Substitution of (50.33) into (50.32) gives, with the help of (50.18),

$$-\frac{1}{c^2} \sum_k A_k [\omega_k^2 - (\omega + i\gamma)^2] \mathbf{u}_k(\mathbf{r}) = -\frac{4\pi}{c} \mathbf{J}(\mathbf{r})$$

This can be solved for A_k with the help of the orthonormality relation (50.21).

$$A_k = \frac{4\pi c}{\omega_k^2 - (\omega + i\gamma)^2} \int \mathbf{u}_k(\mathbf{r}') \cdot \mathbf{J}(\mathbf{r}') d\tau' \tag{50.34}$$

Substitution of (50.34) into (50.33) gives for a cartesian component of $\mathbf{A}(\mathbf{r})$

$$A_s(\mathbf{r}) = 4\pi c \int \sum_{s'} J_{s'}(\mathbf{r}') \left[\sum_k \frac{u_{ks'}(\mathbf{r}') u_{ks}(\mathbf{r})}{\omega_k^2 - (\omega + i\gamma)^2} \right] d\tau' \tag{50.35}$$

The summation in square brackets can be replaced by an integration over real values of ω_k without difficulty, since for finite γ the pole of the integrand is above the real axis. In the limit $\gamma \to 0$, the pole moves into the real axis, and the integral approaches the value computed with the contour C of Eq. (29.24). This is just the integral (50.28), so that we can replace the square-bracket expression in (50.35) by $P + iR$. The intensity of light measured at $\mathbf{r}$ is proportional to the time average of the square of the vector potential (50.31). For a small current source located at the point $\mathbf{r}'$, this intensity is proportional (in the limit $\gamma \to 0$) to

$$\{[(P + iR)e^{i\omega t} + (P - iR)e^{-i\omega t}]^2\}_{\text{time avg.}} = 4[(P \cos \omega t - R \sin \omega t)^2]_{\text{time avg.}}$$
$$= 2(P^2 + R^2)$$

The agreement between this result and (50.29) shows that the probability of finding an ionized atom at a particular point is proportional to the classically computed intensity of light at that point.

Problems

1. Calculate the commutator bracket of [curl $\mathbf{A}(\mathbf{r},t)$]^2 and $P_x(\mathbf{r}',t)$. Use the result to show that the equation of motion for the quantity $\mathbf{P}$ in a vacuum electromagnetic field is given by the second of Eqs. (48.6).

2. Show that if the commutator bracket of two cartesian components of **A** and **P** is given by

$$[A_s(\mathbf{r},t), P_{s'}(\mathbf{r}',t)] = i\hbar\delta_{ss'}\delta(\mathbf{r} - \mathbf{r}') - \frac{i\hbar}{4\pi}\frac{\partial}{\partial r_s}\frac{\partial}{\partial r'_{s'}}\left(\frac{1}{|\mathbf{r} - \mathbf{r}'|}\right)$$

then **A** and div **P** at different space points commute with each other.

3. Show that the replacement of the last of the commutation relations (48.8) by that of Prob. 2 does not affect those commutator brackets that involve the field strengths.

4. Show that div **H** commutes with the electromagnetic field Hamiltonian (48.15), and hence is a constant of the motion.

5. Carry through the calculations implied in Eqs. (48.16), and show that the first two of Maxwell's equations are obtained.

6. Calculate the commutator bracket of each of the bracket expressions in (48.18) and the Hamiltonian (48.22), and show that the bracket expressions are constant in time. This means that these commutation laws are consistent with the equations of motion.

7. Compare the D function given in Eqs. (47.30) and (47.33), and the D_0 function given in Eq. (48.39), from a physical point of view.

8. Derive the expression (48.43) for the commutator bracket of $E_x(\mathbf{r},t)$ and $H_y(\mathbf{r}',t')$.

9. Obtain the Lagrangian equations of motion for ψ, ψ^*, and **A** from Eq. (49.4).

10. Find the quantum equation of motion for ψ when the Hamiltonian is given by (49.11) with the substitution of (49.13) for (49.12). Show that it agrees with (49.1) if ϕ is replaced by $e\int[\psi^*(\mathbf{r}',t)\psi(\mathbf{r}',t)/|\mathbf{r} - \mathbf{r}'|]d\tau'$. What result is obtained if the above subsitution is not made?

11. Show that the bracket expressions in (47.8) and (48.21) are constant in time for the Hamiltonian of Prob. 10.

12. Verify Eq. (49.23) by making use of the anticommutation relations (49.19), and also by making use of operator equations like (46.32).

13. Calculate a typical off-diagonal matrix element of the Coulomb interaction energy (49.21), and show that it is in agreement with what would be obtained from an antisymmetric many-electron wave function like (32.7).

14. Carry through a calculation like that given in the latter part of Sec. 50, except that the diaphragm is omitted and plane waves with periodic boundary conditions are used in place of the real vector functions $\mathbf{u}_k(\mathbf{r})$. Show explicitly that the probability of ionization of the detector atom is inversely proportional to the square of its distance from the source atom. Compare this calculation with that of Sec. 30 which dealt with the production of a cloud-chamber track.

INDEX